HANDBOOK ON COMPUTATIONAL INTELLIGENCE

Volume 2: Evolutionary Computation, Hybrid Systems, and Applications

HANDBOOK ON COMPUTATIONAL INTELLIGENCE

Volume 2: Evolutionary Computation, Hybrid Systems, and Applications

Editor

Plamen Parvanov Angelov

Lancaster University, UK

World Scientific

NEW JERSEY • LONDON • SINGAPORE • BEIJING • SHANGHAI • HONG KONG • TAIPEI • CHENNAI • TOKYO

Published by

World Scientific Publishing Co. Pte. Ltd.
5 Toh Tuck Link, Singapore 596224
USA office: 27 Warren Street, Suite 401-402, Hackensack, NJ 07601
UK office: 57 Shelton Street, Covent Garden, London WC2H 9HE

British Library Cataloguing-in-Publication Data
A catalogue record for this book is available from the British Library.

HANDBOOK ON COMPUTATIONAL INTELLIGENCE
In 2 Volumes

Volume 1: Fuzzy Logic, Systems, Artifical Neural Networks, and Learning Systems
Volume 2: Evolutionary Computation, Hybrid Systems, and Applications

ISBN 978-981-4675-00-0 (Set)
ISBN 978-981-4675-03-1 (Vol. 1)
ISBN 978-981-4675-04-8 (Vol. 2)

In-house Editors: Dipasri Sardar/Amanda Yun

Typeset by Stallion Press
Email: enquiries@stallionpress.com

Printed in Singapore

Dedication

Computational Intelligence is only possible if we have a *Computer*. This work is dedicated to the inventor of the digital computer, John Vincent Atanasoff.

Contents

Introduction by the Editor

The term *Computational Intelligence* was coined more recently (at the end of the last century when a series of high profile conferences were organized by the Institute of Electrical and Electronics Engineers (IEEE) leading to the formation of the Computational Intelligence Society within the IEEE), however, the disciplines and problems it covers have been in existence for a much longer period of time. The very idea of developing systems, devices, algorithms, techniques that possess characteristics of "*intelligence*" and are computational (not just conceptual) dates back to the middle of the 20th century or even earlier and is broadly associated with the so-called "*artificial intelligence*". However, "artificial intelligence" is nowadays rather linked with logic, cognition, natural language processing, induction and so on, while "*computational intelligence*" has been developed in a direction that can be described as "nature-inspired" alternatives to the conventional/traditional computing approaches. This includes, but is not limited to:

- Fuzzy logic (as a more human-oriented approach to reasoning);
- Artificial neural networks (mimicking the human brain);
- Evolutionary algorithms (mimicking the population-based genetic evolution), and
- Dynamically evolving systems based on the above.

Some authors also attribute other areas of research such as belief-based Depmster–Shafer theory, chaos theory, swarm and collective intelligence, etc. on the margins of *Computational Intelligence.* It is also often the case that the application areas such as pattern recognition, image processing, business and video analytics and so on are also attributed or linked closely to *Computational Intelligence*; areas of research that are closer to Statistical Learning (e.g., Support Vector Machines), probability theory, Bayesian, Markov models etc. are also sometimes considered to be a part of *Computational Intelligence.*

In this handbook, while not closing the door to all possible methods and alternatives, we keep clear the picture of *Computational Intelligence* as a distinct area of research that is based on the above mentioned pillars and we assume that the other areas are either applications of *Computational Intelligence* methods, techniques or approaches or research areas that gravitate around Statistical Learning.

The primary goal of the area of *Computational Intelligence* is to provide efficient computational solutions to the existing open problems from theoretical and application points of view in understanding, representation, modeling, visualization, reasoning, decision, prediction, classification, analysis and control of physical objects, environmental or social processes and phenomena to which the traditional methods, techniques and theories (primarily, so-called "first principles", deterministic, often expressed as differential equations and stemming from mass- and energy-balance) cannot provide a valid or useful/practical solution.

Another specific feature of *Computational Intelligence* is that it offers solutions that bear characteristics of "intelligence" which is usually attributed to humans only. This has to be considered broadly rather than literally as in the area of "artificial intelligence". For example, fuzzy logic systems can make decisions like humans do. This is in a stark contrast with the deterministic type expert systems as well as with the probabilistic associative rules. For artificial neural networks, one can argue that they process the data in a manner which is more like what human Brain does. In evolutionary computation, the population of candidate solutions "evolves" towards the optimum in a manner similar to the way species and living organisms evolve in Nature. Finally, in dynamically evolving systems, self-development is very much like in the real life, where we, humans, learn individually from experience in a supervised (from parents, teachers, peers etc.) or unsupervised (self-learning) manner. Learning from experience, we can develop a rule-base starting from "scratch" and constantly update this rule-base by adding new rules or removing the outdated ones; or similarly, the strengths of the links between neurons in our brain can dynamically evolve and new areas of the brain can be activated or deactivated (thus, dynamically evolving neural networks).

In this handbook, a mix of leading academics and practitioners in this area as well as some of the younger generation researchers contributed to cover the main aspects of the exciting area of *Computational Intelligence.* The overall structure and invitations to a much broader circle of contributors were set up initially. After a careful peer review process, a selected set of contributions was organized in a coherent end product aiming to cover the main areas of *Computational Intelligence*; it also aims to cover both, the theoretical basis and, at the same time, to give a flavor of the possible efficient applications.

This handbook is composed of two volumes and five parts which contain 26 chapters.

Volume 1 includes Part I (Fuzzy Logic) and Part II (Artificial Neural Networks and Learning Systems).

Volume 2 includes Part III (Evolutionary Computation), Part IV (Hybrid Systems) and Part V (Applications).

In Part I, the readers can find seven chapters, including:

- Fundamentals of Fuzzy Set Theory
  This chapter sets the tone with a thorough, step by step introduction to the theory of fuzzy sets. It is written by one of the foremost experts in this area, Dr. Fernando Gomide, Professor at University of Campinas, Campinas, Brazil.
- Granular Computing

  Granular computing became a cornerstone of *Computational Intelligence* and the chapter offers a thorough review of the problems and solutions. It is written by two of the leading experts in this area, Dr. Andrzej Bargiela, Professor at Nottingham University, UK (now in Christchurch University, New Zealand) and Dr. Witold Pedrycz, Professor at University of Alberta, Canada.
- Evolving Fuzzy Systems — Fundamentals, Reliability, Interpretability, Useability, Applications

  Since its introduction around the turn of the centuries by the Editor, the area of evolving fuzzy systems is constantly developing and this chapter offers a review of the problems and some of the solutions. It is written by Dr. Edwin Lughofer, Key Researcher at Johannes Kepler University, Linz, Austria, who quickly became one of the leading experts in this area following an exchange of research visits with Lancaster University, UK.
- Modeling of Fuzzy Rule-based Systems

  This chapter covers the important problem of designing fuzzy systems from data. It is written by Dr. Rashmi Dutta Baruah of Indian Institute of Technology, Guwahati, India and Diganta Baruah of Sikkim Manipal Institute of Technology, Sikkim, India. Rashmi recently obtained a PhD degree from Lancaster University, UK in the area of evolving fuzzy systems.
- Fuzzy Classifiers

  This chapter covers the very important problem of fuzzy rule-based classifiers and is written by the expert in the field, Dr. Hamid Bouchachia, Associate Professor at Bournemouth University, UK.
- Fuzzy Model based Control: Predictive and Adaptive Approach

  This chapter covers the problems of fuzzy control and is written by the experts in the area, Dr. Igor Škrjanc, Professor and Dr. Sašo Blažič, Professor at the University of Ljubljana, Slovienia.

- Fuzzy Fault Detection and Diagnosis

  This chapter is written by Dr. Bruno Costa, Professor at IFRN, Natal, Brazil who specialized recently in Lancaster, UK.

Part II consists of six chapters, which cover:

- The ANN and Learning Systems in Brains and Machines

  This chapter is written by Dr. Leonid Perlovsky from Harvard University, USA.

- Introduction to Cognitive Systems

  This chapter is written by Dr. Peter Erdi, Professor at Kalamazoo College, USA, co-authored by Dr. Mihaly Banyai (leading author) from Wigner RCP, Hungarian Academy of Sciences.

- A New View on Economics with Recurrent Neural Networks

  This chapter offers a rather specific view on the recurrent neural networks from the point of view of their importance for modeling economic processes and is written by a team of industry-based researchers from Siemens, Germany including Drs. Hans Georg Zimmermann, Ralph Grothmann and Christoph Tietz.

- Evolving Connectionist Systems for Adaptive Learning and Pattern Recognition: From Neuro-Fuzzy, to Spiking and Neurogenetic

  This chapter offers a review of one of the cornerstones of *Computational Intelligence*, namely, the evolving connectionist systems, and is written by the pioneer in this area Dr. Nikola Kasabov, Professor at Auckland University of Technology, New Zealand.

- Reinforcement Learning with Applications in Automation Decision and Feedback Control

  This chapter offers a thorough and advanced analysis of the reinforcement learning from the perspective of decision-making and control. It is written by one of the world's leading experts in this area, Dr. Frank L. Lewis, Professor at The University of Texas, co-authored by Dr. Kyriakos Vamvoudakis from the same University (the leading author) and Dr. Draguna Vrabie from the United Technologies Research Centre, USA.

- Kernel Models and Support Vector Machines

  This chapter offers a very skilful review of one of the hottest topics in research and applications linked to classification and related problems. It is written by a team of young Russian researchers who are finishing their PhD studies at Lancaster University, UK (Denis Kolev and Dmitry Kangin) and by Mikhail Suvorov. All three graduated from leading Moscow Universities (Moscow State University and Bauman Moscow State Technical University).

Part III consists of four chapters:

- History and Philosophy of the Evolutionary Computation

  This chapter lays the basis for one of the pillars of *Computational Intelligence*, covering its history and basic principles. It is written by one of the well-known experts in this area, Dr. Carlos A. Coello-Coello from CINVESTAV, Mexico and co-authored by Dr. Carlos Segura from the Centre of Research in Mathematics, Mexico and Dr. Gara Miranda from the University of La Laguna, Tenerife, Spain.

- A Survey of Recent Works in Artificial Immune Systems

  This chapter covers one of the important aspects of *Computational Intelligence* which is associated with the Evolutionary Computation. It is written by the pioneer in the area Dr. Dipankar Dasgupta, Professor at The University of Memphis, USA and is co-authored by Dr. Guilherme Costa Silva from the same University who is the leading author.

- Swarm Intelligence: An Introduction, History and Applications

  This chapter covers another important aspect of Evolutionary Computation and is written by Dr. Fevrier Valdez from The Institute of Technology, Tijuana, Mexico.

- Memetic Algorithms

  This chapter reviews another important type of methods and algorithms which are associated with the Evolutionary Computation and is written by a team of authors from the University of Aizu, Japan led by Dr. Qiangfu Zhao who is a well-known expert in the area of *Computational Intelligence*. The team also includes Drs. Yong Liu and Yan Pei.

Part IV consists of five chapters:

- Multi-objective Evolutionary Design of Fuzzy Rule-Based Systems

  This chapter covers one of the areas of hybridization where Evolutionary Computation is used as an optimization tool for automatic design of fuzzy rule-based systems from data. It is written by the well-known expert in this area, Dr. Francesco Marcelloni, Professor at the University of Pisa, Italy, supported by Dr. Michaela Antonelli and Dr. Pietro Ducange from the same University.

- Bio-inspired Optimization of Type-2 Fuzzy Controllers

  The chapter offers a hybrid system where a fuzzy controller of the so-called type-2 is being optimized using a bio-inspired approach. It is written by one of the leading experts in type-2 fuzzy systems, Dr. Oscar Castillo, Professor at The Institute of Technology, Tijuana Mexico.

- Nature-inspired Optimization of Fuzzy Controllers and Fuzzy Models

  This chapter also offers a hybrid system in which fuzzy models and controllers are being optimized using nature-inspired optimization methods. It is written by the well-known expert in the area of fuzzy control, Dr. Radu-Emil Precup, Professor at The Polytechnic University of Timisoara, Romania and co-authored by Dr. Radu Codrut David.

- Genetic Optimization of Modular Neural Networks for Pattern Recognition with a Granular Approach

  This chapter describes a hybrid system whereby modular neural networks using a granular approach are optimized by a genetic algorithm and applied for pattern recognition. It is written by Dr. Patricia Melin, Professor at The Institute of Technology, Tijuana, Mexico who is well-known through her work in the area of hybrid systems.

- Hybrid Evolutionary-, Constructive-, and Evolving Fuzzy Neural Networks

  This is another chapter by the pioneer of evolving neural networks, Professor Dr. Nikola Kasabov, co-authored by Dr. Michael Watts (leading author), both from Auckland, New Zealand.

Part V includes four chapters:

- Applications of Computational Intelligence to Decision-Making: Modeling Human Reasoning/Agreement

  This chapter covers the use of *Computational Intelligence* in decision-making applications, in particular, modeling human reasoning and agreement. It is authored by the leading expert in this field, Dr. Jonathan Garibaldi, Professor at The Nottingham University, UK and co-authored by Drs. Simon Miller (leading author) and Christian Wagner from the same University.

- Applications of Computational Intelligence to Process Industry

  This chapter offers the industry-based researcher's point of view. Dr. Jose Juan Macias Hernandez is leading a busy Department of Process Control at the largest oil refinery on the Canary Islands, Spain and is also Associate Professor at the local University of La Laguna, Tenerife.

- Applications of Computational Intelligence to Robotics and Autonomous Systems

  This chapter describes applications of *Computational Intelligence* to the area of Robotics and Autonomous Systems and is written by Dr. Adham Atyabi and Professor Dr. Samia Nefti-Meziani, both from Salford University, UK.

- Selected Automotive Applications of Computational Intelligence

  Last, but not least, the chapter by the pioneer of fuzzy systems area Dr. Dimitar Filev, co-authored by his colleagues, Dr. Mahmoud Abou-Nasr (leading author) and Dr. Fazal Sayed (all based at Ford Motors Co., Dearborn, MI, USA) offers the industry-based leaders' point of view.

In conclusion, this Handbook is composed with care aiming to cover all main aspects of *Computational Intelligence* area of research offering solid background knowledge as well as end-point applications from the leaders in the area supported by younger researchers in the field. It is designed to be a one-stop-shop for interested readers, but by no means aims to completely replace all other sources in this dynamically evolving area of research.

Enjoy reading it.

Plamen Angelov
Lancaster, UK

About the Editor

Professor Plamen Angelov (www.lancs.ac.uk/staff/angelov) holds a Personal Chair in Intelligent Systems and leads the Data Science Group at Lancaster University, UK. He has PhD (1993) and Doctor of Sciences (DSc, 2015) degrees and is a Fellow of both the IEEE and IET, as well as a Senior Member of the International Neural Networks Society (INNS). He is also a member of the Boards of Governors of both bodies for the period 2014–2017. He also chairs the Technical Committee (TC) on Evolving Intelligent Systems within the Systems, Man and Cybernetics Society, IEEE and is a member of the TCs on Neural Networks and on Fuzzy Systems within the Computational Intelligence Society, IEEE. He has authored or co-authored over 200 peer-reviewed publications in leading journals, peer-reviewed conference proceedings, five patents and a dozen books, including two research monographs by Springer (2002) and Wiley (2012), respectively. He has an active research portfolio in the area of data science, computational intelligence and autonomous machine learning and internationally recognized results into online and evolving learning and algorithms for knowledge extraction in the form of human-intelligible fuzzy rule-based systems. Prof. Angelov leads numerous projects funded by UK research councils, EU, industry, UK Ministry of Defence, The Royal Society, etc. His research was recognized by 'The Engineer Innovation and Technology 2008 Special Award' and 'For outstanding Services' (2013) by IEEE and INNS. In 2014, he was awarded a Chair of Excellence at Carlos III University, Spain sponsored by Santander Bank. Prof. Angelov is the founding Editor-in-Chief of Springer's journal on *Evolving Systems* and Associate Editor of the leading international scientific journals in this area, including *IEEE Transactions on Cybernetics*, *IEEE Transactions on Fuzzy Systems* and half a dozen others. He was General, Program or Technical co-Chair of prime IEEE conferences

(IJCNN-2013, Dallas; SSCI2014, Orlando,WCCI2014, Beijing; IS'14, Warsaw; IJCNN2015, Killarney; IJCNN/ WCCI2016, Vancouver; UKCI 2016, Lancaster; WCCI2018, Rio de Janeiro) and founding General co-Chair of a series of annual IEEE conferences on Evolving and Adaptive Intelligent Systems. He was a Visiting Professor in Brazil, Germany, Spain, France, Bulgaria. Prof. Angelov regularly gives invited and plenary talks at leading conferences, universities and companies.

Acknowledgments

The Editor would like to acknowledge the support of the Chair of Excellence programme of Carlos III University, Madrid, Spain.

The Editor would also like to acknowledge the unwavering support of his family (Rosi, Lachezar and Mariela).

Prologue

The *Handbook on Computational Intelligence* aims to be a one-stop-shop for the various aspects of the broad research area of Computational Intelligence. The *Handbook* is organized into five parts over two volumes:

(1) Fuzzy Sets and Systems (Vol. 1)
(2) Artificial Neural Networks and Learning Systems (Vol. 1)
(3) Evolutionary Computation (Vol. 2)
(4) Hybrid Systems (Vol. 2)
(5) Applications (Vol. 2)

In total, 26 chapters detail various aspects of the theory, methodology and applications of *Computational Intelligence*. The authors of the different chapters are leading researchers in their respective fields or "rising stars" (promising early career researchers). This mix of experience and energy provides an invaluable source of information that is easy to read, rich in detail, and wide in spectrum. In total, over 50 authors from 16 different countries including USA, UK, Japan, Germany, Canada, Italy, Spain, Austria, Bulgaria, Brazil, Russia, India, New Zealand, Hungary, Slovenia, Mexico, and Romania contributed to this collaborative effort. The scope of the *Handbook* covers practically all important aspects of the topic of Computational Intelligence and has several chapters dedicated to particular applications written by leading industry-based or industry-linked researchers.

Preparing, compiling and editing this Handbook was an enjoyable and inspirational experience. I hope you will also enjoy reading it and will find answers to your questions and will use this book in your everyday work.

Plamen Angelov
Lancaster, UK

Volume 2

Part III

Evolutionary Computation

Chapter 14

History and Philosophy of Evolutionary Computation

Carlos A. Coello Coello, Carlos Segura and Gara Miranda

This chapter provides a general overview of evolutionary computation (EC), including a short review of natural evolution theories and some basic concepts from natural evolution and genetics that have been adopted in EC. Then, a historical review of EC is presented, including its three main paradigms: evolution strategies, evolutionary programming and genetic algorithms. In the final part of the chapter, a unified view of EC is provided, together with a short introduction to the design of evolutionary algorithms that includes a practical example.

14.1. Introduction

Evolutionary computation (EC) is a research area within computer science that studies the properties of a set of algorithms — usually called evolutionary algorithms (EAS) — that draw their inspiration from natural evolution. Initially, several algorithms intended to better understand the population dynamics present in evolution were designed (Crosby, 1967). However, although the design of the EC schemes is based on drawing inspiration from natural evolution, a faithful modeling of biologic processes is not usually incorporated. Thus, since EAS are usually overly simplistic versions of their biological counterparts, using EAS to model population dynamics is not too widely accepted by the evolutionary biology community (Mitchell, 1998). Instead, the advances achieved in recent decades have shown that the main strength of EC is that it can be successfully applied to numerous practical problems that appear in several areas such as process control, machine learning and function optimization (Fogel, 1995). For this reason, EC should be seen as a general and robust evolution-inspired framework devoted to problem solving.

Although it is not easy to classify the kinds of problems that can be solved with EC, some taxonomies have been proposed. For instance, Everett distinguished between two main uses of EAs (Everett, 2000): Optimizing the performance of operating systems, and the testing and fitting of quantitative models. Another view was proposed by Eiben and Smith (2003) by providing an analogy between problems and systems. In working systems, the three main components are: inputs, outputs, and the internal model connecting these two. They distinguished between three kinds of problems that can be solved with EC depending on which of the three components is unknown. In any case, the important fact is that EC has been successfully used in a huge number of applications such as numerical optimization, design of expert systems, training of neural networks, data mining and many others. In general, EC might be potentially applied to any problem where we can identify a set of candidate solutions and a quality level associated with each of them.

This chapter is devoted to presenting the history and philosophy behind the use of EC. In Section 14.2, a brief review of natural evolution theories is provided. In addition, some of the main concepts from the fields of evolution and genetics that have inspired developments in EC are introduced. Then, Section 14.3 presents the history and philosophy of the first EC approaches ever developed. Some of the latest developments, as well as the current unifying view of EC, are summarized in Section 14.4. Section 14.5 offers some observations on the design of EAs and describes some of the most popular components that have been used when tackling optimization problems with EC. Finally, some concluding remarks are given in Section 14.6.

14.2. The Fundamentals of Evolution

The term "*evolution*" is defined by the Oxford Dictionary as *the process by which different kinds of living organisms are thought to have developed and diversified from earlier forms during the history of the Earth.* A much more general definition of this term is *the gradual development of something, especially from a simple to a more complex form.* The word "*evolution*" originated from the Latin word "*evolutio*", which means unrolling, from the verb "*evolvere*". Early meanings related to physical movement, first recorded in describing a tactical "wheeling" maneuver in the realignment of troops or ships. Current senses stem from a notion of "opening out" and "unfolding", giving rise to a general sense of "development". The term appeared a couple of centuries before Darwin wrote "*On the Origin of Species*". In fact, Darwin did not even use the word evolution in his book until the last line:

> *There is grandeur in this view of life, with its several powers, having been originally breathed by the Creator into a few forms or into one; and that, whilst this planet has gone circling on according to the fixed law of gravity, from so simple a beginning endless forms most beautiful and most wonderful have been, and are being* ***evolved***.

14.2.1. *A Historical Review*

During the 18th century, a group of researchers, called naturalists, managed to gather a great deal of information on the flora and fauna in many different areas of our planet. In an attempt to organize and classify this remarkable amount of information, **Carl Linnaeus** (1707–1778) proposed a set of rules to assign genus and species labels to all known living beings. His taxonomy, called *System Naturae* (Linnaeus, 1735), focused solely on the morphological properties of living beings to define the classification. Since this classification criterion was purely morphological, to Linnaeus, species identified distinct groups with no relation of origin. This perspective, called *fixity of species*, considered that each species was created as it was, and individuals did not experience changes over time. Linnaeus began his study believing this concept, but later rejected it after observing interbreeding between various species. Due to his extensive work in the field, he is considered the founding father of our current taxonomic system.

The accumulation of information provided by naturalists and the progress achieved in the taxonomies led to the adoption of new approaches, different from the fixity of species, and based on the fact that some species came from other species. This idea required defining a new classification that reflected the relationships among organisms. It was called "*natural classification*". Although **Georges-Louis Leclerc**, Comte de Buffon (1707–1788), was the first to question Linnaeus's fixity of species, the first to propose a hypothesis for how one species could come from another was **Jean-Baptiste Pierre Antoine de Monet**, Chevalier de Lamarck (1744–1829). Lamarck, in his *Zoological Philosophy* (de Monet de Lamarck, 1809) presented a systematic description for the evolution of living beings. For Lamarck, species develop as a result of their reaction and adaptation to the environment. These changes, therefore, must be gradual and will occur over long periods of time. Lamarck suggested that certain organs are strengthened by the use that animals make of them, mainly due to the specific nature of their environment. Other organs, in contrast, are atrophied and eventually eliminated because they fall into disuse. For Lamarck, nature developed in the following way: circumstances create a need, that need creates habits, habits produce the changes resulting from the use or disuse of the organ and the means of nature are responsible for setting these modifications. Lamarck believed that these physiological changes acquired over the life of an organism could be transmitted to offspring. This hypothesis is known as the "*inheritance of acquired characteristics*" and is also commonly referred to as *Lamarckism*. We can say, therefore, that Lamarck was the first to formulate a strictly evolutionary hypothesis, although the word "evolution" was at that time reserved for the development of the embryo, so his proposal was referred to as "*transformism*". Despite Lamarck's hypothesis, there was no experimental evidence for the existence of mechanisms by which individuals could transmit the alleged improvements acquired over the course of their lives. In fact, Lamarckism is now considered an obsolete theory. The principles governing the transformation of the individual characters, which are now commonly accepted by science, were first established by Darwin and Wallace. The principles governing the transmission or inheritance of these characteristics were first established by Mendel.

In 1858, **Charles Robert Darwin** (1809–1882) and **Alfred Russel Wallace** (1823–1913) gave a presentation at the Linnean Society of London on a theory of the evolution of species by means of "*natural selection*" (Darwin and Wallace, 1858). One year later, Darwin published *On the Origin of Species* (Darwin, 1859), a work in which he provided a detailed explanation of his theory supported by numerous experiments and observations of nature. Darwin's theory — usually known as *Darwinism* — is based on a set of related ideas which try to explain different features of biological reality:

- Living beings are not static; they change continuously: Some new organisms are created and some die out. This process of change is gradual, slow and continuous, with no abrupt or discontinuous steps.
- Species diversify, by adapting to different environments or ways of life, thus branching out. The implication of this phenomenon is that all species are somehow related — to varying degrees — and ultimately all species have a single origin in one common and remote ancestor. That is, all living organisms can be traced back to a single and common origin of life.
- Natural selection is the key to the system. It is conceived as a result of two factors: The inherited natural variability of the individuals of a species, and the selection through survival in the struggle for life, i.e., the fittest individuals, who were born with favorable spontaneous modifications better suited to the environment, and are thus more likely to survive, reproduce, and leave offspring with these advantages. This implies that each slight variation, if useful, is preserved.

Although Darwin knew that there should be a mechanism for transmitting these characteristics from parents to offspring, he was unable to discover the transmission mechanism. It was **Gregor Johann Mendel** (1822–1884) who suggested a number of hypotheses which would set the basic underlying principles of heredity. Mendel's research (Mendel, 1865) focused on plants (peas) and, especially on individual features, all unequivocally different from one other and having the peculiarity of not being expressed in a graduated form, i.e., the feature is only present or not present. This research led Mendel to three important conclusions:

- The inheritance of each trait is determined by "units" or "factors" that are passed on to descendants unchanged. These units are now called "*genes*".
- An individual inherits one such unit from each parent for each trait.

- A trait may not show up in an individual but can still be passed on to the next generation. In this sense, the term "*phenotype*" refers to the set of physical or observable characteristics of an organism, while the term "*genotype*" refers to the individual's complete collection of genes. The difference between genotype and phenotype is that the genotype can be distinguished by looking at the deoxyribonucleic acid (DNA) of the cells and the phenotype can be established from observing the external appearance of an organism.

Mendel's laws are the foundation of modern genetics and abolished the idea that characteristics are transmitted from parents to children through bodily fluids so that, when mixed, cannot be separated, thus causing the offspring to have characteristics that will mix the characteristics of the parents. This theory is called "*pangenesis*" and was mainly based on observations such as how crossing plants with red flowers with plants with white flowers produces plants with pink flowers. Starting from Mendel's advances in genetics and the concept of natural selection, in the thirties and forties the "*modern evolutionary synthesis*" was established (Fisher, 1930; Haldane, 1932; Wright, 1931). Basically, this theory (Huxley, 1942) served as a link between the unity of evolution ("the gene") and the mechanism of evolution ("the selection"), i.e., gradual changes and natural selection in populations are the primary mechanism of evolution. According to this theory, genetic variation in populations arises mainly by chance through mutation (alteration or change in the genetic information — genotype — of a living being) and recombination (the mixing of chromosomes produced at meiosis).

14.2.2. *Main Concepts*

In the above description, some important definitions related to evolution and genetics were introduced. This section is devoted to describing some other terms that have been used in some popular books and papers on EC. A complete list of the terms contained in the papers on EC would be too extensive to be included. For this reason, we have selected the most broadly used terms:

- *DNA*: Nucleic acid that consists of two long chains of nucleotides twisted into a double helix and joined by hydrogen bonds between the complementary bases adenine and thymine or cytosine and guanine. It is the main constituent of the chromosome and carries the genes as segments along its strands.
- *Chromosome*: Structure within the nucleus of eukaryotic cells that bears the genetic material as a thread-like linear strand of DNA.
- *Gene*: As seen in the previous section, Mendel regarded "genes" as inherited factors which determine the external features on living beings. In modern genetics, a "gene" is defined as a sequence of DNA that occupies a specific location on a chromosome.

- *Diploid cell*: Cell that contains two sets of paired chromosomes. For example, humans have 2 sets of 23 chromosomes, for a total of 46 chromosomes. Exact replicas of diploid cells are generated through a process called mitosis.
- *Haploid cell*: Cell that contains only one complete set of chromosomes. The genesis of a haploid cell can occur by meiosis of diploid cells or by mitosis of haploid cells. A haploid cell will merge with another haploid cell at fertilization, i.e., sperm and ova (also known as "gametes").
- *Locus*: Specific position of the chromosome where a gene or other DNA sequence is located.
- *Genetic linkage*: Tendency of genes that are located proximal to each other on a chromosome to be inherited together.
- *Alleles*: Variant or alternative forms of a gene which are located at the same position — locus — on a chromosome.
- *Genotype*: Genetic information of an organism. This information — contained in the chromosomes of the organism — may or may not be manifested or observed in the individual.
- *Phenotype*: Property observed in the organism, such as morphology, development, or behavior. It is the expression of the genotype in relation to a particular environment.
- *Epistasis*: Type of interaction between genes located at different loci on the same chromosome consisting of one gene masking or suppressing the expression of the other.

14.3. History of EC

EC is a field of research with a fascinating but complex history. In its origins, several independent researchers proposed numerous approaches with the common feature of using natural evolution to inspire their implementations. Some of the developments were also inspired from other, related fields such as artificial life (Conrad and Pattee, 1970) and other areas of artificial intelligence. EC had many independent beginnings, so different terms have been used to refer to concepts that are broadly similar. Given the similarities of the different schemes proposed, the term EC was invented in the early 1990s in an effort to unify the field of evolution-inspired algorithms (Fogel, 1995).

Determining the merits of the various authors is not easy, which is why several different versions of the history of EC have been told (Fogel, 1998). In this section, we review the origins of EC, focusing on the most important milestones. Many of the bases of EC were developed in the 1960s and 1970s. During that period, three different popular schemes inspired by natural evolution were devised: Evolutionary Programming (EP), Evolution Strategies (ESs), and Genetic Algorithms (GAs). These schemes were inspired by the same ideas but some details, like the nature of the representation and the operators applied, were different. In addition, there were several earlier attempts that highly influenced the advances in this area. Some of these proposals can be considered to be the first designed EAs. In other cases, the schemes were substantially different from what is currently known as an EA. In any case, they are historically important because they had a significant impact on the subsequent studies carried out in the field. This section reviews the origins along with the three aforementioned types of EAs.

14.3.1. *Origins*

Wright and Cannon (Cannon, 1932; Wright, 1932) were probably the first researchers to influence the subsequent development of EC. They viewed natural evolution as a learning process where the genetic information of species is continuously changed through a trial and error mechanism. In this way, evolution can be regarded as a method whose aim is to maximize the adaptiveness of species to their environment. Wright went further and introduced the concept of fitness landscape as a representation of the space of all possible genotypes along with their fitness values. This concept is widely used today to study the performance of EAs (Richter, 2014). In addition, he developed one of the first studies where selection and mutation were linked, concluding that a proper balance between them is required to proceed successfully. These ideas were extended by Campbell (1960). He claimed that a blind-variation-and-selective-survival process is one of the main underlying principles of evolution, and hypothesized that "in all processes leading to expansions of knowledge, a blind-variation-and-selective-survival process is involved". This is one of the principles behind Universal Darwinism, a proposal that extends the applicability of Darwin's theory to other areas beyond natural evolution.

Turing can also be considered another EC pioneer. In Turing (1950), Turing recognized a connection between machine learning and evolution. Specifically, Turing claimed that in order to develop an intelligent computer that passes the famous Turing test, a learning scheme based on evolution might be used. In this regard, the structure of the evolved machine is related to hereditary material, changes made to the machine are related to mutation and the use of an experimenter to evaluate the generated machines are related to natural selection. In addition, Turing had previously suggested that these kinds of methods might be used to train a set of networks which were akin to current neural networks (Turing, 1948). Turing used the term "genetical search" to refer to these kinds of schemes. However, this paper was not published until 1968 (Evans and Robertson, 1968) because his supervisor considered it to be a "schoolboy essay" (Burgin and Eberbach, 2013). By the time of its publication, other EAs had already appeared and the term "genetical search" was never adopted by the EC community.

Some important advances were made in the late 1950s and early 1960s, coinciding with the period in which electronic digital computers became more readily available. In this period, several analyses of the population dynamics appearing in evolution were carried out. A survey of the application of digital computers in this field was presented in (Crosby, 1967). Crosby identified three kinds of schemes:

- Methods based on studying the mathematical formulations that emerge in the deterministic analysis of population dynamics. These schemes usually assume an infinite population size and analyze the distributions of genes under different circumstances. An example of this type of scheme is the one developed by Lewontin (1964), where the interactions between selection and linkage are analyzed.
- Approaches that simulate evolution but do not explicitly represent a population (Crosby, 1960). In these methods, the frequencies of the different potential genotypes are stored for each generation, resulting in a non-scalable scheme in terms of the number of genes. In addition, a faithful mathematical representation of the evolutionary system is required.
- Schemes that simulate evolution by explicitly maintaining a representation of the population. Fraser and some of his colleagues pioneered these kinds of methods and they analyzed this approach in a set of papers published over the course of a decade (Fraser, 1957; Fraser and Burnell, 1967). The main conclusions drawn from these studies were gathered in their seminal book (Fraser and Burnell, 1970). From its inception, this model was widely accepted, and several researchers soon adopted it (Gill, 1965; Young, 1966). In fact, even though there are several implementation details that differ from those used in current EAs, several authors regard the works of Fraser as representing the first invention of a GA (Fogel, 1995). As for the implementation details, the main difference with respect to GAs is that individuals are diploid instead of haploid. However, in our opinion, the key difference is not the implementation but the philosophy behind the use of the scheme. Fraser used its algorithms as a way to analyze population dynamics and not to solve problems, which is the typical current application of EAs.

There were other authors who proposed schemes resembling current EAs. Among them, the works of Friedman, Box, and Friedberg are particularly important and often-cited papers. Friedman (1956) hypothesized on the automatic design of control circuits by using a scheme inspired by natural evolution that was termed "selective feedback". His proposals were very different from current ones. For instance, there was no notion of population and/or generations. Moreover, Friedman did not implement his method, and some of his assumptions seem to be overly optimistic (Fogel, 1998). In any event, his research can be considered as the first efforts in the field of evolvable hardware.

Box proposed a technique called "Evolutionary Operation" (EVOP) (Box, 1957) to optimize the management processes of the chemical industry. His technique essentially used a single parent to generate multiple offspring by modifying a few production parameters at a time. Then, one individual was selected to survive to the next generation by considering certain statistical evidence. The system was not autonomous. Specifically, the variation and selection processes required human intervention, so it can be considered as the first interactive EA.

The most important contribution of Friedberg *et al.* to the field of EC was their attempt to automatically generate computer programs using an evolutionary scheme (Friedberg, 1958; Friedberg *et al.*, 1959). In the previous papers, Friedberg *et al.* did not identify any relationship between their proposal and natural evolution. However, in subsequent publications by his coauthors, such a relationship was explicitly identified (Dunham *et al.*, 1963). In their first attempts, the aim was to automatically generate small programs with some simple functionalities that relied on a tailor-made instruction set. In order to direct the search to promising regions, problem-dependent information was considered by defining a variation scheme specifically tailored to the problem at hand. Even with this addition, their success was limited. Even so, some of the analyses they carried out were particularly important to subsequent achievements in EC. Among their contributions, some of the most important are the following:

- The idea of dividing candidate solutions into classes is a precursor of the notions of *intrinsic parallelism* and *schema*, proposed years later by Holland (1975).
- Several instruction sets were tested, showing, for the first time, the influence of genotype-to-phenotype mapping.
- A credit assignment algorithm was used to measure the influence of the single instructions. This idea is closely related to the work of Holland on GAS and classifier systems.

There are several more papers that did not elicit much attention when they were first published, but that proposed techniques very similar to others that were later reinvented. For instance, the work by Reed, Toombs, and Barricelli (Reed *et al.*, 1967) provides several innovations closely related to self-adaptation, crossover, and coevolution.[1]

[1] Some preliminary work on coevolution was started in (Barricelli, 1962).

14.3.2. *EP*

EP was devised by Fogel (1962) while he was engaged in basic research on artificial intelligence for the National Science Foundation. At the time, most attempts to generate intelligent behavior used man as a model (Fogel, 1999). However, Fogel realized that since evolution had been able to create humans and other intelligent creatures, a model mimicking evolution might be successful. Note that, as previously described, some research into this topic had already been published by then. The basic ideas adopted by Fogel are similar: Use variation and selection to evolve candidate solutions better adapted to the given goals. However, Fogel was not aware of the existing research and his proposals differed substantially from them, meaning that his models can be considered as a reinvention of evolution-based schemes.

Philosophically, the coding structures utilized in EP are an abstraction of the phenotype of different species (Fogel, 1994). As a result, the encoding of candidate solutions can be freely adapted to better support the requirements of the problems at hand. Since there is no sexual communication between different species, this view of candidate solutions also justifies the lack of recombination operators in EP. Thus, the non-application of recombination operators is due to a conceptual rather than a technical view. The lack of recombination, the freedom to adapt the encoding and the use of a probabilistic survivor selection operator — not used in the initial versions of EP — might be considered the main features that distinguished EP from other EC paradigms (Fogel and Chellapilla, 1998).

In his first designs, Fogel reasoned that one of the main features that characterizes intelligent behavior is the capacity to predict one's environment, coupled with a translation of said predictions into an adequate response so as to accomplish a given objective. A finite state transducer is a finite state machine (FSM) that allows a sequence of input symbols to be transformed into a sequence of output symbols. Depending on the states and given transitions, they can be used to model different situations and cause different transformations. Thus, Fogel viewed FSMs as a proper mechanism for dealing with the problem of generating intelligent behavior. In his initial experiments, the aim was to develop a FSM capable of predicting the behavior of an environment. The environment was considered to be a sequence of symbols belonging to a given input alphabet. The aim was to develop a FSM that, given the symbols previously generated by the environment, could predict the next symbol to emerge from the environment.

The initial EP proposal operates as follows. First, a population with N random FSMs is created. Then, each member of the population is mutated, creating as many offspring as parents. Five mutation modes are considered: add a state, delete a state, change the next state of a transition, change the output symbol of a transition, or change the initial state. Mutation operators are chosen randomly — other ways were also tested — and in some cases the offspring are subjected to more than one mutation. Finally, the offspring are evaluated and the best N FSMs are selected to survive. FSMs are evaluated in light of their capacity to correctly predict the next symbols in known sequences. Initially, the fitness is calculated by considering a small number of symbols, but as the evolution progresses more symbols are attached to the training set.

In the first experiments carried out involving EP, different prediction tasks were tested: Periodic sequences of numbers, sequences with noise, non-stationary environments, etc. Subsequently, more difficult tasks were considered. Among other applications, EP was used to tackle pattern recognition, classification, and control system design. All this research resulted in the publication of the first book on EC (Fogel *et al.*, 1966). EP was also used to evolve strategies for gaming (Fogel and Burgin, 1969). This work is particularly important because it is one of the first applications of coevolution.

It is also important to remark that in most of the initial studies on EP, the amount of computational results was not ample because of the limited computational power at the time of its inception. Most of these initial experiments were recapitulated and extended in a later period (Fogel and Fogel, 1986), providing a much deeper understanding of EP.

In the 1970s, most of the research into EP was conducted under the guidance of Dearholt. One of the main contributions of his work was the application of EP to practical problems. EP was applied to pattern recognition in regular expressions (Lyle, 1972) and handwritten characters (Cornett, 1972) and to classify different types of electrocardiograms (Dearholt, 1976). These works incorporated several algorithmic novelties. Among them, the most influential were the use of several simultaneous mutation operators and the dynamic adaptation of the probabilities associated with the different mutation schemes.

Starting in the 1980s, EP diversified by using other arbitrary representations of candidate solutions in order to address different problems. The number of applications that have been addressed with EP is huge. In Fogel and Fogel (1986), EP was used to solve routing problems by considering a permutation-based encoding. In order to tackle the generation of computer programs, tree-based encoding was used in (Chellapilla, 1997). Real-valued vectors were used to deal with continuous optimization problems in (Yao *et al.*, 1999) and to train neural networks in (Porto and Fogel, 1995). During this period, the feeling was that by designing problem-specific representations with operators specifically tailored to face a given problem, more efficient searches might be performed (Fogel, 1999). In fact, most EP practitioners defended that by designing intelligent mutation schemes, the use of recombination operators might be avoided (Chellapilla, 1997; Fogel and Atmar, 1990).

Among the aforementioned topics, the application of EP to continuous optimization problems saw a large expansion in the 1990s. Over this period, great efforts were made into developing self-adaptive schemes. In self-adaptation, some of the parameters required by the algorithm are bound to each individual and evolved with the original variables. The variables of the problem are called *object parameters*, while those newly attached are called *strategy parameters*. Initial proposals adapted the scale factor of Gaussian mutation (Fogel *et al.*, 1991). In more advanced variants of EP, several mutation operators are considered simultaneously (Yao *et al.*, 1999). Since self-adaptive schemes surpassed more traditional EP variants, self-adaptation was adopted by practitioners addressing problems where real encoding was not used, becoming a common mechanism in EP (Fogel *et al.*, 1995). Self-adaptive EP for continuous optimization presents several similarities with ESs. The most important difference is that EP does not include recombination. In addition, some implementation details were also different in the first variants devised (Eiben and Smith, 2003). For instance, the order in which the object and strategy parameters were subjected to mutation was different in the two schemes, though these differences vanished over time. Moreover, it has been shown that there are cases where mutation alone can outperform schemes with recombination and vice versa (Richter *et al.*, 2008). There is also evidence that indicates that it is promising to adapt the parameters associated with crossover (Jain and Fogel, 2000), which further stretches the barriers between EP and ESs. Since self-adaptation for continuous optimization was first proposed in ESs, the history of and advances in self-adaption for continuous optimization is presented in the section devoted to ESs.

14.3.3. *Evolution Strategies*

In the mid-1960s, three students at the Technical University of Berlin — Bienert, Schwefel and Rechenberg — were studying practical problems that arise in fluid mechanics and some related fields. Their desire was to build robots that could autonomously solve engineering problems (Fogel, 1998). They formulated these engineering tasks as optimization problems and developed autonomous machines that were automatically modified using certain rules. They also made some initial attempts at using traditional optimization schemes. However, since the problems were noisy and multimodal, their schemes failed to provide promising solutions. In order to avoid these drawbacks, they decided to apply mutation and selection methods analogous to natural evolution. Rechenberg published the first report on ESs by applying these ideas to minimizing the total drag of a body in a wind tunnel (Rechenberg, 1965). Subsequently, other problems like the design of pipes and efficient flashing nozzles were addressed (Fogel, 1998).

Philosophically, the coding structures utilized in ESs are an abstraction of the phenotype of different individuals (Fogel, 1994). This is why the encoding of candidate solutions can be freely adapted to better support the requirements of the problems at hand. In addition, recombination among individuals is allowed in spite of not being implemented in the initial variants of ESs.

In the first problems tested, a set of quantitative discrete variables had to be adjusted. The initial proposal was very similar to the current $(1+1)-$ES and works as follows. First, a random solution is created and considered to be the current solution. Then, the current solution is mutated by slightly changing each variable. Specifically, mutation is implemented by emulating a Galton pin-board, so binomial distributions are used. The principle behind the design of this operator is to apply small mutations more frequently than large mutations, as is the case in nature. The current solution is replaced by the mutant only if the mutant solution is at least as good. This process is repeated until the stopping criterion is reached. Empirical evidence revealed the promising behavior of these kinds of schemes with respect to more traditional optimization methods.

In 1965, Schwefel first implemented an ES in a general computer (Schwefel, 1965). In this case, ESs were mainly applied to continuous optimization. The most important contribution of the new variant was the incorporation of Gaussian mutation with zero mean, which is still the most typical distribution used nowadays. The mutation operator could be controlled by tuning the standard deviations — or step size — of the Gaussian distribution. Studies on the step size resulted in the first theoretical analyses of ESs.

As previously discussed, initial ES variants only kept a single solution at a time. However, in the late 1960s, the use of populations with several individuals was introduced. The first population-based scheme tested is now known as $(\mu+1)-$ES. This scheme uses a population with μ individuals. These individuals are used to create a new individual through recombination and mutation. Then, the best μ individuals from the $\mu+1$ individuals are selected to survive. This scheme resembles the steady state selection that was popularized much later in the field of GAs (Whitley and Kauth, 1988).

ESs were extended further to support any number of parents and offspring. In addition, two different selection schemes and a notation that is still in use were proposed. The first selection comprises the $(\mu+\lambda)-$ES. In this case, λ offspring are created from a population with μ individuals. Then, the best μ individuals from the union of parents and offspring are selected to survive. Schemes that consider the second kind of selection are known as $(\mu,\lambda)-$ES. In this case, the best μ individuals from the λ offspring are selected to survive.

When ESs were first developed, the papers were written in German and, as a consequence, they were accessible only to a fairly small community. However, in 1981, Schwefel published the first book on ESs in English (Schwefel, 1981). Since then, several researchers have adopted ESs and the number of studies in this area has grown enormously. Schwefel's book focuses on the use of ESs for continuous optimization, which is in fact the field where ESs have been more successful. In his book, Schwefel discusses, among other topics, the use of different kinds of recombinations and the adaptation of the Gaussian distributions adopted for mutation. Regarding recombination, some controversies and misunderstandings have appeared. The use of adaptive mutation is one of the distinguishing features of ESs, and the history of and advances in both topics are described herein. Most of the papers reviewed in this chapter involve continuous single-objective optimization problems. However, it is important to note that the application of ESs has not been limited to these kinds of problems. For instance, multi-objective (Igel *et al.*, 2007), mixed-integer (Li *et al.*, 2013) and constrained problems (Mezura-Montes and Coello Coello, 2005) have also been addressed.

14.3.3.1. *Recombination*

Initially, four different recombination schemes were proposed by combining two different properties (Schwefel, 1981). First, two choices were given for the number of parents taking part in creating an offspring: *bisexual* or *multisexual*. In bisexual recombination — also known as local — two parents are selected and they are used to recombine each parameter value. In the case of multisexual recombination, also known as global, different pairs of parents are selected for each parameter value. Thus, more than two individuals can potentially participate in the creation of each offspring. In addition, two different ways of combining two parameter values were proposed. In the *discrete* case, one of the values is selected randomly. In the *intermediary* case, the mean value of both parameters is calculated.

In the above recombination schemes, the number of parents taking part in each recombination cannot be specified. Rechenberg proposed a generalization that changed this restriction (Rechenberg, 1978). Specifically, a new parameter, ρ, is used to specify the number of parents taking part in each individual creation. The new schemes were called $(\mu/\rho,\lambda)$ and $(\mu/\rho+\lambda)$. Further extensions of the intermediary schemes were developed by weighting the contributions of the different individuals taking part in the recombination (Bäck and Schwefel, 1993). Different ways of assigning weights have been extensively tested. Previous schemes were not proper generalizations of the initial schemes, in the sense that the intermediary case calculates the mean of ρ individuals, and not the mean of two individuals selected from among a larger set, as was the case in the initial schemes. A more powerful generalization that allowed for both the original operators and those proposed by

Rechengerg to be implemented was devised (Eiben and Bäck, 1997). Thus, using the notation proposed in this last paper is preferable.

The situation became even more complicated because of a misinterpretation of the initial crossover schemes. In the survey presented in (Bäck *et al.*, 1991), the authors showed a formula indicating that, in global recombination, one parent is chosen and held fixed while the other parent is randomly chosen anew for each component.[2] This new way of recombination was adopted by many authors over the following years, so when using global recombination, the exact definition must be carefully given.

14.3.3.2. *Adaptive Mutation*

One of the main features that characterizes ESs is its mutation operator. In the case of continuous optimization, mutation is usually based on Gaussian distributions with zero mean. In most cases, individuals are disturbed by adding a random vector generated from a multivariate Gaussian distribution, i.e., the candidate solutions x_i are perturbed using Equation (1). In this equation, C represents a covariance matrix.

$$x_i' = x_i + N_i(0, C). \tag{1}$$

From the inception of ESs, it was clear that the features of C might have a significant effect on search performance. As a result, several methods that adapt C during the run have been developed. Many ES variants can be categorized into one of the following groups depending on how C is adapted (Hansen and Ostermeier, 2001):

- Schemes where the surfaces of equal probability density are hyper-spheres. In these cases, the only free adaptive parameter is the global step size or standard deviation.
- Schemes where the surfaces of equal probability density are axis-parallel hyper-ellipsoids. In these cases, the most typical approach is to have as many free adaptive parameters as there are dimensions.
- Schemes where the surfaces of equal probability density are arbitrarily oriented hyper-ellipsoids. In these cases, any positive-definite matrix can be used, resulting in $(n^2 + n)/2$ free adaptive parameters.

The first adaptive ES considered the global step size as the only free parameter. These schemes originated from the studies presented in (Rechenberg, 1973), which analyzed the convergence properties of ESs depending on the relative frequency of successful mutations. These analyses led to the first adaptive scheme (Schwefel,

[2]To the best of the authors' knowledge, Bäck *et al.* (1991) was the first paper where this definition was given.

1981), where the global step size is adjusted by an online procedure with the aim of producing successful mutations with a ratio equal to $1/5$. This rule is generally referred to as the "$1/5$ success rule of Rechenberg". However, this rule is not general so it does not work properly for many functions, which is why self-adaptive ESs were proposed. In the first such variants, the only strategy parameter was the global step size, and this strategy parameter was subjected to variation using a lognormal distributed mutation.

In the case of schemes where the surfaces of equal probability are axis-parallel hyperellipsoids, a larger number of methods have been devised. A direct extension of previous methods considers the self-adaptation of n strategy parameters, where n is the number of dimensions of the optimization problem at hand. In such a case, each strategy parameter represents the variance in each dimension. Another popular ES variant is the *derandomized* scheme (Ostermeier *et al.*, 1994a). Ostermeier *et al.* realized that in the original self-adaptive ES, the interaction of the random elements can lead to a drop in performance. The scheme is based on reducing the number of random decisions made by ESs. Another interesting extension is termed *accumulation* (Ostermeier *et al.*, 1994b). In these variants, the adaptation is performed considering information extracted from the best mutations carried out during the whole run, and not only in the last generation. Note that these last variants favor adaptation instead of self-adaptation.

By adapting the whole covariance matrix, correlations can be induced among the mutations performed involving the different parameters, thus making ESs more suitable for dealing with non-separable functions. The first adaptive scheme where the whole matrix is adapted was presented in (Schwefel, 1981). In this case, the coordinate system in which the step size control takes place, as well as the step sizes themselves, are self-adapted. In general, this method has not been very successful because it requires very large populations to operate properly. A very efficient and popular scheme is covariance matrix adaptation (cma-es) (Hansen and Ostermeier, 2001). In this scheme, derandomization and accumulation are integrated in an adaptive scheme whose aim is to build covariance matrices that maximize the creation of mutation vectors that were successful in previous generations of the execution. This scheme is very complex and the practitioner must specify a large number of parameters. This has led to simpler schemes being devised. For instance, the covariance matrix self-adaptation (CMSA) scheme (Beyer and Sendhoff, 2008) reduces the number of parameters required by combining adaptation and self-adaptation. Many other not so popular schemes that are capable of adapting the whole covariance matrix have been devised. The reader is referred to (Rudolph, 2012) for a broader review of these kinds of schemes.

Finally, it is important to note that several schemes that favor some directions without adapting a full covariance matrix have been devised. For instance, in (Poland

and Zell, 2001), the main descent direction is adapted. The main advantage of these kinds of schemes is the reduced complexity in terms of time and space. Since the time required for matrix computation is usually negligible in comparison to the function evaluation phase, these schemes have not been very popular. Still, they might be useful especially for large-scale problems, where the cost of computing the matrices is much higher. In addition, several other adaptive and self-adaptive variants that do not fit into the previous categorization have been devised. For instance, some schemes that allow the use of Gaussian distributions with a non-zero mean have been proposed (Ostermeier, 1992). In addition, some methods not based on Gaussian mutation have been designed (Yao and Liu, 1997). In this chapter, we have briefly described the fundamentals of different methods. The reader is referred to (Bäck *et al.*, 2013; Rudolph, 2012) for a discussion of the implementation details for several ES variants.

14.3.4. *Genetic Algorithms*

Holland (1975) identified the relationship between the adaptation process that appears in natural evolution and optimization, and conjectured that it might have critical roles in several other fields, such as learning, control and/or mathematics. He proposed an algorithmic framework inspired by these ideas, which was initially called the "Genetic Plan" and was subsequently renamed the "Genetic Algorithm". GAs are based on progressively modifying a set of structures with the aim of adapting them to a given environment. The specific way of making these modifications is inspired by genetics and evolution. His initial aim was to formally study the phenomenon of adaptation. However, GAs were soon used as problem solvers. Specifically, GAs have been successfully applied to numerous applications, such as machine learning, control, search, and function optimization. A very popular use of GAs appeared in the development of *learning classifier systems*, which is an approach to machine learning based on the autonomous development of rule-based systems capable of generalization and inductive learning. The application of GAs as function optimizers was also soon analyzed (De Jong, 1975), defining metrics, benchmark problems, and methodologies to perform comparisons. This is probably the field where GAs have been most extensively and successfully applied.

The evolutionary schemes devised by Holland are very similar to those previously designed by Bremermann (1962) and Bledsoe (1961). In fact, "by 1962 there was nothing in Bremermann's algorithm that would distinguish it from what later became known as genetic algorithms" (Fogel and Anderson, 2000). Moreover, they pioneered several ideas that were developed much later, like the use of multisexual recombination, the use of real-encoding evolutionary approaches and the adaptation of mutation rates. Moreover, since Bremermann's algorithm was very similar to the schemes described earlier by Fraser, some authors regard GAs as having been reinvented at least three times (Fogel, 1995).

Philosophically, the coding structures utilized in GAs are an abstraction of the genotype of different individuals (Fogel, 1994). Specifically, each trial solution is usually coded as a vector, termed *chromosome*, and each element is denoted with the term *gene*. A candidate solution is created by assigning values to the genes. The set of values that can be assigned are termed *alleles*. In the first variants of GAs, there was an emphasis on using binary representations — although using other encodings is plausible — so even when continuous optimization problems were addressed, the preferred encoding was binary. Goldberg claimed that "GAs work with a coding of the parameter set, not the parameters themselves" (Goldberg, 1989), which is a distinguishing feature of GAs. This results in the requirement to define a mapping between genotype and phenotype.

The working principles of GAs are somewhat similar to those of EP and ESs. However, unlike other schemes, in most early forms of GAs, recombination was emphasized over mutation. The basic operation of one of the first GAs — denoted as canonical GA or simple GA — is as follows. First, a set of random candidate solutions is created. Then, the performance of each individual is evaluated and a *fitness value* is assigned to each individual. This fitness value is a measure of each individual's quality, and in the initial GA variants it had to be a positive value. Based on the fitness values, a temporary population is created by applying *selection*. This selection process was also called *reproduction* in some of the first works on GAs (Goldberg, 1989). The best-performing individuals are selected with larger probabilities and might be included several times in the temporary population. Finally, in order to create the population of the next generation, a set of variation operators is applied. The most popular operators are crossover and mutation, but other operators such as inversion, segregation, and translocation have also been proposed (Goldberg, 1989). In most of the early research on GAs, more attention was paid to the crossover operator. The reason is that crossover was believed to be the major source of the power behind GAs, while the role of mutation was to prevent the loss of diversity (Mitchell, 1998). This first variant was soon extended by Holland's students. Some of these extensions include the development of game-playing strategies, the use of diploid representations and the use of adaptive parameters (Bäck *et al.*, 1997).

Among Holland's many contributions, the schema theorem was one of the most important. Holland developed the concepts of schemata and hyperplanes to explain the working principles of GAs. A schema is basically a template that allows grouping candidate solutions. In a problem where candidate solutions are represented with l genes, a schema consists of l symbols. Each symbol can be an allele of the corresponding gene or "*", which is the "do not care" symbol. Each schema designates the subset of candidate solutions in which the corresponding representations match every position in the schema that is different from "*". For instance, the candidate solutions "0 0 1 1" and "0 1 0 1" belong to the schema "0 * * 1". Note that the candidate solutions belonging to a schema form a hyperplane in the space of solutions. Holland introduced the concept of *intrinsic parallelism* — subsequently renamed as *implicit parallelism* — to describe the fact that the evaluation of a candidate solution provides valuable information on many different schemata. He hypothesized that GAs operate by better sampling schemata with larger mean fitness values.

The concept of schema was also used to justify the use of binary encoding. Specifically, Holland showed that by using binary encoding the number of schemata sampled in each evaluation can be maximized. However, the use of binary encoding was not extensively tested in his preliminary works, and its application has been a source of controversy. One of the first problems detected with the use of binary encoding is that, depending on the length of the vector, precision or efficiency might be sacrificed. It is not always easy to strike a proper balance, so dynamic parameter encoding methods have also been proposed (Schraudolph and Belew, 1992). Goldberg weakened the binary-encoding requirement by claiming that "the user should select the smallest alphabet that permits a natural expression of the problem" (Goldberg, 1989). A strict interpretation of this means that the requirement for binary alphabets can be dropped (Bäck *et al.*, 1997). In fact, several authors have been able to obtain better results by using representations different from the binary encoding, such as floating point representations. For instance, Michalewicz carried out an extensive comparison between binary and floating point representations (Michalewicz, 1994). He concluded that GAs operating with floating-point representations are faster, more consistent and provide a higher precision. Subsequently, Fogel and Ghozeil demonstrated that there are equivalences between any bijective representation (Fogel and Ghozeil, 1997). Thus, for GAs with bijective representations, the interactions that take place between the representation and other components are one of the keys to their success.

Holland used the above concepts to develop the *schema theorem*, which provides lower bounds to the change in the sampling rate for a single hyperplane from one generation to the next. For many years, the schema theorem was used to explain the working operation of GAs. However, several researchers have pointed out some weaknesses that call into question some of the implications of the theorem (Altenberg, 1995). Some of the most well-known weaknesses pointed out by several researchers are the following. First, the schema theorem only provides lower bounds for the next generation and not for the whole run. Second, the schema theorem does not fully explain the behavior of GAs in problems that present large degrees of inconsistencies in terms of the bit values preferred (Heckendorn *et al.*, 1996). Finally, considering the typical population sizes used by most practitioners, the number of samples belonging to high-order schemata — those with few "*" — is very low, so in these cases the theorem is not very accurate. In general, the controversies are not with the formulae, but with the implications that can be derived from them. The reader is referred to (Whitley and Sutton, 2012) for a more detailed discussion of this topic. Finally, we should note that other theoretical studies not based on the concept of schema have also been proposed to explain the behavior of GAs. In some cases, the model is simplified by assuming infinitely large population sizes (Vose and Liepins, 1991). In other cases, the Markov model has been used to analyze simple GAs with finite population sizes (Nix and Vose, 1992).

Due to the complexity of analyzing the mathematics behind GAs, there is a large amount of work focused on the practical use of GAs. For instance, the initial GA framework has been extended by considering several selection and variation operators. Regarding the former, note that initially, selection was only used to choose the individuals that were subjected to variation. This operator is now known as *parent selection* or *mating selection* (Eiben and Smith, 2003). However, in most current GAs, a *survivor selection* or *environmental selection* is also carried out. The aim of this last selection — also called *replacement* — is to choose which individuals survive to the next generation. In its most general form, survivor selection can operate on the union of parents and offspring. The number of selection operators defined in recent decades is very large, ranging from deterministic to stochastic schemes. Parent selection is usually carried out with stochastic operators. Some of the most well-known stochastic selectors are: *fitness proportional selection*, *ranking selection*, and *tournament selection*. Alternatively, survivor selection is usually based on deterministic schemes. In the case of the survivor selection schemes, not only is the fitness used, but the age of individuals might also be considered. Some of the most well-known schemes are *age-based replacement* and *replace-worst*. Also of note is the fact that *elitism* is included in most current GAs. Elitist selectors ensure that the best individual from among parents and offspring is always selected to survive. In these kinds of schemes, and under some assumptions, asymptotic convergence is ensured (Eiben *et al.*, 1991) and, in general, there is empirical evidence of its advantages. A topic closely related to replacement is the *steady state model* (Whitley and Kauth, 1988). In the steady state model, after the creation of one or maybe a few offspring, the replacement phase is executed. Note that this model is closely related to the *generation gap* concept previously defined in (De Jong, 1975). The generation gap was introduced into GAs to permit overlapping populations.

In the same way, several crossover schemes have been proposed in the literature. The first GAs proposed by Holland operated with one-point crossover, whose operation is justified in light of the schema theorem. Specifically, Goldberg (1989) claimed that in GAs with one-point crossover, short, low-order, and highly fit schemata — which received the name of building blocks[3] — are sampled, recombined, and resampled to form strings of potentially higher fitness. However, this hypothesis has been very controversial. One of the basic features of one-point crossover is that bits from a single parent that are close together in the encoding are inherited together, i.e., it suffers from *positional bias*. This idea was borrowed in part from the biological concept of *coadapted alleles*. However, several authors have questioned the importance of this property (Whitley and Sutton, 2012). In fact, Goldberg claimed that since many encoding decisions are arbitrary, it is not clear that a GA operating in this way might obtain the desired improvements (Goldberg, 1989). The inversion operator might in some way alleviate this problem by allowing the reordering of genes so that linkages between arbitrary positions can be created. Another popular attempt to identify linkages was carried out in the messy GA (Goldberg *et al.*, 1989), which explicitly manipulates schemata and allows linking non-adjacent positions. More advanced linkage learning mechanisms have been depicted recently (Chen and Lim, 2008). In addition, given the lack of a theory that fully justifies the use of one-point crossover, several different crossover operators, as well as alternative hypotheses to explain the effectiveness of crossover, have been proposed. Among these hypotheses, some of the most popular view crossover as a macro-mutation or as an adaptive mutation (Sivanandam and Deepa, 2007). Regarding alternative definitions of crossover operators, it has been shown empirically that depending on the problem, operators different from one-point crossover might be preferred. For instance, Syswerda showed the proper behavior of uniform crossover with a set of benchmark problems (Syswerda, 1989). In the case of binary encoding, some of the most well-known crossover operators are the two-point crossover, multi-point crossover, segmented crossover and uniform crossover (Eiben and Smith, 2003). Note that some multisexual crossover operators have also been provided. In fact, well before the popularization of GAs, Bremermann had proposed their use (Fogel, 1998). For other representations, a large set of crossover operators have been devised (Eiben and Smith, 2003).

As mentioned earlier, several components and/or parameters in GAs have to be tuned. The first GA variants lacked procedures to automatically adapt these parameters and components. However, several adaptive GAs have also been proposed (Lobo *et al.*, 2007). In these schemes, some of the parameters and/or components are adapted by using the feedback obtained during the search. In addition, most current GAs do not operate on binary strings, relying instead on encodings that fit naturally with the problem at hand. As a result, several variation operators specific to different

[3]The term building block has also been used with slightly different definitions (Radcliffe, 1997).

chromosome representations have been defined. The reader is referred to (Eiben and Smith, 2003) for a review of these operators.

14.4. A Unified View of EC

The three main branches of EC — (EP, GAS, and ESS) — developed quite independently of each other over the course of about 25 years, during which several conferences and workshops devoted to specific types of EAS were held, such as the Evolutionary Programming Conference. However, in the early 1990s, it was clear to some researchers that these approaches had several similarities, and that findings in one kind of approach might also be useful for the other types of EAS. Since these researchers considered that the topics covered by the conferences at the time period were too narrow, they decided to organize a workshop called "Parallel Problem Solving From Nature" that would accept papers on any type of EA, as well as papers based on other metaphors of nature. This resulted in a growth in the number of interactions and collaborations among practitioners of the various EC paradigms, and as a result the different schemes began to merge naturally. This unification process continued at the *Fourth International Conference on Genetic Algorithms*, where the creators of EP, GAS, and ESS met. At this conference, the terms EC and EA were proposed and it was decided to use these terms as the common denominators of their approaches. Basically, an EA was defined as any approach towards solving problems that mimics evolutionary principles.[4] Similar efforts were undertaken at other conferences, such as in the *Evolutionary Programming Conference*. Finally, these unifying efforts resulted in the establishment in 1993 of the journal *Evolutionary Computation*, published by MIT Press. Furthermore, the original conferences were soon replaced by more general ones, like the *Genetic and Evolutionary Computation Conference*[5] and the *IEEE Congress on Evolutionary Computation*. In addition, other journals specifically devoted to EC have appeared, like the *IEEE Transactions on Evolutionary Computation*.

It is worth noting that since the different types of EAS were developed in an independent way, many ideas have been reinvented and explored more than once. In addition, there was no clear definition for each kind of scheme, so the boundaries between EC paradigms become blurred. Thus, for many contemporary EAS it is very difficult and even unfair to claim that they belong to one or another type of EA. For instance, a scheme that adopts proportional parent selection, self-adaptation and stochastic replacement merges ideas that were originally depicted in each of the

[4]See http://ls11-www.cs.uni-dortmund.de/rudolph/ppsn.

[5]The conference originally known as "International Conference on Genetic Algorithms" was renamed "Genetic and Evolutionary Computation Conference".

Algorithm 1.1 Pseudocode of an EA — A Unified View

Initialization: Generate an initial population with N individuals
Evaluation: Evaluate every individual in the population
while (not fulfilling the stopping criterion) **do**
    Mating selection: Select parents to generate the offspring
    Variation: Apply variation operators to the mating pool to create a child population
    Evaluation: Evaluate the child population
    Survivor selection: Select individuals for the next generation
end while

initial types of EAs. For this reason, when combining ideas that were originated by practitioners of the different EC paradigms — which is very typical — it is preferable to use the generic terms EC and EA.

In recent decades, several papers comparing the differences and similarities of the different types of EAs have appeared (Bäck *et al.*, 1993). In addition, some authors have proposed unifying and general frameworks that allow for the implementation of any of these schemes (Bäck, 1996; De Jong, 2006). In fact, note that with a pseudocode as simple as the one shown in Algorithm 1.1, any of the original schemes can be implemented. Although this simple pseudocode does not fit with every contemporary EA, it does capture the main essence of EC by combining population, random variation and selection. Two interesting books where the unifying view is used are: (De Jong, 2006; Eiben and Smith, 2003).

The last two decades have seen an impressive growth in the number of EC practitioners. Thus, the amount of research that has been conducted in the area is huge. For instance, EAs have been applied to several kinds of optimization problems, such as constrained (Mezura-Montes, 2009) and multi-objective (Coello Coello *et al.*, 2006) optimization problems. Also, several efforts have been made to address the problem of premature convergence (Črepinšek *et al.*, 2013). Studies conducted on this topic include the use of specific selection schemes such as fitness sharing (Goldberg and Richardson, 1987), crowding schemes (De Jong, 1975), restarting mechanisms (Eshelman, 1991) and the application of multi-objective concepts to tackle single-objective problems (Segura *et al.*, 2013b). Other highly active topics include the design of parallel EAs (Alba, 2005) and memetic (Moscato, 1989) algorithms — related to Lamarck's hypothesis which was discussed before — which allows hybridizing EAs with more traditional optimization schemes. Note that for most of the topics that have been studied over these past decades, there were some preliminary works that were developed in the 1960s. For instance, the island-based model — which is one of the most popular parallel models — was proposed in (Bossert, 1967), while some preliminary works on hybrid models were presented as early as 1967 (Kaufman, 1967). The aforementioned works represent only a very small cross-section of the topics that have been covered in recent years. It is beyond the scope of this chapter to present an extensive review of current research, so readers are referred to some of the latest papers published in some of the most popular conferences and journals in the field.

Interestingly, it is also remarkable that while considerable efforts have been made to unify the different EC paradigms, some new terms for referring to specific classes of EAs have also appeared in recent decades. However, in these last cases, their distinguishing features are clear, so there is no ambiguity in the use of such terms. For instance, Differential Evolution (Storn and Price, 1995) is a special type of EA where the mutation is guided by the differences appearing in the current population. Another popular variant is Genetic Programming (Koza, 1990), which focuses on the evolution of computer programs.

Finally, we would like to state that while there has been considerable research into EC in the last decade, the number of topics that have yet to be addressed and further explored in the field is huge. Moreover, in recent years there has been a remarkable increase in the number of proposals based on alternative nature-inspired phenomena. In some cases, they have been merged with evolutionary schemes. Thus, similarly to the period where synergies were obtained by combining ideas that arose within different evolutionary paradigms, the interactions among practitioners of different nature-inspired algorithms might be beneficial for advancing this field.

14.5. Design of EAs

EC is a general framework that can be applied to a large number of practical applications. Among them, the use of EC to tackle optimization problems is probably the most popular one (Eiben and Smith, 2003). The generality of EC and the large number of different components that have been devised imply that when facing new problems, several design decisions must be made. These design decisions have an important impact on the overall performance (Lobo *et al.*, 2007), meaning they must be made very carefully. This section discusses some of the main decisions involved in the design of EAs and describes some of the most well-known components that have been used to handle optimization problems.

One of the first decisions to be made when applying EAs is the way in which individuals are represented. Let us consider a simple optimization problem such as the minimization of the function $f(x, y, z)$ [Equation (2)], where each variable is an integer number in the range $[0, 15]$. Considering some of the first GAs designed, an alternative is to represent each number in base-2 with 4 binary digits.

Values of variables	Binary representation	Integer representation
x = 5, y = 8, z = 3	0 1 0 1 1 0 0 0 0 0 1 1	5 8 3
x = 7, y = 0, z = 11	0 1 1 1 0 0 0 0 1 0 1 1	7 0 11

Figure 14.1: Individuals with binary and integer encoding.

In such a case, individuals consist of 12 binary digits or genes (based on the GAs nomenclature). Another possible choice — which is more extended nowadays — is to use a gene for each variable, where each gene can have any value between 0 and 15. Figure 14.1 shows some candidate solutions considering both the binary and integer representations. Each cell represents a gene of the chromosome. The representation chosen influences other decisions. For instance, the design of the variation operators depends on the representation, which is why it must be carefully selected.

$$f(x, y, z) = (x - 1)^2 + (y - 2)^2 + (z - 7)^2 - 2. \tag{2}$$

Another important component of EAs is the fitness function. The role of the fitness function is to assign a quality measure to each individual, which is then used mainly in the selection stages. The term *fitness function* is usually associated with maximization, so it has caused some controversy when applied to minimization problems. However, changing minimization into maximization or vice versa is trivial, so when connecting selection operators and fitness functions both components must consider maximization or minimization. Depending on the selection operators used, some requirements might be fulfilled by the fitness function. For instance, some selectors cannot operate with negative fitness values. Let us consider an even simpler optimization problem, such as the minimization of the function $f(x)$ [Equation (3)], where x is a real number in the range [0, 15]. In this case, a plausible fitness function for the minimization of $f(x)$ that guarantees that the fitness value of any candidate solution is positive is given by f_1 [Equation (4)]. Note that 191 is the maximum value of the function $f(x)$ in the range considered. Usually, this value is not known. However, any value greater than 191 can also be used. Alternatively, a maximization fitness function that might produce negative values is given by the simpler function $f_2(x) = -f(x)$. In this last case, estimating the maximum value of the function is not a requirement. However, with f_2 not every selection operator can be used.

$$f(x) = (x - 1)^2 - 5, \tag{3}$$

$$f_1(x) = -f(x) + 191. \tag{4}$$

The selection operator is another important component that has a large impact on the overall performance of the EAS (Blickle and Thiele, 1996). The aim of selection is to focus the search on the most promising regions. Some of the first selectors designed made their decisions considering only the individuals' fitness values. However, other factors, such as age or diversity, are usually considered in state-of-the-art EAS (Segura *et al.*, 2013a). Selection operators are applied in two different stages: parent selection and replacement. In both cases, stochastic and deterministic operators can be used, though the most popular choice is to apply stochastic operators in the parent selection stage and deterministic operators in the replacement phase (Eiben and Smith, 2003).

A very popular stochastic selection operator is the *fitness proportional* operator. In the fitness proportional selection, the total fitness F is first calculated as the sum of the fitness values of the individuals in the current population. Then, the selection probability of an individual I_i (p_i) is calculated using Equation (5), where *fit* represents the fitness function. In order to apply this selection scheme, the fitness function of every individual must be positive. Let us assume that we are using the fitness function established in Equation (4) and that our current population consists of three individuals with $x = 2$, $x = 5$, and $x = 12$. Table 14.1 shows the fitness value and the selection probability associated with each individual. One of the weaknesses of this operator is that it is susceptible to function transposition, i.e., its behavior changes if the fitness function of every individual is transposed by adding a constant value. This is illustrated in Figure 14.2. In this figure, a population consisting of individuals A, B, and C is used. Two fitness functions are considered: the first one (f_1) is shown in Equation (4), while the second one (f_2) is generated by substituting the value 191 in Equation (4) by the value 1000. Figure 14.2 shows the fitness values of the different individuals, as well as the selection probabilities associated with the individuals when f_1 and f_2 are applied. Since the selection scheme is susceptible to function transposition, these probabilities differ, as can be seen in the pie charts. In addition, note that with f_2, the selection pressure is very low, i.e., all individuals are selected with very similar probabilities. The reason is that when the differences between the fitness values are small with respect to their

Table 14.1: Fitness values and selection probabilities induced by the fitness proportional selection.

Individual	Fitness	Selection Prob.
$x = 2$	195	0.43
$x = 5$	180	0.40
$x = 12$	75	0.17

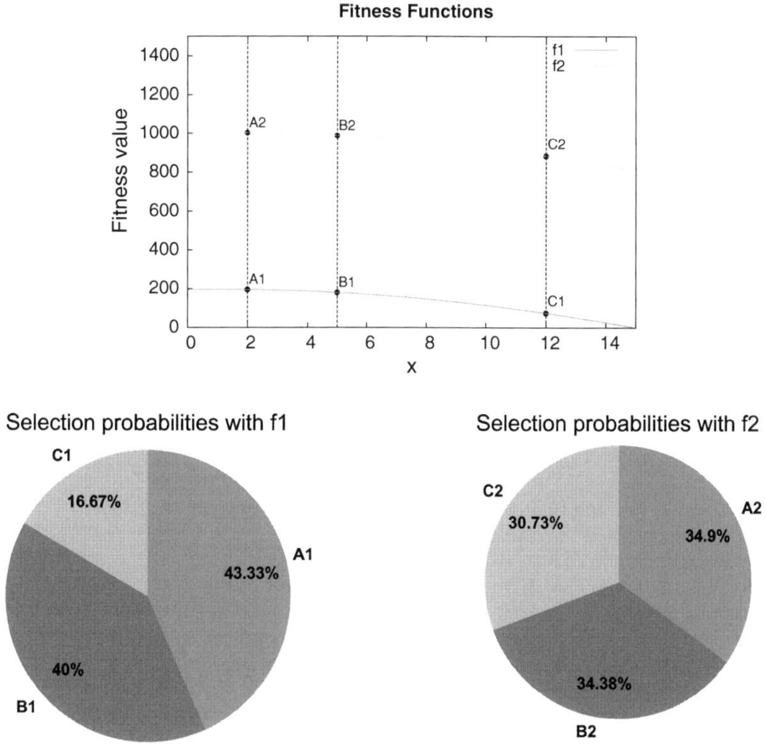

Figure 14.2: Effect of transposition on fitness proportional selection.

absolute values, the selection pressure vanishes. This last effect is a well-known weakness of fitness proportional selection.

$$p_i = \frac{fit(I_i)}{F}. \tag{5}$$

Another quite popular stochastic selection operator is the *tournament selection*. In this case, each time that an individual must be selected, there is a competition between k randomly selected individuals, with the best one being chosen. Tournament selection has very different features than *fitness proportional* selection. For instance, it is invariant to transposition of the fitness function. However, this does not mean that it is superior to *fitness proportional* selection. For instance, when facing some fitness landscapes, *fitness proportional* selection can induce a larger focus on exploitation than *tournament selection*. Depending on the problem at hand, on the stopping criterion and on the other components applied, this might be desired or counterproductive, so it is the task of the designer to analyze the interactions between the selectors and the fitness landscape.

Finally, another quite important stage of EAs is the variation phase. Among the different operators, the crossover and mutation operators are the most popular, and a

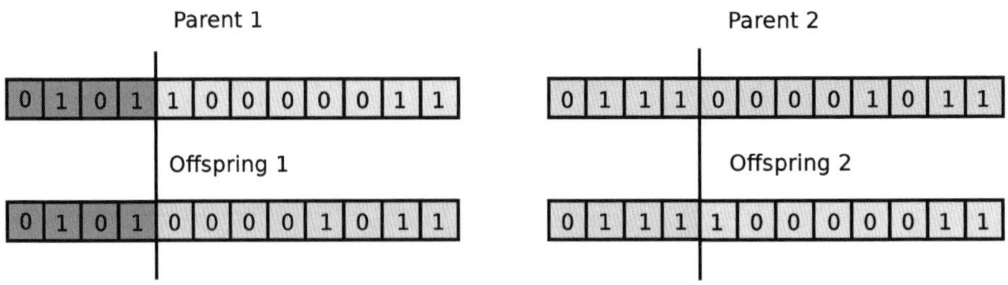

Figure 14.3: Operation of one-point crossover.

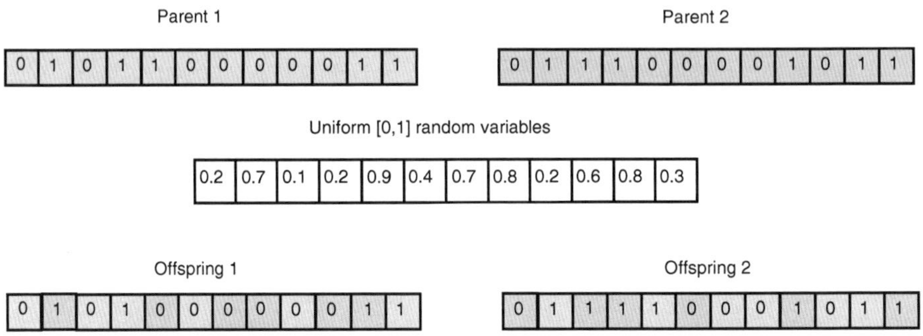

Figure 14.4: Operation of uniform crossover.

large number of different choices have been devised for each. For instance, in (Eiben and Smith, 2003) several operators that can be applied with binary, integer, floating-point, and permutation representations are discussed. In order to better illustrate the working operation of crossover, two popular crossover operators that can be applied with binary, integer, and floating-point representations are presented: one-point and the uniform crossover. One-point crossover (Figure 14.3) operates by choosing a random gene, and then splitting both parents at this point and creating the two children by exchanging the tails. Alternatively, uniform crossover (Figure 14.4) works by treating each gene independently, so the parent associated with each gene is selected randomly. This is implemented by generating a string with L random variables from a uniform distribution over $[0, 1]$, where L is the number of genes. In each position, if the value is below a given value (usually 0.5), the gene is inherited from the first parent; otherwise, it is inherited from the second parent. The second offspring is created using inverse mapping.

It is important to note that the crossover schemes discussed induce different linkages between the genes. For instance, in one-point crossover, genes that are close in the chromosome are usually inherited together, while this is not the case in uniform crossover. Depending on the meaning of each gene and on its position in the chromosome, introducing this kind of linkage might make sense or not. Thus, when selecting the crossover operator, the representation of individuals must be taken into account. Finally, note that as mentioned before, operators that try to learn a proper linkage between genes have been devised (Chen and Lim, 2008). These kinds of operators have provided important benefits in several cases.

Note that not all the components involved in the design of EAS have been presented in this section. In addition, the components discussed are very simple, as most of them were devised at the time when the foundations of EC were being established. In spite of this, many of them are used in several state-of-the-art schemes, so mastering them is important. Regarding their performance, it is not possible to make any categorical assertions. The reason is that the performance depends on all the components, on the interactions that arise among them, and on the fitness landscape. Depending on the components used, different balances between exploitation and exploration can be induced. It is very important to recognize how to modify this balance because it is one of the keys to success. Thus, when designing EAS to solve new problems, several components and parameterizations are usually tested. By analyzing the performance of different components and the reasons for their good or poor performance, some alternative designs might be tested until an acceptable scheme is obtained. Moreover, note that not only do the components have to be selected, but also a set of parameters have to be adapted to the problem at hand. Table 14.2 enumerates some of the most important aspects to define when designing and running EAS. It is necessary not only to define the representation of individuals,

Table 14.2: Some aspects to consider when designing EAS.

Component or aspect	Related decisions
Individual	Representation Evaluation (*fitness function*)
Population	Size Population sizing scheme Initialization
Evolution	Mutation operator Crossover operator Repair operator Intensification operator Probabilities for applying operators Parent selection Replacement scheme
Stopping criterion	Number of evaluations of individuals Generations Time Given signs of stagnation Achievement of a certain quality of solution

but also to specify all the variation operators and selection schemes involved in the evolution process. We must also decide the criterion for terminating the execution of the algorithm. In addition to all of these aspects, we also have to consider the internal parameters associated with many of the operators mentioned above. Since all of these decisions have an important effect on the algorithm's behavior, parameter tuning strategies should be used at this stage. It is also very important to know the features and implications of using the different components and parameter values and recognize the drawbacks that each of them can circumvent. This is because testing every parameter and component combination is not possible given how time and computationally consuming this task is. Moreover, it might also be desirable to use several components and parameterizations simultaneously. Parameter control techniques can be used for such a purpose. Thus, designing efficient EAs for new problems is a complex task that requires using a variety of tools (León *et al.*, 2009; Liefooghe *et al.*, 2011; Luke *et al.*, 2007) and knowledge that has been developed in recent decades through both experimental and theoretical studies.

14.6. Concluding Remarks

EC is a very active area of research that studies the design and application of a set of algorithms that draw their inspiration from natural evolution. The first studies that influenced the development of EC date back to at least the 1930s. However, it was during the 1960s when the roots of EC were established. During the first stages of EC, several independent researchers devised different schemes that were applied to a diverse number of applications. Three different types of schemes were developed: EP, ESs, and GAs. Although each type of scheme had its own features, further developments made it clear that these schemes had more in common than not, so they began to merge naturally. In the 1990s, the terms EC and EA were proposed with the aim of unifying the terminology and they were soon widely adopted by the community. In fact, it is now very difficult to claim that a given state-of-the-art EA belongs to any of the previous classes because they usually combine components from several types of schemes. The number of studies that has been carried out in the last decades is vast. These studies have yielded significant advances in EC; as a result, the number of problems that have been addressed with EAs has grown enormously.

One of the main handicaps of EC is that mastering EAs is a very complex task. One of the reasons is that despite the huge amount of research conducted in recent years, the discipline cannot yet be considered as fully mature. For instance, we are still in a period where different researchers have opposing views with respect to several aspects of EAs, so much more research is still required to fully understand EAs and the large number of different components that have been devised by various authors. Fortunately, many tools that facilitate the use of EAs are now available and recent years have seen significant efforts made to facilitate the application of EAs. In the near future, we expect this area to grow even more as it continues to develop on its path to maturity.

Acknowledgments

The first author gratefully acknowledges the support obtained from CONACyT Project No. 221551. The second author acknowledges the financial support from CONCYTEG as part of the plan "Investigadores Jóvenes — DPP-2014" (project14-IJ-DPP-Q182-11).

References

Alba, E. (2005). *Parallel Metaheuristics: A New Class of Algorithms*. NJ, USA: John Wiley & Sons.

Altenberg, L. (1995). The schema theorem and Price's theorem. In Whitley, D. and Vose M. D. (eds.), *Foundations of Genetic Algorithms 3*. San Francisco: Morgan Kaufmann, pp. 23–49.

Bäck, T. (1996). *Evolutionary Algorithms in Theory and Practice: Evolution Strategies, Evolutionary Programming, Genetic Algorithms*. Oxford, UK: Oxford University Press.

Bäck, T., Fogel, D. B. and Michalewicz, Z. (1997). *Handbook of Evolutionary Computation*, 1st edn. Bristol, UK: IOP Publishing Ltd.

Bäck, T., Foussette, C. and Krause, P. (2013). *Contemporary Evolution Strategies*, Natural Computing Series. New York: Springer.

Bäck, T., Hoffmeister, F. and Schwefel, H.-P. (1991). A survey of evolution strategies. *Proc. Fourth Int. Conf. Genetic Algorithms*, Morgan Kaufmann, pp. 2–9.

Bäck, T., Rudolph, G. and Schwefel, H.-P. (1993). Evolutionary programming and evolution strategies: Similarities and differences. In Fogel, D. B. and Atmar, J. W. (eds.), *Second Annual Conference on Evolutionary Programming*. San Diego, CA, pp. 11–22.

Bäck, T. and Schwefel, H.-P. (1993). An overview of evolutionary algorithms for parameter optimization. *Evol. Comput.*, 1(1), pp. 1–23.

Barricelli, N. A. (1962). Numerical testing of evolution theories. *Acta Biotheor.* 16(1–2), pp. 69–98.

Beyer, H.-G. and Sendhoff, B. (2008). Covariance matrix adaptation revisited — the CMSA evolution strategy. In Rudolph, G., Jansen, T., Lucas, S., Poloni, C. and Beume, N. (eds.), *Parallel Problem Solving from Nature — PPSN X, Lecture Notes in Computer Science*, Vol. 5199. Berlin Heidelberg: Springer, pp. 123–132.

Bledsoe, W. W. (1961). The use of biological concepts in the analytical study of systems. Tech. Rep. Technical report of talk presented to ORSA-TIMS national meeting, San Francisco, CA.

Blickle, T. and Thiele, L. (1996). A comparison of selection schemes used in evolutionary algorithms. *Evol. Comput.*, 4(4), pp. 361–394.

Bossert, W. (1967). Mathematical optimization: Are there abstract limits on natural selection? In Moorehead, P. S. and Kaplan, M. M. (eds.), *Mathematical Challenges to the Neo-Darwinian Interpretation of Evolution*. Philadelphia, PA: The Wistar Institute Press, pp. 35–46.

Box, G. E. P. (1957). Evolutionary operation: A method for increasing industrial productivity. *Appl. Stat.*, 6(2), pp. 81–101.

Bremermann, H. J. (1962). Optimization through evolution and recombination. In Yovits, M. C., Jacobi, G. T. and Golstine, G. D. (eds.), *Proceedings of the Conference on Self-Organizing Systems*. Washington, DC: Spartan Books, pp. 93–106.

Burgin, M. and Eberbach, E. (2013). Recursively generated evolutionary turing machines and evolutionary automata. In Yang, X.-S. (ed.), *Artificial Intelligence, Evolutionary Computing and Metaheuristics, Studies in Computational Intelligence*, Vol. 427. Berlin Heidelberg: Springer, pp. 201–230.

Campbell, D. T. (1960). Blind variation and selective survival as a general strategy in knowledge-processes. In Yovits, M. C. and Cameron, S. (eds.), *Self-Organizing Systems*. New York: Pergamon Press, pp. 205–231.

Cannon, W. B. (1932). *The Wisdom of the Body*. W. W. Norton & Company, Inc.

Chellapilla, K. (1997). Evolving computer programs without subtree crossover. *IEEE Trans. Evol. Comput.* 1(3), pp. 209–216.

Chen, Y. and Lim, M. H. (2008). *Linkage in Evolutionary Computation*, Studies in Computational Intelligence. New York: Springer.

Coello Coello, C. A., Lamont, G. B. and Veldhuizen, D. A. V. (2006). *Evolutionary Algorithms for Solving Multi-Objective Problems*, Genetic and Evolutionary Computation. Secaucus, NJ, USA: Springer-Verlag New York, Inc.

Conrad, M. and Pattee, H. H. (1970). Evolution experiments with an artificial ecosystem. *J. Theor. Biolo.* 28(3), pp. 393–409.

Cornett, F. N. (1972). *An application of evolutionary programming to pattern recognition*. Master's thesis, Las Cruces.

Črepinšek, M., Liu, S.-H. and Mernik, M. (2013). Exploration and exploitation in evolutionary algorithms: A survey. *ACM Comput. Surv.*, 45(3), pp. 35:1–35:33.

Crosby, J. L. (1960). The use of electronic computation in the study of random fluctuations in rapidly evolving populations. *Philos. T. Roy. Soc. B*, 242(697), pp. 550–572.

Crosby, J. L. (1967). Computers in the study of evolution. *Science Progress Oxford*, 55, pp. 279–292.

Darwin, C. (1859). *On the Origin of Species by Means of Natural Selection* (Murray), or *the Preservation of Favored Races in the Struggle for Life*.

Darwin, C. and Wallace, A. (1858). On the tendency of species to form varieties; and on the perpetuation of varieties and species by natural means of selection. *Zool. J. Linn. Soc.* 3, pp. 46–50.

De Jong, K. A. (1975). An analysis of the behavior of a class of genetic adaptive systems. Ph.D. thesis, Ann Arbor, MI, USA.

De Jong, K. A. (2006). *Evolutionary Computation — A Unified Approach*. MIT Press.

de Monet de Lamarck, J. B. P. A. (1809). *Philosophie zoologique*: *Ou Exposition des considérations relative à l'histoire naturelle des animaux*.

Dearholt, D. W. (1976). Some experiments on generalization using evolving automata. *9th Hawaii Int. Conf. System Sciences*, Western Periodicals, Honolulu, pp. 131–133.

Dunham, B., Fridshal, D., Fridshal, R. and North, J. H. (1963). Design by natural selection. *Synthese*, 15(1), pp. 254–259.

Eiben, A. E., Aarts, E. H. L. and Hee, K. M. (1991). Global convergence of genetic algorithms: A Markov Chain analysis. In Schwefel, H.-P. and Männer, R. (eds.), *Parallel Problem Solving from Nature, Lecture Notes in Computer Science*, Vol. 496. Berlin Heidelberg: Springer, pp. 3–12.

Eiben, A. E. and Bäck, T. (1997). Empirical investigation of multiparent recombination operators in evolution strategies. *Evol. Comput.*, 5(3), pp. 347–365.

Eiben, A. E. and Smith, J. E. (2003). *Introduction to Evolutionary Computing*, Natural Computing Series. New York: Springer.

Eshelman, L. (1991). The CHC adaptive search algorithm: How to have safe search when engaging in nontraditional genetic recombination. *Foundations of Genetic Algorithms*, pp. 265–283.

Evans, C. R. and Robertson, A. D. J. (eds.) (1968). *Cybernetics: Key Papers*. Baltimore, MD, USA: University Park Press.

Everett, J. E. (2000). Model building, model testing and model fitting. In *The Practical Handbook of Genetic Algorithms: Applications*, 2nd edn., Boca Raton, FL, USA: CRC Press, Inc.

Fisher, R. (1930). *The Genetical Theory of Natural Selection*. Oxford University Press.

Fogel, D. B. (1994). An introduction to simulated evolutionary optimization. *IEEE Trans. Neural Netw.*, 5(1), pp. 3–14.

Fogel, D. B. (1995). *Evolutionary Computation: Toward a New Philosophy of Machine Intelligence*. Piscataway, NJ, USA: IEEE Press.

Fogel, D. B. (1998). *Evolutionary Computation: The Fossil Record*. New york: Wiley-IEEE Press.

Fogel, D. B. and Anderson, R. W. (2000). Revisiting Bremermann's genetic algorithm. I. Simultaneous mutation of all parameters. In *2000 IEEE Congress on Evolutionary Computation*, Vol. 2, pp. 1204–1209.

Fogel, D. B. and Atmar, J. W. (1990). Comparing genetic operators with gaussian mutations in simulated evolutionary processes using linear systems. *Biol. Cybern.*, 63(2), pp. 111–114.

Fogel, D. B. and Chellapilla, K. (1998). Revisiting evolutionary programming, pp. 2–11.

Fogel, D. B., Fogel, L. J. and Atmar, J. W. (1991). Meta-evolutionary programming. In *Asilomar Conference in Signals Systems and Computers*, pp. 540–545.

Fogel, D. B. and Ghozeil, A. (1997). A note on representations and variation operators. *IEEE Trans. Evol. Comput.*, 1(2), pp. 159–161.

Fogel, L. J. (1962). Autonomous automata. *Industrial Research*, 4, pp. 14–19.

Fogel, L. J. (1999). *Intelligence Through Simulated Evolution: Forty Years of Evolutionary Programming*. Wiley series on intelligent systems. New york: Wiley.

Fogel, L. J., Angeline, P. J. and Fogel, D. B. (1995). An evolutionary programming approach to self-adaptation on finite state machines. *Annual Conference on Evolutionary Programming IV*, pp. 355–365.

Fogel, L. J. and Burgin, G. H. (1969). Competitive goal-seeking through evolutionary programming. Tech. Rep. Contract AF 19(628)-5927, Air Force Cambridge Research Labs.

Fogel, L. J. and Fogel, D. B. (1986). Artificial intelligence through evolutionary programming. Tech. Rep. PO-9-X56-1102C-1, U.S. Army Research Institute, San Diego, CA.

Fogel, L. J., Owens, A. J. and Walsh, M. J. (1966). *Artificial Intelligence Through Simulated Evolution*. New York: John Wiley & Sons.

Fraser, A. S. (1957). Simulation of genetic systems by automatic digital computers. I. Introduction. *Aust. J. Bio. Sci.*, 10, pp. 484–491.

Fraser, A. S. and Burnell, D. (1967). Simulation of genetic systems XII. Models of inversion polymorphism. *Genetics*, 57, pp. 267–282.

Fraser, A. S. and Burnell, D. (1970). *Computer Models in Genetics*. NY: McGraw-Hill.

Friedberg, R. M. (1958). A learning machine: Part I. *IBM J. Res. Dev.*, 2(1), pp. 2–13.

Friedberg, R. M., Dunham, B. and North, J. H. (1959). A learning machine: Part II. *IBM J. Res. Dev.*, 3(3), pp. 282–287.

Friedman, G. J. (1956). Selective feedback computers for engineering synthesis and nervous system analogy. Master's thesis, University of California, Los Angeles.

Gill, J. L. (1965). Effects of finite size on selection advance in simulated genetic populations. *Aust. J. Biol. Sci.*, 18, pp. 599–617.

Goldberg, D. E. (1989). *Genetic Algorithms in Search, Optimization, and Machine Learning*, Artificial Intelligence. New York: Addison-Wesley.

Goldberg, D. E., Korb, B. and Deb, K. (1989). Messy genetic algorithms: Motivation, Analysis, and First Results. *Complex Systems*, 3(5), pp. 493–530.

Goldberg, D. E. and Richardson, J. (1987). Genetic algorithms with sharing for multimodal function optimization. *Proc. Second Int. Conf. Genetic Algorithms and their Application*, L. Erlbaum Associates Inc., Hillsdale, NJ, USA, pp. 41–49.

Haldane, J. B. S. (1932). *The Causes of Evolution*. Longman, Green and Co.

Hansen, N. and Ostermeier, A. (2001). Completely derandomized self-adaptation in evolution strategies. *Evol. Comput.*, 9(2), pp. 159–195.

Heckendorn, R. B., Whitley, D. and Rana, S. (1996). Nonlinearity, Hyperplane Ranking and the Simple Genetic Algorithm. In Belew, R. K. and Vose, M. D. (eds.), *Foundations of Genetic Algorithms 4*, pp. 181–201.

Holland, J. H. (1975). *Adaptation in Natural and Artificial Systems*. Ann Arbor, MI, USA: University of Michigan Press.

Huxley, J. S. (1942). *Evolution: The Modern Synthesis*. Allen and Unwin.

Igel, C., Hansen, N. and Roth, S. (2007). Covariance matrix adaptation for multi-objective optimization. *Evol. Comput.*, 15(1), pp. 1–28.

Jain, A. and Fogel, D. B. (2000). Case studies in applying fitness distributions in evolutionary algorithms. II. Comparing the improvements from crossover and Gaussian mutation on simple neural networks. *2000 IEEE Sympo. Combinations of Evolutionary Computation and Neural Networks*, pp. 91–97.

Kaufman, H. (1967). An experimental investigation of process identification by competitive evolution. *IEEE Trans. Syst. Sci. Cybern.*, 3(1), pp. 11–16.

Koza, J. R. (1990). Genetic programming: A paradigm for genetically breeding populations of computer programs to solve problems. Tech. Rep., Stanford, CA, USA.

León, C., Miranda, G. and Segura, C. (2009). Metco: A parallel plugin-based framework for multi-objective optimization. *Int. J. Artificial Intelligence Tools*, 18(4), pp. 569–588.

Lewontin, R. C. (1964). The interaction of selection and linkage. I. General considerations; Heterotic models. *Genetics*, 49(1), pp. 49–67.

Li, R., Emmerich, M. T. M., Eggermont, J., Bäck, T., Schütz, M., Dijkstra, J. and Reiber, J. H. C. (2013). Mixed integer evolution strategies for parameter optimization. *Evol. Comput.*, 21(1), pp. 29–64.

Liefooghe, A., Jourdan, L. and Talbi, E.-G. (2011). A software framework based on a conceptual unified model for evolutionary multiobjective optimization: Paradiseo-moeo. *Eur. J. Oper. Res.*, 209(2), pp. 104–112.

Linnaeus, C. (1735). *Systema Naturae, Sive Regna Tria Naturae Systematice Proposita Per Secundum Classes, Ordines, Genera, & Species, Cum Characteribus, Differentiis, Synonymis, Locis*. Theodorum Haak.

Lobo, F. G., Lima, C. F. and Michalewicz, Z. (2007). *Parameter Setting in Evolutionary Algorithms*, 1st edn. New York: Springer Publishing Company, Inc.

Luke, S., Panait, L., Balan, G. and Et (2007). ECJ: A Java-based Evolutionary computation research system.

Lyle, M. R. (1972). An investigation into scoring techniques in evolutionary programming. Master's thesis, Las Cruces.

Mendel, G. (1865). Experiments in plant hibridization. In *Brünn Natural History Society*, pp. 3–47.

Mezura-Montes, E. (2009). *Constraint-Handling in Evolutionary Optimization*, 1st edn. New York: Springer.

Mezura-Montes, E. and Coello Coello, C. A. (2005). A simple multimembered evolution strategy to solve constrained optimization problems. *IEEE Trans. Evol. Comput.*, 9(1), pp. 1–17.

Michalewicz, Z. (1994). *Genetic Algorithms + Data Structures = Evolution Programs*. New York, NY, USA: Springer-Verlag New York, Inc.

Mitchell, M. (1998). *An Introduction to Genetic Algorithms*. Cambridge, MA, USA: MIT Press.

Moscato, P. (1989). On evolution, search, optimization, genetic algorithms and martial arts: Towards memetic algorithms. Tech. Rep. C3P Report 826, California Institute of Technology.

Nix, A. and Vose, M. D. (1992). Modeling genetic algorithms with Markov chains. *Ann. Math. Artif. Intell.* 5(1), pp. 79–88.

Ostermeier, A. (1992). An evolution strategy with momentum adaptation of the random number distribution. In Männer, R. and Manderick, B. (eds.), *Parallel Problem Solving from Nature 2, PPSN-II*. Brussels, Belgium: Elsevier, pp. 199–208.

Ostermeier, A., Gawelczyk, A. and Hansen, N. (1994a). A derandomized approach to self-adaptation of evolution strategies. *Evol. Comput.*, 2(4), pp. 369–380.

Ostermeier, A., Gawelczyk, A. and Hansen, N. (1994b). Step-size adaptation based on non-local use of selection information. In Davidor, Y., Schwefel, H.-P. and Männer, R. (eds.), *Parallel Problem Solving from Nature PPSN III, Lecture Notes in Computer Science*, Vol. 866. Springer: Berlin Heidelberg, pp. 189–198.

Poland, J. and Zell, A. (2001). Main vector adaptation: A CMA variant with linear time and space complexity. In Spector, L., Goodman, E. D., Wu, A., Langdon, W. B., Voigt, H.-M., Gen, M., Sen, S., Dorigo, M., Pezeshk, S., Garzon, M. H. and Burke E. (eds.), *Proceedings of the Genetic and Evolutionary Computation Conference* (*GECCO-2001*). San Francisco, California, USA: Morgan Kaufmann, pp. 1050–1055.

Porto, V. W. and Fogel, D. B. (1995). Alternative neural network training methods [active sonar processing]. *IEEE Expert*, 10(3), pp. 16–22.

Radcliffe, N. J. (1997). Schema processing. In Bäck, T., Fogel, D. B. and Michalewicz, Z. (eds.), *Handbook of Evolutionary Computation*. Bristol, New York: Institute of Physics Publishing and Oxford University Press, pp. 1–10.

Rechenberg, I. (1965). Cybernetic solution path of an experimental problem. Tech. Rep. Library Translation 1122, Royal Air Force Establishment.

Rechenberg, I. (1973). *Evolutions strategie: Optimierung technischer Systeme nach Prinzipien der biologischen Evolution*. Stutgart: Frommann-Holzboog.

Rechenberg, I. (1978). Evolutionsstrategin. In Schneider, B. and Ranft, U. (eds.), *Simulations methoden in der Medizin und Biologie*. Berlin, Germinay: Springer-Verlag, pp. 83–114.

Reed, J., Toombs, R. and Barricelli, N. A. (1967). Simulation of biological evolution and machine learning: I. Selection of self-reproducing numeric patterns by data processing machines, effects of hereditary control, mutation type and crossing. *J. Theor. Biol.* 17(3), pp. 319–342.

Richter, H. (2014). Fitness landscapes: From evolutionary biology to evolutionary computation. In Richter, H. and Engelbrecht, A. (eds.), *Recent Advances in the Theory and Application of Fitness Landscapes, Emergence, Complexity and Computation*, Vol. 6. Berlin Heidelberg: Springer, pp. 3–31.

Richter, J. N., Wright, A. and Paxton, J. (2008). Ignoble trails — where crossover is provably harmful. In Rudolph, G., Jansen, T., Lucas, S., Poloni, C. and Beume, N. (eds.), *Parallel Problem Solving from Nature PPSN X, Lecture Notes in Computer Science*, Vol. 5199. Berlin Heidelberg: Springer, pp. 92–101.

Rudolph, G. (2012). Evolutionary strategies. In Rozenberg, G., Bäck, T. and Kok, J. (eds.), *Handbook of Natural Computing*. Berlin Heidelberg: Springer, pp. 673–698.

Schraudolph, N. and Belew, R. (1992). Dynamic parameter encoding for genetic algorithms. *Machine Learning*, 9(1), pp. 9–21.

Schwefel, H.-P. (1965). *Kybernetische Evolution als Strategie der experimentellen Forschung in der Strömungstechnik.* Dipl.-Ing. Thesis, Technical University of Berlin, Hermann Föttinger–Institute for Hydrodynamics.

Schwefel, H.-P. (1981). *Numerical Optimization of Computer Models*. New York, NY, USA: John Wiley & Sons, Inc.

Segura, C., Coello, C., Segredo, E., Miranda, G. and Leon, C. (2013a). Improving the diversity preservation of multi-objective approaches used for single-objective optimization. *2013 IEEE Congress on Evolutionary Computation (CEC)*, pp. 3198–3205.

Segura, C., Coello Coello, C. A., Miranda, G. and León, C. (2013b). Using multi-objective evolutionary algorithms for single-objective optimization. *4OR* 11(3), pp. 201–228.

Sivanandam, S. N. and Deepa, S. N. (2007). *Introduction to Genetic Algorithms*. New York: Springer.

Storn, R. and Price, K. (1995). Differential evolution: A simple and efficient adaptive scheme for global optimization over continuous spaces. Tech. rep., International Computer Science Institute, Berkeley, Tech. Rep. TR95012.

Syswerda, G. (1989). Uniform crossover in genetic algorithms. In *Proc. 3rd Int. Con. Genetic Algorithms*. San Francisco, CA, USA: Morgan Kaufmann Publishers Inc., pp. 2–9.

Turing, A. M. (1948). Intelligent Machinery. Report, National Physical Laboratory, Teddington, UK.

Turing, A. M. (1950). Computing machinery and intelligence. *Mind*, 59, pp. 433–460.

Vose, M. D. and Liepins, G. (1991). Punctuated equilibria in genetic search. *Complex Systems*, 5, pp. 31–44.

Whitley, D. and Kauth, J. (1988). *GENITOR: A different genetic algorithm*. Colorado State University, Department of Computer Science.

Whitley, D. and Sutton, A. (2012). Genetic algorithms — A survey of models and methods. In Rozenberg, G., Bäck, T. and Kok, J. (eds.), *Handbook of Natural Computing*. Berlin Heidelberg: Springer, pp. 637–671.

Wright, S. (1931). Evolution in mendelian populations. *Genetics*, 16, pp. 97–159.

Wright, S. (1932). The roles of mutation, in breeding, crossbreeding and selection in evolution. *VI International Congress of Genetics*, Vol. 1, pp. 356–366.

Yao, X. and Liu, Y. (1997). Fast evolution strategies. In Angeline, P., Reynolds, R., McDonnell, J. and Eberhart, R. (eds.), *Evolutionary Programming VI*, *Lecture Notes in Computer Science*, Vol. 1213. Berlin Heidelberg: Springer, pp. 149–161.

Yao, X., Liu, Y. and Lin, G. (1999). Evolutionary programming made faster. *IEEE Trans. Evol. Comput.*, 3(2), pp. 82–102.

Young, S. S. (1966). Computer simulation of directional selection in large populations. I. the programme, the additive and the dominance models. *Genetics*, 53, pp. 189–205.

Chapter 15

A Survey of Recent Works in Artificial Immune Systems

Guilherme Costa Silva and Dipankar Dasgupta

This report aims to bring the state-of-the-art of artificial immune systems (AISs) and the literature review during the last five years, presenting some Immune-based methods, their applications and provides several considerations on how immune analogies can contribute to the development of more efficient and robust immunity-inspired algorithms.

15.1. Introduction

Artificial immune systems (AISs), alternatively known as immune-inspired systems or immuno-logical computation, is a research line which are developed based on abstractions derived from the biological immune system. Many researches related to computational algorithms have used immunological abstractions as an inspiration, through algorithms based on some immunological theories or models and capable of solving computational or engineering real-world applications.

The biological immune system is an autonomic system able to provide a defense mechanism against possible diseases and threats to the body. Many studies have been performed in order to explain exactly how this mechanism is important in biology. Each theory or model of immune systems can provide analogies to many computational and engineering problems, these analogies serve as metaphors for the development of methods and techniques to reproduce some features found in the biological immune system and then, provide an efficient solution to a specific problem.

These systems can be applied to a wide set of problems in Engineering and in Computer Science, such as optimization, clustering, information retrieval, anomaly detection, machine learning and pattern recognition, among other problems, adopting different abstractions associated to system components or the application environment, depending on the context of the problem studied.

AIS has been widely studied throughout the years, with several approaches and applications in literature, with the development and improvement of these, as well as their applications which have become very popular in literature. In addition, there are some other aspects that can be considered as relevant and recent remarks in the research, such as the increasing of hybrid AIS approaches, the contributions of research in some multidisciplinary studies, and the contributions of AIS approaches in the immunology whose impact is so far unknown, among others.

This survey aims to present the highlights of AIS research during the last five years, including new approaches, improvements in classical techniques and reviews in these algorithms, as well as their applications in different problems in literature. This paper will also review some information about AIS according to biological points of view, but often presenting their relation to the AIS researches. In addition, the survey in (Dasgupta *et al.*, 2011), will be revisited according to these aspects. Further sections will discuss the state-of-the-art, approaches according to analogies and applications of models.

15.2. State-of-the-Art

Early works, starting from (Forrest *et al.*, 1994), are focused on the Self/Non-self Discrimination principle applied to anomaly detection. These methods consist of supervised learning based techniques inspired on the negative selection process, which has a censoring feature occurred in the thymus. The Negative Selection Algorithms (NSA) use Self-based training data for detectors generation through Non-self space, which may be equivalent to an anomaly detection.

The reason for inspiration in the biological immune system may be related to its robustness and the faster response provided in the human immune system, in which a more effective and faster response to an antigen is expected for its next occurrences, after the first time this same antigen was seen in the body. The expected objective of using an immune-inspired approach, once applied to an engineering problem, is to provide a similar behavior for an engineering problem solution, mainly in the concept of anomaly detection.

A first survey about AIS was done in (Dasgupta and Attoh-Okine, 1997). A brief description about immune models, such as Immune Networks and Negative Selection, and applications of first immune-inspired approach, such as Computer Security, Pattern Recognition, Time Series Anomaly Detection and Fault Diagnosis, were reported in the survey, and then, in the first book about these systems in, (Dasgupta, 1998).

The development of novel engineering tools based on immunological theories and models have been provided for many applications as seen on (De Castro and Timmis, 2002), in which a framework for the development of immune-inspired engineering systems, as well as their applications, comparisons to other computational intelligence paradigms and also proposal for some hybrid systems were considered. Since then, applications such as Optimization approaches based on the Clonal Selection Theory or on the B cells, Pattern Recognition approaches and Clustering approaches based on the Immune Idiotypic Network.

Novel approaches to anomaly detection based on alternate models of the biological immune system, like the infectious non-self and danger models, have appeared. These models, implied by their biological counterpart, may depend on prior expert knowledge which defines normal and abnormal events, suggested by biological analogies, as the Self-Non-self principle, which relies on the Negative Selection process, analogous to a supervised machine learning method that defines the normal and anomalous feature space.

Most aspects of these algorithms, including alternate versions and improvements developed, are seen in (Dasgupta and Niño, 2008), a book in which many aspects and most immunological computation objectives and proposals are reviewed and discussed. This book has the most updated information about the research field so far. This survey will cover most aspects of AIS within these last five years, discussing novel approaches and other aspects of the research, as well as providing additional information on how AIS research has been lead during these years in terms of models, applications and approaches developed.

15.3. Artificial Immune System Approaches

Several immune-inspired systems have been developed in order to provide more efficient results for problems such as anomaly detection, optimization, clustering, time series and pattern recognition, among other applications.

Algorithms that adopt multiple models for immunological abstraction (i.e., clonal selection algorithm (CSA) applied to optimization of negative selection algorithms), the predominant model related to its research and applications focus will be considered in the list of methods in each subsection, since these methods can be combined and are not mutually exclusive.

15.3.1. *Immune Response Models*

In biology, the main bottleneck was to define how the nature of the immune responses is in fact. The most accepted model is related to the concepts of Self-non-self Discrimination, which consists in recognizing foreign antigens. This model has inspired the computer virus detection approach of Forrest *et al.* (1994), and many approaches and improvements were done since then.

As in biology, it was discovered that "non-self" antigens alone are not sufficient to trigger T cell activation, the model of costimulation signals would explain this issue, and then, other models of immune response were proposed to explain several immunological phenomena. These models have offered other analogies for AIS approaches, mainly related to anomaly detection systems, which would be applied to different problems, depending on the analogy.

Each approach has differences related to data analysis. However, all of them have a transitional link as described in (Costa Silva *et al.*, 2012b). With complementary functions to be further discussed, each immunological model has advantages and disadvantages that should be taken into account for each application environment.

Usually, Self-non-self and negative selection approaches are seen as a distinct group in AIS approaches, as well as immune networks and clonal selection approaches. In this survey, Self-non-self approaches and most models of immune response are grouped into algorithms based on the immune response, since these techniques are applied to anomaly detection and they have points in common, being a part of a transitional link.

The response models which inspire anomaly detection systems will be further discussed regarding the corresponding model, usually based on T cells or their interaction with antigen presenting cells (APCs), but not limited to this analogy. Since the immune system analogy is closely related to the anomaly detection problem, by providing a response to pathogens which may threaten the body, most algorithms are related to anomaly detection, but not all of them, as there are other aspects to be explored in these models. The following section will bring some concepts and advances in these approaches.

15.3.1.1. *Self-non-self/negative selection-based algorithms*

The concept of Self-non-self Discrimination defines the Biological Immune System with the purpose to defend the body against foreign substances (non-self). Considering these substances as potential causes of diseases, the body must respond to these. For this purpose, the immune cells, especially lymphocytes, should not recognize the substances in the body (Self) through a maturation process, known as the negative selection. This process eliminates all lymphocytes which have high affinity to self antigens.

In order to improve the training mechanism of these algorithms, several approaches were considered, as the *V-detector*, a well-developed Negative Selection-based approach with coverage estimation. This algorithm was exposed to sensitivity tests in (Ji and Dasgupta, 2009), in order to expose its advantages and drawbacks.

Some other improvements for NSA were employed, as in (Almeida *et al.*, 2010) with some operators such as radius and detector overlap checking, in (Li *et al.*, 2010) with an outlier robust inspired by immune suppression and applied for noise in (Wang *et al.*, 2011) with boundary management for detectors and in (Gong *et al.*, 2012) with a further training mechanism. Detector generation aspects were reviewed in (Jinyin and Dongyoung, 2011), and the cooperative co-evolution detector generation, a parallel gene-based model, is included. In (Wang *et al.*, 2012), fractional distances are tested in order to verify their applicability to high dimensional problems, since data relative contrast is related to data dimensionality.

The development of NS-based approaches without detectors was considered in (Liskiewicz and Textor, 2010), for string-based applications. In (Costa Silva *et al.* 2012), a fuzzy view of negative and positive selection processes was discussed with approaches proposed. In this view, antigen recognition has a fuzzy nature and the objective of thymic selection is the maturation of cells with an intermediate affinity to self. This model considers both positive and negative selection mechanisms. Two approaches were proposed based on the model, one of them without detector generation but considering the non-self space as a deviation of self patterns according to a fuzzy inference system.

Recently, shape-space representations were evaluated in (McEwan and Hart, 2009), then, some classifiers and an alternative representational abstraction based on linear squares were presented to demonstrate the flaws of a n-dimensional-based technique and how they can be outperformed by alternative representations. The basis discovery and decomposition in the immune repertoire representation were represented by a Matching Pursuit like process and based on equivalent algebraic and algorithmic mechanisms. The shape-space representation for machine learning AIS was considered inferior, because it is considered to reduce potential value of immune-inspired approaches.

Some other interesting improvements or applications of self-non-self-based methods are listed in Table 15.1.

The main advantages of negative selection-based algorithms are the ease implementation and intuitive principle, based on the input training data, the shape-space concept and distance metrics like euclidean or hamming distance, depending on the data. The training phase of the algorithm also favors the approach by the management of the non-self Space. However, the algorithm has issues regarding the test phase, mainly because of its limitations due to the *curse of dimensionality* issue. In addition, these approaches may have some context issues that may represent a hindrance to a proper anomaly detection.

15.3.1.2. *The infectious non-self/pattern recognition receptors-based algorithms*

Some models were proposed in order to provide a proper explanation about biological immune system and its problems. One of them was the Infectious Non-self model, which extends the two-signal costimulatory model and tries to explain some elements that could lead to an immune response.

Table 15.1: Some other negative selection-based related works.

Approach	Reference	Description	Application
Negative Selection	(Poggiolini and Engelbrecht, 2013)	Introduction of a feature detection rule with the correlation between rules of a particular problem domain.	Car evaluation dataset
Negative Selection	(Ghosh and Srinivasan, 2011)	Use of spherical detectors in the non-self space as detectors with a boundary detection feature.	The Distillation Column Startup Case Study
Arisytis	(Ma *et al.*, 2008)	Addition of an antigen feedback mechanism that provides maturing process and once activated by more antigens they become legitimate detectors.	Intrusion Detection Dataset (KDD Cup'99)
T-detector Maturation Algorithm (TMA)	(Chen *et al.*, 2012)	Addition of overlap rate metric, suppression operator to control distance among detectors according to logic operators and the combination of these features and of a self-radius learning mechanism in another version.	—
NSA with Mahalanobis Distance (MDNS)	(Chen, 2013)	Employment of Mahalanobis distance metric to improve the classification power and provide more quality to detectors.	Medical diagnosis and quality inspection problems
Negative Selection	(Mahapatra *et al.*, 2013)	Use of NSA as an operator that combines the different results of maximum information entropy and global thresholding.	Image thresholding problems
NSA	(Zeng *et al.*, 2013)	Improvement of NSA through a bidirectional matching rule for a detector.	—
NSA	(Chen *et al.*, 2013)	Addition of operators based on Clonal Selection.	Wireless sensor network problems
GB-RNSA	(Chen *et al.*, 2013)	Use of detectors allocation based on the coverage of grids in non-self space. Comparition of its performance to real-valued NSA and V-Detector.	—
Evolutionary NSA	(Xu *et al.*, 2009)	Evaluation of complexity and influence of self set in average time of the algorithm.	Anomaly Detection problems
Multilevel Immune Learning Algorithm	(Chen, 2013)	Improvements in the algorithm regarding the detection generation using a variable-recessive based threshold.	Intrusion Detection problems

(*Continued*)

Table 15.1: (*Continued*)

Approach	Reference	Description	Application
Self-non-self based method	(Wang and Jiang, 2011)	"*A dynamically assigned sense of self of the protected program*", which aims to prevent re-classification of data in problems.	Malware Detection problems
Self-non-self based method	(Secker *et al.*, 2008)	Application of cloning, mutation and memory mechanisms and a confirmation signal to affinity of information based in costimulatory signals.	Web mining
Negative Database (NDB)	(Zhao and Luo, 2013)	Use of real-valued representation in an alternative to binary representation to improve reversal of database.	Privacy-preserving data publication problems
Negative Survey	(Bao *et al.*, 2013)	Review of methods to estimate positive surveys.	Information retrieval
Negative Survey	(Groat *et al.*, 2013)	An alternate application of negative surveys.	Participatory sensing applications
Negative Authentication	(Dasgupta and Azeem, 2008)	Generation of invalid credentials (anti-passwords) in order to detect or filter invalid attempts of authentication.	Computer security
Negative Authentication	(Dasgupta and Saha, 2010)	Validation and sensitive analysis (number of passwords, confusion parameters and coverage) of the model.	Computer security

An approach considered in this group was the Conserved Self Pattern Recognition Algorithm, applied to a recurrent database of anomaly detection problems and improved with selective mechanisms and tests performed with comparative datasets among different approaches. The algorithm is also based on the Negative Selection, however, with costimulatory mechanisms based in the Pattern Recognition Receptors. An improved version of the algorithm applied to computer security was developed in (Yu and Dasgupta, 2011) with a near deterministic mechanism of detector allocation.

The Infectious Non-self model has also inspired a Dendritic Cell-based approach: The Toll-like Receptor Algorithm was designed to intrusion detection problems with training mechanisms and a simplified signal scheme. The interaction between APCs and T cells is the basis of the algorithm. A Structured version of the algorithm was proposed in (Nejad *et al.*, 2012), this version considers the Non-self space analysis a criterion for antigen recognition after signal exposure.

A NSA-based approach with PRR inspired mechanisms was proposed in (Zheng *et al.*, 2013). The named PRR-2NSA combines the inspiration on Pattern Recognition Receptors, whose data are generated via hard clustering and dissimilarity measurements, and a "Dual Negative Selection" strategy, in which NSA is applied to classifier maturation to assure it does not match with any other classifier, and once again to training data, to assure it does not match with any normal data. The proposed algorithm is tested to dataset benchmarks and is compared to the 2NSA without PRR and the V-detector, with better performance. A similar strategy for APC data generation was adopted in the semi-supervised Immune Classifier Generation Algorithm (SICGA) in (Ying, 2003), but with APC and PRR data being generated based on k-means algorithm and APC radius metric, and tests being performed in Iris, Chess, and Breast Cancer Wisconsin datasets in comparison to V-detector results.

In summary, there are few approaches inspired on the Infectious Non-self model of immune response. However, this model is supposed to be halfway between Self-Non-self-based Model and the Danger Model in terms of development of AIS approaches, as the concept of signals, implied by the pattern recognition receptors, and contextualization of anomaly represented by PAMPs or by a conserved self pattern are features that indicate anomalies in an application.

15.3.1.3. *Danger model-based algorithms*

Another proposal was the Danger Model, usually referred as Danger Theory,[1] which defines that the immune response occurs during a distress event from the body, and activation signals are sent by damaged cells. Both models also define a higher influence of innate immunity on adaptive immunity.

Once introduced as a new immune-inspired paradigm and designed for computer security applications, this immunological model would provide a second generation of immune-inspired algorithms. Mainly represented by the Dendritic Cell Algorithm, evaluated in (Greensmith and Aickelin, 2009), these algorithms were based in the correlation between system behavior (Danger and Safe signals) and potential anomalous processes (Antigens).

The algorithm was further simplified in order to work as a deterministic algorithm, with further formalization, formulations, advances, comparison to other algorithms, functionality analysis and complexity analysis, which clarifies most implementing issues for the algorithm. Mathematical aspects related to its geometrical interpretation and linearity are also discussed. A progress analysis and

[1] The Danger Model is seen as a theory, but according to immunologists, it is postulated as a model rather than a theory. This is also applied to Infectious Non-self Model.

Table 15.2: Some other Danger Model-based related works.

Approach	Ref.	Description	Application
A Danger Model-based Architecture	(Elsadig and Abdullah, 2009)	An autonomous and self-responding system with robustness, capacity of detection and prevention of threats and even to recover from damages.	Intrusion prevention system with self-Healing
A machine learning ensemble framework	(Zhu and Tan, 2011)	Application of signals, danger signals and danger zones concepts, to define interactions between classifiers and some operations such as the self-trigger process to evaluate conflicting results.	Spam filtering
DM-FD	(De Almeida *et al.*, 2010)	A Danger Model inspired method which evaluates anomalous data using an input for a fuzzy inference system based on APC signal transduction and its output being based on a mathematical model of NK cells reaction against tumors.	Fault detection
Danger Model Immune Algorithm (DMIA)	(Xu *et al.*, 2013)	An optimization algorithm which employs some danger operators applied to population, and an adaptive danger zone radius.	General optimization problems
DTAIS	(Zhang *et al.*, 2013)	An optimization algorithm which employs three different types of cell and co-evolution mechanisms.	Dynamic nonlinear constrained and single-objective problems
Danger Model-based classification	(Zhang and Yi, 2010)	A classification method based on shape-space representations.	Classification datasets

some suggestions about all these DCA mechanisms were discussed in (Ding *et al.*, 2013), and an updated study is seen in (Gu *et al.*, 2013). Other Danger model related works can be seen in Table 15.2, which in a comparison to the Infectious Non-self model, there are more approaches inspired on this immunological model and some advances in their study.

The Danger Model inspiration can provide many interpretations about the problem environment, mainly in anomaly detection problems, for which this paradigm is widely employed. The expert knowledge is one of the main forms of representation for the analogy, which does not necessarily need to represent danger contexts. Unlike most models representation, Danger Model based approaches may not need a training phase for its algorithms, but a proper representation of its signals is necessary, as stated in (Costa Silva *et al.*, 2012b), and how to obtain this representation for some problems is still a recurring challenge in literature. Some tests in malware detection in (Shafiq *et al.*, 2008) indicate that DCA detection is good, as it has a low rate of false alarms, but compared to other approaches, is far from perfect, even the real-valued negative selection has a higher detection rate according to some results.

Even in some intrusion detection problems, the Danger Model has some limitations such as antigen sampling, robust signal selection and time correlation problems, and some adaptations may be provided for the analogy, as discussed in (Vella *et al.*, 2010). Depending on the context, these algorithms may need an expert model to be employed and provide proper results.

15.3.2. *Clonal Selection-Based Algorithms*

The Clonal Selection Theory[2] is related to the expansion of lymphocytes, antibody formation in response to the antigen presence, and faster responses in further new exposures to the same antigen. This theory has inspired the Clonal Algorithm (CLONALG) applied to optimization and machine learning problems, as well as classification problems, as in (Sharma and Sharma, 2011). The algorithm has somatic hypermutation, with some insights reported in (Jansen and Zarger, 2011), and their importance to an application context in (Ulutas and Kulturel-Konak, 2013), diversity features and is able to search for local and global optima solutions. Since then, it has been widely applied to many optimization problems in the literature. A deep and comparative survey of some approaches, with the emerging research about these algorithms are discussed in (Al-Sheshtawi *et al.*, 2010; Ulutas and Kulturel-Konak, 2011).

In (McEwan and Hart, 2010), the Competitive Exclusion mechanism of clonal selection was discussed, based on generation and filtering aspects, the mathematical models involved and some biological aspects discussed, such as competition factors between clones. As clonal selection has been often seen as an "asexual" selection-based evolutionary approach since its proposal, the authors have proposed two models for the competitive exclusion mechanism: as an approximator with greedy heuristics and global optimization, and as a learning approach. Both approaches were developed in terms of dynamic systems approach rather than the evolutionary approach, and the authors have reinforced that both approaches can

[2]The Clonal Selection, according to immunologists, is in fact accepted as a theory.

coexist and be integrated, and the model developed in the work should be resumed as well.

The research in (Oliveira *et al.*, 2013) adopts an alternative representation for the algorithm inspired by the Pittsburgh-style representation in Genetic-Based Machine Learning. In this representation, the main objective is to select as few instances as possible to represent the training set data without accuracy losses and number of required instances is set dynamically and evaluated during the affinity assessment. The main features of the model are the measurement of the performance of all selected prototypes during execution, representation without redundancy, faster distance calculation between prototypes. For validation purposes, several algorithms were compared to the new approach, and the novel method has shown some promising results.

Some other interesting works are reviewed in Table 15.3.

Table 15.3: Some other clonal selection theory-based related works.

Approach	Ref.	Description	Application
CSA	(Cuevas *et al.*, 2012)	Development of Clonal Selection to deal with estimation of gaussian mixture models with fast convergence and a low sensitivity to initial conditions	Multithreshold segmentation problem
CSA	(Muddada *et al.*, 2010)	The application of Structural Similarity Index to solution evaluation in exploiting the solution structures and its use in threshold divergence, normalization, and proper mutation and cloning operators	General optimization problems
Several CSA approaches	(Yunfang, 2012)	Proposal of a framework to analyze four algorithms: CLONALG, MISA, NNIA, and CMOIA as its principles, mainly used operators and processing methods	Multiobjective optimization problems
NNIA	(Gong *et al.*, 2013)	Improvements on the algorithm to optimize Modified Ratio Association and Ratio Cut objectives for revealing multi-resolution community structures in complex networks	Complex networks optimization
Novel immune clonal algorithm (NICA)	(Shang *et al.*, 2012)	Proposal of an algorithm with dominance function and a selection operator according to it	Multiobjective optimization problems

(*Continued*)

Table 15.3: (*Continued*)

Approach	Ref.	Description	Application
CSA	(Ma *et al.*, 2009)	Proposal of an algorithm with the concept of immunodominance and three measurements, with different strategies to each population generated through each measurement	Multi-objective clustering problems
CSA	(Jabeen and Baig, 2010)	Proposal of a Genetic Programming approach with main features of clonal-based algorithms, aiming to avoid bloat and reduce training time	Classification problems
CSA	(Gan *et al.*, 2009)	Another Genetic Programming-based CSA	Fault detection
CSA	(Karakasis and Stafylopatis, 2008)	Combination of Gene Expression Programming (GEP) to Clonal Selection	Classification problems
CSA	(Tang *et al.*, 2010)	Another GEP-based CSA	Intrusion detection system
Immunoglobulin based artificial immune system (IAIS)	(Chung and Liao, 2013)	A novel clonal-based technique with the isotype switching, which combines different mutation methods	Hybrid flow shop scheduling
GT-AIS	(Jarosz and Burczyski, 2010)	A CSA with Game theory-based fitness evaluation mechanism	Multi-objective optimization problems
AIRS	(Jenhani and Elouedi, 2012)	Literature review and a new version of the algorithm with a new parameter	Classification Problems
EXPAIRS	(Golzari *et al.*, 2011)	Improvement on the algorithm by a nonlinear resource allocation employment to improve affinity metrics	Classification Problems
RL-AIS	(Karakose, 2013)	A CSA with a reinforcement learning mechanism based in Q-learning	Remote sensing data.
CSA	(Riff *et al.*, 2013)	An application of CSA for reinforcement learning with the (C, n)-strategy applied to parameter control	Combinatorial Optimization
CSA	(Hu *et al.*, 2013)	A CSA based on multi-attribute decision-making with co-evolution mechanisms	Clothing uniform assignment problem

(*Continued*)

Table 15.3: (*Continued*)

Approach	Ref.	Description	Application
CSA	(Ding *et al.*, 2011)	Another CSA with co-evolution applied to decision-making in optimization	Clothing uniform assignment problem
CSA	(Liu *et al.*, 2012)	An algorithm which applies B cells as bases and combines different T cells analogies to improve solutions and maintain diversity of them	Grid scheduling problems
AC-CS	(Mohammadi *et al.*, 2012)	An associative classification algorithm inspired on clonal selection and whose affinity measure is based on rules confidence	Classification datasets
AISLFS	(Dudek, 2012)	A classification algorithm local feature selection mechanism	Classification datasets
AIFSA	(Fouad *et al.*, 2011)	A clonal-based algorithm used as a wrapper and weighting algorithm	Feature selection
Motif Tracking Algorithm (MTA)	(Wilson *et al.*, 2010)	A clonal-based algorithm applied to motif detection	Time-series analysis
CSA	(Wilson *et al.*, 2010)	A clonal-based algorithm applied to optimization of SCGM1,1 forecasting	Network security

Clonal selection theory has contributed in several aspects for the development of different systems, many of them applied to optimization related problems. Immunological memory and cloning have been explored, and some operations such as hypermutation, affinity maturation and the selection itself, have been exploited, as several algorithms with different objectives have been proposed, since CLONALG until some multiobjective and well-defined algorithms, in order to solve more complex optimization, or even machine learning problems. Since the proposal of Clonal Selection-based algorithms, these approaches have been widely studied and some improvements were proposed.

The next model of algorithms, based on the Artificial Immune Network theory, shares many features with Clonal Selection-based approaches and employs more sophisticated features in addition to the ones studied in these approaches. These algorithms are also applied to a diverse set of more complex applications, in comparison to Clonal-based algorithms.

15.3.3. *Immune Network-Based Algorithms*

The Artificial Immune Network paradigm is inspired on the Idiotypic Network Hypothesis, in which is postulated that immune responses may be triggered through idiotypes, possibly unique to antibody and supposely expressed on Immunoglobins (B-cells), also discovered on TCRs. These idiotypes not only recognize antigens, but also recognize paratopes from other receptors, allowing mutual interactions between immune cells and providing more effective responses. The network theory has inspired some approaches, such as an immune network for diagnosis, learning and data mining application, among other models.

Some interesting applications of immune network theory are in automated systems, such as in (Khan and de Silva, 2012), in which the immune network is applied to a self-regulated fault tolerant multi-robot cooperation system, as a robot is modeled as an antibody and its interaction environment is modeled as an antigen. The objective of the application is to provide coordination and cooperation among robots. Other robotic-based applications of immune-inspired systems can be seen in (Raza and Fernandez, 2012).

Most Immune Network approaches are reviewed in Table 15.4.

Table 15.4: Some other Immune Network theory-based related works.

Approach	Ref.	Description	Application
Immune Network Architecture	(Fernandez-Leon *et al.*, 2011)	Development of autonomous mobile robot with immune network metaphor applied to different low-level behavior coordination influenced by environmental conditions	Robotics
A decentralized Immune Network algorithm	(Swięcicki, 2008)	An algorithm with levels of decentralization of the network measured according to antigens and their number during network training	Data mining
Adaptive Immune Response Network (AIRN)	(Liu *et al.*, 2009)	An algorithm with a processing feature based on matching between features, as the network has to reveal patterns in the original dataset	Clustering datasets
The Immune Feature Extracting Network (IFEN)	(Ge *et al.*, 2012)	A feature extraction algorithm with a different features such as selection, cloning and diversity maintenance	Feature extraction related
RA-AIS	(Li and He, 2013)	An Immune Network approach with proper mutation, cloning and suppression operators applied to RFID reader collision avoidance problem	Resource allocation

(*Continued*)

Table 15.4: (*Continued*)

Approach	Ref.	Description	Application
opt-aiNET	(Yang *et al.*, 2011)	Application of the immune-inspired approach to collaborative RFID problem	Resource allocation
aiNET	(De França *et al.*, 2010)	Review of aiNet conceptual and practical aspects	Literature review
dt-aiNET	(Zhang *et al.*, 2013)	Proposal of an aiNet with danger zone-based local search operators	General optimization problems
Predication based aiNET	(Xu *et al.*, 2010)	Proposal of an aiNet with immune predication operator and defined local and global search phases	General optimization problems
aiNET	(Xu *et al.*, 2010)	Proposal of two operators: self-organized criticality based suppression and q-gaussian mutation operator	General optimization problems
WBMOIA	(Xu *et al.*, 2010)	Proposal of an aiNET based algorithm with a weighted sum of objectives as an affinity function and truncation of similar individuals	Multiobjective optimization problems
Immune Network based	(Chen and Zang, 2011)	Proposal of a clustering algorithm in which its components can change and learn patterns. Hierarchical clustering mechanism and antibody memory cells are adopted	Clustering
AIMCA & IMCS	(Liu *et al.*, 2010)	Proposal of two aiNET based algorithms: AIMCA, with dynamical adjust of parameters, and IMCS, with evolution of parameters and a poly-clonal operator in antibodies	Combinatorial optimization problems
Immune Network based	(Liu *et al.*, n.d.)	Proposal of a single B-cell based method aiming to avoid high scale of network and suppression rates	SAR image classification
DHPAINC	(Deng *et al.*, 2013)	Proposal of an approach in which the decision hyperplane is constructed through decision antibodies and those with high quality are stable, defined by a recognition ability function	Classification and speech recognition

(*Continued*)

Table 15.4: (*Continued*)

Approach	Ref.	Description	Application
Autopoietic Model based	(Nanas *et al.*, 2010)	Proposal of an information filtering system inspired by the Autopoietic model of immune networks, with self organization and distributed mechanisms	Web data mining
Agent-based immune network architecture	(Hilaire *et al.*, 2010)	Immune network based model of adaptive cooperation at the local level and of emergent behavior at the global level in Multi-Agent Systems	Robo soccer experiments

Some of earlier immune network approaches have been developed as an extension for the clonal selection-based methods. However, since the analogy has been more explored throughout last years, some novel and interesting approaches have also been appeared in literature in order to provide solution of other problems, such as robotics and data mining. Clustering and optimization are still a recurrent application of the immune network-based approaches as well. These aspects will be further discussed in the research analysis.

15.3.4. *Algorithms Based on Other Models*

The further approaches presented here are based on other models or features of the immune system and these approaches are focused on other analogies provided by the immune system, as presented in Table 15.5. Some of them can serve as alternative approaches to different applications.

Interestingly, the cognitive paradigm of immune system (Cohen, 2000), which states that immune system recognizes both self and non-self and immune responses are mediated through cooperation of immune cells has lately inspired an information retrieval architecture in (Hu *et al.*, 2008). The proposed system relies on interactive networks between agents of the system and a co-evolutionary mechanism led by an affinity maturation through the networks. Studies about development of systems inspired on this paradigm have started in (Andrews and Timmis, 2007; Voigt *et al.*, 2007), but since then, few works have explored this paradigm of immune system, which can provide interesting analogies.

According to Hart *et al.* (2009), modeling collaborative network among immune entities can lead to the development of novel approaches fit for their purpose of solving engineering problems. Analogies are taken from innate immunity and their interaction to the adaptive immunity elements, modern models of immune networks,

Table 15.5: AIS related works based on other aspects.

Approach	Ref.	Description	Application
T-Cell receptor density	(Owens *et al.*, 2013)	Algorithm based in a mathematical model of TCR density and feedback estimation, with a comparative to some kernel density estimation-based techniques	Anomaly detection
AIDEN	(Pathak *et al.*, 2012)	A method that adopts a density concept and considers TCRs stimulation and interaction to B cells in the form of Antigen Recognition Balls	Clustering datasets
Complement System based	(Aitken *et al.*, 2008)	Proposal of a method based on one of pathways of the complement system, based on message passing processes. Requires a matching function	Engineering problems
NK cells based	(Laurentys *et al.*, 2011)	Proposal of an algorithm inspired by Natural Killer Cells functions: Receptor balance and the education processes	Fault detection
NK cells based	(Fu *et al.*, 2012)	An algorithm inspired by Natural Killer Cells with activating and inhibition cytokines signals applied to spyware detection	Malware detection
T cells based	(Aragon *et al.*, 2011)	An algorithm inspired by T Cells with three groups and idynamic tolerance factor and population change evaluation mechanisms	Dynamic optimization problems
Dynamic Effector Regulatory Algorithm	(Guzella *et al.*, 2007)	A method that incorporates cytokines and regulatory cells and adopts different concepts of Self and Non-self spaces, based on effector and regulatory cells distribution and recognition of normal and abnormal processes	Fault detection
Innate immunity based	(Guzella *et al.*, 2007)	Discussion of modeling aspects of innate immunity based algorithms in terms of multi-level data fusion mechanisms and how real-world problems should reflect on these algorithms	Intrusion detection systems

(Continued)

Table 15.5: (*Continued*)

Approach	Ref.	Description	Application
Humoral Artificial Immune System	(Narayanan and Ahmad, 2012)	Novel technique with diverse concepts exploited for supervised learning using mechanisms as similarity measures, affinity thresholds, maturation, hyper-mutation, and memory cells, among others	Machine Learning
Artificial Immune Privilege Site Model	(Singh *et al.*, 2011)	Method based on antigen tolerance without inflammatory responses	Robotics and Computer security
Memory Cells based	(Suarez-Tangil *et al.*, 2011)	Learning and memory analogies are explored to provide the generation of event correlation rules as a novel multi-step attacks detector	Computer security
Immune models	(Suarez-Tangil *et al.*, 2011)	Proposal of comparison regarding two types of simulation: Simulation of Dynamic System (SDS), a mathematics-based immune model, and Simulation Based in Agents (ABS), based on models	Approach evaluation
Cross-regulation based	(Abi-Haidar and Rocha, 2011)	An agent-based method inspired by the dynamics of a population of T-cells and APCs for antigen recognition	Data classification and feature selection
Tunable activation threshold (TAT-AIS)	(Antunes and Correia, 2010)	A novel algorithm inspired on two concepts: homeostasis and clonal size regulation	Temporal anomaly detection
TAT-AIS	(Antunes and Correia, 2010)	Employment of TAT-AIS in another application	Network Intrusion detection systems

and the cognitive paradigm. These analogies were discussed and then related to some real-world applications.

15.4. A Brief Summary about Hybrid AIS Approaches

AIS can also be combined to other approaches as described in (De Castro and Timmis, 2002), with description of diverse combinations of paradigms, and in (Dasgupta and Niño, 2008), with the example of NS-SOM model described.

The development of hybrid systems has increased in the literature, not only for AIS, but also for many other nature-inspired algorithms. This survey will further describe the influence of hybrid approaches in AIS research.

Hybrid system can be divided in two groups. In the first group, the use of tools or methods that can extend or enhance AIS to provide proper features in problem solving will be discussed, such as Probability Theory, Fuzzy Logic, Information-based Tools, among others. In the other group, systems that employ different algorithms or techniques with their functions mixed will be discussed, such as Artificial Neural Networks, Evolutionary Algorithms, Swarm Intelligence Algorithms, other machine learning methods, among others.

15.4.1. *Useful Tools for AIS Enhancement*

Several tools can be employed in order to extend AIS features or to enhance most aspects, such as probability or bayesian tools, fuzzy set theory, information theory, kernel methods, and other tools since they are not considered as specific algorithms. Hybrid approaches involving multiple algorithms will be further discussed in the other group.

Some of these tools have been already adopted in early approaches, as in the example of the first Self-Non-self-based system in (Forrest *et al.*, 1994), whose detection is probabilistic. Several methods rely on these tools for modeling purposes, according to features that should be provided for a particular problem. In addition, algorithms based on clonal selection need these features because of their stochastic nature as these are applied to generation of antibodies and in the somatic hypermutation operators. However, since these features were not the focuses of their respective approaches, but features incorpored to these systems, they cannot be considered as hybrid approaches at all. As each tool can enhance AIS functionalities, a further discussion will be presented of some of these tools.

In this group, some tools can be used to provide enhancement for AIS, in terms of functions and mechanisms. The following list includes, but is not limited to these considered approaches:

- Probabilistic methods, such as gaussian or bayesian tools;
- Fuzzy and Rough sets theory;
- Information theory tools;
- Kernel Functions;
- Other learning and memory mechanisms;
- Chaos theory, quantum computing and other methods.

These tools can be used to improve or replace mechanisms on AIS approaches, in the case of probabilistic methods. Examples of these techniques are the family of Probabilistic Artificial immune Systems based on Negative Selection in (Mohammadi *et al.*, 2012) and both Bayesian Artificial Immune System (BAIS) (Castro and Von Zuben, 2010) and Gaussian Artificial Immune System (GAIS) (Castro and Von Zuben, 2008) applied to optimization, with these algorithms also having multiobjective versions.

Fuzzy Set Theory, which can deal with uncertain or imprecise information, may offer proper models of aspects and mechanisms of the immune systems, providing powerful interactions, according to De Castro and Timmis (2002). These aspects are considered mainly for adaptive immunity features, as the antigen recognition is approximate. However, the use of Fuzzy Logic is not limited to these aspects, as the immune system has several components. Some examples of algorithms are an Immune Network based in (Szabo *et al.*, 2012), a Dendritic Cell-based in (Chelly *et al.*, 2012), and the fuzzy recognition algorithms proposed in (Costa Silva *et al.*, 2012a).

Information theory tools have been used to enhance AIS functions through entropic divergence metrics, such as Kullback–Leibler, Rényi and von Neumann, or the Dempster-belief Theory, which performs classification by computing evidences. One example of these approaches are the Local Concentration (LC), proposed in (Zhu and Tan, 2011), to perform feature extraction and is based on tendency calculation via probability of occurrences, the vector of LCs is constructed by sliding window measurements of both censored and legitimate genes. The LC model can be constructed based on term selection that can be employed by information-based methods.

The use of kernel functions was less considered, and the discussion in (Guzella *et al.*, 2008) has presented how kernel functions should extend AIS functions and features in the same way as used in machine learning paradigms such as SVM algorithms. The possibility of replacement of affinity functions by kernel functions were considered to map feature space. A test using aiNet approach mapped in a Gaussian space was performed in the research. In (Ozsen *et al.*, 2009), a kernel-based AIS for classification inspired on clonal selection was proposed, and the affinity function between Ag–Ab is replaced by a kernel-based distance measurement. Benchmarks of UCI Database were applied to the proposed method.

These are some examples of useful tools in the development of different techniques or the improvement of existing ones without alter significantly the main idea of either the abstract model of an algorithm or functions for which these algorithms were designed for. Instead, these tools should provide a better suitability of the model or even permit the feasibility of an analogy for the development of new techniques applied to problem solving. Approaches that are developed mixing multiple techniques or employing features of different algorithms or even paradigms will be further discussed in the next subsection.

15.4.2. *Hybridization of AIS and Other Paradigms*

In this subsection, hybrid approaches that use mechanisms from AIS and other algorithms or even multiple algorithms will be discussed. Differently from the other group, in which paradigms or tools are implemented in terms of AIS modeling, in this group, all approaches employ different algorithms in the same system, in a high level of system hybridization. The list of approaches that can be used for this purpose include, but are not limited to the following:

- Nature Inspired approaches:
  - Artificial Neural Networks.
  - Genetic Algorithms and other evolutionary algorithms.
  - Swarm intelligence approaches.
- Other Machine Learning systems:
  - Naive Bayes.
  - k-Nearest Neighbors (kNN).
  - Support Vector Machines (SVMs).
  - Most Clustering algorithms.
- Fuzzy systems:
  - Fuzzy C-means.
  - Takagi-Sugeno systems.
- Meta-heuristics.
- Meta-learning tools.

Examples of applications for possible hybrid AIS are mining rules from neural, weight optimization, ensemble in classification problems and generation of rule-bases. Some examples of these approaches can be seen in Table 15.6. The ones based in Swarm Intelligence have some interesting aspects and a further discussion is presented.

Swarm Intelligence-based approaches is another nature-inspired paradigm that have been widely applied to optimization problems and then, comparisons to AIS approaches have been discussed in (Timmis *et al.*, 2010), since both paradigms have many aspects of direct parallels, since Swarm Intelligence exploits the result of individual behaviors in coordinated population behavior as a whole and AIS exploits immune functions and models. Both approaches have been also discussed in terms of self-organization, positive and negative feedbacks, amplification factors and multiple signals of phenomena. The scientific and abstract aspects of swarm interactions have been discussed and both approaches can be considered as complementary fields of research that also can be combined to develop new techniques. Similarities between both approaches have been discussed in (Xiao *et al.*,

Table 15.6: Some Hybrid AIS related works.

Approach	Ref.	Hybrid with	Description	Application
RABNET	(Masutti and Castro, 208)	Self-organizing Neural Network	Antibody based system with cloning and pruning mechanisms applied to real-valued problems	CVRP problem
Negative Selection	(Davis *et al.*, 2010)	Genetic Algorithm	NSA enhanced by GA optimization of detector generation	Anomaly detection
T-Cell receptor density algorithm (RDA)	(Hilder *et al.*, 2011)	Genetic Algorithm	Parameters of RDA are enhanced by genetic operators	Anomaly detection
Imaboost	(Taud *et al.*, 2010)	Several classifiers	Transformation of Adaboost with clonal selection operators into a novel technique	Machine Learning Ensemble
CSA	(Aydin *et al.*, 2011)	SVMs	Optimization of SVM parameters	Fault diagnosis
CSA	(Bernardino *et al.*, 2010)	k-NN algorithm	Development of a Similarity-based Surrogate Model to clonal selection	Optimization
NSA and CSA	(Chao and Tan, 2009)	Machine Learning approaches	Training of classifiers using the immune approaches	Computer Security

2011), such as structure of individuals, their interaction, and system structures, as well as their learning, memory, feedback, and adaptability aspects, among other points. It is possible that Swarm Intelligence-based approaches, as well as AIS, are emerging approaches whose potential is still high for analogy exploiting.

Main examples of these approaches are combinations of AIS and PSO, as PSO may be applied to antibody improvements under mutation operators in classifiers or clustering methods. Several approaches were discussed in (Wu, 2012), including a novel immune-inspired method, presented to solve constrained global optimization problems.

There are many possibilities of hybrid approaches, since there are many paradigms to be considered. How these algorithms can be applied to a given problem is also another aspect of these mixed systems, since these algorithms, as well as AIS approaches, can serve as ensemble for one or many algorithms, or improve features or results of a given algorithm, or even be a part of the algorithm processing. The approaches cited here are some examples of how AIS can improve or be improved by other techniques to solve harder problems, as for their complexity, a single algorithm may not be enough.

Some of these combinations, however, may imply on redundant features, since AIS have features in common with other paradigms of machine learning or mainly nature-inspired applications, which are subject to similarities between paradigms, as in the example of Clonal Selection algorithms and Evolutionary Algorithms approaches. Some other examples will be further discussed in the sense of AIS research.

15.5. Impacts in Biological Research

Immunology serving as a source of inspiration for computational systems may provide some multidisciplinary links and many interactions among researchers from different fields of study and a perspective of benefits for immunology, computer science and engineering respective researches, as further discussed in terms of AIS impact in biology and how computation could inspire biological models in research.

Reviews done in (Timmis *et al.*, 2008) point that the development of AIS algorithms may provide interdisciplinary links between immunology, computer science, mathematics, and engineering, since the immunology provides metaphors for the creation of novel solutions to problems. The authors have provided a framework for modeling novel approaches from immunology through a methodology evaluation, some reference models and the further development of techniques from the abstract model, as well as some features to be provided in newer AIS approaches. It is also suggested that these models may help immunologists in bringing some understanding of the immune system as well as proper representations in AIS for engineering systems through greater interaction between each group of researchers.

As immunology may inspire computer systems, computation can also be an inspiration for insights about immunology, as defined by Cohen (2007), in this work are described the view of the immune system as a computational entity and immunological concepts and functions in terms of computation. Some computation concepts were applied to immunological components, such as the system states, its cells and their actions in the immune system. The paper also reinforces the need of interactions between immunologists and computer scientists.

The research in (Navlakha and Bar-Joseph, 2011) was related to biological modeling and inspiration for strategies to problem solving as well as the similarities between computation and biology and their differences. According to the authors, computational systems are often focused on speed and biological systems are focused in dynamic adaptability to changes and their decision-making mechanisms. This suggests that biological inspirations are very useful to computational systems. Features of biological and analogous computational systems are discussed and their research was considered as a *computational thinking of biological systems*, which provides more understanding of biological processes as well as improvements in algorithms development.

The ecology of immune system is discussed in (Tauber, 2008), in this paper, the author also discuss the 'Immunocomputing' research described as immunology formalization aspects and its quality as a fruitful source for applications to various problems. It is also implied that AIS is involved in multidisciplinary studies including fields of immunology modeling, mathematical modeling and computer simulations, among other forms of simulating immune models.

The artificial immune systems research, as seen on these works, may provide some significant contributions to immunology in the sense of understanding the immune system, as well as providing a multidisciplinary research between immunologists and computer scientists or engineers in order to establish interactions that should improve the understanding of the real functions of immune systems and reinforce the development of novel techniques and provide better results in problem solving.

At the present moment, there are few works pointing this aspect of AIS. However, there are some definitions stated in (Hart *et al.*, 2009), such as 'Immunoengineering', which is inspired on immunoecology (study of principles applied to immunological functions) and immunoinformatics (related to decision-making paradigms), whose elements are reunited to provide adaption and applications. These studies would provide a framework that supports the development of mathematical and computational models, as well as their validation through benchmark problems. In summary, understanding AIS may reinforce the understanding of immunological principles and models, as well as provide the growth of the research on bio-inspired systems.

15.6. Research and Applications

In this section, a summary about AIS applications and focuses is presented in the sense of how AIS research is being currently applied, as most aspects of current state of the research about AIS have been discussed on the survey in (Dasgupta *et al.*, 2011). The main remarks discussed are the popularity of techniques, mainly negative selection and clonal selection algorithms, and the advances in the research, such as interdisciplinary aspects, emerging research about other immunological models, AIS textbooks and their highlights and conferences about AIS or which provides the spreading of current state of AIS related works.

Immune-inspired methods are still appearing in most computational intelligence or evolutionary computation conferences. However, during this year, the International Conferences on Artificial Immune Systems (ICARIS) has become a part of

Advances in Artificial Life, ECAL 2013 Conference, due to a drop in submissions of the conference that was supposed to happen during the current year.

Some AIS related up-to-date textbooks have been published. Regarding the current state-of-the-art, in (Dasgupta and Niño, 2008) is described the overview of most AIS techniques and models that have been developed, as well as their related analogies and the applications for which they were applied. An optimization focused book in (Mo, 2008), presents some AIS and other nature-inspired methods and improvements and discusses them. Since then, most AIS related books recently published are related to applications, such as computer security problems in (Al-Anezi and Al-Dabagh, 2012) applied to intrusion detection and malware, or in (Unterleitner, 2012) also applied to virus detection.

In these years, some reviews were done, as in (Ramakrishnan and Srinivasan, 2009) for AIS applied to computer security systems and using agent-based approaches to solve the problem, Network Intrusion Detection-based approaches are reviewed in (Chauhan *et al.*, 2013, Singh *et al.*, 2013) in terms of developing techniques, in (Wong and Lau, 2009) a review about optimization methods was done with description of design, benchmark and applications to real life problems, in (Malhotra *et al.*, 2012) a survey on the applications of AIS in various fields related to pattern recognition is presented, in (Raza and Fernandez, 2012), robotic-based applications of AIS are presented, many of them inspired on the immune network theory, and in (Dalal and Singh, 2012), a review of AIS-based applications to Mobile Ad-hoc Networks was presented.

A graphical illustration regarding publications per year within last five years is shown in Figure 15.1.

A list of recent applications is presented in a quantitative illustration of published papers in Figure 15.2.

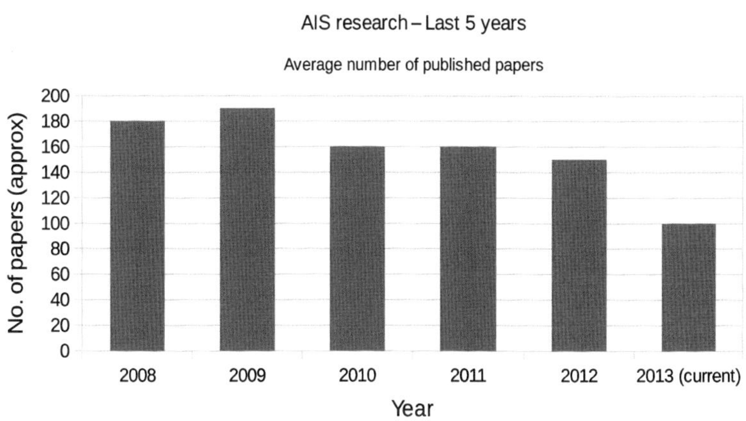

Figure 15.1: Papers published per year.

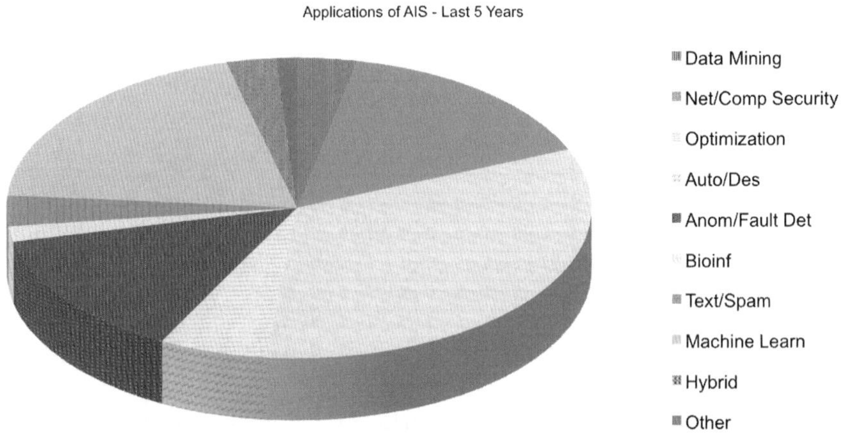

Figure 15.2: Distribution of AIS applications.

These data imply that AIS researches has emerged and then is currently updated with more publications, mainly in optimization, in which clonal selection based approaches is constantly applied. Applications to security and anomaly detection are also updated with more approaches and improvements for negative selection-based algorithms. The other immune response models are currently emerging, mainly the dendritic cell algorithm, which is being applied for computer or network security as well. Immune networks has also some remarkable applications, such as clustering, robotics, and some optimization problems.

The Figure 15.3 illustrates these publications distributed per immune model or algorithm developed. These data are considered by their features, as Negative Selection approaches are based on Self-Non-self Discrimination, Clonal Selection are based on antibody production, cloning and mutation features, Immune Networks are based on network models, and PRR and Danger approaches uses features of the other immune response models. If these approaches have different features than the previous models, they are included in Other category and if more than one model or approach are developed, they are included in Multi category, which means that more than one AIS approach was adopted.

From previous data, the Figure 15.4 is regarding the research of these algorithms during these years. According to these data, Clonal Selection-based approaches have been consolidated, because of its application to optimization problems. Negative Selection and Immune Networks based approaches are also popular, due to their applicability and features provided. The other immune response models are emerging approaches that had many researches, but they are still in development.

Figure 15.4 presents the relationship between AIS models and their applications through number of papers published in these last five years, for Computer and Network Security, Anomaly Detection, Optimization, Machine Learning and the

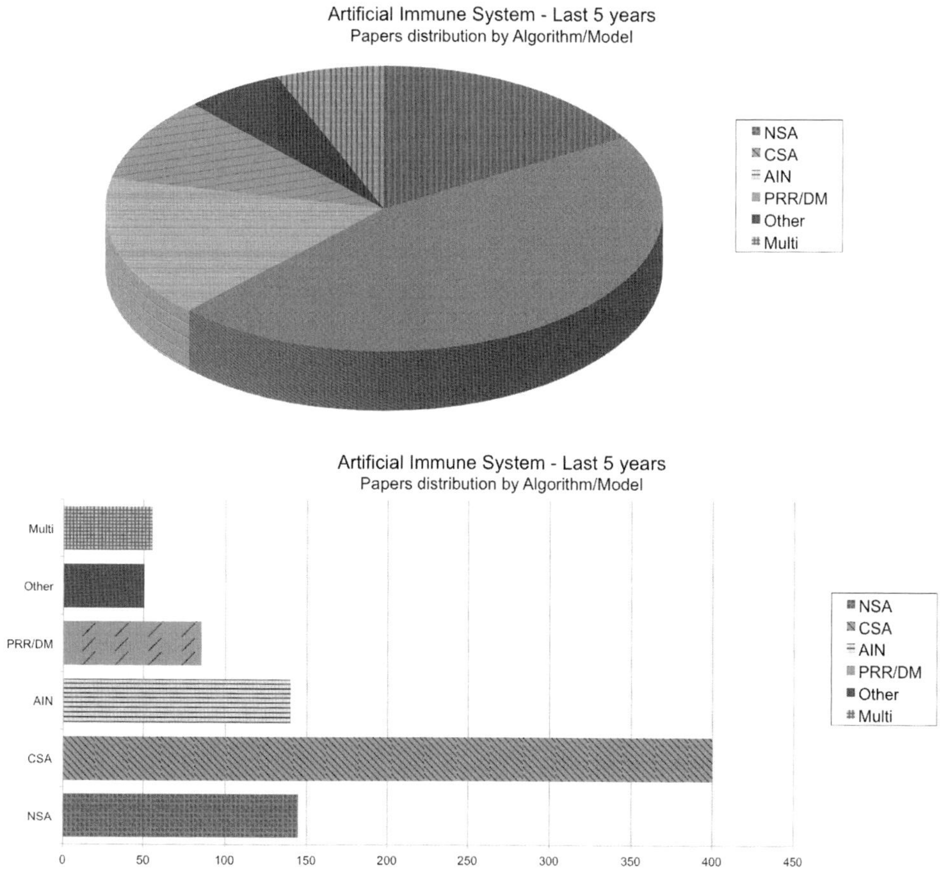

Figure 15.3: Quantitative distribution of papers published of AIS models.

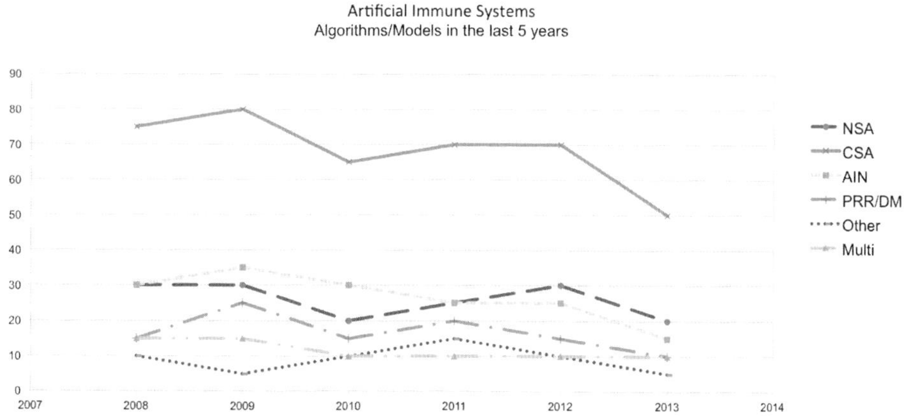

Figure 15.4: Quantitative distribution of papers published of AIS models per year.

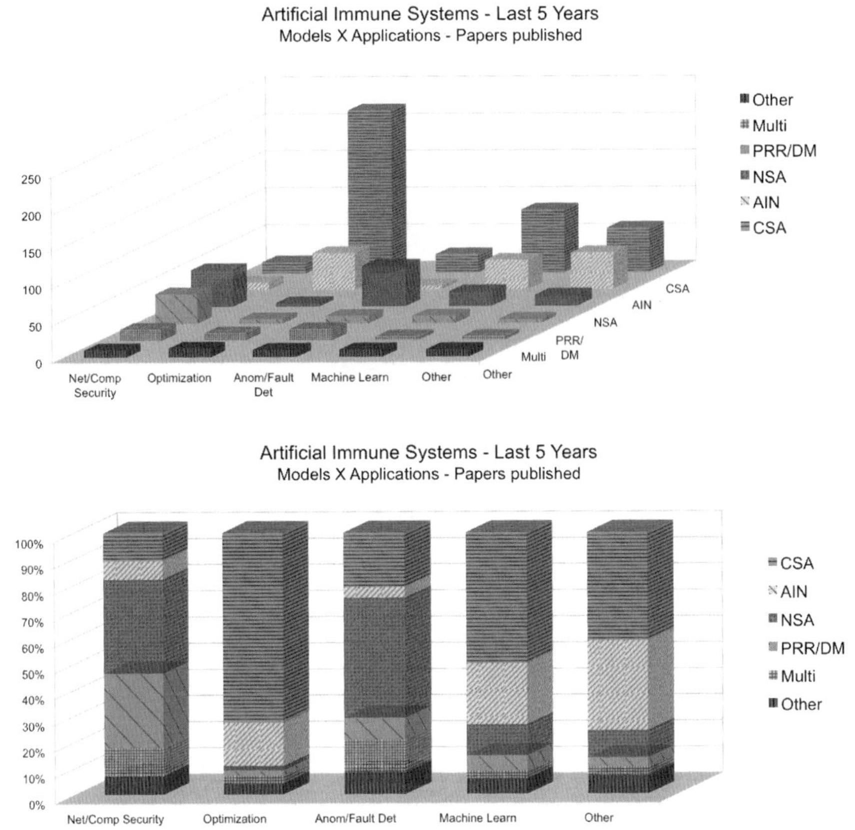

Figure 15.5: Distribution of papers published of AIS models per applications.

other applications (including Data Mining and Text for example). As expected, clonal selection and optimization are typically related. There are other relations, such as negative selection and anomaly detection, or danger model based approaches and applications for computer and network security, as some examples.

In Figure 15.6, paper distribution is categorized by classical or hybrid approaches, illustrating the proportion of these approaches in these last five years and the quantitative analysis throughout years.

The Figure 15.7 considers the development of classical and hybrid approaches by the based model and their proportional distribution. As presented by these graphics, hybridized versions of Clonal and Immune Networks algorithms are the most popular in AIS research.

The Figure 15.8 considers the situation of classical and hybrid AIS approaches regarding to their application. Except for Anomaly Detection, in which hybrid approaches has more papers published, classical approaches are more dominant for most applications. For hybrid approaches, it was also considered the employment

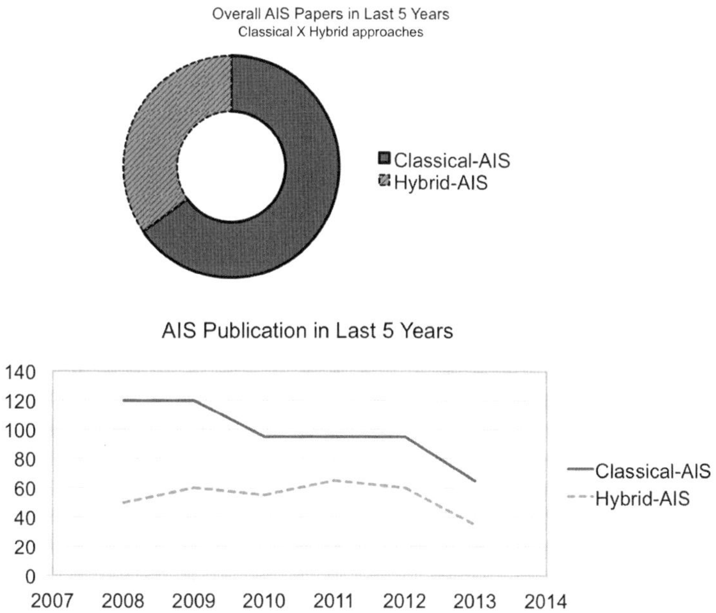

Figure 15.6: Classical X Hybrid approaches in these last five years.

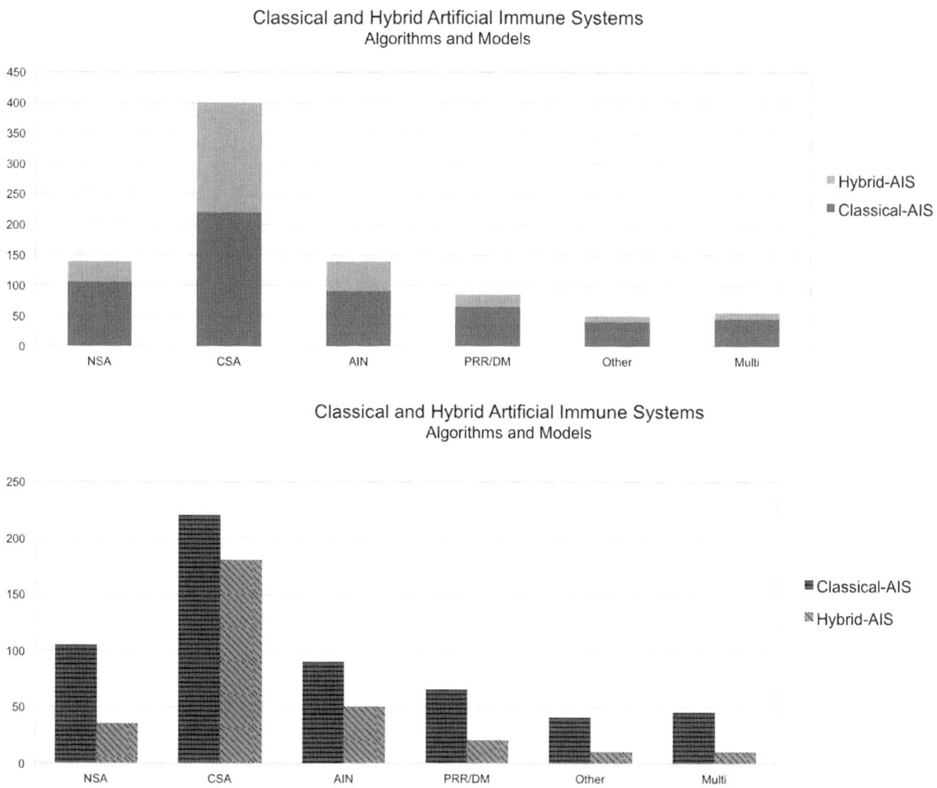

Figure 15.7: Classical X Hybrid approaches regarding the model studied.

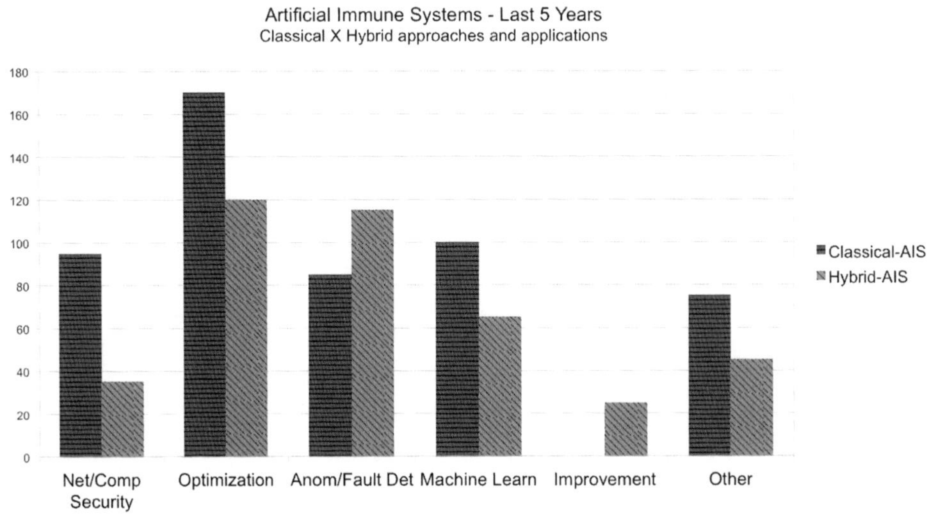

Figure 15.8: Classical X Hybrid approaches regarding the application. For hybrid approaches, AIS as improvements are also listed.

of AIS as an improvement of these systems, which is becoming a recurring approach.

In a global view of this analysis, Artificial Immune Systems can be considered as a well developed and consolidated field of research as many publications are presented, considering the several applications of these techniques to be exploited.

15.7. Remarks

This work has presented the current state-of-the-art of the research field and some aspects such as current state of approaches, their applications, some contributions to multidisciplinary researches and the distribution of research according to many aspects within these last five years.

AIS has been consolidated as a nature-inspired paradigm that employs metaphors by reproducing models and mechanisms from immunology in order to solve problems. Several works have been published and some models have appeared throughout these last years.

State-of-the-art models, such as Negative Selection and Clonal Selection have been successfully employed in their proper applications and are currently consolidated as successful immune-inspired algorithms. Immune network-based applications are also well applied to some problems in literature, and the other immune response models, which have inspired some novel algorithms, such as CSPRA and DCA, are emerging as their potential are still to be properly explored for their applications.

In other part, the development and study of hybrid approaches in which AIS methods are being implemented is increasing, as different techniques or their combination may reproduce different and improved results. In this view, AIS are being improved by some methods, as well as serving as improvement for other systems. Possibly, each mechanism may be isolated for the better exploitation, as some researches are focused on specific algorithms, in order to provide better problem solving through different combinations.

Actually, as the biological immune system has many features to be exploited, there are many possibilities of approaches, considering mechanisms, models and even biological mechanisms involved on immune processes. The current state of the art has exploited few of these characteristics, most of them in a high level of abstraction and focusing features. Newer approaches are exploiting more biological factors and providing mathematical or computational models for these mechanisms, as they are being studied. Biological analogies may not be perfect, but they have to be suitable for development of proper algorithms for a given problem.

However, the success of Artificial Immune Systems may be explained by the results provided by these analogies and the intensive research regarding these algorithms and how to improve them in terms of technique or by providing better results. Seemingly, not only AIS, but most nature-inspired methods have several features to be exploited, serving as analogies in development of new systems.

Acknowledgments

The authors acknowledge the support of Brazilian funding agency CAPES, which supported the first author during this study.

References

Abi-Haidar, A. and Rocha, L. M. (2011). Collective classification of textual documents by guided self-organization in t-cell cross-regulation dynamics. *Evolutionary Intelligence*, 4(2), pp. 69–80.

Aitken, J. M., Clarke, T. and Timmis, J. I. (2008). The pathways of complement. In Bentley, P. J., Lee D. and Jung, S. (eds.), *Artificial Immune Systems, Lecture Notes in Computer Science*. Berlin Heidelberg: Springer, pp. 364–375.

Al-Anezi, M. M. K. and Al-Dabagh, N. B. I. (2012). *Multilayer Artificial Immune Systems for Intrusion & Malware Detection: Concepts, Methods, Design and Implementation*. Germany: LAP Lambert Academic Publishing.

Al-Sheshtawi, K. A., Abdul-Kader, H. M. and Ismail, N. A. (2010). Artificial immune clonal selection algorithms: A comparative study of clonalg, opt-ia, and bca with numerical optimization problems. *Int. J. Computer Science and Network Security* (*IJCSNS*), 10(4), pp. 24–30.

Andrews, P. and Timmis, J. (2007). Alternative inspiration for artificial immune systems: Exploiting cohen's cognitive immune model. In Flower, D. and Timmis, J. (eds.), *In Silico Immunology*. US: Springer, pp. 119–137.

Antunes, M. and Correia, M. E. (2011). Tunable immune detectors for behaviour-based network intrusion detection. In Lio, P., Nicosia, G. and Stibor, T. (eds.), *Artificial Immune Systems, Lecture Notes in Computer Science*. Berlin Heidelberg: Springer, pp. 334–347.

Antunes, M. J. and Correia, M. E. (2010). Temporal anomaly detection: An artificial immune approach based on t cell activation, clonal size regulation and homeostasis. In Arabnia, H. R. (ed.), *Advances in Computational Biology*, Advances in Experimental Medicine and Biology. New York: Springer, pp. 291–298.

Aragón, V. S., Esquivel, S. C and Coello, C. A. C. (2011). A t-cell algorithm for solving dynamic optimization problems. *Inform. Sci.*, 181(17), pp. 3614–3637.

Aydin, I., Karakose, M. and Akin, E. (2011). A multi-objective artificial immune algorithm for parameter optimization in support vector machine. *Appl. Soft Comput.*, 11(1), pp. 120–129.

Bao, Y., Luo, W. and Zhang, X. (2013). Estimating positive surveys from negative surveys. *Stat. Probabil. Lett.*, 83(2), pp. 551–558.

Bernardino, H., Barbosa, H. and Fonseca, L. (2010). A faster clonal selection algorithm for expensive optimization problems. In Hart, E., McEwan, C., Timmis, J. and Hone, A. (eds.), *Artificial Immune Systems, Lecture Notes in Computer Science*. Berlin Heidelberg: Springer, pp. 130–143.

Castro, P. A. D. and Von Zuben, F. (2010). A gaussian artificial immune system for multi-objective optimization in continuous domains. *Hybrid Intelligent Systems (HIS), 2010 10th Int. Conf.*, pp. 159–164.

Castro, P. A. D. and Von Zuben, F. J. (2008). MOBAIS: A Bayesian artificial immune system for multi-objective optimization. In Bentley, P. J., Lee D. and Jung, S. (eds.), *ICARIS, Lecture Notes in Computer Science*. Berlin Heidelberg: Springer, pp. 48–59.

Chao, R. and Tan, Y. (2009). A virus detection system based on artificial immune system. *Computational Intelligence and Security, 2009. CIS '09. Int. Conf.*, Vol. 1, pp. 6–10.

Chauhan, P., Singh, N. and Chandra, N. (2013). Article: A review on intrusion detection system based on artificial immune system. *Int. J. Comput. Appli.*, 63(20), pp. 36–40.

Chelly, Z., Smiti, A. and Elouedi, Z. (2012). Coid-fdcm: The fuzzy maintained dendritic cell classification method. In Rutkowski, L., Korytkowski, M., Scherer, R., Tadeusiewicz, R., Zadeh, L. and Zurada, J. (eds.), *Artificial Intelligence and Soft Computing, Lecture Notes in Computer Science*. Berlin Heidelberg: Springer, pp. 233–241.

Chen, B. and Zang, C. (2011). Emergent damage pattern recognition using immune network theory. *Smart Structures and System*, 8(1), pp. 69–92.

Chen, G., Zhang, L. and Bao, J. (2013). An improved negative selection algorithm and its application in the fault diagnosis of vibrating screen by wireless sensor networks. *J. Comput. Theor. Nanos.*, 10(10), pp. 2418–2426.

Chen, J., Zhang, Q. and Fang, Z. (2012). Improve the adaptive capability of tma-or. In Omatsu, S., De Paz Santana, J. F., González, S. R., Molina, J. M., Bernardos, A. M. and Rodríguez, J. M. C. (eds.), *Distributed Computing and Artificial Intelligence, Advances in Intelligent and Soft Computing*. Berlin Heidelberg: Springer, pp. 665–671.

Chen, L.-F. (2013). An improved negative selection approach for anomaly detection: with applications in medical diagnosis and quality inspection. *Neural Comput. Appl.*, 22(5), pp. 901–910.

Chen, S. (2013). Optimized multilevel immune learning algorithm in abnormal detection. *Information Technology Journal*, 12(3), pp. 514–517.

Chung, T.-P. and Liao, C.-J. (2013). An immunoglobulin-based artificial immune system for solving the hybrid flow shop problem. *Appl. Soft Comput.*, 13(8), pp. 3729–3736.

Cohen, I. (2000). *Tending Adam's Garden: Evolving the Cognitive Immune Self.* Academic Press.

Cohen, I. R. (2007). Real and artificial immune systems: computing the state of the body. *Nat. Rev. Immunol.*, 07(07), pp. 569–574.

Costa Silva, G., Palhares, R. M. and Caminhas, W. M. (2012a). Immune inspired fault detection and diagnosis: A fuzzy-based approach of the negative selection algorithm and participatory clustering. *Expert Syst. Appl.*, 39(16), pp. 12474–12486.

Costa Silva, G., Palhares, R. M. and Caminhas, W. M. (2012b). A transitional view of immune inspired techniques for anomaly detection. In Yin, H., Costa J. A. F. and Barreto, G. (eds.), *Intelligent Data Engineering and Automated Learning — IDEAL 2012, Lecture Notes in Computer Science.* Berlin Heidelberg: Springer, pp. 568–577.

Cuevas, E., Osuna-Enciso, V., Zaldivar, D., Pérez-Cisneros, M. and Sossa, H. (2012). Multithreshold segmentation based on artificial immune systems. *Math. Prob. Eng.*, pp. 1–20.

Dalal, T. and Singh, G. (2012). Review of artificial immune system to enhance secu review of artificial immune system to enhance security in mobile ad-hoc networks. *Int. J. Computer Science & Management Studies (IJCSMS)*, 12(02), pp. 82–85.

Dasgupta, D. (1998). *Artficial Immune Systems and Their Applications*, 1st edn. New York: Springer-Verlag.

Dasgupta, D. and Attoh-Okine, N. (1997). Immunity-based systems: A survey. *Systems, Man, and Cybernetics, 1997. Computational Cybernetics and Simulation, 1997 IEEE Int. Conf.*, Vol. 1, pp. 369–374.

Dasgupta, D. and Azeem, R. (2008). An investigation of negative authentication systems. *Proc. 3rd Int. Conf. Information Warfare and Security*, CSIIRW '09.

Dasgupta, D. and Niño, L. (2008). *Immunological Computation: Theory and Applications*, 1st edn. Boston, MA, USA: Auerbach Publications.

Dasgupta, D. and Saha, S. (2010). Password security through negative filtering. *2010 International Conference on Emerging Security Technologies* (*EST*), pp. 83–89.

Dasgupta, D., Yu, S. and Niño, F. (2011). Recent advances in artificial immune systems: Models and applications. *Appl. Soft Comput.*, 11(2), pp. 1574–1587.

Davis, J., Perhinschi, M. G. and Moncayo, H. (2010). Evolutionary algorithm for artificial-immune-system-based failure-detector generation and optimization. *J. Guid. Control Dynam.*, 33(2), pp. 305–320.

de Almeida, C. A. L., Palhares, R. M. and Caminhas, W. M. (2010). Design of an artificial immune system based on danger model for fault detection. *Expert Syst. Appl.*, 37, pp. 5145–5152.

de Almeida, C. A. L., Ronacher, G., Palhares, R. M. and Caminhas, W. M. (2010). Design of an artificial immune system for fault detection: A negative selection approach. *Expert Syst. Appl.*, 37(7), pp. 5507–5513.

De Castro, L. N. and Timmis, J. (2002). *Artificial Immune Systems: A New Computational Intelligence Approach.* Berlin: Springer-Verlag.

de França, F. O., Coelho, G. P., Castro, P. A. D. and von Zuben F. J. (2010). Conceptual and practical aspects of the ainet family of algorithms. *Int. J. Natural Computing Research (IJNCR)*, 1, pp. 1–35.

Deng, Z.-L., Tan, G.-Z., He, P. and Ye, J.-X. (2013). A decision hyper plane heuristic based artificial immune network classification algorithm. *J. Cent. South Univ.*, 20(7), pp. 1852–1860.

Ding, L., Yu, F. and Yang, Z. (2013). Survey of dca for abnormal detection. *J. Softw.*, 8(8), pp. 2087–2094.

Ding, Y.-S., Hu, Z.-H. and Zhang, W.-B. (2011). Multi-criteria decision making approach based on immune co-evolutionary algorithm with application to garment matching problem. *Expert Syst. Appl.*, 38(8), pp. 10377–10383.

Dudek, G. (2012). An artificial immune system for classification with local feature selection. *IEEE Trans. Evolutionary Computation*, 16(6), pp. 847–860.

Elsadig, M. and Abdullah, A. (2009). Biological inspired intrusion prevention and self healing system for network security based on danger theory. *Int. J. Video & Image Processing and Network Security* (*IJVIPNS-IJENS*) 09, pp. 16–28.

Fernandez-Leon, J. A., Acosta, G. G. and Mayosky, M. A. (2011). From network-to-antibody robustness in a bio-inspired immune system. *Biosystems*, 104(3), pp. 109–117.

Figueredo, G. P., Aickelin, U. and Siebers, P.-O. (2011). Systems dynamics or agent-based modelling for immune simulation? *Proc. 10th Int. Conf. Artificial Immune Systems*, Berlin, Heidelberg, ICARIS'11, Springer-Verlag, pp. 81–94.

Forrest, S., Perelson, A. S., Allen, L. and Cherukuri, R. (1994). Self-non-self discrimination in a computer. *Proc. 1994 IEEE Sympo. Research in Security and Privacy*, p. 202.

Fouad, W., Badr, A. and Farag, I. (2011). Aifsa: A new approach for feature selection and weighting. In Abd Manaf, A., Zeki, A., Zamani, M., Chuprat, S. and El-Qawasmeh, E. (eds.), *Informatics Engineering and Information Science, Communications in Computer and Information Science.* Berlin Heidelberg: Springer, pp. 596–609.

Fu, J., Yang, H., Liang, Y. and Tan, C. (2012). Bait a trap: Introducing natural killer cells to artificial immune system for spyware detection. *Proc. 11th Int. Conf. Artificial Immune Systems*, Berlin, Heidelberg, ICARIS'12, Springer-Verlag, pp. 125–138.

Gan, Z., Zhao, M.-B. and Chow, T. W. (2009). Induction machine fault detection using clone selection programming. *Expert Syst. Appl.*, 36(4), pp. 8000–8012.

Gao, J., Fang, L. and Wang, J. (2010). A weight-based multiobjective immune algorithm: Wbmoia. *Eng. Optimiz.*, 42(8), pp. 719–745.

Ge, H., Yan, X., Okada, K. and Li, Y. (2012). Alpha matting using immune feature extraction network. In Wang, F., Lei, J., Lau, R. and Zhang, J. (eds.), *Multimedia and Signal Processing, Communications in Computer and Information Science.* Berlin Heidelberg: Springer, pp. 207–214.

Ghosh, K. and Srinivasan, R. (2011). Immune-system-inspired approach to process monitoring and fault diagnosis. *Ind. Eng. Chemi. Res.*, 50(3), pp. 1637–1651.

Golzari, S., Doraisamy, S., Sulaiman, M. N. and Udzir, N. I. (2011). An efficient and effective immune based classifier. *J. Comput. Sci.*, 7(2), pp. 148–153.

Gong, M., Chen, X., Ma, L., Zhang, Q. and Jiao, L. (2013). Identification of multi-resolution network structures with multi-objective immune algorithm. *Appl. Soft Comput.*, 13(4), pp. 1705–1717.

Gong, M., Zhang, J., Ma, J. and Jiao, L. (2012). An efficient negative selection algorithm with further training for anomaly detection. *Knowl. Based Syst.*, 30, pp. 185–191.

Greensmith, J. and Aickelin, U. (2009). Artificial dendritic cells: Multi-faceted perspectives. In Bargiela, A. and Pedrycz, W. (eds.), *Human-Centric Information Processing Through Granular Modelling, Studies in Computational Intelligence.* Berlin/Heidelberg: Springer, pp. 375–395.

Groat, M. M., Edwards, B., Horey, J., He, W. and Forrest, S. (2013). Application and analysis of multidimensional negative surveys in participatory sensing applications. *Pervasive Mob. Comput.*, 9(3), pp. 372–391.

Gu, F., Greensmith, J. and Aickelin, U. (2013). Theoretical formulation and analysis of the deterministic dendritic cell algorithm. *Biosystems*, 111(2), pp. 127–135.

Guzella, T. S., Mota-Santos, T. A. and Caminhas, W. M. (2007). A novel immune inspired approach to fault detection. *Proc. 6th Int. Conf. Artificial Immune Systems*, Berlin, Heidelberg, ICARIS'07. Springer-Verlag, pp. 107–118.

Guzella, T., Mota-Santos, T. and Caminhas, W. (2008). Artificial immune systems and kernel methods. In Bentley, P., Lee, D. and Jung, S. (eds.), *Artificial Immune Systems, Lecture Notes in Computer Science.* Berlin, Heidelberg: Springer, pp. 303–315.

Haktanirlar Ulutas, B. and Kulturel-Konak, S. (2011). A review of clonal selection algorithm and its applications. *Artif. Intell. Rev.*, 36(2), pp. 117–138.

Hart, E., McEwan, C. and Davoudani, D. (2009). Exploiting collaborations in the immune system: The future of artificial immune systems. In Mumford, C. and Jain, L. (eds.), *Computational Intelligence, Intelligent Systems Reference Library.* Berlin, Heidelberg: Springer, pp. 527–558.

Hilaire, V., Lauri, F., Gruer, P., Koukam, A. and Rodriguez, S. (2010). Formal specification of an immune based agent architecture. *Eng. Appl. Artif. Intel.*, 23(4), pp. 505–513.

Hilder, J., Owens, N., Hickey, P., Cairns, S., Kilgour, D., Timmis, J. and Tyrrell, A. (2011). Parameter optimisation in the receptor density algorithm. In Lió, P., Nicosia, G. and Stibor, T. (eds.), *Artificial Immune Systems*, Lecture Notes in Computer Science. Berlin Heidelberg: Springer, pp. 226–239.

Hu, Z.-H., Ding, Y.-S. and Lua, X.-J. (2008). Cognitive immune system-based co-evolutionary information retrieval model. *2007 Workshop on Intelligent Information Technology Applications*, 3, pp. 212–215.

Hu, Z.-H., Yu, X.-K. and Sheng, Z.-H. (2013). An immune co-evolutionary algorithm based approach for problems related to clothing uniform assignment. *Int. J. Cloth. Sci. Tech.*, 25(1), pp. 70–82.

Jabeen, H. and Baig, A. (2010). Clonal-gp framework for artificial immune system inspired genetic programming for classification. In Setchi, R., Jordanov, I., Howlett R. and Jain, L. (eds.), *Knowledge-Based and Intelligent Information and Engineering Systems*, Lecture Notes in Computer Science. Berlin, Heidelberg: Springer, pp. 61–68.

Jansen, T. and Zarges, C. (2011). Variants of immune inspired somatic contiguous hypermutations. *Theor. Comput. Sci.*, 412(6), pp. 517–533.

Jarosz, P. and Burczyski, T. (2010). Coupling of immune algorithms and game theory in multiobjective optimization. In Rutkowski, L., Scherer, R., Tadeusiewicz, R., Zadeh, L. and Zurada, J. (eds.), *Artifical Intelligence and Soft Computing*, Lecture Notes in Computer Science. Berlin, Heidelberg: Springer, pp. 500–507.

Jenhani, I. and Elouedi, Z. (2012). Re-visiting the artificial immune recognition system: A survey and an improved version. *Artif. Intel. Rev.*, pp. 1–13.

Ji, Z. and Dasgupta, D. (2009). V-detector: An efficient negative selection algorithm with "probably adequate" detector coverage. *Inform. Sciences*, 179(10), pp. 1390–1406.

Jinyin, C. and Dongyong, Y. (2011). A study of detector generation algorithms based on artificial immune in intrusion detection system. *2011 3rd Int. Conf. Computer Research and Development* (*ICCRD*), Vol. 1, pp. 4–8.

Karakasis, V. and Stafylopatis, A. (2008). Efficient evolution of accurate classification rules using a combination of gene expression programming and clonal selection. *Evolutionary Computation, IEEE Trans.*, 12(6), pp. 662–678.

Karakose, M. (2013). Reinforcement learning based artificial immune classifier. *The Scientific World Journal*, p. 7.

Khan, M. T. and de Silva, C. W. (2012). Autonomous and robust multi-robot cooperation using an artificial immune system. *Int. J. Robot. Autom.*, 27(1).

Knidel, H., de Castro, L. N. and Zuben, F. J. V. (2005). Rabnet: A real-valued antibody network for data clustering. *Genetic and Evolutionary Computation Conference, GECCO 2005, Proc., Washington DC, USA*, June 25–29, Beyer, H.-G. and Reilly, U.-M. O. (eds.), ACM, pp. 371–372.

Laurentys, C. A., Palhares, R. M. and Caminhas, W. M. (2011). A novel artificial immune system for fault behavior detection. *Expert Syst. Appl.*, 38(6), pp. 6957–6966.

Li, G., Li, T., Zeng, J. and Li, H. (2010). An outlier robust negative selection algorithm inspired by immune suppression. *J. Comput.*, 5(9).

Li, Z. and He, C. (2013). Optimal scheduling-based {RFID} reader-to-reader collision avoidance method using artificial immune system. *Appl. Soft Comput.*, 13(5), pp. 2557–2568.

Liskiewicz, M. and Textor, J. (2010). Negative selection algorithms without generating detectors. *Proc. 12th Annual Conf. Genetic and Evolutionary Computation*, New York, NY, USA, GECCO'10, ACM, pp. 1047–1054.

Liu, C.-H., Huang, W.-H. and Chang, P.-C. (2012). A two-stage ais approach for grid scheduling problems. *Int. J. Prod. Res.*, 50(10–12), pp. 2665–2680.

Liu, R., Jiao, L., Li, Y. and Liu, J. (2010). An immune memory clonal algorithm for numerical and combinatorial optimization. *Frontiers of Computer Science in China*, 4(4), pp. 536–559.

Liu, R., Niu, M. and Jiao, L. (n.d.). A new artificial immune network classifier for SAR image. 7496, pp. 74960W.

Liu, T., Zhang, L. and Shi, B. (2009). Adaptive immune response network model. In Huang, D.-S., Jo, K.-H., Lee, H.-H., Kang, H.-J. and Bevilacqua, V. (eds.), *Emerging Intelligent Computing Technology and Applications. With Aspects of Artificial Intelligence*, Lecture Notes in Computer Science. Berlin Heidelberg: Springer, pp. 890–898.

Ma, W., Jiao, L. and Gong, M. (2009). Immunodominance and clonal selection inspired multiobjective clustering. *Prog. Nat. Sci.*, 19(6), pp. 751–758.

Ma, W., Tran, D. and Sharma, D. (2008). Negative selection with antigen feedback in intrusion detection. In Bentley, P., Lee, D. and Jung, S. (eds.), *Artificial Immune Systems*, Lecture Notes in Computer Science. Berlin, Heidelberg: Springer, pp. 200–209.

Mahapatra, P. K., Kaur, M., Sethi, S., Thareja, R., Kumar, A. and Devi, S. (2013). Improved thresholding based on negative selection algorithm (nsa). *Evolutionary Intelligence*, pp. 1–14.

Malhotra, A., Baheti, A. and Gupta, S. (2012). Pattern recognition approaches inspired by artificial immune system. *Int. J. Comput. Appl.*, 44(20), pp. 12–16.

Masutti, T. and Castro, L. (2008). A neuro-immune algorithm to solve the capacitated vehicle routing problem. In Bentley, P., Lee, D. and Jung, S. (eds.), *Artificial Immune Systems*, Lecture Notes in Computer Science. Berlin, Heidelberg: Springer, pp. 210–219.

McEwan, C and Hart, E. (2009). Representation in the (artificial) immune system. *J. Mathematical Modelling and Algorithms*, 8(2), pp. 125–149.

McEwan, C and Hart, E. (2010). Clonal selection from first principles. In Hart, E., McEwan, C., Timmis J. and Hone, A. (eds.), *Artificial Immune Systems*, Lecture Notes in Computer Science. Berlin, Heidelberg: Springer, pp. 18–32.

Mo, H. (2008). *Handbook of Research on Artificial Immune Systems and Natural Computing: Applying Complex Adaptive Technologies*. Hershey, PA: IGI Publishing.

Mohamed Elsayed, S., Rajasekaran, S. and Ammar, R. (2012). An artificial immune system approach to associative classification. In Murgante, B., Gervasi, O., Misra, S., Nedjah, N., Rocha, A., Taniar, D. and Apduhan, B. (eds.), *Computational Science and Its Applications* âĂŞ ICCSA 2012, Lecture Notes in Computer Science. Berlin Heidelberg: Springer, pp. 161–171.

Mohammadi, M., Akbari, A., Raahemi, B. and Nassersharif, B. (2012). A real time anomaly detection system based on probabilistic artificial immune based algorithm. In Coello Coello, C. A., Greensmith, J., Krasnogor, N., Lio, P., Nicosia, G. and Pavone, M. (eds.), *Artificial Immune Systems*, Lecture Notes in Computer Science. Berlin, Heidelberg: Springer, pp. 205–217.

Muddada, R., Zhang, F., Tiwari, M. and Zhang, W. (2010). A new index to evaluate solutions in the clonalg algorithm: Structural similarity index. In Huang, G., Mak, K. and Maropoulos, P. (eds.), *Proceedings of the 6th CIRP-Sponsored International Conference on Digital Enterprise Technology, Advances in Intelligent and Soft Computing*. Berlin Heidelberg: Springer, pp. 1119–1132.

Nanas, N., Vavalis, M. and Roeck, A. (2010). Words, antibodies and their interactions. *Swarm Intelligence*, 4(4), pp. 275–300.

Narayanan, A. and Ahmad, W. (2012). Humoral artificial immune system (hais) for supervised learning. *Int. J. Comput. Int. Appl.*, 11(01), p. 1250004.

Navlakha, S. and Bar-Joseph, Z. (2011). Algorithms in nature: The convergence of systems biology and computational thinking. *Mol. Syst. Biol.*, 7, 546.

Nejad, F., Salkhi, R., Azmi, R. and Pishgoo, B. (2012). Structural tlr algorithm for anomaly detection based on danger theory. *9th International ISC Conf. Information Security and Cryptology* (*ISCISC*), pp. 156–161.

Oliveira, L. O. V. B., Drummond, I. N. and Pappa, G. L. (2013). A new representation for instance-based clonal selection algorithms. In *Evolutionary Computation (CEC), 2013 IEEE Congress on*, pp. 2259–2266.

Owens, N. D., Greensted, A., Timmis, J. and Tyrrell, A. (2013). The receptor density algorithm. *Theor. Comp. Sci.*, 481, pp. 51–73.

Ozsen, S., Gunes, S., Kara, S. and Latifoglu, F. (2009). Use of kernel functions in artificial immune systems for the nonlinear classification problems. *Information Technology in Biomedicine, IEEE Trans.*, 13(4), pp. 621–628.

Pathak, V., Dhyani, P. and Mahanti, P. (2012). Aiden: A density conscious artificial immune system for automatic discovery of arbitrary shape clusters in spatial patterns. *Broad Research in Artificial Intelligence and Neuroscience* (*BRAIN*), 3(3), pp. 5–11.

Poggiolini, M. and Engelbrecht, A. (2013). Application of the feature-detection rule to the negative selection algorithm. *Expert Syst. Appl.*, 40(8), pp. 3001–3014.

Ramakrishnan, S. and Srinivasan, S. (2009). Intelligent agent based artificial immune system for computer security — a review. *Artif. Intel. Rev.*, 32(1–4), pp. 13–43.

Raza, A. and Fernandez, B. R. (2012). Immuno-inspired robotic applications: A review. *CoRR abs/1202.4261*.

Riff, M. C, Montero, E. and Neveu, B. (2013). Reducing calibration effort for clonal selection based algorithms: A reinforcement learning approach. *Knowl.-Based Syst.*, 41, pp. 54–67.

Secker, A., Freitas, A. A. and Timmis, J. (2008). Aisiid: An artificial immune system for interesting information discovery on the web. *Appl. Soft Comput.*, 8(2), pp. 885–905.

Shafiq, M. Z., Khayam, S. A. and Farooq, M. (2008). Improving accuracy of immune-inspired malware detectors by using intelligent features. *Proc. 10th Annual Conf. Genetic and Evolutionary Computation*, New York, NY, USA, GECCO '08, ACM, pp. 119–126.

Shang, R., Jiao, L., Liu, F. and Ma, W. (2012). A novel immune clonal algorithm for mo problems. *Evolutionary Computation, IEEE Trans.*, 16(1), pp. 35–50.

Sharma, A. and Sharma, D. (2011). Clonal selection algorithm for classification. In Lio, P., Nicosia, G. and Stibor, T. (eds.), *Artificial Immune Systems*, Lecture Notes in Computer Science. Berlin, Heidelberg: Springer, pp. 361–370.

Shi, Y., Xie, G., Zhang, Y., Peng, X., Huang, B., Yao, D. and Yue, G. (2013). An immune-based scgm(1,1)c prediction model for network security situation. *J. Comput. Inform. Syst.*, 9, pp. 4395–4406.

Shimo, H. K. and Tinos, R. (2013). Use of self-organizing suppression and q-gaussian mutation in artificial immune systems. *International Journal of Intelligent Computing and Cybernetics*, 6(3), pp. 296–322.

Singh, C. T., Sahoo, G. and Ghose, M. K. (2011). Artificial immune privileged sites as an enhancement to immuno-computing paradigm. *CoRR abs/1102.3971*.

Singh, S., Singh, J. P. and Shrivastva, G. (2013). A review: A is based intrusion detection system. *Int. J. Adv. Res. Comput. Commun. Eng.*, 2(6), pp. 2387–2391.

Suarez-Tangil, G., Palomar, E., Pastrana, S. and Ribagorda, A. (2011). Artificial immunity-based correlation system. In *SECRYPT 2011 — Proceedings of the International Conference on Security and Cryptography, Seville, Spain, July, 18–21 SECRYPT is part of ICETE — The International Joint Conference on e-Business and Telecommunications*, Lopez, J. and Samarati, P. (eds.), SciTePress, pp. 422–425.

Swiecicki, M. (2008). An algorithm of decentralized artificial immune network and its implementation. In Darzentas, J., Vouros, G., Vosinakis, S. and Arnellos, A. (eds.), *Artificial Intelligence: Theories, Models and Applications*, Lecture Notes in Computer Science. Berlin, Heidelberg: Springer, pp. 407–412.

Szabo, A., de Castro, L. and Delgado, M. (2012). Fainet: An immune algorithm for fuzzy clustering. In *2012 IEEE Int. Conf. Fuzzy Systems* (*FUZZ-IEEE*), pp. 1–9.

Tang, W., Peng, L.-M., Yang, X.-M., Xie, X. and Cao, Y. (2010). Gep-based framework for immune-inspired intrusion detection. *TIIS*, 4(6), pp. 1273–1293.

Tauber, A. I. (2008). The immune system and its ecology. *Philos. Sci.* 75(2), pp. 224–245.

Taud, H., Herrera-Lozada, J. C. and Alvarez-Cedillo, J. (2010). Adaboost classifier by artificial immune system model. In Martínez-Trinidad, J. F., Carrasco-Ochoa, J. A. and Kittler, J. (eds.), *Advances in Pattern Recognition*, Lecture Notes in Computer Science. Berlin Heidelberg: Springer, pp. 171–179.

Timmis, J., Andrews, P. and Hart, E. (2010). On artificial immune systems and swarm intelligence. *Swarm Intelligence*, 4(4), pp. 247–273.

Timmis, J., Andrews, P., Owens, N. and Clark, E. (2008). Immune systems and computation: An interdisciplinary adventure. In Calude, C., Costa, J., Freund, R., Oswald, M. and Rozenberg, G. (eds.), *Unconventional Computing*, Lecture Notes in Computer Science. Berlin Heidelberg: Springer, pp. 8–18.

Twycross, J. and Aickelin, U. (2010). Information fusion in the immune system. *CoRR abs/1003.1598.*

Ulutas, B. H. and Kulturel-Konak, S. (2013). Assessing hypermutation operators of a clonal selection algorithm for the unequal area facility layout problem. *Eng. Optim.*, 45(3), pp. 375–395.

Unterleitner, M. (2012). *Computer Immune System for Intrusion and Virus Detection: Adaptive detection mechanisms and their implementation.* AV Akademikerverlag.

Vella, M., Roper, M. and Terzis, S. (2010). Danger theory and intrusion detection: Possibilities and limitations of the analogy. In Hart, E., McEwan, C., Timmis, J. and Hone, A. (eds.), *Artificial Immune Systems*, Lecture Notes in Computer Science. Berlin, Heidelberg: Springer, pp. 276–289.

Voigt, D., Wirth, H. and Dilger, W. (2007). A computational model for the cognitive immune system theory based on learning classifier systems. In *Proc. 6th Int. Conf. Artificial Immune Systems*, Berlin, Heidelberg, ICARIS'07, Springer-Verlag, pp. 264–275.

Wang, D., Zhang, F. and Xi, L. (2011). Evolving boundary detector for anomaly detection. *Expert Syst. Appl.*, 38(3), pp. 2412–2420.

Wang, S., Yang, T. and Wang, K. (2012). Self/non-self discrimination based on fractional distance. In *Computer Science Service System (CSSS), 2012 Int. Conf.*, pp. 1777–1780.

Wang, X. and Jiang, X. (2011). Artificial malware immunization based on dynamically assigned sense of self. In Burmester, M., Tsudik, G., Magliveras, S. and Ilić, I. (eds.), *Information Security*, Lecture Notes in Computer Science. Berlin, Heidelberg: Springer, pp. 166–180.

Wilson, W. O., Birkin, P. and Aickelin, U. (2010). The motif tracking algorithm. *CoRR abs/1006.1526.*

Wong, E. and Lau, H. Y. K. (2009). Advancement in the twentieth century in artificial immune systems for optimization: Review and future outlook. *Systems, Man and Cybernetics, 2009. SMC 2009. IEEE Int. Conf.*, pp. 5195–4202.

Wu, J.-Y. (2012). Solving constrained global optimization problems by using hybrid evolutionary computing and artificial life approaches. *Math. Probl. Eng.*, 36.

Xiao, R., Chen, T. and Tao, Z. (2011). An analytical approach to the similarities between swarm intelligence and artificial immune system. *Innovations in Bio-inspired Computing and Applications (IBICA), 2011 Second Int. Conf.*, pp. 112–115.

Xu, B., Luo, W., Pei, X., Zhang, M. and Wang, X. (2009). On average time complexity of evolutionary negative selection algorithms for anomaly detection. *Proc. first ACM/SIGEVO Summit on Genetic and Evolutionary Computation*, New York, NY, USA, GEC '09, ACM, pp. 631–638.

Xu, Q., Wang, L. and Si, J. (2010). Predication-based immune network for multimodal function optimization. *Eng. Appl. Artif. Intel.*, 23(4), pp. 495–504.

Xu, Q., Wang, S. and Zhang, C. (2012). Structural design of the danger model immune algorithm. *Inf. Sci.*, 205, pp. 20–37.

Yang, H., Guo, J. and Deng, F. (2011). Collaborative RFID intrusion detection with an artificial immune system. *J. Intell. Inf. Syst.*, 36(1), pp. 1–26.

Ying, W. (2013). The semi-supervised immune classifier generation algorithm based on data clustering. *J. Computational Information Systems*, 9(9), pp. 3407–3414.

Yu, S. and Dasgupta, D. (2011). An effective network-based intrusion detection using conserved self pattern recognition algorithm augmented with near-deterministic detector generation. *Computational Intelligence in Cyber Security (CICS), 2011 IEEE Symp.*, pp. 17–24.

Yunfang, C. (2012). A General Framework for Multi-Objective Optimization Immune Algorithms. *Int. J. Intell. Syst. Appli.*, 4(6), pp. 1–13.

Zeng, J., Qin, Z. and Tang, W. (2013). Anomaly detection using a novel negative selection algorithm. *J. Comput. Theor. Nanosci.*, 10(12), pp. 2831–2835.

Zhang, C. and Yi, Z. (2010). A danger theory inspired artificial immune algorithm for on-line supervised two-class classification problem. *Neurocomputing*, 73(7–9), pp. 1244–1255.

Zhang, R., Li, T., Xiao, X. and Shi, Y. (2013). A danger-theory-based immune network optimization algorithm. *The Scientific World J.*, p. 13.

Zhang, Z., Yue, S., Liao, M. and Long, F. (2013). Danger theory based artificial immune system solving dynamic constrained single-objective optimization. *Soft Comput.*, pp. 1–22.

Zhao, D. and Luo, W. (2013). Real-valued negative databases. *Proc. 12th European Conf. Artificial Life* (*ECAL 2013*), pp. 884–890.

Zheng, X., Zhou, Y. and Fang, Y. (2013). The dual negative selection algorithm based on pattern recognition receptor theory and its application in two-class data classification. *J. Comput.*, 8(8), pp. 1951–1959.

Zhu, Y. and Tan, Y. (2011). A danger theory inspired learning model and its application to spam detection. In Tan, Y., Shi, Y., Chai Y. and Wang, G. (eds.), *Advances in Swarm Intelligence*, Lecture Notes in Computer Science. Berlin, Heidelberg: Springer, pp. 382–389.

Zhu, Y. and Tan, Y. (2011). A local-concentration-based feature extraction approach for spam filtering. *Information Forensics and Security, IEEE Trans.*, 6(2), pp. 486–497.

Chapter 16

Swarm Intelligence: An Introduction, History and Applications

Fevrier Valdez

In this paper, a survey about the algorithms based in swarm intelligence (SI) is presented. In this case, are analyzed the most popular algorithms such as the particle swarm optimization (PSO), ant colony optimization (ACO), bee swarm optimization (BCO), and the Bat algorithm (BA). These algorithms are mentioned in the paper because they have demonstrated be superior with respect to the other optimization methods based in swarms in some applications, and also the algorithms are inspired in swarm intelligence and are similar in some aspects.

16.1. Introduction

Swarm intelligence (SI) originated from the study of colonies, or swarms of social organisms. Studies of the social behavior of organisms in swarms prompted the design of very efficient optimization and clustering algorithms. For example, simulation studies of the graceful, but unpredictable, choreography of bird flocks led to the design of the particle swarm optimization (PSO) algorithm, and studies of the foraging behavior of ants resulted in ant colony optimization (ACO) algorithms. A major thrust in algorithmic development is the design of algorithmic models to solve increasingly complex problems. Enormous successes have been achieved through the modeling of biological and natural intelligence, resulting in so-called "intelligent systems". These intelligent algorithms include artificial neural networks, evolutionary computation, swarm intelligence, artificial immune systems, and fuzzy systems. Together with logic, deductive reasoning, expert systems, case-based reasoning, and symbolic machine learning systems, these intelligent algorithms form part of the field of *Artificial Intelligence* (AI). Just looking at this wide variety of AI techniques, AI can be seen as a combination of several research disciplines, for example, computer science, physiology, philosophy, sociology, and biology.

Studies of social animals and social insects have resulted in a number of computational models of SI. Biological swarm systems that have inspired computational models include ants, termites, bees, spiders, fish schools, and bird flocks. Within these swarms, individuals are relatively simple in structure, but their collective behavior is usually very complex. The complex behavior of a swarm is a result of the pattern of interactions between the individuals of the swarm over time. This complex behavior is not a property of any single individual, and is usually not easily predicted or deduced from the simple behaviors of the individuals. This paper is organized as follows: in Section 16.1, a brief introduction about the swarm intelligence is presented, Section 16.2 describe with detail the methods analyzed in the paper, Section 16.3 shows the applications that have been used for these methods. In Section 16.4, the conclusion are presented and finally the references are included in the last section.

16.2. History

Nowadays application of SI algorithms has been very popular because they are able to solve a variety of complex optimization problems. The term "Swarm intelligence", that denotes this "collective intelligence" has come into use (Beni, 1988, 1989, 1992; Bonabeau *et al.*, 1997). Swarm Intelligence (Bonabeau *et al.*, 1997) is the part of AI based on study of actions of individuals in various decentralized systems. Therefore, in this paper, we explain some heuristic techniques based on population and throughout history have been used by researchers as optimization methods to solve problems of everyday life and industry. This chapter relates the history and description of the stochastic algorithms PSO, ACO, BCO, and BA. However, in this section, the most popular optimization algorithms based in populations in chronological order are presented in Table 16.1.

16.2.1. *Ant Colony Optimization*

One of the first behaviors studied by researchers was the ability of ants to find the shortest path between their nest and a food source. From these studies and observations followed the first algorithmic models of the foraging behavior of ants, as developed by Marco Dorigo (Dorigo, 1992, 1994). Since then, research in the development of Algorithms, based on Ants have been very popular, resulting in a large number of algorithms and applications. These algorithms that were developed

Table 16.1: Popular optimization methods inspired in populations in chronological order.

Year	Optimization methods inspired in populations
2010	Bat Algorithm (BA) [5]
2010	Artificial Bee Algorithm [6]
2009	Gravitational Search Algorithm [7]
2007	Intelligent water drops [8]
2005	Harmony Search Algorithm [9]
2005	Honey Bee Algorithm [10]
2002	Bacterial Foraging Algorithm [11]
2002	Estimation of Distribution Algorithm [12]
1995	PSO [13]
1992	ACO [14]
1989	Tabu Search [15]
1983	Simulated Annealing [16]
1979	Cultural Algorithms [17]
1975	GAs [18]
1966	Evolutionary Programming [19]
1965	Evolution Strategies [20]

as a result of studies of ant foraging behavior are referred to as instances of the ant colony optimization metaheuristic (Dorigo *et al.*, 2000; Dorigo and Caro, 1999). This paper provides an overview of the ACO algorithms, and the first algorithms that have been developed. Section 16.2.1 gives an overview of the foraging behavior of real ants, and introduces the concepts of stigmergy and artificial ants. This section presents a very simple ant algorithm implementation to illustrate the basic principles of these algorithms. Sections 16.2.1.1 to 16.2.1.4 respectively, discuss the ant system (AS), elitist system (EAS), rank-based AS (ASrank) and max–MIN ant system (MMAS). These algorithms were the first set of ant algorithms implemented, mainly with reference to the traveling salesman problem (TSP).

The first ACO algorithm has been applied to the TSP (Dorigo, 1992, 1994; Dorigo *et al.*, 2000; Dorigo and Caro, 1999). Given a set of cities and the distances between them, the TSP is the problem of finding the shortest possible path which visits every city exactly once. Possible path which visits every city exactly once, it can be represented by a complete weighted graph $G = (N, E)N$ is the set of nodes representing the cities and E is the set of edges. Each edge is assigned a value d_{ij} which is the distance between cities i and j. When applying the ACO algorithm to the TSP, a pheromone strength $\tau_{ij}(t)$ is associated to each edge (i, j), where $\tau_{ij}(t)$ is a numerical value which is modified during the execution of the algorithm and t is the iteration counter.

The skeleton of the ACO algorithm applied to the TSP is:

procedure ACO algorithm for TSPs
set parameters, initialize pheromone
trails while
(termination
condition not
met) do Tour
construction
Pheromone
update end
end

The ACO metaheuristic is inspired by observing the behavior of real ant colonies, which presented an interesting feature, on how to find the shortest paths between the nest and food, on its way the ants deposit a substance called pheromone, this trail allows the ants back to their nest from the food; it uses the evaporation of pheromone to avoid a unlimited increase of pheromone trails and allow to forget the bad decisions (Dorigo and Gambardella, 1996, 1997). Where is the probability of ant k goes from node i to node j, is the heuristic information, say, prior knowledge, is the possible neighborhood of an ant k when in the city i, is the pheromone trail, α and β are parameters that determine the influence of the pheromone and prior knowledge, respectively.

16.2.2. *Ant System*

Initially, three different versions of AS were proposed (Dorigo, 1992, 1994; Dorigo *et al.*, 2000; Dorigo and Caro, 1999). These were called ant-density, antquantity, and ant-cycle. Whereas in the ant-density and ant-quantity versions the ants updated the pheromone directly after a move from one city to an adjacent city, in the ant-cycle version the pheromone update was only done after all the ants had constructed the tours and the amount of pheromone deposited by each ant was set to be a function of the tour quality. Nowadays, when referring to AS, one actually refers to ant-cycle since the two other variants were abandoned because of their inferior performance.

The two main phases of the AS algorithm constitute the ants' solution construction and the pheromone update. In AS a good heuristic to initialize the pheromone trails is to set them to a value slightly higher than the expected amount of pheromone deposited by the ants in one iteration; a rough estimate of this value can be obtained by setting, $\forall(i, j), \tau_{ij} = \tau_0 = m/C^{nn}$, where m is the number of ants, and c^{nn} is the length of a tour generated by the nearest-neighbor heuristic.

The reason for this choice is that if the initial pheromone values τ_0's are too low, then the search is quickly biased by the first tours generated by the ants, which in general leads toward the exploration of inferior zones of the search space. On the other side, if the initial pheromone values are too high, then many iterations are lost waiting until pheromone evaporation reduces enough pheromone values, so that pheromone added by ants can start to bias the search.

In AS, m ants build a tour of the TSP. Initially, ants are put on randomly chosen cities. At each construction step, ant k applies a probabilistic action choice rule, called *random proportional rule*, to decide which city to visit next. In particular, the probability with which ant k, currently at city i, chooses to go to city j is

$$p_{ij}^{k} \frac{[\tau_{ij}]^{\alpha}[\eta_{ij}]^{\beta}}{\sum l \in N_i^k [\tau_{ij}]^{\alpha}[\eta_{ij}]^{\beta}}, \quad \text{if } j \in N_i^k, \tag{1}$$

where $\eta_{ij} = 1/d_{ij}$ is a heuristic value that is available *a priori*, α and β are two parameters which determine the relative influence of the pheromone trail and the heuristic information, and N_i^k is the feasible neighborhood of ant k when being at city i, that is, the set of cities that ant k has not visited yet. The update of pheromone trails is as follow:

After all the ants have constructed their tours, the pheromone trails are updated. This is done by first lowering the pheromone value on all arcs by a constant factor, and the adding pheromone on the arcs the ants have crossed in their tours, pheromone evaporation is made by

$$\tau_{ij} \leftarrow (1-\rho)\tau_{ij}, \quad \forall (i, j) \in L, \tag{2}$$

where $0 < p \leq 1$. The parameter ρ is used to avoid unlimited accumulation of the pheromone trails and it enables the algorithm to delete bad decisions previously taken by ants. In fact, if an arc is not chosen by the ants, its associated pheromone value decreases exponentially in the number of iterations. After evaporation, all ants deposit pheromone on the arcs they have crossed in their tour:

$$\tau_{ij} \leftarrow \tau_{ij} + \sum_{k=1}^{m} \Delta\tau_{ij}^{k} \forall (i, j) \in L, \tag{3}$$

where $\Delta\tau_{ij}^k$ is amount of pheromone ant k deposits on the arcs it has visited.

16.2.3. *Elitist Ant System*

A first improvement on the initial AS, called the elitist strategy for Ant System (EAS), was introduced in Dorigo (Dorigo and Caro, 1999; Dorigo and Gambardella, 1996, 1997). The idea is to provide strong additional reinforcement to the arcs belonging to the best tour found since the start of the algorithm; this tour is denoted as T^{bs} (best-so-far tour) in the following. Note that this additional feedback to the best-so-far tour (which can be viewed as additional pheromone deposited by an additional ant called best-so-far ant) is another example of a daemon action of the ACO metaheuristic. The update of pheromone trails is very similar as in AS and the only difference in the additional reinforcement of tour T^{bs} is achieved by adding a quantity e/C^{bs} to its arcs, where e is a parameter that defines the weight given to the best-so-far tour T^{bs}, and C^{bs} is its length. Thus, the following equation for the pheromone deposit becomes

$$\tau_{ij} \leftarrow \tau_{ij} + \sum_{k=1}^{m} \Delta\tau_{ij}^{k} + e\Delta\tau_{ij}^{bs}, \tag{4}$$

where $\Delta\tau_{ij}^{k}$ is defined as in AS.

In EAS, the pheromone evaporation is implemented as in AS. Computational results presented in Dorigo (Dorigo, 1992, 1994; Dorigo and Gambardella, 1996, 1997) suggest that the use of the elitist strategy with an appropriate value for parameter e allows AS to both find better tours and find them in a lower number of iterations.

16.2.4. *Rank-Based Ant System*

Bullnheimer *et al.* (1997) proposed a modification of AS as follows: Equation (1) to allow only the best ant to update pheromone concentrations on the links of the global-best path, Equation (2) to use elitist ants, and Equation (3) to let ants update pheromone on the basis of a ranking of the ants. In ASrank the ants are sorted by increasing tour length and the quantity of pheromone that an ant deposits is weighted according to the rank r of the ant. In the iteration only the $(w - 1)$ best-ranked ants and the ant that produced the best-so-fat tour are allowed to deposit pheromone. The best-so-far tour gives the strongest feedback, with w. For ASrank, the global update rule is defined as follow:

$$\tau_{ij} \leftarrow \tau_{ij} + \sum_{r=1}^{w-1}(w - r)\Delta\tau_{ij}^{r} + w\Delta\tau_{ij}^{bs}. \tag{5}$$

The results of an experimental evaluation by Bullnheimer *et al.* (1999c) suggest that ASrank performs slightly better than EAS and significantly better than AS.

16.2.5. *MAX-MIN Ant System*

MMAS (Stützle, 1997a, 1997b) introduces four main modifications with respect to AS. First, it strongly exploits the best tours found: only either the iteration-best ant, that is, the ant that produced the best tour in the current iteration, or the best-so-far ant is allowed to deposit pheromone. Unfortunately, such a strategy may lead to a stagnation situation in which all the ants follow the same tour, because of the excessive growth of pheromone trails on arcs of a good, although suboptimal, tour. To counteract this effect, a second modification introduced by MMAS is that it limits the possible range of pheromone trail values to the interval $[\tau_{min}, \tau_{max}]$. Third, the pheromone trails are initialized to the upper pheromone trail limit, which, together with a small pheromone evaporation rate, increases the exploration of tours at the start of the search. Finally, in MMAS, pheromone trails are reinitialized each time the system approaches stagnation or when no improved tour has been generated for a certain number of consecutive iterations. The update of pheromone trail is as follows:

$$\tau_{ij} \leftarrow \tau_{ij} + \Delta\tau_{ij}^{best}. \tag{6}$$

Experimental results indicate that for small TSP instances it may be best to use only iteration-best pheromone updates, while for large TSPs with several hundreds of cities the best performance is obtained by giving an increasingly stronger emphasis to the best-so-far tour T^{bs} is chosen for the trail update (Stüzle, 1999).

16.2.6. *Particle Swarm Optimization*

PSO is a population-based stochastic optimization technique developed by Eberhart and Kennedy in 1995, inspired by the social behavior of bird flocking or fish schooling (Kennedy and Eberhart, 1995).

PSO shares many similarities with evolutionary computation techniques such as GA (Castillo and Melin, 2002). The system is initialized with a population of random solutions and searches for optima by updating generations. However, unlike the GA, the PSO has no evolution operators such as crossover and mutation. In PSO, the potential solutions, called particles, fly through the problem space by following the current optimum particles (Angeline, 1998).

Each particle keeps track of its coordinates in the problem space, which are associated with the best solution (fitness) it has achieved so far (The fitness value is also stored). This value is called *pbest*. Another "best" value that is tracked by the particle swarm optimizer is the best value, obtained so far by any particle in the neighbors of the particle. This location is called *lbest*. When a particle takes all the population as its topological neighbors, the best value is a global best and is called *gbest*.

The particle swarm optimization concept consists of, at each time step, changing the velocity of (accelerating) each particle toward its *pbest* and *lbest* locations (local version of PSO). Acceleration is weighted by a random term, with separate random numbers being generated for acceleration toward *pbest* and *lbest* locations.

In the past several years, PSO has been successfully applied in many research and application areas. It is demonstrated that PSO gets better results in a faster, cheaper way compared with other methods (Angeline, 1998).

Another reason that PSO is attractive is that there are few parameters to adjust. One version, with slight variations, works well in a wide variety of applications. Particle swarm optimization has been used for approaches that can be used across a wide range of applications, as well as for specific applications focused on a specific requirement.

The pseudo code of the PSO is as follows

```
For each particle
  Initialize particle
End
Do
  For each particle
     Calculate fitness value
     If the fitness value is better than the best fitness value (pBest) in history
        set current value as the new pBest
  End
  Choose the particle with the best fitness value of all the particles as the gBest
  For each particle
    Calculate particle velocity
    Update particle position
  End
While maximum iterations or minimum error criteria is not attained
```

16.2.7. *Bee Colony Optimization*

The Bee Colony Optimization (BCO) metaheuristic (Lučić and Teodorović, 2001, 2002, 2003a, 2003b; Teodorović, 2003b) was proposed recently by Lučić and Teodorović as a new direction method in the field of Swarm Intelligence. The BCO has been successfully applied to various engineering and management problems by Teodorović and coauthors (Teodorović and Dell'Orco, 2005; Teodorović *et al.*, 2006; Marković *et al.*, 2007; Teodorović and Šelmić, 2007). The BCO approach is a "bottom-up" approach to modeling where special kinds of artificial agents are created by analogy with bees. Artificial bees represent agents, which collaboratively solve complex combinatorial optimization problem.

Lučić and Teodorović (Lučić and Teodorović, 2001, 2002, 2003a, 2003b) were among first who used basic principles of collective bee intelligence in solving combinatorial optimization problems. The BCO is a population-based algorithm. Population of *artificial bees* searches for the optimal solution. Artificial bees represent agents, which collaboratively solve complex combinatorial optimization problems. Every artificial bee generates one solution to the problem. The algorithm consists of two alternating phases: *forward pass* and *backward pass*. In each forward pass, every artificial bee is exploring the search space. It applies a predefined number of moves, which construct and/or improve the solution, yielding to a new solution. Having obtained new partial solutions, the bees go again to the nest and start the second phase, the so-called backward pass. In the backward pass, all artificial bees share information about their solutions.

In nature, bees would perform a dancing ceremony, which would notify other bees about the quantity of food they have collected, and the closeness of the patch to the nest. In the BCO, the artificial bees publicize the quality of the solution, i.e., the objective function value. During the backward pass, every bee decides with a certain probability whether to abandon the created partial solution and become again uncommitted follower, or dance and thus recruit the nest mates before returning to the created partial solution. During the second forward pass bees expand previously created partial solutions, by a predefined number of nodes, and after that perform again the backward pass and return to the hive. In the hive, bees again participate in a decision-making process, make a decision, perform third forward pass, etc. The two phases of the search algorithm, forward and backward pass, are performed *iteratively*, until a stopping condition is met. The possible stopping conditions could be, for example, the maximum total number of forward/backward passes, the maximum total number of forward/backward passes without the improvement of the objective function, etc.

The algorithm parameters whose values need to be set prior the algorithm execution are as follows:

B — The number of bees in the hive.
NC — The number of constructive moves during one forward pass.

In the beginning of the search, all the bees are in the hive. The following is the pseudocode of the BCO algorithm (Lučić and Teodorović, 2001, 2002):

1. Initialization: every bee is set to an empty solution;
2. For every bee do the forward pass:
(a) Set $k = 1$; //counter for constructive moves in the forward pass;
(b) Evaluate all possible constructive moves;
(c) According to evaluation, choose one move using the roulette wheel;
(d) $k = k + 1$; If $k \leq$ NC Go To Step b.
3. All bees are back to the hive; // backward pass starts;
4. Sort the bees by their objective function value;

5. Every bee decides randomly whether to continue its own exploration and become a recruiter, or to become a follower (bees with higher objective function value have greater chance to continue its own exploration);
6. For every follower, choose a new solution from recruiters by the roulette wheel;
7. If the stopping condition is not met Go To Step 2;
8. Output the best result.

16.2.8. *Bat Algorithm*

BA is a bio-inspired algorithm developed by Yang in 2010 and BA has been found to be very efficient. If we idealize some of the echolocation characteristics of microbats, we can develop various bat-inspired algorithms or bat algorithms. For simplicity, we now use the following approximate or idealized rules (Yang, 2010):

1. All bats use echolocation to sense distance, ant they also 'know' the difference between food/prey and background barriers in some magical way.
2. Bats fly randomly witch velocity $\mathbf{v}_i$ at position $\mathbf{x}_i$ witch a fixed frequency $\boldsymbol{f}_{\mathbf{min}}$, varying wavelength $\boldsymbol{\lambda}$ and loudness $\boldsymbol{A}_0$ to search for prey. They can automatically adjust the wavelength (or frequency) of their emitted pulses and adjust the rate of pulse emission r [0, 1], depending on the proximity of their target.
3. Although loudness can vary in many ways, we assume that the loudness varies from a large (positive) $\boldsymbol{A}_0$ to a minimum constant value $\boldsymbol{A}_{\mathbf{min}}$.

For simplicity, the frequency $f[0, f_{max}]$, the new solutions $\mathbf{x}_i^t$ and velocity $\mathbf{v}_i^t$ at a specific time step t are represented by a random vector drawn from a uniform distribution (Goel *et al.*, 2013).

The basic pseudocode developed by the authors for the bat algorithm is described as follows (Yang, 2010):

Objective function f(x), $\boldsymbol{x} = (x_1, \ldots, xd)^T$
Initialize the bat population $\boldsymbol{x}_i$ $(i = 1, 2, \ldots, n)$ *and* $\boldsymbol{v}_i$
Define pulse frequency f_i *at* $\boldsymbol{x}_i$
Initialize pulse rates r_i *and the loudness* $\boldsymbol{A}_i$
While *(t < Max numbers of iterations)*
Generate new solutions by adjusting frequency and updating velocities and locations/solutions [equations (1) *to* (3)*]*
if *(rand>*r_i*)*
Select a solution among the best solutions
Generate a local solution around the selected best solution
end if
Generate a new solutions by flying randomly

if *(rand <$\boldsymbol{A}_i$ & f($\boldsymbol{x}_i$) <f($\boldsymbol{x}_*$))*
Accept the new solutions and increase r_i and reduce $\boldsymbol{A}_i$
end if
Rank the bats and find the current best $\boldsymbol{x}_*$
end while
Postprocess results and visualization

The movements of each bat is associated with a velocity $\mathbf{v_i}^t$ and location $\mathbf{x_i}^t$, alt iteration t, in a dimensional search or solution space. Among all the bats, there exist a current best solution $\boldsymbol{x}_*$. Therefore, the above three rules can be translated into the updating equations for $\mathbf{x_i}^t$ and velocities $\mathbf{v_i}^t$:

$$f_i = f_{\min} + (f_{\max} - f_{\min})\beta, \tag{7}$$

$$v_i^t = v_i^{t-1} + (x_i^{t-1} - x_*) f_i, \tag{8}$$

$$x_i^t = x_i^{t-1} + v_i^t, \tag{9}$$

where β [0, 1] is a random vector drawn from a uniform distribution (Rodrigues, 2013). As mentioned earlier, we can either use wavelengths or frequencies for implementation, we will use $f_{\min} = 0$ and $f_{\max} = 1$, depending on the domain size of the problem of interest. Initially, each bat is randomly assigned a frequency which is drawn uniformly from $[f_{\min} - f_{\max}]$. The loudness and pulse emission rates essentially provide a mechanism for automatic control and auto zooming into the region with promising solutions (Yang, 2013).

The loudness and pulse rates is used to provide an affective mechanism to control the exploration and exploitation and switch to exploitation stage when necessary, we have to vary the loudness $\boldsymbol{A}_i$ and the rate $\boldsymbol{r}_i$ of pulse emission during the iterations. Since the loudness usually decreases once a bat has found its prey, while the rate of pulse emission increases, the loudness can be chosen as any value of convenience, between $A_{\min}$ and $A_{\max}$, assuming $A_{\min} = 0$ means that a bat has just found the prey and temporarily stop emitting any sound. With these assumptions, we have

$$A_i^{t+1} = \alpha A_i^t, \quad r_i^{t+1} = r_i^0[1 - \exp(-\gamma^t)], \tag{10}$$

where α and γ are constants. In essence, here α is similar to the cooling factor of a cooling schedule in simulated annealing. For any $0 < \alpha < 1$ and $\gamma > 0$, we have

$$A_i^t \to 0, \quad r_i^t \to r_i^0, \quad \text{as } t \to \infty. \tag{11}$$

16.3. Applications

In this chapter, a review about the applications of the above mentioned algorithms is presented. In this case, we describe only the applications that have used swarm computing. In particular, in this paper, we have analyzed in detail only four algorithms based in swarm such as ACO, PSO, BCO, and BA algorithms. However, in this section some applications with these algorithms are shown.

16.3.1. *ACO in Control and Classification*

First, some applications with the ACO algorithm is presented in this section. Several applications have been developed using ACO, in this part the most relevant are shown. In the first paper, Li *et al.*, developed in their work, a one-piece flow production system with the purpose of ensuring just-in-time production. Three approaches are applied to achieve the goal: adopting straightforward schedule policies, relaxing the Talk time, and decreasing the risk of machine failures and operator mistakes. Consequently, a multi-objective design model is proposed, whose aim is to minimize cycle time, changeover count, cell load variation and the number of cells to maximize the extent to which items are completed in a cell. The fuzzy ant colony optimization (FACO) is also presented to solve the formulated problem. In FACO, the fuzzy logic controller (FLC) is used to adapt the evaporated and deposited value of pheromone trail based on the ant's fitness and pheromone trail age. Furthermore, domain knowledge of facility layout, generated based on the travel chart method, is also adaptively injected to improve the performance of FACO. The proposed method is evaluated with real-world data and experimental results demonstrate that the FACO method outperforms many other methods in efficiency, solution quality and facilitation measures (Li and Rong, 2009). Also, in (Castillo *et al.*, 2013) ACO was used to find the correct parameters for the fuzzy logic controller in a complex robotics problem; it is also a task that consumes considerable time (Alcalá-Fdez *et al.*, 2009). Because of their ability to solve complex NP problems, in these papers the authors proposed an algorithm ACO for the selection of the optimal fuzzy controller parameters (Castillo *et al.*, 2013).

Also, in (Ahmadizar and Soltanpanah, 2011) fuzzy logic is used by Ahmadizar *et al.* to improve ACO. In this paper, a solution is generated by an ant based on both pheromone trails modified by previous ants and heuristic information considered as a fuzzy set. Constructed solutions are not guaranteed to be feasible; consequently, applying an appropriate procedure, an infeasible solution is replaced by a feasible one. Then, feasible solutions are improved by a local search. The proposed approach is compared with the existing metaheuristic available in the literature. Computational results demonstrate that the approach serves to be a better performance for large problems.

In 2011, a fuzzy classification system based on Ant Colony Optimization for diabetes disease diagnosis is proposed by Ganji *et al.* The aim of this paper is to use an Ant Colony-based classification system to extract a set of fuzzy rules for diagnosis of diabetes disease, named FCS-ANTMINER. This paper describes some recent methods and describes a new and efficient approach that leads to considerable results for diabetes disease classification problem. FCS-ANTMINER has new characteristics that make it different from the existing methods that have utilized the ACO for classification tasks. The obtained classification accuracy is 84.24% which reveals that FCS-ANTMINER outperforms several famous and recent methods in classification accuracy for diabetes disease diagnosis (Ganji and Abadeh, 2011). On the other hand, Chang *et al.* developed a fuzzy sliding-mode control for ball and beam system with FACO. This paper mainly addresses the balance control of a ball and beam system, where a pair of decoupled fuzzy sliding-mode controllers (DFSMCs) is proposed. The DFSMC has the advantage of reducing the design complexity, in which the coupling dynamics of the state-error dynamics are considered as disturbance terms. Stability analysis of the ball and beam system with DFSMCs is also discussed in detail. To further improve the control performance, an improved ACO is proposed to optimize the controller parameters. The proposed ACO algorithm has the enhanced capability of fuzzy pheromone updating and adaptive parameter tuning. The proposed ACO-optimized scheme is utilized to tune the parameters of the fuzzy sliding-mode controllers for a real ball-and-beam system. Compared to some conventional ACO algorithms, simulation and experimental results all indicate that the proposed scheme can provide better performance in the aspect of convergence rate and accuracy (Chang *et al.*, 2012).

16.3.2. *PSO in Neural Networks, Mathematical Functions and Control*

In the first approach of PSO, particles could be a swarm of neural networks attempting to find the lowest error on some classification or regression task. See Particle Swarm Optimization of Neural Network Architectures and Weights (de Lima and Ludermir, 2011).

Also in (Valdez *et al.*, 2010), an Evolutionary method combining Particle Swarm Optimization and GAs using fuzzy logic for parameter adaptation and aggregation is used to optimize the architecture of the modular neural network for face recognition. In this approach, the authors proposed a combination of Genetic Algorithms and PSO to improve the performance of the Neural Network.

Also in (Argha *et al.*, 2013) the adaptation of network weights using PSO was proposed as a mechanism to improve the performance of artificial neural network (ANN) in classification of IRIS dataset. Classification is a machine learning technique used to predict group membership for data instances. To simplify, the problem of classification neural networks are being introduced. This paper focuses on IRIS plant classification using Neural Network. The problem concerns the identification of IRIS plant species on the basis of plant attribute measurements. Classification of IRIS dataset would be discovering patterns from examining petal and sepal size of the IRIS plant and how the prediction was made from analyzing the pattern to form the class of IRIS plant.

In 2013, Melin *et al.* propose an improvement to the convergence and diversity of the swarm in PSO using fuzzy logic. Simulation results show that the proposed approach improves the performance of traditional PSO. First, benchmark mathematical functions are used to illustrate the feasibility of the proposed approach. Then a set of classification problems are also used to show the potential applicability of fuzzy logic in dynamic parameter adaptation of PSO.

Chiou *et al.* developed a novel method for determining the optimal fuzzy PID-controller parameters of active automobile suspension system using the PSO algorithm. This paper demonstrated in detail how to help the PSO with a Q-learning cooperation method to search efficiently for the optimal fuzzy-PID controller parameters of a suspension system. The design of a fuzzy system can be formulated as a search problem in high-dimensional space where each point represents a rule set, membership functions, and the corresponding system's behavior. In order to avoid obtaining the local optimum solution, a pure PSO global exploration method to search for fuzzy-PID parameter (Li and Wu, 2011) was adopted.

16.3.3. *BCO in Traveling Salesman Person and Other Applications*

The main goal of Lučić and Teodorović (Lučić and Teodorović, 2001, 2002, 2003a, 2003b) research was not to develop a new heuristic algorithm for the traveling salesman problem but to explore possible applications of Swarm Intelligence (particularly collective bee intelligence) in solving complex engineering and control problems. The TSP is only an illustrative example, which shows the characteristics of the proposed concept. Lučić and Teodorović tested the BCO approach on a large number of numerical examples.

Also, BCO has been successfully tested (Teodorović *et al.*, 2006) in the case of the Routing and Wavelength Assignment (RWA) in All-Optical Networks. This problem is, by its nature similar to the traffic assignment problem. The results achieved, as well as experience gained when solving the RWA problem could be used in the future research of the traffic assignment problem. The RWA problem is described as follows: every pair of nodes in optical networks is characterized by a number of requested connections. The total number of established connections in the network depends on the RWA procedure. RWA problem in all-optical networks could be defined in the following way: Assign a path through the network and a wavelength on that path for each considered connection between a pair of nodes in such a way to maximize the total number of established connections in the network.

16.3.4. *BA in Several Applications*

Musikapun and Pongcharoen (2012) solved multistage, multi-machine, multi-product scheduling problems using bat algorithm, and they solved a class of non-deterministic polynomial time (NP) hard problems with a detailed parametric study. They also implied that the performance can be further improved by about 8.4% using optimal set of parameters.

Yang (2013) used the bat algorithm to study topological shape optimization in microelectronic applications so that materials of different thermal properties can be placed in such a way that the heat transfer is most efficient under stringent constraints. It can also be applied to carry out parameter estimation as an inverse problem. If an inverse problem can be properly formulated, then bat algorithm can provide better results than least-squares methods and regularization methods.

Lin *et al.* (2012) presented a chaotic Levy flight bat algorithm to estimate parameters in nonlinear dynamic biological systems, which proved the effectiveness of the proposed algorithm.

Komarasamy and Wahi (2012) studied k-means clustering using bat algorithm and they concluded that the combination of both k-means and BA can achieve higher efficiency and thus performs better than other algorithms.

Khan and Sahai (2012a) presented a study of a clustering problem for office workplaces using a fuzzy bat algorithm. Khan and Sahai (2012a) also presented a comparison study of bat algorithm with PSO, GA, and other algorithms in the context for e-learning, and thus suggested that bat algorithm has clearly some advantages over other algorithms.

Then, they (Khan and Sahai, 2012a) also presented a study of clustering problems using bat algorithm and its extension as a bi-sonar optimization variant with good results.

16.4. Conclusions

After making an exhaustive study of the different optimization algorithms inspired in swarms, we can conclude the importance of these algorithms and we can see that they are capable to improve the performance of many applications, which is usually required in complex optimization problems. For example, BCO is a metaheuristic motivated by foraging behavior of honeybees. It represents general algorithmic framework that can be applied to various optimization problems in management, engineering, and control. ACO takes inspiration from the shortest path searching behavior of various ant species. PSO developed by

Eberhart and Kennedy in 1995, inspired by the social behavior of bird flocking or fish schooling also is able for solving many complex optimization problems. Finally BA is the more recent method, inspired in the behavior of the micro bats, however is able to achieve very good results as the methods based in populations. In this paper, we only analyzed the most relevant proposed methods in the last years; however, there are other works with other algorithms where the researchers can find other similar metaheuristics. Therefore, in this study we focused on the methods based in swarm intelligence. Recently, many researchers have been applying swarm intelligence in for solving complex applications and obtain better results than with conventional methods. Also, we can observe in this review that the fuzzy systems can be used to improve methods and not only work with control systems for example or other applications. The swarm intelligence is nowadays used by researchers to achieve the best results in the algorithms and obtain better results than the other techniques.

Acknowledgment

We would like to express our gratitude to CONACYT, Tijuana Institute of Technology for the facilities and resources granted for the development of this research.

References

Ahmadizar, F. and Soltanpanah, H. (2011). Reliability optimization of a series system with multiple-choice and budget constraints using an efficient ant colony approach. *Expert Syst. Appl.*, 38(4), pp. 3640–3646.

Alcalá-Fdez, R., Alcalá, MJ. and Gacto, F. (2009). Herrera, learning the membership function contexts forming fuzzy association rules by using genetic algorithms. *Fuzzy Sets Syst.*, 160(7), pp. 905–921.

Angeline P. J. (1998). Using selection to improve particle swarm optimization. *Proc. 1998 IEEE World Congress on Computational Intelligence*, Anchorage, Alaska, IEEE, pp. 84–89.

Angeline P. J. (1998). Evolutionary optimization versus particle swarm optimization: Philosophy and performance differences, Evolutionary Programming VII, Lecture Notes in Computer Science 1447, Springer, pp. 601–610.

Argha R., Diptam D. and Kaustav C. Training artificial neural network using particle swarm optimization 3(3), *Int. J. of Adv. Res. Comp. Sci. and Soft. Eng. Res. Paper*. Retrieved from www.ijarcsse.com.

Beni, G. (1988). The concept of cellular robotic system. *Proc. of the 1988 IEEE Int. Symp. Intell. Control*. Los Alamitos, CA: IEEE Computer Society Press, pp. 57–62.

Beni, G. and Wang, J. (1989). Swarm intelligence. *Proc. of the Seventh Ann. Meeting of the Robotics Society of Japan*. RSJ Press, Tokyo, pp. 425–428.

Beni, G. and Hackwood, S. (1992). Stationary waves in cyclic swarms. *Proc. of the 1992 Int. Symp. on Intelligent Control*. IEEE Computer Society Press, Los Alamitos, CA, pp. 234–242.

Bonabeau, E., Dorigo, M. and Theraulaz, G. (1997). *Swarm Intelligence*. Oxford University Press, Oxford.

Bullnheimer, B., Kotsis, G. and Strauss, C. (1997). Parallelization strategies for the ant system. In Toraldo, G., Murli, A. and Pardalos, P. (eds.), *Kluwer Series on Applied Optimization*, pp. 87–100.

Castillo, O. and Melin, P. (2002). Hybrid intelligent systems for time series prediction using neural networks, fuzzy logic, and fractal theory. *Neural Networks, IEEE Transactions* 13(6), pp. 1395–1408.

Castillo, O., Neyoy, H., Soria, J., García, M. and Valdez, F. (2013). Dynamic fuzzy logic parameter tuning for ACO and its application in the fuzzy logic control of an autonomous mobile robot. *Int. J. Adv. Robot Syst.*, 10(51), pp. 1–10.

Chang, Y. H., Chang, C. W., Tao, C. W., Lin, H. W. and Taur, J. S. (2012). Fuzzy sliding-mode control for ball and beam system with fuzzy ant colony optimization. *Expert Systems with Applications*, 39(3), pp. 3624–3633.

Colorni, A., Dorigo, M. and Maniezzo, V. (1992a). Distributed optimization by ant colonies. In Varela, F. J. and Bourgine, P. (eds.), *Proceedings of the First European Conference on Artificial Life*. Cambridge, MA: MIT Press, pp. 134–142.

de Lima, N. F. and Ludermir, T. B. Frankenstein PSO applied to neural network weights and architectures, *Evolutionary Computation (CEC), 2011 IEEE Congress*. pp. 2452–2456.

Dorigo. M. (1992). *Optimization, Learning and Natural Algorithms*. Ph.D. thesis, Politecnico di Milan, Milano, Italy.

Dorigo, M. (1994). Learning by probabilistic boolean networks. *Proc. IEEE Int. Conf. Neural Netw.*, pp. 887–891.

Dorigo, M., Bonabeau, E. and Theraulaz, G. (2000). Ant algorithms and stigmergy. *Future Generation Computer Systems*, 16(9), pp. 851–871.

Dorigo, M. and Di Caro, G. (1999). Ant colony optimization: A new meta-heuristic. *Proc. of the IEEE Congress on Evolutionary Computation*, 2, p. 1477.

Dorigo, M. and Di Caro, G. (1999). The ant colony optimization meta-heuristic. In Corne, D., Dorigo, M. and F. Glover, (eds.), *New Ideas in Optimization*, pp. 11–32. London: McGraw-Hill.

Dorigo M. and Gambardella, L. (1996). A study of some properties of Ant-Q. *Proc. of the Fourth Int. Conf. on Parallel Problem Solving from Nature*, pp. 656–665.

Dorigo, M. and Gambardella, L. M. Ant colonies for the travelling salesman problem. *Biosystems*, 43(2), pp. 73–81.

Eberhart, R. C. and Kennedy, (1995). A new optimizer using particle swarm theory, *Proc. Sixth Int. Symposium on Micro Machine and Human Science*, Nagoya, Japan, pp. 33–43.

Ganji, M. F. and Abadeh, M. S. (2011). A fuzzy classification system based on Ant Colony Optimization for diabetes disease diagnosis. *Expert Systems with Applications*, 38(12), pp. 14650–14659.

Geem, Z. W. (2008). Novel derivative of harmony search algorithm for discrete design variables. *Appl. Math. Comput.*, 199(1), pp. 223–230.

Glover, F. (1989). Tabu Search — Part I, ORSA. *Journal on Computing*, 1, No. 3, pp. 190–206. First comprensive description of tabu search.

Goel N., Gupta D. and Goel S. (2013). *Performance of Firefly and Bat Algorithm for Unconstrained Optimization Problems*, Department of Computer Science Maharaja Surajmal Institute of Technology GGSIP University C-4, Janakpuri, New Delhi, India.

Holland, J. H. (1975). Adaptation in Natural and Artificial Systems: An Introductory Analysis with Applications to Biology, Control, and Artificial Intelligence. Ann Arbor, MI: University of Michigan Press.

Karaboga, D. and Akay, B. (2009). A survey: Algorithms simulating bee swarm intelligence. *Artificial Intelligence Rev*. 31(1), pp. 68–85.

Kennedy, J. and Eberhart, R. C. (1995). Particle swarm optimization. *Proc. of IEEE Int. Conf. on Neural Networks*, Piscataway, NJ, pp. 1942–1948.

Kennedy, J. and Eberhart, R. C. Particle swarm optimization. *Proc. IEEE Int. Conf. on Neural Networks*, Piscataway, NJ, pp. 1942–1948.

Khan, K. and Sahai, A. (2012a). A comparison of BA, GA, PSO, BP and LM for training feed forward neural networks in e-learning context, *Int. J. Intelligent Systems and Applications* (*IJISA*), 4, No. 7, pp. 23–29.

Kirkpatrick, S., Gelatt, C. D. and Vecchi, M. P. (1983). Optimization by simulated annealing. *Science*, 220(4598), pp. 671–680.

Komarasamy, G. and Wahi, A. (2012). An optimized K-means clustering technique using bat algorithm, *European J. Scientific Research*, 84, No. 2, pp. 263–273.

Lin, J. H., Chou, C. W., Yang, C. H. and Tsai, H. L. (2012). A chaotic levy flight bat algorithm for parameter estimation in nonlinear dynamic biological systems, *J. Computer and Info. Tech.* 2, No. 2, pp. 56–63.

Li, S. G. and Rong, Y. L. (2009). The reliable design of one-piece flow production system using fuzzy ant colony optimization, *Computers & Operations Research*, 36(5), pp. 1656–1663.

Li, C. and Wu, T. (2011). Adaptive fuzzy approach to function approximation with PSO and RLSE. *Expert Systems with Applications*, 38, pp. 13266–13273.

Lučić, P. and Teodorović, D. (2001). Bee system: Modeling combinatorial optimization transportation engineering problems by swarm intelligence. In *Preprints of the RISTAN IV Triennial Symposium on Transportation Analysis*, Sao Miguel, Azores Islands, Portugal, pp. 441–445.

Lučić, P. and Teodorović, D.: Transportation modeling: An artificial life approach. *Proc. of the 14th IEEE 'Int. Conf. on Tools with Artificial Intelligence*, Washington, DC, pp. 216–223.

Lučić, P. and Teodorović, D. (2003a). Computing with bees: Attacking complex transportation engineering problems. *Int. J. Artif. Intell. T.* 12, pp. 375–394.

Lučić, P. and Teodorović, D. (2003b). Vehicle routing problem with uncertain demand at nodes: The bee system and fuzzy logic approach. Verdegay, J. L. (ed.), *Fuzzy Sets in Optimization*. Heidelberg, Berlin: Springer-Verlag, pp. 67–82.

Marković, G., Teodorović, D. and Aćimović, Raspopović, V. (2007). Routing and wavelength assignment in all-optical networks based on the bee colony optimization. *AI Commun.* 20, pp. 273–285.

Melin, P., Olivas, F., Castillo, O., Valdez, F., Soria, J. and Valdez, M. (2013). Optimal design of fuzzy classification systems using PSO with dynamic parameter adaptation through fuzzy logic. *Expert Syst. Appl.* 40(8): pp. 3196–3206.

Musikapun, P. and Pongcharoen, P. (2012). Solving multi-stage multi-machine multi-product scheduling problem using bat algorithm. *2nd Int. Conf. on Management and Artificial Intelligence* (*IPEDR*), 35, IACSIT Press, Singapore, pp. 98–102.

Ocenasek, J. and Schwarz, J. (2002). Estimation of distribution algorithm for mixed continuous-discrete optimization problems. In *Proc. of the 2nd Euro-International Symposium on Computational Intelligence*, IOS Press, Amsterdam, the Netherlands, (pp. 227–232).

Rashedi, E., Nezamabadi-pour, H. and Saryazdi, S. (2009). GSA: A Gravitational Search Algorithm. *Inf. Sci.*, 179(13), pp. 2232–2248.

Reynolds, R. G. (1994). An introduction to cultural algorithms, *Proc. of the 3rd Ann. Conf. on Evolutionary Programming*, World Scientific Publishing, RiverEdge NJ, pp. 131–139.

Rodrigues, D., Pereira, L., Nakamura, R., Costa, K., Yang, X., Souza, A. and Papa, J. P. (2013). *A wrapper approach for feature selection based on Bat Algorithm and Optimum-Path Forest*, Department of Computing, Universidade Estadual Paulista, Bauru, Brazil.

Shah-Hosseini, H. (2009). The intelligent water drops algorithm: A nature-inspired swarm-based optimisation algorithm, *Int. J. Bio-Inspired Computation*, 1(1/2), pp. 71–79.

Stützle, T. (1997a). An ant approach to the flow shop problem. Technical report AIDA-97-07, FG Intellektik, FB Informatik, TU Darmstadt, Germany.

Stützle, T. (1997b). MAX–MIN Ant System for the quadratic assignment problem. Technical report AIDA-97-4, FG Intellektik, FB Informatik, TU Darmstadt, Germany.

Tang, W. J., Wu, Q. H. and Saunders, J. R. (2006). Bacterial foraging algorithm for dynamic environments. *IEEE Congress on Evolutionary Computation Sheraton Vancouver Wall Centre Hotel*, Vancouver, BC, Canada, July 16–21.

Teodorović, D. (2003b). Transport modeling by multi-agent systems: A swarm intelligence approach. *Transport. Plan. Techn.* 26, pp. 289–312.

Teodorovic, D. and Dell'orco, M. (2005). Bee colony optimization — A cooperative learning approach to complex transportation problems, *Advanced OR and AI Methods in Transportation*, pp. 51–60.

Teodorović, D. and Dell'Orco, M. (2005). Bee colony optimization — A cooperative learning approach to complex transportation problems. In advanced OR and AI methods in transportation. *Proc. of the 10th Meeting of the EURO Working Group on Transportation*, Poznan, Poland, pp. 51–60.

Teodorović, D., Lučić, P., Marković, G. and Dell' Orco, M. (2006). Bee colony optimization: Principles and applications. In Reljin, B. and Stanković, S. (eds.), *Proc. of the Eight Seminar on Neural Network Applications in Electrical Engineering — NEUREL* 2006, University of Belgrade, Belgrade, pp. 151–156.

Teodorović, D. and Šelmić, M. (2007). The BCO algorithm for the *p* median problem. *In Proc. of the XXXIV Serbian Operations Research Conf.* Zlatibor, Serbia.

Valdez, F., Melin, P. and Castillo, O. (2010). Evolutionary method combining Particle Swarm Optimisation and Genetic Algorithms using fuzzy logic for parameter adaptation and aggregation: The case neural network optimisation for face recognition. *IJAISC*, 2(1/2), pp. 77–102.

Yang, X. (2010). *A New Metaheuristic Bat-Inspired Algorithm*. Department of Engineering, University of Cambridge, Trumpington Street, Cambridge CB2 1PZ, UK.

Yang, X. S. (2010). A new metaheuristic bat-inspired algorithm. In Gonzalez, J. R. (ed.), *Nature Inspired Cooperative Strategies for Optimization (NISCO 2010). Studies in Computational Intelligence*. Berlin: Springer, pp. 65–74.

Yang, X. (2013). *Bat Algorithm: Literature Review and Applications, School of Science and Technology*, Middlesex University, The Burroughs, London NW4 4BT, United Kingdom.

Chapter 17

Memetic Algorithms

Qiangfu Zhao and Yong Liu

Roughly speaking, genes carry information for constructing a body, in which they usually work in groups to construct a meaningful body. Similarly, memes carry information for constructing a culture, in which many memes usually work together to construct a meaningful culture. Although in real world genes and memes are realized in different forms (e.g., DNA for genes and language for memes), in evolutionary computation (EC), both of them can be represented using strings defined on some alphabetic set. Thus, in EC we can study genetic evolution and memetic evolution in the same way. We can also combine them together to improve the efficiency and efficacy of the evolutionary search process. *Memetic algorithms (MAs) are search algorithms obtained by combining genetic evolution and memetic evolution.* In MAs, genetic evolution is often used for global search and memetic evolution is used to find the best local search strategy. So far, a great number of MAs have been proposed in the literature. In this chapter, we first define some fundamental concepts related to memetic evolution, and then introduce several templates that may cover most existing MAs. For each template, we provide a pseudo code, so that readers can understand the algorithms easily, and can develop programs to solve their own problems.

17.1. Introduction

Heuristic algorithms often use some *a priori* domain knowledge called *heuristics* to determine the next search point, given the current one. The main purpose of using heuristics is to improve search efficiency, although global optimal solutions may not be guaranteed. To increase the opportunity of obtaining the global optimal solutions, some higher level heuristics are often required. Search algorithms using multiple levels of heuristics are called *metaheuristic algorithms.* To improve the efficiency and the efficacy of search, different heuristics can be hybridized without considering levels. These kinds of hybridized algorithms in general are called *hyper-heuristic algorithms.* Hyper-heuristics are more general than metaheuristics.

In hyper-heuristic algorithms, we often use some heuristics for local search, and some other heuristics for controlling the whole search process, so that the global optimal solution(s) can be obtained with a higher probability (Miller *et al.*, 1993). A simple example is to hybridize *a population based* algorithm with an *individual based* one. The former is used for global search, and the latter for local adaptation. This hybridization, although simple, often leads to very good results for solving hard problems (Krasnogor and Smith, 2005; Ong *et al.*, 2006; Chen *et al.*, 2011).

Noting that some good local search heuristics or strategies can be shared by many individuals, these heuristics together can be considered as the "culture" of a population. It is for this reason that Moscato has named hyper-heuristic algorithms as *memetic algorithms* (MAs) (Moscato, 1989). Here, the term "meme" was produced by Dawkins to mean "a *unit of imitation in cultural transmission which in some aspects is analogues to the gene*" (Dawkins, 1976). In MAs, memes are often considered as local search strategies. The common goal of MAs is to incorporate some good memes into a global search procedure, so that we can find the global optimal solution(s) more efficiently and effectively.

In recent years, a great number of MAs have been proposed in the literature, and many survey papers have been published in several good journals (Krasnogor and Smith, 2005; Ong *et al.*, 2006; Chen *et al.*, 2011). Although authors of these papers have tried different ways to summarize and classify MAs, it is still difficult for the beginners to understand the relationships between different MAs. The goal of this chapter is to summarize different MAs in a more systematic way, so that readers can study, use, and propose their own MAs easily.

The rest of the chapter is organized as follows. Section 17.2 provides a brief introduction to memetic evolution theory, so that readers can understand what a meme really is, and what an MA should be. In Sections 17.3 and 17.4, we investigate, respectively, some *adaptive* MAs and *evolutionary* MAs, and provide pseudo codes for them. Section 17.5 is the conclusion of this chapter.

17.2. Meme and Memetic Evolution

It is known that *Darwin's theory of evolution* is universal, and is not limited to evolution of *biological lives* on the earth. In fact, the universal Darwinism is also applicable to evolution of cultures (Hodgson, 2005). For the latter, Dawkins introduced the term *meme* to represent "a unit of imitation in cultural transmission which in some aspects is analogues to the gene" (Dawkins, 1976). Memes, according to Dawkins, are a kind of *replicators* that can evolve. That is, they have the three fundamental properties for evolution, namely *variation, selection, and retention.*

In this section, we try to define meme and some related concepts more clearly, and build a foundation for the following sections.

17.2.1. *Meme, Memotype, and Memeplex*

Some people argue that unlike genes, we still cannot define the *units or building blocks* for cultures, and thus the meme metaphor may not be correct (Blackmore, 1999). In fact, when talking about memes, Dawkins did not distinguish meme, memotype, and memeplex clearly. This is the main reason why people could not understand the meme theory well. It is a pity that many MA researchers actually do not understand what a meme really is.

Similar to gene, *genotype,* and *phenotype,* we have meme, *memotype,* and *memeplex* (short for *meme complex).* Roughly speaking, a group of memes form a memotype; and a memotype defines a memeplex. For example, to make an origami airplane, a kindergarten teacher may tell the children how to do, step by step, while she makes a demonstration. The ways she selects the paper, folds the corners, folds the edges, etc., can be seen and imitated by the children. Children in group A may try to remember what their teacher says, memorize the instructions, and then make the origami airplane in *the same way.* On the other hand, children in group B may imitate their teacher step by step, try to describe the process using their own languages and memorize, and then make the paper airplanes in *similar ways.* Here, the ways for selecting the paper, folding the corners, folding the edges, etc., form the memeplex; the instructions form the memotype; and the words used in the instructions are memes.

From the origami example we can understand that memes can be defined as *words* or *phrases* in different languages, and be used as the building blocks of different cultures. It is not proper to consider the whole process for doing something as a single meme. Rather, this whole process should be considered as a memeplex. In general, we may define memes as *concepts* represented in words (or Chinese characters) or phrases. Some concept can be very complicated and must be defined using many lower level concepts. In such cases we may define the corresponding meme using its *name or label* (e.g., "*meme*" is the name of the main concept described in this paragraph). Similar to genes, memes contain information for constructing different memeplexes (e.g., ideas, rules, instructions, and methods).

Similar to genotype, memotype represents *a group of memes.* Speaking more precisely, it is memotype, not memeplex, which is transmitted from brain to brain. A memotype is the seed or egg of a memeplex. Once it is accepted by a brain, it can grow up using resources of the brain, and become a memeplex. We may classify the memotypes into two categories, namely *strictly described* (SD) memotypes, and *weakly described* (WD) ones. An SD memotype usually describes the memeplex precisely. It can be passed from one brain to another with few variations, and the memeplex can be almost the same as the memotype. On the other hand, a WD memotype is usually short, and may vary greatly when it is passed to other brains. A WD memotype, once accepted by a brain, may grow up in the brain, and generate a big memeplex later.

In the case the memotype is how to ride a bicycle for instance, it can be a very simple instruction like *"just practice and you will do it"*. In such cases, some *tacit knowledge* (Polanyi, 1966) must be learned through practice to compensate the instruction. The same thing happens in genotype based phenotype construction. It is reasonable to consider that information contained in the genotype alone is not enough to construct a phenotype (e.g., a human body) if the egg is not put into a proper environment. That is, some outside information or materials are supposed *to be there* for constructing the phenotype. Similarly, when a person imitates a memeplex, not all information is memorized in the brain. A *seed* or an *egg* will be sufficient, and this seed is nothing but the memotype. The memotype will utilize resources of the brain to construct a memeplex, with variations.

Note that there are memeplexes that cannot be described by *speaking languages.* Examples include music, fashions, hair styles, gestures, videos, etc. However, the memotypes of these memeplexes can also be described using a set of *symbols or attributes.* In general, the memotypes can be represented in strings defined on some alphabetic set, which are nothing but *languages in the sense of computer science.*

17.2.2. *Fitness of Memes*

Memes can transmit from one brain to another via *imitation* or learning, and their different versions can survive in different brains for a relatively long period. For the memes to evolve, it is necessary to define their goodness or fitness first. Intuitively, good memes can form good memotypes, good memotypes can form good memeplexes, and many good memeplexes together can form a good *mental brain* (or *mind).* The memeplexes can be defined as *agents,* and the mental brain is actually a *society of agents* (Minsky, 1986). In turn, a person with a good mental brain can be very clever, and can be more successful than others. A successful person has more chances to be imitated or learned by others. Through imitation or learning people wish to be equally or more successful. Thus, good memes can be passed from brain to brain easily, and can survive for a long time.

After all, what is the fitness of a meme? Like a gene, a single meme cannot be evaluated directly. A meme can become meaningful only when it is put together with other memes and form a memotype; and only if this memotype can obtain some brain recourses and become a memeplex. Only when a memeplex is meaningful, the corresponding memotype can be accepted more easily by many brains. Here, the term "meaningful" should be defined based on the principle of *survival of the fittest.* Normally, we accept some memotypes if we *believe* (through observations) that the corresponding memeplexes are useful. However, what we believe may not be true or correct. In the process of memetic evolution, some memotypes may become so *clever* that they can be easily passed and accepted by many brains and can grow up inside the brains gradually later. These memotypes may not be useful or even harmful to our humans. But we may accept them before knowing their real values.

Thus, we cannot define the fitness of the memes based on human belief. The memes or memotypes are selected or selected against based only on their own fitness for survival. Similar to evaluation of a gene, the fitness of a meme is evaluated indirectly based on the fitness of the memotypes containing this meme. The memotypes in turn are evaluated by the fitness of the corresponding memeplexes. In fact, any method used for evaluating genes based on genotypes and phenotypes can be used to evaluate memes based on memotypes and memeplexes.

It is also worthwhile to note that the fitness of a meme does not depend, at least does not only depend, on the fitness of the human body. People with weak bodies may have strong *mental brains,* which are constructed by strong memeplexes. However, clever memes do seek for more chances to immigrate to brains with strong bodies so that they can have more opportunity to influence other people and thus have more chances to spread. Clever memes must also govern the brains in which they live to keep the bodies healthy and strong, so that they can have longer time to seek for chances to spread.

17.2.3. *Process of Memetic Evolution*

In the above discussions, we have already mentioned here and there something related to memetic evolution. For example, through transmission a memotype can find more resources to survive by joining other memotypes (*recombination or crossover*). When a memotype is transmitted to a brain, agents (or memeplexes) already living there often do not accept this new comer, at least they will not accept the new comer as it is. Existing agents will make a collective decision, force the new comer to make some changes (*mutation*), and then accept it. As a result, the same memotype (and thus the corresponding memeplex) can have different variations in different brains. Memotypes that cannot find any place to go will die and disappear (*selected against*). Even this chapter, as a memotype, will be selectively accepted by the readers — some parts may transmit from my brain to this book and from this book to the brains of some readers, and others will be forgotten.

There are many memeplexes, and they can exist in different forms. Some *are living* in the human brains, some *are sleeping* in the libraries, and some *are wandering* around in the internet. Each person accepts (via imitation or learning) some memeplexes (exist in the brains or other places) that he/she believes useful, recombines them with the memeplexes already in the brain, produces variations, and posts them to some mass media (e.g., books, papers, reports, etc.) if he/she believes that the new memeplexes are useful to other people (and this paragraph is an example of a new memeplex). Thus, we human beings are one of the media for receiving, carrying, reproducing, amplifying, and distributing the memeplexes. In certain sense, we are just the computing machines for the memeplexes to evolve. There is no evidence that memetic evolution is for human. In future, the memeplexes may find better computing machines (e.g., the cyber-space) to evolve and forget completely the old machines that they are using now.

17.3. Adaptive MAs

In this section, we introduce several basic MAs. Although these MAs do not *evolve* the memes, they are very useful for solving many practical problems. Before starting, let us first review briefly the standard genetic algorithm (SGA), and define some terminologies that will be used throughout this chapter.

17.3.1. *Standard Genetic Algorithm*

SGA (Goldberg, 1989) is used as a basis algorithm of this chapter; although discussions given here can be extended easily to genetic programming (Koza, 1992; 2002), evolution strategies (Beyer and Schwefel, 2002), evolutionary programming (Fogel *et al.*, 1996), and other population based metaheuristic algorithms.

Program-0 is the pseudo code of SGA. In this *program*, we consider each individual in a population P as an *agent,* which is defined as a *structure* containing several elements. In this chapter, whenever we provide a pseudo-code, we use a style *similar to* C language, and try to use full English words as much as possible to make the code more understandable. We use a semicolon to terminate a line, and a double slash "//" to make some short comments. In the program, "`DefineType`" is used to define a new type, the type "`Genotype`" is usually a binary bit string, the type "`Fitness`" is a real number, and the population `P` is an array of type Agent. `P` contains `NumberAgent` individuals. As in C language, we use `x.g` and `x.f` to denote the genotype and the fitness, respectively, of an individual `x`; and use `P [i]` to denote the ith element of `P`.

Program-0: SGA

```
DefineType Agent {
  Genotype: g; // Genotype of the agent.
  Fitness : f; // Fitness of the agent.
};
Agent P[NumberAgent];

Begin
  P=Initialize(); // Initialize population.
  For t=1 to NumberGeneration
    For i=1 to NumberAgent
      p=Decoding(P[i].g); // Find phenotype.
      P[i].f=Evaluation(p); // Find fitness.
    End
    If (Terminating condition) break;
    P=Reproduction(P); // Update population.
  End
End
```

Note that in SGA, it is not necessary for each individual to have a phenotype. The phenotype can be generated and stored in a *working memory* which is shared by all individuals. The genotype of each individual is usually initialized at random. Although some algorithm can also be used to find a better starting point, we do not consider this kind of hybridization in SGA. During evolution, the phenotype of each individual is first decoded (reconstructed) from the genotype, and is then evaluated. Different methods for evaluation can be used for different applications. The *terminating condition* also depends on applications, but usually we may just check if the fitness value of the current best individual is already good enough (e.g., higher than a pre-specified value) or not; or the number of *generations* reaches to a given value (i.e., `NumberGeneration`) or not.

To reproduce a new population, we first select some parent individuals, then produce new individuals (offspring) by recombining (crossover) these parents, and finally mutate the new individuals. The new individuals together form the population for the next generation. That is, reproduction can be defined as a product of three operators as follows:

$$P(t+1) = \text{Reproduction}(P(t)) = \text{Mutation (Crossover (Selection }(P(t)))).$$

In this chapter, we suppose that the population size does not change during evolution. For practical applications, however, we may consider the population as a hybrid of the medium-term and long-term memories used in Tabu search (TS) for intensification (exploitation) and diversification (exploration) (Glover, 1986; 1989; 1990), and use some other meta-heuristics to adjust the population size. We will not discuss this issue in detail here.

Program-1: SHA

```
Begin
  P=Initialize(); // Initialize population.
  For t=1 to NumberGeneration
    For i=1 to NumberAgent
      p=Decoding(P[i].g); // Find phenotype.
      P[i].f=Evaluation(p); // Find fitness.
    End
    If (Terminating condition) break;
    P=Reproduction(P);
  End
  x=FindBest(P); // find the best individual.
  p=Decoding(x.g); // Find phenotype.
  p=LocalSearch(p); // Fine tune phenotype.
End
```

17.3.2. *Sequential Hybrid Algorithm (SHA)*

It is known that population-based algorithms like SGA are good for global search, but weak for local fine tuning. That is, even if we have already found the rough position of the global optimal solution x^*, it may take time to find the exact position of x^*. A simple idea to solve this problem is to use SGA first and then use some local search algorithm to fine-tune the solution. Many algorithms have been proposed based on this idea (Thangaraj *et al.*, 2011). In this chapter, we call these algorithms SHAs. Program-1 is the pseudo code of an SHA.

The local search algorithm used in SHA can be TS (Glover, 1989), simulated annealing (SA) (Goffe *et al.*, 1994), or any algorithms proposed in the literature. If the problem is to find a multilayer neural network, we may also use the back propagation (BP) algorithm or any of its improved versions for local search (Schaffer *et al.*, 1992). In addition, we may use particle swarm optimization (PSO) (Eberhart and Shi, 2001) or other population-based *Lamarckian* algorithms for fine tuning. In this case, we may just use the whole population P obtained by SGA as the initial population for further search (Thangaraj *et al.*, 2011).

17.3.3. *Two-Layered Hybrid Algorithms (TLHAs)*

Instead of fine tuning after global search, we may embed the local search into the global search algorithm. This way, we can obtain hybrid algorithms with two layers, namely the global search layer and the local search layer. In this chapter, we call these TLHAs. Program-2 is the pseudo code of a TLHA.

In Program-2, we have assumed that TLHA is a *Baldwinian evolution.* That is, the new phenotype acquired through local search is used only for evaluation. This can be considered as a *default* because Baldwinian evolution is usually better than *Lamarckian* in the sense that better results can be obtained in changing environments. If the environment does not change or does not change quickly, we may also use Lamarckian evolution.

To change the algorithm to Lamarckian, we can introduce an *encoder* that converts the phenotype obtained via local search to a genotype, and then assign the new genotype to the individual under concern. In practice, we may accept the local search result *partially,* to make a balance between full Baldwinian and full Lamarckian evolutions. For example, we may use some of the intermediate results found during local search, encode and then assign the results to the genotype of the current individual.

There is an important difference between local searches in SHA and TLHA. In the former, local search is usually *full,* that is, it should be conducted until convergence; while in the latter local search can *be partial,* that is, we may just run local search for several iterations without waiting for convergence. In fact, full local search for TLHA can be harmful because the evolution process may fall into local minimum easily. In addition, using TLHA we may not have to employ complex algorithms for local search. For example, to solve the traveling salesman problem (TSP) or other combinatorial problems, simple local searches like swapping and visiting neighboring nodes might be sufficient.

Program-2: TLHA

```
Begin
  P=Initialize(); // Initialize population.
  For t=1 to NumberGeneration
    For i=1 to NumberAgent
      p=Decoding(P[i].g); // Find phenotype.
      p=LocalSearch(p); // Update phenotype.
      P[i].f=Evaluation(p);// Find fitness.
// Use the following line for Lamarckian Evolution
     /* P[i].g=Encoding(p); */
     End
     If (Terminating condition) break;
     P=Reproduction(P);
   End
End
```

In the literature, TLHA is often considered as the standard or canonical MA (Ong *et al.*, 2006), although in this chapter we do not adopt this name. We may define the local search strategy used for fine tuning as a memeplex. This memeplex is the culture of the whole population, and is shared by all individuals. However, this memeplex is completely pre-defined, rather than found through evolution. Thus, we can define TLHA as a zeroth-order MA. In fact, SHA is also a zeroth-order MA because the memeplex is pre-defined. In this chapter, we define the *order* of an MA according to its *degree of evolution.* That is, if an MA does not evolve the memeplexes, it is a zeroth-order MA; if the MA uses one or two factors (among variation, selection, and retention) of evolution, it is a first-order MA; and if the MA possesses all features of memetic evolution, it is a second-order or true MA.

17.3.4. *Adaptive Two-Layered Hybrid Algorithm (a-THLA)*

In using TLHAs, we just employ a local search algorithm without fine tuning the search parameters. To make the algorithms more effective, we can introduce a mechanism to fine-tune the local search parameters. The pseudo code of an improved algorithm is Program-3. Here, the type `Parameter` can be a parameter array or a structure containing different types of parameters.

Program-3: a-TLHA

```
Agent P[NumberAgent];
Parameter par;
Begin
   P=Initialize(); // Initialize population.
   par=InitializeParameter(); // Initialize parameters
   For t=1 to NumberGeneration
      For i=1 to NumberAgent
        p=Decoding(P[i].g);// Find phenotype.
        pp=LocalSearch(p); // Update phenotype.
        P[i].f=Evaluation(pp); // Find fitness.
        Gain=P[i].f-Evaluation(p); // Find fitness gain.
        par=Adaptation(par,p,pp,Gain); // Update parameters.
     End
     If (Terminating condition) break;
     P=Reproduction(P);
   End
End
```

In Program-3, a local search parameter set (i.e., `par`) is defined for the whole population and is shared by all individuals. This parameter set is adapted based on local search result of each individual. If we use TS for local search, the parameter set may include the number of iterations, the sizes of different memories (e.g., Tabu list or short-term memory, medium-term memory, and long-term memory), the Tabu-tenure, rates for intensification and diversification, and so on. If we use SA, local search parameters may include the initial temperature, the speed for temperature cooling down, and the number of iterations for obtaining equilibrium. In general, the parameter set should be properly defined for different local search algorithms.

As mentioned earlier, for many problems we may just use *neighborhood-based* search strategies like visiting several points in a neighborhood and swapping adjacent nodes. In such cases, search parameters may include the number of iterations, the radius of the neighborhood, the step size for search, etc. We may fine tune the parameters as follows:

- If the *fitness gain* obtained through local search is *high* (in a fuzzy logic sense), that is, if the local search is successful, we may increase the step size, or increase the neighborhood radius, to accelerate the search process.
- If the fitness gain is negative, that is, if the local search fails, we may decrease the step size, reduce the neighborhood radius, and increase the number iterations, to search more carefully.

The above rules are *local* in the sense that only the current position of the search point is used to make a judgment. To adapt the parameters more effectively, we should also consider memorizing the search history. For example, even if we just use a few values of the fitness gains, say `Gain[t]`, `Gain[t-1]`, and `Gain[t-2]`, we can estimate roughly the trend of the fitness function in the current neighborhood, and can modify the parameters more properly. To estimate the trend of the fitness function, we can use a neural network or some other regression model. The regression model can make the search space more *transparent*, and the local search parameters can be adapted more efficiently.

In Program-3, the parameters are updated based on information acquired by each individual. Thus, the parameters actually *evolve* in the same way as the pheromone trails do in ant colony optimization (ACO) (Dorigo and Stützle, 2004). In this sense, a-TLHA is already an evolutionary MA. In TLHA, there is no imitation between individuals, but the memeplex is saved in a library, and is shared by all individuals as a culture of the whole population. Thus, we may define a-TLHA as the first-order MA. That is, at least *variation and retention* for memetic evolution is employed in the algorithm.

In Program-3, we have implicitly assumed that the local search algorithm is fixed, and the purpose of adaptation is to fine tune the parameters. We may also assume that the parameters are fixed (to some default values), and through adaption we can select the most suitable local search algorithm. This is actually the meta-Lamarckian learning algorithm given in (Ong and Keane, 2004). In this case, we can select the most appropriate local search algorithm based on the current search position and the fitness gain. For more detailed information, please refer to (Ong and Keane, 2004).

Program-4: Ga-TLHA

```
DefineType Agent {
   Genotype : g;
   Fitness  : f;
   Parameter: par;
};
Agent P[NumberAgent];

Begin
   P=Initialize(); // Initialize population.
   For t=1 to NumberGeneration
      For i=1 to NumberAgent
         p=Decoding(P[i].g);// Find phenotype.
         pp=LocalSearch(p,P[i].par); // Update phenotype.
         P[i].f=Evaluation(pp); // Find fitness.
         Gain=P[i].f-Evaluation(p); // Find fitness gain.
         P[i].par=Adaptation(P[i].par,p,pp,Gain);
                 // Update parameters.
      End
      If (Terminating condition) break;
      P=Reproduction(P);
   End
End
```

17.3.5. *General Adaptive Two-Layered Hybrid Algorithm (Ga-TLHA)*

Now, let us consider some of the extensions of a-TLHA. First, as described above, we may prepare *a set of local search algorithms,* so that individuals can select and use different algorithms for local search. Second, we may use *a unique parameter set* for each individual, so that individuals can have different search strategies even if they may share the same local search algorithm. Third, we may allow each individual to memorize its search history, so that different search strategies can be used in different situations.

In fact, the phenotypes of different individuals represent different points in the search space. At different points the landscape of the search space can be completely different. Even for the same individual, it may move from one region to another during search, and the landscapes of these regions can be different. Thus, it is reasonable to use different local search strategies for different individuals or the same individual at different search points.

Program-4 is the pseudo code of an algorithm summarizing the above considerations. This algorithm is called Ga-TLHA. Here, the type `Parameter` is a *queue* (i.e., a sliding window) containing several historical parameter sets. In Ga-TLHA, each individual has its own parameter set(s) for local search, and the parameter set(s) can be updated based on the individual's search behavior.

Before local search, we need to select one algorithm first from the set Ω of local search algorithms based on the parameter set `par`, and then conduct local search using parameters specified, again, by `par`. A memeplex (i.e., one element of `par`) can be defined as follows:

$$par[t] = (j, \pi_1, \pi_2, \ldots, \pi_K), \tag{1}$$

where $1 < j \leq |\Omega|$ is the index of a local search algorithm in Ω and $\pi_k (1 < k \leq K)$ is the kth parameter used by this algorithm, and where K is the maximum number of parameters (or slots) that can be used by a local search algorithm.

In Ga-TLHA, the adaptation mechanism is basically the same as that used in the algorithm a-TLHA, except that we should include a method for selecting local search algorithms. The basic idea for selecting the local search algorithm is as follows:

- If the current local search is successful, the local search algorithm used right now is considered good, and we should increase the probability of choosing this algorithm again next time.
- If the local search does not provide a good result, we should reduce the probability of choosing this algorithm.

That is, each individual can assign a probability to each local search algorithm, and choose a proper algorithm based on the probability, which can be considered as the *belief of an* individual to a certain local search algorithm.

Note that although the algorithm Ga-TLHA is a generalized a-TLHA, it is again a first-order MA. That is, although the memeplex is generalized, there is no big difference for evolving the memeplex. Even if we use different sets of parameters for different individuals, the parameters acquired by one individual are not imitated by other individuals during evolution. That is, good memeplex are neither selected nor transmitted.

17.3.6. *Further Generalization*

To make some preparations for changing a-TLHA or Ga-TLHA into a full evolutionary MA, let us try to generalize the memeplex again. In general, we may allow each individual to use several local search algorithms *sequentially*, and the same local search algorithm can be used again in this sequence. Thus, a memeplex can have the following form:

$$par = (par_1, par_2, \ldots), \tag{2}$$

where each element of par is given by (1). For example, an individual may conduct local search using the following strategy:

$$\text{LocalSearch} = L_1(\theta_1)L_5(\theta_5)L_9(\theta_9)L_5(\theta_5).$$

This local search is conducted in four steps, by using the fifth, the ninth, the fifth (again), and the first local search algorithms in turn. That is, local search in this case is a product of four *local search operators*. The parameter sets may contain parameters such as the number of iterations, the search step size, the number of points to search, etc. Among the parameters, there should be a parameter to specify or limit the computing resources (e.g., time and memory) used by each local search operator. The total resource allocated to local search should not be too long. Otherwise, the computational cost will be too high (Bambha *et al.*, 2004). Also, each time a local operator (say L_5 in the above example) is called, a different set of parameters should be used because the parameters depend on the current location of the search point, too.

Using Ga-TLHA and the above generalizations, we may expect that a good local search strategy can appear during evolution, and the individual using this strategy can have a high fitness. However, it is very difficult to pre-define the rules to adapt the memeplexes of the individuals during evolution. Therefore, we need an algorithm that can evolve the memeplexes fully automatically.

Program-5: D-EMA

```
DefineType Agent {
    Genotype: [g1,g2]; // g2 = memotype
    Fitness : f;
}
Agent P[NumberAgent];

Begin
    P=Initialize(); // Initialize population.
    For t=1 to NumberGeneration
```

```
      For i=1 to NumberAgent
        p=PhenotypeDecoding(P[i].g1); // Find phenotype.
        par=MemeplexDecoding(P[i].g2); // Find memeplex.
        p=LocalSearch(p,par); // Update phenotype.
        P[i].f=Evaluation(p); // Find fitness.
      End
      If (Terminating condition) break;
      P=Reproduction(P);
   End
End
------------------------------------------------------------
```

17.4. Evolutionary MAs

To use the adaptive MAs introduced in the previous section, we must answer several questions. Examples include:

- How often should the local search be applied?
- On which agent should local search be used?
- How long should a local search run?

To answer the above questions through trial and error is certainly not efficient. A better way to answer the above questions and others is evolution. Based on the discussions given so far, in this section we introduce several evolutionary MAs. In some sense, only evolutionary MAs are true MAs (Krasnogor and Gustafson, 2002). Of course, this does not mean that evolutionary MAs are better than adaptive MAs for solving all problems (Wolpert and Macready, 1997). In fact, to obtain good memeplexes through evolution might be computationally expensive. In case we have some *a priori* domain knowledge, we may solve the problem more efficiently by using adaptive MAs. In case we do not have enough domain knowledge, it might be better to use evolutionary MAs.

17.4.1. *Direct Evolutionary Memetic Algorithm (D-EMA)*

The first evolutionary MA to consider is D-EMA, which is a simple extension of SGA or TLHA. The pseudo code of D-EMA is given as Program-5. In this program, the memotype is encoded as the second part of the genotype.

In D-EMA, the memeplex is first constructed (decoded) from the second part of the genotype, and is then used in local search. By default, it is not necessary to include the phenotype and the memeplex in the definition of the individuals. Further, the memeplex represented in (2) can be encoded in a binary bit string. We may also use a character string defined on any alphabetic set. The memeplex is not imitated from other individuals, but is inherited from the parents only. That is, memeplex transmission is done only *vertically*. It is known that this vertical transmission alone can improve the efficiency of search significantly (Krasnogor and Smith, 2001).

Speaking strictly, D-EMA may not be considered as a true MA. According to the definition given in Section 2, memeplexes are cultures that can be shared by part or all individuals in the population. The memeplexes evolved in D-EMA, however, are just *instincts*. The instinct of a good individual may control the individual to behave smartly, and may be helpful for improving search efficiency; but it is not shared by other individuals. However, the memotypes do evolve during the evolution process, and thus in this chapter we define D-EMA as a first-order evolutionary MA.

17.4.2. *Two-Level D-EMA (TLD-EMA)*

The algorithm D-EMA can be modified or improved in many directions. First, we may evolve the genotype and the memotype one by one. That is, we may consider a double-loop evolution. The outer loop can be used to evolve the local search or learning strategy, and the inner loop can be used to evolve the solution of the given problem. Or the outer loop can be used to evolve the search point, and the inner loop can be used to evolve the local search strategy (Figure 17.1). In fact, the latter has a clearer physical meaning. That is, at any search point, it is necessary to find a suitable search strategy based on the position of the search point in the search space. Only if the search strategy fits the current search point, we can search more effectively and efficiently.

17.4.3. *Canonical Evolutionary Memetic Algorithm (C-EMA)*

Another direction to change the D-EMA is to allow the memeplexes to imitate. This results in C-EMA. The pseudo code is given by Program-6. In C-EMA, each individual has its own memeplex, which can be modified before local search. The memeplex `par` of an individual can be recombined (crossover) with that of some other individual in P, and be mutated before being used for local search. In the pseudo code, IMITAION and VARIATION are conditions for conducting imitation

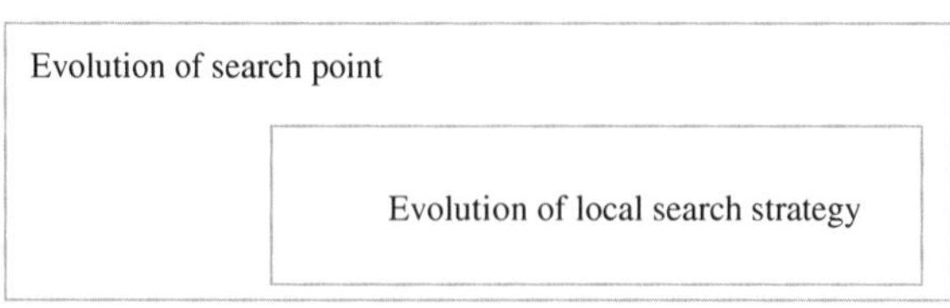

Figure 17.1: A TLD-EMA.

and variation, respectively. The main difference between C-EMA and D-EMA is that the latter only allows vertical transmission of memeplexes, but the former *also* allows *horizontal transmission* of memeplexes, i.e., each individual can imitate the strategies of other (possibly better) individuals through recombination.

We can consider individuals with *personal* memeplexes as *search agents.* Each individual in the population tries to find the best strategy for local search (i.e., the memeplex), and then tries to find the best solution of the given problem (i.e., the phenotype). When we modify the memeplex of an individual using imitation, the individual to be imitated can be anyone in the population. However, if we observe the human societies, we may have the following considerations:

Program-6: C-EMA

```
DefineType Agent {
   Genotype: [g1,g2]; // g2 is the memotype.
   Fitness : f;
};
Agent P[NumberAgent];

Begin
   P=Initialize(); // Initialize population.
   For t=1 to NumberGeneration
     For i=1 to NumberAgent
       p=PhenotypeDecoding(P[i].g1); // Find phenotype.
       m=P[i].g2;
       If(IMITATION) m=Imitation(SelectMemotype(P),m);
       // Imitating another individual selected from P.
       If(VARIATION) m=Variation(m); // Memeplex mutation.
       par=MemeplexDecoding(m);
       p=LocalSearch(p,par); // Update phenotype.
       P[i].f=Evaluation(p); // Find fitness.
    End
    If (Terminating condition) break;
    P=Reproduction(P);
  End
End
```

- The influence of the parents (or direct ancestors) to a child is usually very high, especially in the early stage. Thus, we may assign a higher probability to select the parents to imitate.

- It is better to imitate the elite individual(s) with a higher probability, to improve the fitness of the current individual quickly.
- We may also preserve some search history of each agent, and improve the search strategy properly based on the history.

Thus, a mechanism similar to PSO can be used to modify the memeplex of a given individual, and the updating equations can be given as follows:

$$v(t+1) = av(t) + bw_1(x(t) - x_p(t)) + cw_2(x(t) - x_b) + dw_3(x(t) - x_g),$$
$$x(t+1) = x(t) + v(t+1), \quad (3)$$

where $v(t)$ and $x(t)$ are the search velocity and the position, respectively, of the agent under concern; $x_p(t)$ is the position of one of the parents, x_b is the best position found by the agent itself, x_g is the position of the best agent in the population; a is the inertial, b is the *inheritance influence,* c is the *personal influence,* and d is the *social influence*; and w_1, w_2, and w_3 are random numbers generated in [0,1].

Note that although Program-6 allows each individual to have its own memeplex, the memeplex so obtained is valid only for one generation. That is, by default C-EMA is Baldwinian evolution. The memeplex acquired through recombination and imitation is not passed to the offspring, and is used only for evaluation. We can change the algorithm to a Lamarckian evolution by introducing an encoding mechanism that can encode the acquired memeplex into a memotype. When the landscape of the search space is complex, however, Lamarckian learning can easily fall into a local minimum. Thus, instead of accepting the acquired memeplex directly, we may replace some parts of the memotype with the new materials.

17.4.4. *Co-Evolutionary MAs (Co-EMA)*

As discussed in Section 2, memeplexes can evolve independently. That is, the population of memeplexes can be separated from that of the phenotypes. In fact, human bodies and human cultures are evolving in a co-existence manner. Some authors referred to this kind of evolution as co-evolution (Smith *et al.*, 2002; Smith, 2003; 2007), although it is neither cooperative co-evolution nor competitive evolution (Zhao, 1997; 1998).

Program-7 is the pseudo code of a Co-EMA. In this program, there are two populations, namely the agent population P and the *spirit* population `M`. Each individual in `M` has a memotype and a fitness value. The maximum number of spirits is `NumberSpirit`. Initially, `M` can be empty or generated at random. During evolution, `M` is updated based on the fitness values of the existing spirits and the newly generated ones.

In Program-7, a local search strategy for each agent is defined by a new memotype `newMeme[i]`, which in turn is obtained through variation (e.g., recombination and mutation) of two parent memotypes. There are several ways for selecting the parent memotypes (Smith, 2007). If the agents and their spirits are closely *linked,* we may just select the two parents based on the fitness of the agents.

Otherwise, we can select the parent memotypes based on their own fitness values, or just at random.

Program-7: Co-EMA

```
DefineType Agent {
   Genotype: g;
   Fitness : f;
};
DefineType Spirit {
   Memotype: m;
   Fitness : f;
}
Agent P[NumberAgent];
Spirit M[NumberSpirit], newMeme[NumberAgent];

Begin
   (P, M)=Initialize(); // Initialize populations.
   For t=1 to NumberGeneration
     For i=1 to NumberAgent
       p=PhenotypeDecoding(P[i].g); // Find phenotype.
       (m1,m2)=SelectMemotype(M); // Select parent memotypes.
       newMeme[i]=Variation(m1,m2); // Find a new memotype.
       par=MemeplexDecoding(newMeme[i]); // Find memeplex.
       pp=LocalSearch(p,par); // Update phenotype.
       P[i].f=Evaluation(pp); // Find agent fitness.
       Gain=P[i].f-Evaluation(p); // Find fitness gain.
       newMeme[i].f=MemeEvaluation(Gain, p, pp);
          // Find fitness of new memotype;
    End
    If (Terminating condition) break;
    (P,M)=Reproduction(P,M,newMeme);
  End
End
```

Each time when we fine-tune a phenotype, we obtain a fitness gain. We can then define the fitness of the local search strategy based on the fitness gain, the current position `p`, and the new position `pp`. In each generation, we produce `NumberAgent` new spirits. These spirits along with the existing ones can be used together to produce M for the next generation. In this sense, the way for updating M is similar to that used in evolutionary strategy (ES), rather than that of SGA.

As pointed out earlier, the fitness of a local search strategy depends highly on the current position of the search point. Thus, the memeplex fitness defined in Program-7 is local, and a spirit good for one agent may not be good for other agents. To solve this problem, we may define the *effective region*(s) of a spirit using a set ω of phenotypes. That is, the spirit is useful only for phenotypes (and their close neighbors) in ω. For any agent, we can select spirits based on its own phenotype and the effective regions of the spirits.

17.4.5. *General Evolutionary Memetic Algorithm (G-EMA)*

Both Co-EMA and C-EMA are second-order evolutionary MAs, and they are very similar. The only difference is that in C-EMA each agent has an inherited memeplex. This difference may make C-EMA more stable. This is because the fitness of a local search strategy depends on the current search point, and the parent memotypes selected independent of the phenotype fitness may not fit the current search position. Thus, Co-EMA in its current form may take a large number of generations to find a good combination of agent and spirit.

To solve this problem, we can combine C-EMA and Co-EMA, and obtain the G-EMA, whose pseudo code is given by Program-8. In this program, each agent has its personal memotype (the second part of the genotype). During evolution, this personal memotype is first combined with some other memotype and mutated, and is then used for local search. Hopefully, G-EMA is better than both Co-EAM and C-EMA.

In the literature, the population M of memotypes is often referred to as the meme pool. This meme pool is actually the library or knowledge base for the whole population. In G-EMA, each agent has its inherited instincts. It can imitate its parents or learn knowledge from the library. Hopefully, through imitation and learning, each agent can find a suitable strategy to find a better solution (for the problem under concern).

By default, the knowledge learned by each agent is used only for one generation. That is, the memetic evolution is Baldwinian. We may allow Lamarckian or partial Lamarckian evolution, so that memotypes can be modified in each generation, and re-used in future generations. This way, each agent can conduct *life-time learning,* that is, it can learn in many generations before being selected against. This kind of evolution may encourage agents that can acquire good phenotypes and memeplexes slowly but steadily.

Program-8: G-EMA

```
DefineType Agent {
   Genotype: [g1,g2];
   Fitness : f;
};
DefineType Spirit {
   Memotype: m;
   Fitness : f;
}
Agent P[NumberAgent] ;
Spirit M[NumberSpirit], newMeme[NumberAgent];

Begin
   (P, M)=Initialize(); // Initialize populations.
   For t=1 to NumberGeneration
     For i=1 to NumberAgent
       p=PhenotypeDecoding(P[i].g1); // Find phenotype.
       m=SelectMemotype(M); // Select parent memotype.
       newMeme[i]=Variation(P[i].g2,m);// Find a new memotype.
       par=MemeplexDecoding(newMeme[i]); // Find memeplex.
       pp=LocalSearch(p,par); // Update phenotype.
       P[i].f=Evaluation(pp); // Find agent fitness.
       Gain=P[i].f-Evaluation(p); // Find fitness gain.
       newMeme[i].f=MemeEvaluation(Gain, p, pp);
          // Find fitness of new memotype;
    End
    If (Terminating condition) break;
    (P,M)=Reproduction(P,M,newMeme);
  End
End
```

17.4.6. *A Simple Example*

To show how to use G-EMA, let us consider a simple example. In this example, we suppose that the search space is the parameter space of a neural network controller for navigating a mobile robot. The genotype of each agent is the system parameter set represented in binary string, the phenotype is the system parameter set itself, and the fitness is defined as the performance of the robot (e.g., ability to track a target, efficiency to reach a goal, etc.).

For this example, we can use reinforcement learning (e.g., Q-learning) only for local search (Sutton and Barto, 1998), and define the memeplex as the learning parameters (e.g., the learning rate, the discount factor, and the number of learning cycles). The memotype is the binary representation of the memeplex, and is included in the second part of the genotype.

During evolution, each agent `P[i]` is evaluated as follows:

- Find the phenotype `p` from the first part of the genotype;
- Select a memotype m from the meme pool `M` (which is initialized at random);
- Find a new memotype `newMeme[i]` by crossover and mutation, based on m and the second part of the genotype;
- Find a parameter set par based on `newMeme[i]`;
- Conduct reinforcement learning on the phenotype `p`, and obtain a new phenotype `pp`;
- Evaluate p and pp, and find the fitness gain `Gain`; and
- Evaluate `newMeme[i]` based on `p`, `pp`, and `Gain`.

Figure 17.2 illustrates the above evaluation process. Based on the evaluation results, the agent population `P` can be updated in the same way as in SGA, and the meme pool `M` can be updated using methods proposed for ES.

17.4.7. *Hierarchical Evolutionary MA (H-EMA)*

So far, we have considered each individual in a population as a search agent. That is, during evolution each agent searches for the best local search strategy while

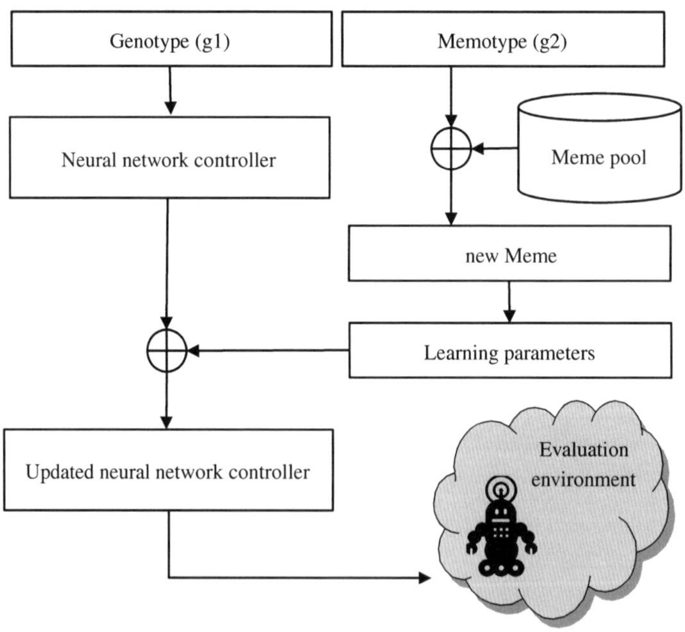

Figure 17.2: Illustration of evaluation process of an agent.

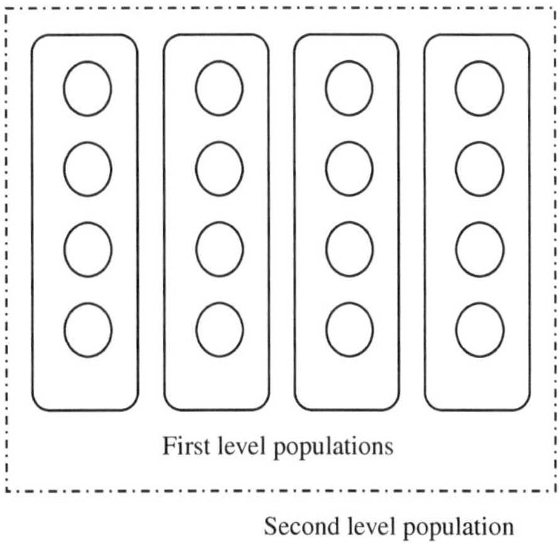

Figure 17.3: Illustration of (H-EMA).

searching for the best position in the problem space. We may consider the whole population as a search agent, and define another higher level population. Thus, in principle we can have a H-EMA.

Figure 17.3 illustrates the basic idea of H-EMA. In Figure 17.3, circles represent the *first level agents,* and many of them form a *first level population,* or a *second level agent.* Many second level agents form a *second level population,* which can be defined as a *third level agent.* This way, we can define many levels or hierarchies of evolution. In general, for the jth level, we can use SGA or any MAs to evolve the jth level agents using the jth level population. During evolution, genetic or memetic materials can be transmitted from one agent to another, and this is equivalent to immigration between the $(j-1)$th level populations.

17.5. Conclusions and Remarks

In this chapter, we have defined the memes, memotypes, and memeplexes more clearly, and introduced several MAs. Although these algorithms have been summarized in several survey papers, we believe that this chapter is more readable and comprehensible for the beginners of this area. Readers can easily master the whole picture of MAs, and ready to write programs for solving their own problems based on the pseudo codes given here.

In this chapter, we have tried to be *neutral* about the performance of the MAs. We have neither mentioned whether MAs are better than existing meta-heuristic algorithms (e.g., TS, SA-PSO, and ACO), nor pointed out which MA is the best. Based on no free lunch theory (Wolpert and Macready, 1997), any single algorithm cannot be the best for solving all problems. For instance, evolutionary MAs may not be more efficient than adaptive ones. If we have *a priori* domain knowledge, we may try adaptive MAs first. Otherwise, we may try evolutionary MAs, gain some knowledge, and then try to fix some parameters to narrow the search space for memetic evolution.

Note also that this chapter focused only on the algorithm aspect. We have tried to use the pseudo codes to explain the algorithms, so that readers can understand and use them straightforwardly. Encoding and decoding of individuals (i.e., phenotypes and memeplexes), evaluation of fitness, terminating condition, evolutionary operators, and so on, depend on the problem under concern, and are common to all population based algorithms. Readers who are interested in applications may find more information in the references (Choi and Moon, 2005; Garcia *et al.*, 2008; Cowling *et al.*, 2000; Krasnogor *et al.*, 2002).

Further, in this chapter we have put local search just before evaluation of a phenotype. In practice, local search can be put in different positions. For example, local search can be conducted in initialization of the individuals, after evaluation, after crossover and/or mutation, and so on. In fact, *the timing of local search* itself can be considered as one of the memes, and can be determined through evolution. Agents who conduct local search in good timing may find good solutions (for the given problem) more efficiently and effectively.

In this chapter, we did not consider MAs for multi-objective search problems. In principle, if we can formulate multiple objectives into one function (e.g., using different penalties), all results given here can be applied straightforwardly. Otherwise, we need fitness sharing or some other mechanism to keep all solutions close to the Pareto front. Readers who are interested in this topic may refer to (Ishibuchi *et al.*, 2003) and (Knowles and Corne, 2001), and references therein.

References

Bambha, N. K., Bhattacharyya, S. S., Teich, J. and Zitzler, E. (2004). Systematic integration of parameterized local search into evolutionary algorithms. *IEEE Trans. Evolutionary Computation*, 8, pp. 137–154.

Beyer, H. G. and Schwefel, H. P. (2002). Evolution strategies: A comprehensive introduction. *Natural Computing*, 1(1), pp. 3–52.

Blackmore, S. (1999). *The Meme Machine.* New York: Oxford University Press.

Chen, X., Ong, Y. S., Lim, M. H. and Tan, K. C. (2011). A multi-facet survey on memetic computation. *IEEE Trans. Evolutionary Computation*, 15(5), pp. 591–607.

Choi, S. S. and Moon, B. R. (2005). A graph-based Lamarckian-Baldwinian hybrid for the sorting network problem. *IEEE Trans. Evolutionary Computation*, 9(1), pp. 105–114.

Cowling, P., Kendall, G. and Soubeiga, E. (2000). A hyperheuristic approach to scheduling a sales summit. *PATAT 2000*, Springer Lecture Notes in Computer Science, Konstanz, Germany, pp. 176–190.

Dawkins, R. (1976). *The Selfish Gene*. Oxford, UK: Oxford University Press.

Dorigo, M. and Stützle, T. (2004). *Ant Colony Optimization.* Cambridge, MA: MIT Press.

Eberhart, R. C. and Shi, Y. (2001). Particle swarm optimization: Developments, applications and resources. *Proc. IEEE Congress of Evolutionary Computation*, 1, pp. 27–30.

Fogel, L. J., Owens, A. J. and Walsh, M. J. (1966). *Artificial Intelligence through a Simulation of Evolution*. New York: John Wiley & Sons.

Garcia, S., Cano, J. R. and Herrera, F. (2008). A memetic algorithm for evolutionary prototype selection: A scaling up approach. *Pattern Recognition*, 41(8), pp. 2693–2709.

Glover, F. (1986). Future paths for integer programming and links to artificial intelligence. *Computers and Operations Research*, 13(5), pp. 533–549.

Glover, F. (1989). Tabu Search — (Part 1). *ORSA Journal on Computing*, 1(2), pp. 190–206.

Glover, F. (1990). Tabu Search — (Part 2).*ORSA Journal on Computing*, 2(1), pp. 4–32.

Goffe, W. L., Ferrier, G. D. and Rogers, J. (1994). Global optimization of statistical functions with simulated annealing. *Journal of Econometrics*, 60, pp. 65–99.

Goldberg, D. E. (1989). *Genetic Algorithms in Search, Optimization and Machine Learning*. Reading, MA: Addison-Wesley.

Hodgson, G. M. (2005). Generalizing Darwinism to social evolution: Some early attempts. *Journal of Economic Issues*, pp. 899–914.

Ishibuchi, H., Yoshida, T. and Murata, T. (2003). Balance between genetic search and local search in memetic algorithms for multiobjective permutation flowshop scheduling. *IEEE Trans. Evol. Comput.*, 7, pp. 204–223.

Knowles, J. and Corne, D. (2001). A comparative assessment of memetic, evolutionary and constructive algorithms for the multi-objective d-MST problem. *Proc. Genetic and Evolutionary Computation Workshop*.

Koza, J. R. (1992). *Genetic Programming: On the Programming of Computers by Means of Natural Selection*. MIT Press.

Koza, J. R. (1994). *Genetic Programming II: Automatic Discovery of Reusable Programs*. MIT Press.

Krasnogor, N., Blackbourne, B., Burke, E. and Hirst, J. (2002). Multimeme algorithms for protein structure prediction. *Proc. Parallel Problem Solving From Nature*, Lecture Notes in Computer Science, New York: Springer, pp. 769–778.

Krasnogor, N. and Gustafson, S. (2002). Toward truly 'memetic' memetic algorithms: Discussion and proof of concepts. In *Proc. Advances in Nature-Inspired Computation: The PPSN VII Workshops*, pp. 21–22.

Krasnogor, N., and Smith, J., (2001). Emergence of profitable search strategies based on a simple inheritance mechanism. In Spector, L., Goodman, E., Wu, A., Lang don, W., Voigt, H. M., Gen, M., Sen, S., Dorigo, M., Pezeshk, S., Garzon, M. and Burke, E. (eds.). *Proc. Genetic and Evolutionary Computation Conference*, San Francisco: Morgan Kaufmann, pp. 432–439.

Krasnogor, N. and Smith, J. (2005). A tutorial for competent memetic algorithms: Model, taxonomy, and design issues. *IEEE Trans. Evol. Comput.*, 9, pp. 474–488.

Miller, J. A., Potter, W. D., Gandham, R. V. and Lapena, C. N. (1993). An evaluation of local improvement operators for genetic algorithms. *IEEE Trans. Syst. Man. Cybern.*, 23, pp. 1340–1351.

Minsky, M. L. (1986). The *Society of Mind*. New York: Simon and Schuster.

Moscato, P. (1989). On evolution, search, optimization, genetic algorithms and martial arts: Towards memetic algorithms. *Caltech Concurrent Computation Program*, Publication Rep. 790.

Ong, Y. S. and Keane, A. J. (2004). Meta-Lamarckian in memetic algorithm. *IEEE Trans. Evol. Comput.*, 8, pp. 99–110.

Ong, Y. S., Lim, M. H. and Chen, X. (2010). Memetic computation: Past, present and future. *IEEE Comput. Intell. Mag.*, 5(2), pp. 24–31.

Ong, Y. S., Lim, M. H., Zhu, N. and Wong, K. W. (2006). Classification of adaptive memetic algorithms: A comparative study. *IEEE Trans. Syst. Man. Cybern. B*, 36(1), pp. 141–152.

Polanyi, M. (1966). *The Tacit Dimension*. Chicago: University of Chicago Press.

Schaffer, J. D., Whitley, D. and Eshelman, L. I. (1992). Combinations of genetic algorithms and neural networks: A survey of the state-of-the-art. *COGANN-92 Combinations of Genetic Algorithms and Neural Networks*, IEEE Computer Society Press, Los Alamitos, CA, pp. 1–37.

Smith, J. E. (2003). Co-evolving memetic algorithms: A learning approach to robust scalable optimization. In *IEEE Congress on Evolutionary Computation.* Piscataway, NJ: IEEE Press, 1, pp. 498–505.

Smith, J. E. (2007). Coevolving memetic algorithms: A review and progress report. *IEEE Trans. Systems, Man, and Cybernetics — Part B*, 37(1), pp. 6–17.

Smith, J. E. *et al.*, (2002). Co-evolution of memetic algorithms: Initial investigations. In Guervos, G. *et al.* (eds.) *Parallel Problem Solving From Nature — PPSN VII.* Berlin, Germany: Springer, pp. 537–548.

Sutton, R. S. and Barto, A. G. (1998). *Reinforcement Learning: An Introduction.* Cambridge: The MIT Press.

Thangaraj, R., Pant, M., Abraham, A. and Bouvry, P. (2011). Particle swarm optimization: Hybridization perspectives and experimental illustrations. *Applied Mathematics and Computation.*

Wolpert, D. and Macready, W., (1997). No free lunch theorems for optimization. *IEEE Transactions on Evolutionary Computation*, 1, 67–82.

Zhao, Q. F. (1997). A society model for cooperative co-evolutionary algorithms: Some case studies. *Proc. Australia-Japan Joint Workshop on Intelligent and Evolutionary Systems.* Canberra, Australia, pp. 30–36.

Zhao, Q. F. (1998). A general framework for cooperative co-evolutionary algorithms: A society model. *Proc. IEEE Int. Conf. Evolutionary Computation*, Anchorage, Alaska, pp. 57–62.

Part IV

Hybrid Systems

Chapter 18

Multi-Objective Evolutionary Design of Fuzzy Rule-Based Systems

Michela Antonelli, Pietro Ducange and Francesco Marcelloni

In the last years, the generation of fuzzy rule-based systems (FRBSs) from data has been tackled by using a multi-objective optimization approach, with accuracy and interpretability as the objectives to be optimized. Multi-objective evolutionary algorithms have been so often used in this context that the FRBSs generated by exploiting these algorithms have been denoted as multi-objective evolutionary fuzzy systems (MOEFSs). Recent MOEFSs allow concurrently learning the rule-bases (RBs) of the FRBSs and some elements of the database (DB), such as the granularity and the membership function parameters of the fuzzy partitions, during the evolutionary approach. At the end of the execution, a number of FRBSs with different trade-offs between accuracy and interpretability are produced: the designer can choose the FRBS with the most suitable trade-off for the specific application domain. The aim of this chapter is to present the main features of MOEFSs and to discuss how they are applied to both regression and classification problems. Some example of application is also shown and discussed.

18.1. Introduction

Fuzzy rule-based systems (FRBSs) are widely used in different engineering fields such as control, pattern recognition, system identification and signal analysis. They allow achieving accuracies comparable to other approaches and have the capability of explaining how their outputs are generated from the input values. An FRBS consists of a linguistic rule-base (RB), a database (DB) containing the fuzzy sets associated with the linguistic terms used in the RB and a fuzzy logic inference engine. RB and DB compose the knowledge base (KB) of the FRBS. Formally, an FRBS is a mathematical model that, given an input vector, computes an output value, exploiting the knowledge coded in the RB and in the DB, and an inference process based on fuzzy logic.

The most natural approach to build an FRBS is to elicit the knowledge from a human expert and to codify this knowledge in the KB, but sometimes the complexity of the application domain can make this approach hardly viable. Thus, several methods have been proposed in the literature to generate the KB from data (typically expressed as input–output patterns). When FRBSs are generated with the only objective of maximizing the accuracy, they are generally characterized by a high number of rules and by linguistic fuzzy partitions with a low level of comprehensibility, thus loosing that feature which may make FRBSs preferable to other approaches, namely their interpretability (Alonso *et al.*, 2009; Cordón, 2011; Gacto *et al.*, 2011; Zhou and Gan, 2008). Thus, in the last years, the generation of FRBSs from data has been modeled as a multi-objective optimization problem, taking accuracy and interpretability as the objectives to be optimized. Multi-objective evolutionary algorithms have been so widely used as optimization technique in this framework that the term multi-objective evolutionary fuzzy systems (MOEFSs) has been coined (Cordón, 2011; Ducange and Marcelloni, 2011; Fazzolari *et al.*, 2013a).

In the first MOEFSs proposed in the literature, multi-objective evolutionary algorithms have been used to select (Ishibuchi *et al.*, 1997; Ishibuchi and Yamamoto, 2004) or learn (Cococcioni *et al.*, 2007; Ducange *et al.*, 2010; Ishibuchi *et al.*, 2001) rules, and to perform the tuning (Botta *et al.*, 2009) of the DB with prefixed DB and RB, respectively. On the other hand, the most recent MOEFSs perform the learning (Alcalá *et al.*, 2009; Antonelli *et al.*, 2009, 2011a, 2011b; Pulkkinen and Koivisto, 2010) or the selection (Alcalá *et al.*, 2007; Gacto *et al.*, 2009, 2010; Nguyen *et al.*, 2013) of the rules concurrently with the learning of some elements of the DB, namely the granularity and the membership function parameters of the fuzzy partitions. While in rule selection (RS), rules are selected from a initial set of candidate rules generated from data by some heuristic, in rule learning (RL), rules are created during the evolutionary process.

The aim of this chapter is to present the main features of MOEFSs and to discuss how they are applied to both regression and classification problems. For the different solutions we also show some experimental results. The chapter is organized as follows. Section 18.2 introduces the FRBSs and discusses their interpretability. Section 18.3 describes the most popular multi-objective evolutionary algorithms used in the framework of MOEFSs. Section 18.4 introduces the main features of MOEFSs, such as chromosome coding, mating operators, and objective functions. Section 18.5 shows how the results of MOEFSs can be analyzed and compared. In Section 18.6, we discuss some experimental results obtained by applying MOEFSs to both regression and classification problems. Finally, Section 18.7 draws some conclusions.

18.2. Fuzzy Rule-Based Systems

A fuzzy set A defined on a universe of discourse U is characterized by a membership function $A(x) : U \rightarrow [0, 1]$ which associates with each element $\hat{x}$ of U a number $A(\hat{x})$ in the interval [0, 1]: $A(\hat{x})$ represents the grade of membership of $\hat{x}$ in A (Zadeh, 1965). The support and the core of A are the crisp subsets of A with, respectively, non-zero membership grades and membership grades equal to 1.

Different types of membership functions such as Gaussian, triangular, and trapezoidal, have been proposed and used for designing FRBSs. For the sake of simplicity, in this chapter, we consider triangular fuzzy sets, which are identified by the tuples (a, b, c), where a and c correspond to the left and right extremes of the support of the fuzzy set, and b to the core. Formally, a triangular membership function can be defined as follows:

$$A(x) = \begin{cases} \dfrac{a-x}{b-a} & a \leq x \leq b \\ \dfrac{c-x}{c-b} & b < x \leq c \\ 0 & \text{otherwise.} \end{cases} \tag{1}$$

Based on the notion of fuzzy set, Zadeh introduced the concept of linguistic variable (Zadeh, 1965). A linguistic variable X is a variable whose values are linguistic terms. X is characterized by the term set $T(X)$ of X, that is, the set of linguistic values of X with each value being a fuzzy set defined on universe U. The set $P = \{A_1, \ldots, A_{|T(X)|}\}$, where $|T(X)|$ is the cardinality of $T(X)$, of the fuzzy sets used in defining the terms in $T(X)$ composes a fuzzy partition of the universe U.

Let $X = \{X_1, \ldots, X_F\}$ be the set of input variables and X_{F+1} be the output variable. Let U_f, with $f = 1, \ldots, F+1$, be the universe of the fth variable X_f. Let $P_f = \{A_{f,1}, \ldots, A_{f,T_f}\}$ be a fuzzy partition of T_f fuzzy sets on variable X_f. Let $\{(\mathbf{x}_1, x_{F+1,1}), \ldots, (\mathbf{x}_N, x_{F+1,N})\}$ be a training set composed of N input–output pairs, with $\mathbf{x}_t = [x_{t,1} \ldots, x_{t,F}] \in \Re^F$, $t = 1, \ldots, N$.

In regression problems, X_{F+1} is a continuous variable and, therefore, $\forall t \in [1 \ldots N]$, $x_{F+1,t} \in \Re$. With the aim of estimating the output value corresponding to a given input vector, we adopt an RB composed of M linguistic fuzzy rules expressed as:

$$\begin{aligned} R_m : \textbf{IF } X_1 \textbf{ is } A_{1,j_{m,1}} \textbf{ AND} \ldots \textbf{AND } X_f \textbf{ is } A_{f,j_{m,f}} \textbf{ AND} \ldots \\ \ldots \textbf{AND } X_F \textbf{ is } A_{F,j_{m,F}} \textbf{ THEN } X_{F+1} \textbf{ is } A_{F+1,j_{m,F+1}}, \end{aligned} \tag{2}$$

where $j_{m,f} \in [1, T_f]$, $f = 1, \ldots, F+1$, identifies the index of the fuzzy set (among the T_f linguistic terms of partition P_f), which has been selected for X_f in rule R_m.

In classification problems, X_{F+1} is categorical and $x_{F+1,t} \in C$, where $C = \{C_1, \ldots, C_K\}$ is the set of K possible classes. With the aim of determining the class of a given input vector, we adopt an RB composed of M rules expressed as:

$$\begin{aligned} R_m : \textbf{IF } X_1 \textbf{ is } A_{1,j_{m,1}} \textbf{ AND} \ldots \textbf{AND } X_f \textbf{ is } A_{f,j_{m,f}} \textbf{ AND} \ldots \\ \ldots \textbf{AND } X_F \textbf{ is } A_{F,j_{m,F}} \textbf{ THEN } X_{F+1} \textbf{ is } C_{j_m} \, with \, RW_m \end{aligned} \tag{3}$$

where C_{j_m} is the class label associated with the mth rule and RW_m is the rule weight, i.e., a certainty degree of the classification in the class C_{j_m} for a pattern belonging to the fuzzy subspace delimited by the antecedent of the rule R_m. The FRBS designed for classification problems is often denoted as fuzzy rule-based classifier (FRBC).

Usually, a new fuzzy set $A_{f,0}$ ($f = 1, \ldots, F$) is defined for all the F input variables. This fuzzy set, which represents the "don't care" condition, is characterized by a membership function equal to 1 on the overall universe. The term $A_{f,0}$ allows generating rules that contain only a subset of the input variables (Ishibuchi *et al.*, 2004).

Given an input pattern $\hat{\mathbf{x}} \in \Re^F$, the strength of activation (*matching degree* of the rule with the input) of the rule R_m is computed as:

$$w_m(\hat{\mathbf{x}}) = \prod_{f=1}^{F} A_{f,j_{m,f}}(\hat{x}_f), \tag{4}$$

where $A_{f,j_{m,f}}(X_f)$ is the membership function associated with the fuzzy set $A_{f,j_{m,f}}$. For the sake of simplicity, in the formula, we have only considered the product as t-norm for implementing the logical conjunction.

In regression problems, the estimated output $\hat{x}_{F+1}$ is obtained by computing the output of any rule R_m, by aggregating these outputs and finally applying a defuzzification strategy. The output of a rule R_m is a fuzzy set $\hat{A}_m(X_{F+1})$ calculated by applying the implication operator I between $w_m(\hat{x})$ and the output fuzzy set $A_{F+1,j_{m,F+1}}$:

$$\hat{A}_m(X_{F+1}) = I(w_m(\hat{\mathbf{x}}), A_{F+1,j_{m,F+1}}(X_{F+1})). \tag{5}$$

In the context of MOEFSs, the implication operator is typically implemented as minimum or product. The fuzzy sets inferred from each rule are therefore aggregated to produce the fuzzy set $\hat{A}(X_{F+1})$ as follows:

$$\hat{A}(X_{F+1}) = \max_{m=1,\ldots,M} I(w_m(\hat{\mathbf{x}}), A_{F+1,j_{m,F+1}}(X_{F+1})), \tag{6}$$

where the aggregation operator is implemented as maximum. Finally, $\hat{A}(X_{F+1})$ is defuzzified by applying some defuzzification strategy to produce the output $\hat{x}_{F+1}$. For example, by using the center of gravity strategy (Klir and Yuan, 1995) we obtain:

$$\hat{x}_{F+1} = \frac{\int \hat{A}(X_{F+1}) \cdot X_{F+1} \cdot dX_{F+1}}{\int \hat{A}(X_{F+1}) \cdot dX_{F+1}}. \tag{7}$$

In classification problems, the estimated output class $\hat{C}$ is obtained by computing the *association degree* $h_m(\hat{x})$ with class C_{jm} for each rule R_m, and then by applying a reasoning method.

The *association degree* $h_m(\hat{\mathbf{x}})$ is calculated as:

$$h_m(\hat{\mathbf{x}}) = w_m(\hat{\mathbf{x}}) \cdot RW_m. \tag{8}$$

Two different definitions of the rule weight RW_m are commonly found in the literature (Cordon *et al.*, 1999; Ishibuchi *et al.*, 2004):

(1) *The certainty factor*:

$$CF_m = \frac{\sum_{\mathbf{x}_t \in C_{jm}} w_m(\mathbf{x_t})}{\sum_{t=1}^{N} w_m(\mathbf{x_t})}. \tag{9}$$

(2) *The penalized certainty factor*:

$$PCF_m = CF_m - \frac{\sum_{\mathbf{x}_t \notin C_{jm}} w_m(\mathbf{x}_t)}{\sum_{t=1}^{N} w_m(\mathbf{x}_t)}. \tag{10}$$

The *reasoning method* uses the information from the RB to determine the class label for a specific input pattern. Two different approaches are often adopted in the literature:

(1) *The maximum matching*: An input pattern is classified into the class corresponding to the rule with the maximum association degree calculated for the pattern.
(2) *The additive combination*: An input pattern is classified into the class corresponding to the maximum total strength of the vote. For each class C_k, the total strength V_{C_k} is computed as follows:

$$V_{C_k}(\hat{\mathbf{x}}) = \sum_{R_m \in RB; C_{jm} = C_k} h_m(\hat{\mathbf{x}}). \tag{11}$$

Thus, for each pattern $(\hat{x})$, each fuzzy rule gives a vote for its consequent class.

For the sake of brevity, in this chapter we consider only the two types of FRBSs described in this section. Actually, other typologies of FRBSs, such as TSK-FRBSs (Cococcioni *et al.*, 2011), FRBSs with DNF rules (Casillas *et al.*, 2009) and

FRBSs based on multiple granularities (Ishibuchi and Nojima, 2007), have been also considered in the MOEFS specialized literature.

One of the most appealing aspects of FRBSs is their interpretability. Interpretability has been widely discussed in the last years, also in the framework of MOEFSs. Since interpretability is a subjective concept, it is hard to find a worldwide agreed definition and consequently a universal measure of interpretability. Thus, researchers have focused their attention on discussing some factors, which characterize interpretability, and on proposing some constraints which have to be satisfied for these factors. Considerations on the main factors that influence interpretability can be found in Guillaume (2001) and de Oliveira (1999). A homogeneous description of semantic and syntactic interpretability issues regarding both the RB and the DB has been recently published in a survey on interpretability constraints (Mencar and Fanelli, 2008).

In Zhou and Gan (2008), a taxonomy of fuzzy model interpretability has been proposed in terms of both low-level and high-level interpretability. Low-level interpretability is related to the semantic constraints that ensure fuzzy partition interpretability, while high-level interpretability is associated with a set of criteria defined on the RB. Furthermore, a conceptual framework for characterizing interpretability of fuzzy systems has been introduced in (Alonso *et al.*, 2009): this framework includes a global description of the FRBS structure, on the basis of the taxonomy and constraints discussed in (Mencar and Fanelli, 2008) and (Zhou and Gan, 2008), respectively, and a local explanation for understanding the system behavior. This local explanation considers a number of factors such as inference mechanisms, aggregation, conjunction and disjunction operators, defuzzification, and rule type, which affect the system behavior.

Recently, the most relevant measures and strategies exploited to design interpretable FRBSs have been reviewed in Gacto *et al.* (2011). Here, a taxonomy of the interpretability measures has been proposed by considering two different dimensions, namely semantic and complexity, at RB and DB levels. As shown in Figure 18.1, extracted from Gacto *et al.* (2011), this taxonomy is therefore organized into four quadrants. In the figure, the main measures used for each combination dimension/level are presented in the corresponding quadrant. In the context of MOEFSs, measures in the complexity-RB and semantic-DB quadrants have been mainly employed as objectives of the evolutionary optimization process.

18.3. Multi-Objective Evolutionary Optimization

Multi-objective evolutionary algorithms (MOEAs) have proved to be very effective to search for optimal solutions to problems that incorporate multiple performance criteria (Coello *et al.*, 2007; Zitzler *et al.*, 2004). Typically, these criteria are in

	Rule Base Level	*Data Base Level*
Complexity	Number of Rules Number of Conditions Average Rule Length	Number of Features Number of Membership Functions
Semantic	Consistency of Rules Rules Fired at the Same Time Transparency of the Structure Cointension	Coverage Normalization Distinguishability Order Relative and Combined Measures

Figure 18.1: Taxonomy of interpretability measures proposed in the literature.

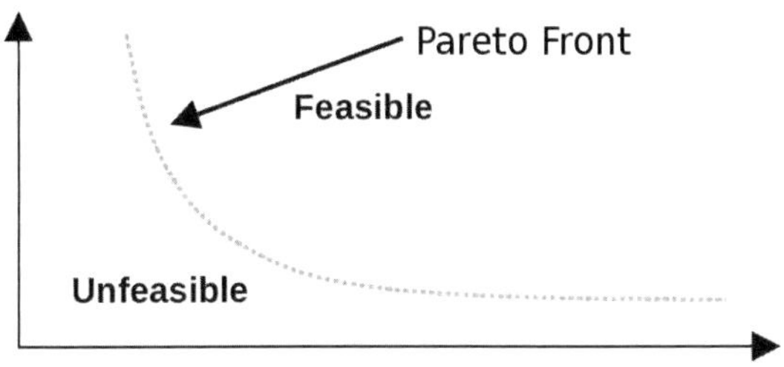

Figure 18.2: An example of Pareto front.

competition with each other. Thus, an MOEA has to determine a trade-off between the objectives, since improvement in one objective cannot be generally achieved without detriment to another. Thus, a family of equally valid solutions will exist, where each solution will tend to satisfy a criterion to a higher extent than another.

Different solutions are compared with each other by using the notion of Pareto dominance. Let I be the number of objectives. A solution x associated with a performance vector $\mathbf{u}$ dominates a solution y associated with a performance vector $\mathbf{v}$ if and only if, $\forall i \in \{1, \ldots, I\}$, u_i performs better than, or equal to, v_i and $\exists i \in \{1, \ldots, I\}$ such that u_i performs better than v_i, where u_i and v_i are the ith element of vectors $\mathbf{u}$ and $\mathbf{v}$, respectively.

A solution is said to be Pareto optimal if it is not dominated by any other possible solution. The set of points that correspond to the Pareto-optimal solutions is denoted as *Pareto front*. Thus, the aim of a multi-objective search algorithm is to discover a family of solutions that are a good approximation of the Pareto front. In Figure 18.2, we show an example of Pareto front for a two-objective minimization problem.

A number of MOEAs have been proposed in the literature (Coello *et al.*, 2007; Zitzler *et al.*, 2004). Some of the most popular among these algorithms are the strength pareto evolutionary algorithm (SPEA) and its evolution (SPEA2) (Zitzler *et al.*, 2001), the Niched Pareto Genetic Algorithm (NPGA) (Horn *et al.*, 1994), the different versions of the Pareto Archived Evolution Strategy (PAES) (Knowles and Corne, 2000), and the Non-dominated Sorting Genetic Algorithm (NSGA) and its evolution (NSGA-II) (Deb *et al.*, 2002). Some of these algorithms have been used in the context of MOEFSs. SPEA2 and NSGA-II have been employed, for instance, in (Alcalá *et al.*, 2007; Gacto *et al.*, 2009) and (Ducange *et al.*, 2010; Ishibuchi and Nojima, 2007), respectively. PAES has been employed in most of our works on MOEFSs and has also been used for the MOEFSs discussed in the experimental results shown in this chapter. For the sake of brevity, in the following, we will shortly discuss only this MOEA.

18.3.1. *PAES and (2+2)M-PAES*

PAES (Knowles and Corne, 2000) probably represents the simplest possible nontrivial algorithm capable of generating diverse solutions in the Pareto optimal set. PAES consists of three parts: the candidate solution generator, the candidate solution acceptance, and the non-dominated-solutions archive. The candidate solution generator maintains a single current solution c, and, at each iteration, produces a new solution m from c, by using a mutation operator. The candidate solution acceptance compares m with c. Three different cases can arise:

(1) c dominates m: m is discarded;
(2) m dominates c: m is inserted into the archive and possible solutions in the archive dominated by m are removed; m replaces c in the role of current solution;
(3) Cases 1 and 2 are not satisfied: m is added to the archive only if it is dominated by no solution contained in the archive; m replaces c in the role of current solution only if m belongs to a region with a crowding degree smaller than, or equal to, the region of c.

The *crowding degree* is computed by firstly dividing the space where the solutions of the archive lie into a number of equally sized regions, generating in this way a grid, and then by counting the solutions that belong to the regions. The number of these solutions determines the crowding degree of a region. The recursive subdivision of the space and assignment of grid locations is carried out using an adaptive method that eliminates the need for a niche size parameter. This adaptive method works by calculating the range in the objective space of the current solutions in the archive and adjusting the grid so that it covers this range. Grid locations are then recalculated. This is done only when the range of the objective space of archived solutions changes by a threshold amount to avoid recalculating the ranges too frequently. The only parameter that must then be set is the number of divisions of the space (and hence grid locations) required.

This approach tends to prefer solutions which belong to poorly crowded regions, so as to guarantee a uniform distribution of solutions along the Pareto front. If the archive is full, the solution m is added to the archive if it lies in a less crowded region of the archive than some members of the archive. In this case, a member of the archive from the most crowded region is removed from the archive. PAES terminates after a given number Z of iterations or when no solution is inserted into the archive for a number G of iterations, with $G < Z$. The candidate solution acceptance strategy generates an archive which contains only non-dominated solutions. On PAES termination, the archive includes the set of solutions which are an approximation of the Pareto front. At the beginning, the archive is empty and the first current solution is randomly generated. The aforementioned PAES is called (1+1)PAES, since it uses a single current solution and generates a single mutant. A more general version of PAES, denoted $(\mu + \gamma)$PAES, uses μ current solutions and generates γ mutants: each mutant is created by mutating one of the μ current solutions, which is selected via binary tournament selection using the fitness values assigned in the previous iteration. The fitness values are computed by considering the dominance of the current solutions with respect to the archive and their crowding degree.

In the context of MOEFSs, in the work discussed in Cococcioni *et al.* (2007), we have proposed a modified version of $(\mu + \gamma)$PAES, with $\mu = 2$ and $\gamma = 2$. We denoted this version as $(2 + 2)$M-PAES, where M-PAES stands for modified PAES. Unlike the original $(2+2)$PAES, which uses only mutation to generate new candidate solutions, our approach exploits the crossover and a set of appropriately mutation operators. We experimentally verified that crossover helps create an approximation of the Pareto front where solutions are uniformly distributed along the front. We start with two randomly generated current solutions c_1 and c_2. At each iteration, the application of crossover and mutation operators produces two new solutions s_1 and s_2 from the current solutions c_1 and c_2. Unlike classical PAES, which maintains c_1 and c_2 as current solutions until they are not replaced by solutions with particular characteristics, we randomly extract, at each iteration, the current solutions. If the archive contains a unique solution, c_1 and c_2 correspond to this unique solution. We experimentally verified that the random extraction of the current solutions from the archive allows us to extend the set of non-dominated solutions contained in the archive so as to obtain a better approximation of the Pareto front. As regards the candidate solution acceptance, s_1 and s_2 are added to the archive only if they are dominated by no solution contained in the archive; possible solutions in the archive dominated by s_1 or s_2 are removed.

18.4. MOEFSs

When designing FRBSs, accuracy and interpretability are objectives in competition with each other: an increase in accuracy corresponds typically to a decrease in interpretability. The best trade-off between accuracy and interpretability generally depends on the application context and cannot be fixed *a priori*. Thus, it would be desirable to produce a set of possible optimal FRBSs with different values of accuracy and interpretability, and let the user decide for the best solution on the basis of the specific application context. MOEAs appear to be a very suitable tool for achieving this objective: we can determine an approximation of the Pareto front, where each point in the front represents an FRBS characterized by a different trade-off between accuracy and interpretability.

Once fixed the type of FRBS, i.e., the model for regression or classification, and the specific defuzzification or reasoning method, the design process of an FRBS consists in determining the rules in the RB and the parameters of the DB that define the membership functions associated with each linguistic term used in the rules. In MOEFSs, the design process is performed as a multi-objective evolutionary optimization process. In the following, we will discuss the different chromosome coding, mating operators and fitness functions used in the literature. Then, we will present a pseudo-code which describes an example of implementation of an MOEFS.

18.4.1. *Chromosome Coding*

The RB can be derived by selecting rules from a pre-defined set of candidate rules or by evolving the antecedent and consequent parts of each rule from scratch. We denote the two strategies as RS and RL, respectively. Moreover, in order to handle high dimensional datasets, we have recently proposed a new approach based on rule and condition selection (RCS) (Antonelli *et al.*, 2013b). In RCS, starting from a pre-defined set of candidate rules, a reduced number of rules together with a reduced number of conditions for each rule are selected during the evolutionary process.

In MOEFSs based on RS (see for example the work in Alcalá *et al.* (2007)), a binary chromosome is used to codify the overall RB. The ith binary gene identifies if the ith rule of a predefined set of candidate rules has been selected or not. The initial set of rules is generated by exploiting some heuristic: in a number of contributions, the Wang and Mendel algorithm (Wang and Mendel, 1992) for regression problems, and its modified version for classification problems, have been used for generating the set of candidate rules.

Also in MOEFSs based on RL a chromosome codifies the overall RB: in this case each gene in the chromosome identifies the index $j_{m,f}$ of the fuzzy set selected for the corresponding linguistic variable X_f in each rule of the RB. When dealing with evolutionary rule learning, in order to generate compact rule-bases, the maximum number of rules M_{max}, which can be contained in the RB, is fixed. In Figure 18.3 we show an example of RL chromosome for regression problems.

$j_{1,1}$	...	$j_{1,F}$	$j_{1,F+1}$	...	$j_{M,1}$	...	$j_{M,F}$	$j_{M,F+1}$

Figure 18.3: RL chromosome for regression problems.

$j_{1,1}$	...	$j_{1,F}$	C_{j_1}	...	$j_{M,1}$	...	$j_{M,F}$	C_{j_M}

Figure 18.4: RL chromosome for classification problems.

In the case of FRBCs, the chromosome structure is slightly different. As shown in Figure 18.4, for each rule R_m the chromosome contains the indexes $j_{m,f}$ of the antecedent, for each input variable X_f, and the consequent class C_{j_m}.

The dimension of the chromosome, and consequently of the search space, increases with the increase of the number of input variables. Thus, when this number is high, the multi-objective evolutionary algorithm generally needs a large amount of evaluations to adequately explore the search space and therefore achieve good solutions. To reduce the number of evaluations, the RCS strategy can be used. Let J_{IN} be the set of the M_{IN} candidate rules generated, for example, by applying the Wang and Mendel algorithm to the training set. We recall that, in this case, the antecedents of each candidate rule have a condition for each linguistic variable, since the Wang and Mendel algorithm performs no selection of the conditions. The C_{RB} part of the chromosome is a vector of M_{max} pairs $\mathbf{p_m} = (k_m, \mathbf{v_m})$, where $k_m \in [0, \ldots, M_{IN}]$ identifies the index of the rule in J_{IN} selected for the current RB and $\mathbf{v_m} = [v_{m,1}, \ldots, v_{m,F}]$ is a binary vector which indicates, for each condition in the rule, if the condition has to be preserved in the rule ($v_{m,f} = 1$) or replaced by a "don't care" condition ($v_{m,f} = 0$). If $k_m = 0$, the mth rule is not included in the RB. In this way we manage to generate RBs with a lower number of rules than M_{max}. As an example, let us consider $M_{max} = 3$ and let us suppose to have a two-inputs fuzzy model with four rules generated by the Wang and Mendel algorithm and described by the following J_{IN} matrix:

$$J_{IN} = \begin{bmatrix} 3 & 2 & 2 \\ 5 & 4 & 1 \\ 1 & 5 & 5 \\ 2 & 2 & 4 \end{bmatrix}. \quad (12)$$

In the matrix, rows and columns identify rules and linguistic variables, respectively, and each cell (i, j) contains the fuzzy set used in rule R_m for variable X_f. Let us assume that, during the evolutionary process, the C_{RB} chromosome part shown in Figure 18.5 is generated.

k_1	$v_{1,1}$	$v_{1,2}$	k_2	$v_{2,1}$	$v_{2,2}$	k_3	$v_{3,1}$	$v_{3,2}$
1	1	0	3	0	1	0	0	0

Figure 18.5: An example of RCS chromosome.

Then, the corresponding RB will be represented by the following matrix J:

$$J = \begin{bmatrix} 3 & 0 & 2 \\ 0 & 5 & 5 \end{bmatrix}. \tag{13}$$

As regards the representation of the DB parameters, as stated before, in this chapter we consider triangular fuzzy sets. Further, we suppose that the granularities of each linguistic variable X_f, i.e., the value of T_f, is fixed.

Usually, the parameters which codify triangular fuzzy sets can be coded in a real-valued chromosome. For each fuzzy set $A_{f,j}$, three genes are used for codifying the tuples $(a_{f,j}, b_{f,j}, c_{f,j})$, where $f = 1, \ldots, F + 1$ for regression problems and $f = 1, \ldots, F$ for classification problems, and $j \in [1, T_f]$. In order to reduce the number of parameters to be identified and, consequently, the search space, in Alcalá *et al.* (2007) and Antonelli *et al.* (2009), two different strategies have been adopted. In (Alcalá *et al.*, 2007), a new coding scheme for the DB has been proposed considering the linguistic 2-tuple representation introduced in Herrera and Martínez (2000), which allows the lateral displacement of the support of a fuzzy set and maintains the interpretability at a good level. This scheme is based on the concept of symbolic translation of a fuzzy set, which is a number in the interval $[-0.5, 0.5)$. The interval defines the domain of a fuzzy set when it is moving between its two adjacent fuzzy sets. Let us consider a generic linguistic fuzzy partition $P_f = \{A_{f,1}, \ldots, A_{f,T_f}\}$. Formally, we represent the symbolic translation of a fuzzy set $A_{f,j}$ in P_f by means of the 2-tuple notation, $(A_{f,j}, \alpha_{f,j})$, $A_{f,j} \in P_f$, $\alpha_{f,j} \in [-0.5, 0.5)$. The symbolic translation of a fuzzy set involves the lateral displacement of its associated parameters. This coding scheme decreases the complexity of the parameter optimization, since the 3 parameters considered per fuzzy set are reduced to only 1 symbolic translation parameter.

Figure 18.6 shows the symbolic translation of a label represented by the 2-tuple $(A_{f,3}, -0.3)$ together with the associated lateral displacement. When using this representation a real-coded chromosome, as shown in Figure 18.7, is used. The chromosome contains a sequence of real genes $\alpha_{f,j}$, where $\alpha_{f,j}$, with $j \in [1, T_f]$, $f \in [1, F + 1]$ in regression contexts and $f \in [1, F]$ in classification contexts, is the translation parameter associated with the label $A_{f,j}$ of partition P_f.

In the contribution in Antonelli *et al.* (2009), we have exploited a real-coded chromosome for regression problems, which codifies the positions of the centroids of each fuzzy set in each linguistic variable. Indeed, since we adopt strong fuzzy

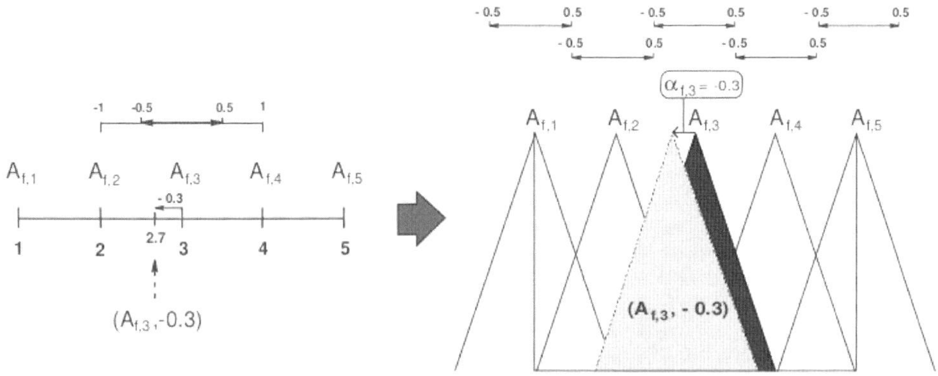

(a) Symbolic Translation of a label (b) Lateral Displacement of a Membership Function

Figure 18.6: Symbolic translation (a) and lateral displacement (b) of the associated fuzzy set.

$\alpha_{1,1}$	$\cdots$	α_{1,T_1}	$\cdots$	$\alpha_{F+1,1}$	$\cdots$	$\alpha_{F+1,T_{F+1}}$

Figure 18.7: Chromosome associated with the linguistic 2-tuple representation.

$b_{1,2}$	$\cdots$	b_{1,T_1-1}	$\cdots$	$b_{F+1,2}$	$\cdots$	$b_{F+1,T_{F+1}-1}$

Figure 18.8: Real-coded chromosome for strong fuzzy partitions.

partitions with, for $j = 2, \ldots, T_f - 1$, $b_{f,j} = c_{f,j-1}$, and $b_{f,j} = a_{f,j+1}$, in order to define each fuzzy set of the partition it is sufficient to fix the positions of the cores $b_{f,j}$ along the universe U_f of the fth variable (we normalize each variable in [0,1]). Since $b_{f,1}$ and b_{f,T_f} coincide with the extremes of the universe, the partition of each linguistic variable X_f is completely defined by $T_f - 2$ parameters. Figure 18.8 shows the chromosome part which consists of $F + 1$ vectors of real numbers: the fth vector contains the $[b_{f,2}, \ldots, b_{f,T_f-1}]$ cores which define the positions of the membership functions for the linguistic variable X_f. To ensure a good integrity level of the membership functions, in terms of order, coverage and distinguishability (Gacto *et al.*, 2011),$\forall j \in [2..T_f - 1]$, we force $b_{f,j}$ to vary in the definition interval $\left[b_{f,j} - \frac{b_{f,j}-b_{f,j-1}}{2}, b_{f,j} + \frac{b_{f,j+1}-b_{f,j}}{2}\right]$.

18.4.2. *Mating Operators*

During the evolutionary process of an MOEA, offspring populations, i.e., new solutions from the current solutions, are generated by applying mating operators such as crossover and mutation. Further, in order to select the candidate parents for generating new solutions, appropriate selection strategies are adopted in each specific MOEA.

The half uniform crossover (HUX) and the flip-flop mutation have been used as crossover and mutation operators, respectively, for the binary RS chromosome employed in Alcalá *et al.* (2007). The HUX crossover randomly interchanges the half of the genes that are different in the parents. The flip-flop mutation operator complements each gene with a predefined probability.

For the RL chromosome, operators which allow, respectively, adding, removing or modifying one or more rules have been adopted. For example, in Cococcioni *et al.* (2007), where the chromosome shown in Figure 18.3 has been employed, the following two mutation operators have been defined. The first mutation operator adds γ rules to the RB, where γ is randomly chosen in $[1 \ldots \gamma_{max}]$. The upper bound γ_{max} is fixed by the user. If $\gamma + M > M_{max}$, then $\gamma = M_{max} - M$. For each rule R_m added to the chromosome, a random number $\xi \in [1 \ldots F]$, which indicates the number of input variables used in the antecedent of the rule, is generated. Then, ξ natural random numbers between 1 and F are generated to determine the input variables which compose the antecedent part of the rule. Finally, for each selected input variable X_f, a random natural number $j_{m,f}$ between 1 and T_f, which determines the linguistic label $A_{f,j_{m,f}}$ to be used in the corresponding input variable of rule R_m, is generated. To select the consequent linguistic term, a random number in $[1..T_{F+1}]$ is generated. The second mutation operator randomly changes δ antecedent conditions of the RB. The number is randomly generated in $[1..\delta_{max}]$. The upper bound δ_{max} is fixed by the user. For each condition to be modified, a number is randomly generated in $[0..T_f]$, where f is the input variable corresponding to the selected condition.

In (Ducange *et al.*, 2010) we have used the chromosome in Figure 18.4 and, in addition to the previously described mutation operators, have defined an operator which removes λ rules from the RB, where λ is randomly extracted from $[1..\lambda_{max}]$. In the experiments, $\lambda_{max} = min(\phi_{max}, M - M_{min})$, where ϕ_{max} is fixed by the user, M is the number of rules of RB coded by the chromosome and M_{min} is the minimum number of rules that must be contained in the RB for performing the classification task (at least one per each class).

For both the chromosomes in Figures 18.3 and 18.4, the one point crossover has been used in Cococcioni *et al.* (2007) and Ducange *et al.* (2010). This operator has been applied as follows: it cuts the selected parent chromosomes c_1 and c_2 at some chosen common gene and swaps the resulting sub-chromosomes. The common gene is chosen by extracting randomly a number in $[M_{min}, \rho_{min}]$, where ρ_{min} is the minimum number of rules in c_1 and c_2.

As regards RCS, in Antonelli *et al.* (2013b) we have applied the one-point crossover and have defined two mutation operators. Let c_1 and c_2 be two selected parent chromosomes. For the crossover operator, we choose the common gene by extracting randomly a number in $[1,\rho_{max}-1]$, where ρ_{max} is the maximum number of rules in c_1 and c_2. The crossover point is always chosen between two rules and not within a rule. The one-point crossover can generate an RB with one or more pairs of equal rules. In this case, we simply eliminate one of the rules from each pair setting the corresponding k_m to zero. This allows us to reduce the total number of rules. The first step for both the mutation operators is to randomly select a rule (i.e., a pair $\mathbf{p_m} = (k_m, \mathbf{v_m})$) in the chromosome. The first operator replaces the value of k_m in the selected pair with an integer value randomly generated in $[1, \ldots, M_{IN}]$, where M_{IN} is the number of candidate rules. If the old value of k_m was equal to zero, the new chromosome will contain an additional rule. The second operator modifies the antecedent $\mathbf{v_m}$ of the selected rule by complementing each gene $v_{m,f}$ with a probability equal to P_{cond} ($P_{cond} = 2/F$ in the experiments). The two operators are applied with two different probabilities. After applying the two mutation operators, we check the chromosome for duplicate rules in the RB.

Finally, as regards the real-coded chromosome, which codifies the parameters of the membership functions, the BLX-α operator has been applied in a number of contributions (Alcalá *et al.*, 2007; Alcalá *et al.*, 2007; Antonelli *et al.*, 2013b). Let us assume that $c_1 = (x_1 \ldots x_g)$ and $c_2 = (y_1 \ldots y_g)$, $(x_i, y_i \in \Re, i = 1, \ldots, g)$, are the two real-coded chromosomes that are going to be crossed. Using the BLX-α crossover, one descendent $z = (z_1, \ldots, z_g)$ is obtained, where z_i is randomly (uniformly) generated within the interval $[l_i, u_i]$, with $l_i = max\{a_i, c_{min} - \chi\}$, $u_i = min\{b_i, c_{max}+\chi\}$, $c_{min} = min\{x_i, y_i\}$, $c_{max} = max\{x_i, y_i\}$, and $\chi = (c_{max}-c_{min})\cdot\alpha$. As regards the mutation operator, it is often defined an operator that simply changes a gene value at random.

18.4.3. *Fitness Functions*

In the context of MOEFSs, accuracy and interpretability are two objectives that usually are taken into consideration in designing FRBSs. The two objectives are in conflict: indeed, an increase in system accuracy generally corresponds to a decrease in interpretability and vice versa. In the literature, several definitions of accuracy and interpretability can be found.

As regards the accuracy, the definition of a specific measure depends on the type of problem, namely regression or classification, to be tackled. In the case of regression problems, the approximation error between the actual and the estimated outputs is usually used to evaluate the accuracy of the FRBSs. For example, in (Alcalá *et al.*, 2007; Antonelli *et al.*, 2013b) the half of the mean squared error (*MSE*/2) has been adopted. MSE/2 is defined as:

$$MSE/2 = \frac{1}{2 \cdot |S|} \sum_{l=1}^{|S|} \left(x^l_{F+1} - \hat{x}^l_{F+1}\right)^2, \qquad (14)$$

where $|S|$ is the cardinality of the dataset, $\hat{x}^l_{F+1}$ is the output obtained by the FRBS when the lth input pattern is considered, and x^l_{F+1} is the desired output.

When dealing with classification problems, the classification rate (CR) is typically used as accuracy measure. *CR* is calculated as follows:

$$CR = 100 \cdot \frac{NCC}{|S|}, \tag{15}$$

where $|S|$ is the cardinality of the dataset and *NCC* is the number of patterns correctly classified. Sometimes, in order to optimize the accuracy of the generated solutions, during the evolutionary process, the error rate (ER) is directly minimized (Ishibuchi and Nojima, 2007). *ER* is computed as follows:

$$ER = 100 - CR. \tag{16}$$

In the framework of binary classifiers, i.e., when the number of classes is equal to 2, the Receiver Operating Characteristic (ROC) curve analysis (Fawcett, 2006) is typically adopted to evaluate the capability of correctly classifying patterns. Indeed, especially in the case of imbalanced datasets (Ducange *et al.*, 2010), the True positive rate (TPR) and the False positive rate (FPR) are calculated instead of *CR*. These two metrics are defined as follows:

$$TPR = \frac{TP}{TP + FN}, \quad FPR = \frac{FP}{TN + FP}, \tag{17}$$

where TP = true positive (number of positives correctly classified), TN = true negative (number of negatives correctly classified), FP = false positive (number of negatives classified as positives), FN = false negative (number of positives classified as negatives). *TPR* and *FPR* coincide, respectively, with the sensitivity and the complement to 1 of the specificity.

Actually, another measure which aggregates *TPR* and *FPR*, namely the area under the curve (AUC), can be also used for evaluating the accuracy of a single binary classifier. The *AUC* is computed as:

$$AUC = \frac{1 + TPR - FPR}{2}. \tag{18}$$

As regards the interpretability measure, a common approach is to distinguish between interpretability of the RB, also known as complexity, and interpretability of the fuzzy partitions, also known as integrity of the DB.

The most used measures of complexity are the *total number of rules* in the RB (Alcalá *et al.*, 2007; Ishibuchi and Nojima, 2007) and the *sum of the conditions* which compose the antecedents of the rules in the RB (Antonelli *et al.*, 2009; Cococcioni *et al.*, 2007; Ishibuchi and Nojima, 2007), also known as *total rule length*. As regards the integrity of the DB, there is no agreement regarding the choice of an appropriate measure. A deep discussion regarding this topic can be found in Gacto *et al.* (2011).

For the sake of brevity, in this chapter we just discuss a simple integrity index (I_{int}) that we have introduced in Antonelli *et al.* (2011b). I_{int} measures the similarity between the partitions learned during the evolutionary process and the initial interpretable partitions defined by an expert. Let $b_{f,j}$ and $\tilde{b}_{f,j}$ be the cores of the fuzzy sets of, respectively, the current partition $P_f = \{A_{f,1}, \ldots, A_{f,T_f}\}$ and the initial partition $\tilde{P}_f = \{\tilde{A}_{f,1}, \ldots, \tilde{A}_{f,T_f}\}$ defined by an expert for the linguistic variable X_f. The index is defined as follows:

$$I_{int} = 1 - \frac{D}{D_{max}}, \tag{19}$$

where $D = \frac{1}{F+1} \sum_{f=1}^{F+1} \sum_{j=1}^{T_f-1} |b_{f,j} - \tilde{b}_{f,j}|$ is a dissimilarity measure which expresses how much, on average, the partitions generated by the multi-objective evolutionary optimization are different from the initial partitions, and D_{max} is the possible maximum value of D. We suppose that $\tilde{b}_{f,j}$ identifies the core of the jth fuzzy set of the fth initial partition $\tilde{P}_f = \{\tilde{A}_{f,1}, \ldots, \tilde{A}_{f,T_f}\}$ defined by an expert for the linguistic variable X_f.

The value of I_{int} ranges in [0, 1]. If the transformed partitions are equal to the initial partitions, then $I_{int} = 1$. The higher the difference between the initial partitions and the transformed partitions, the lower the value of I_{int} (at the minimum, $I_{int} = 0$). If all the partitions are uniform and $T_f = \widehat{T}$ for each linguistic variable X_f, from simple mathematical considerations, we derive that $D_{max} = \frac{1}{2}(\widehat{T} - 2)$.

18.4.4. *An Example of MOEFS Implementation*

In Figure 18.9, we show a pseudo-code which describes an example of implementation of an MOEFS. The pseudo-code basically follows the (2 + 2)M-PAES optimization scheme.

At the beginning, the archive is empty and two initial current solutions c_1 and c_2 are randomly generated. The core of the pseudo-code shows how, at each iteration, two candidate solutions s_1 and s_2 are generated from current solutions c_1 and c_2 by using crossover and mutation operators. In particular, we show a general scheme in which we suppose that both the RB and the DB are concurrently optimized and a chromosome C composed of two parts (C_{RB}, C_{DB}) is exploited. In the example, we suppose that two different crossover operators are applied to the C_{RB} and C_{DB}, with probabilities equal to P_{CRB} and P_{CDB}, respectively. Further, H specific mutation operators are supposed to be independently applied to C_{RB}. The hth mutation operators, with $h \in [1, H]$, is applied with a specific probability set to P_{MRBh}. As regards C_{DB}, we suppose that just one mutation operator is applied with a probability

```
(2+2)M-PAES(TrainingSet)
begin
 initialize(archive);
 [c1, c2] = random_generation();
 loop i=1,...,Z
  s1 = c1
  s2 = c2
  if (rand() < PCRB)
   [s1.CRB,s2.CRB]=crossover_CRB (c1.CRB,c2.CRB);
  endif
  if (rand() < PCDB)
   [s1.CDB,s2.CDB]=crossover_CDB (c1.CDB,c2.CDB);
  endif
  loop i=1,2
    if (rand() < PMRB1)
      si.CRB=RB_mutation_operator_1(si.CRB);
    endif
    .
    .
    .
    if (rand() < PMRBH)
      si.CRB=RB_mutation_operator_H(si.CRB);
    endif
    if (rand() < PMDB)
      si.CDB = DB_mutation_operator(si.CDB);
    endif
    evaluate(si,TrainingSet)
    if (!dominate(archive,si);
      insert_into_archive(si);
    endif
  endloop
  [s1, s2] = random_selection(archive);
 endloop
 return archive
end
```

Figure 18.9: A pseudo-code which describes an example of MOEFS implementation.

equal to P_{MDB}. Obviously, additional mutation operators for C_{DB} can be easily added to the learning scheme.

The function *evaluate*() implements a set of fitness functions for evaluating both the accuracy and the interpretability of each solution. The candidate solutions are added to the archive only if they are dominated by no solution contained in the archive; possible solutions in the archive dominated by the candidate solutions are removed. Typically, the size of the archive is fixed at the beginning of the execution of the $(2 + 2)$M-PAES. In this case, when the archive is full and a new solution s_i, where $i = 1, 2$, has to be added to the archive, if it dominates no solution in the archive, then we insert s_i into the archive and remove the solution (possibly s_i

itself) that belongs to the region with the highest crowding degree (these steps are implemented by the function *insert_into_archive* ()).

18.5. Analyzing and Comparing the Performances of MOEFSs

To evaluate the performance of an MOEFS, typically a number of benchmark datasets are considered. For each dataset, an n-fold cross validation is performed and a number of trials are executed for each fold with different seeds for the random function generator. Then, the results are evaluated along two different perspectives: the effectiveness of the evolutionary process and the generalization capabilities of the generated solutions. The former is generally evaluated by using well-known metrics, such as the hypervolume and the epsilon dominance (Zitzler *et al.*, 2003), commonly used in the literature to assess the quality of Pareto front approximations. Hypervolume and epsilon dominance represent a means to quantify the differences between Pareto front approximations by mapping each set of solutions to a real number. The hypervolume indicator measures the hypervolume of the portion of the objective space that is weakly dominated by a Pareto front approximation. In order to compute this indicator, the objective space must be either bounded or a bounding reference point, that is (at least weakly) dominated by all the solutions, must be defined. The epsilon dominance was proposed in Zitzler *et al.* (2003) and makes direct use of the concept of Pareto dominance. Let us consider two Pareto front approximations A and B, where A dominates B. The epsilon dominance is a measure of the smallest distance one would need to translate every solution in B so that B dominates A. If C is chosen to be a reference Pareto front approximation, such that it dominates the A and B Pareto front approximations, then A and B can be directly compared with each other on the basis of the epsilon dominance with respect to C.

In Antonelli *et al.* (2013b), the computations of the two indicators were performed using the performance assessment package provided in the PISA toolkit Bleuler *et al.* (2003). First, the maximum values of accuracy and total rule length of the Pareto front approximations generated in the 30 trials executed for each of the 3 MOEAs (90 Pareto front approximations in total) are computed in order to obtain the bounds for normalizing in [0, 1] the objectives of each approximation. Then, the objectives are normalized. The hypervolume is calculated by using $(1, 1)$ as reference point. To compute the epsilon dominance, the reference Pareto front approximation consists of the non-dominated solutions among the solutions on the 90 Pareto front approximations. As a consequence of the normalization, the value of the two indicators is normalized in [0, 1].

The generalization capabilities of the generated solutions are evaluated by considering the accuracies on the test set. Since several solutions can lie on the Pareto front approximations, typically only some representative solutions are considered. In our previous papers (Alcalá *et al.*, 2009; Antonelli *et al.*, 2011b) and also in Gacto *et al.* (2010), for each fold and each trial, the Pareto front approximations of each algorithm are computed and the solutions are sorted in each approximation for decreasing accuracies on training set. Then, for each approximation, we select the first (the most accurate), the median, and the last (the least accurate) solutions. We denote these solutions as FIRST, MEDIAN, and LAST, respectively. Finally, for the three solutions, we compute the mean values over all the folds and trials of the accuracy on the training and test sets, and of the interpretability. On the one side, the three solutions allow us to graphically show the average trend of the Pareto front approximations obtained in the executions performed on the different folds. On the other side, we can analyze how these solutions are able to generalize when applied to the test set.

Figure 18.10 shows an example of FIRST, MEDIAN, and LAST solutions obtained by the execution of an MOEFS for classification problems (Antonelli *et al.*, 2012b). The algorithm has been executed for 3 trials for each fold in a 10-fold cross validation. In the figure, the complexity has been calculated as the total rule length and the accuracy is expressed in terms of *CR*. We can realize how the three solutions allow us to visualize the trend of the average Pareto front approximations. Further, by comparing the accuracies of the three solutions on the training and test sets, we can appreciate whether these solutions, especially the FIRST solution, suffer from overfitting. Indeed, the FIRST solution is in general the most prone to overfitting since it achieves the higher accuracy on the training set.

The use of numeric values for evaluating the effectiveness and quality of the evolutionary process and the use of the three representative solutions for assessing

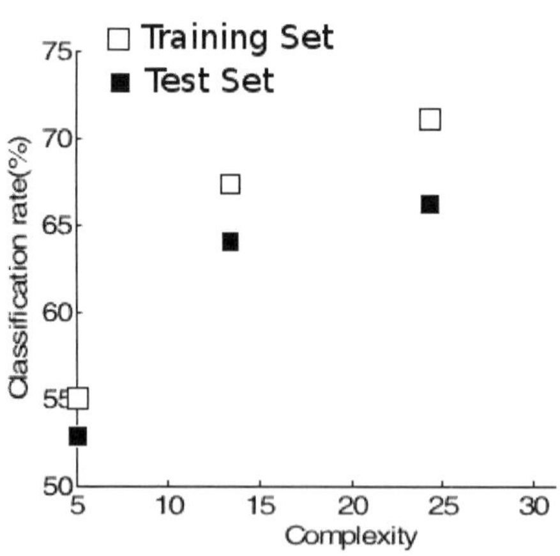

Figure 18.10: An example of Pareto front approximation visualized by using the three representative points.

the generalization capabilities of the solutions on the Pareto front approximations allow comparing different MOEFSs along these two perspectives by using statistical tests. We have to distinguish two different cases: pairwise comparisons and multiple comparisons. In both the cases, the MOEFSs are executed on a number of datasets by employing an n-fold cross validation for each dataset. As regards the first case, the Wilcoxon signed-rank test (Sheskin, 2003; Wilcoxon, 1945), a non-parametric statistical test that detects significant differences between two sample means (Wilcoxon, 1945), has been extensively used. Let d_i be the difference between the performance scores of the two algorithms on the ith out of N_{ds} datasets. The differences are ranked according to their absolute values. Ranks of $d_i = 0$ are split evenly among the sums; if there is an odd number of them, one is ignored. Let $R^+ = \sum_{d_i>0} rank(d_i) + \frac{1}{2}\sum_{d_i=0} rank(d_i)$ and $R^- = \sum_{d_i<0} rank(d_i) + \frac{1}{2}\sum_{d_i=0} rank(d_i)$ be the sum of ranks for the datasets on which the first algorithm outperforms the second, and the sum of ranks for the opposite case, respectively. If $min(R^+, R^-)$ is lower than, or equal to, the value of the distribution of Wilcoxon for N_{ds} degrees of freedom (Table B.12 in Zar (1999)), the null hypothesis of equality is rejected.

The Wilcoxon signed-rank test is more sensible than the t-test. From the statistical point of view, the test is safer than t-test since it does not assume normal distributions. Also, the outliers have less effect on the Wilcoxon test than on the t-test.

As regards non-parametric statistical test for multiple comparisons, first a distribution consisting of the mean values of the metric (hypervolume, epsilon dominance, or accuracy) under consideration is generated for each comparison algorithm by using all the datasets. Then, in the MOEFS literature, the Friedman test is generally applied in order to compute a ranking among the distributions (Friedman, 1937), and the Iman and Davenport test (Iman and Davenport, 1980) is used to evaluate whether there exists a statistical difference among the distributions. If the Iman and Davenport p-value is lower than the level of significance α (in the experiments $\alpha = 0.05$ is generally adopted), we can reject the null hypothesis and affirm that there exist statistical differences between the multiple distributions associated with each approach. Otherwise, no statistical difference exists. If there exists a statistical difference, a *post hoc* procedure, for instance, the Holm test (Holm, 1979), is applied. This test allows detecting effective statistical differences between the control approach, i.e., the one with the lowest Friedman rank, and the remaining approaches.

18.6. Some Experimental Results

In this section, we show and discuss some experimental results obtained in regression and classification problems. These results are extracted from two (Antonelli *et al.*

(2013b) and Antonelli *et al.* (2013a) for, respectively, regressions and classification problems) of our recent papers.

18.6.1. *Example of MOEFS Application to Regression Problems*

In Antonelli *et al.* (2013b), we have discussed and compared the results achieved by two different MOEFSs based on the $(2+2)$M-PAES algorithm which learn concurrently the RB and the membership function parameters of a set of FRBSs in the same multi-objective evolutionary framework. To this aim, each MOEFS exploits a chromosome C composed of two parts (C_{RB}, C_{DB}), which define the RB and the membership function parameters of the linguistic variables, respectively. We denoted these two MOEFs as PAES–RCS and PAES–RL, respectively. Both algorithms exploit the C_{DB} chromosome part shown in Figure 18.8. The only difference between the two MOEFSs lies on the generation of the RB: PAES–RCS uses a rule and condition selection scheme and is based on the C_{RB} shown in Figure 18.5, while PAES–RL employs a classical rule learning approach and is based on the C_{RB} shown in Figure 18.3. Further, both MOEFSs consider the half of the *MSE*, calculated as in Equation (14), and the *total rule length*, calculated as the sum of the conditions which compose the antecedents of the rules in the RB, as objectives to be optimized during the evolutionary process.

We tested the different MOEFSs on twelve regression datasets extracted from the Keel (available at http://sci2s.ugr.es/keel/datasets.php) and TorgoâŁ™s (available at http://www.liaad.up.pt/ ltorgo/Regression/DataSets.html) repositories. As shown in Table 18.1, the datasets are characterized by different numbers (from 7 to 40) of input variables and different numbers (from 4052 to 40768) of input/output instances.

Table 18.1: Regression datasets used in the experiments.

Dataset	#Instance	#Input Variables	Repository
Delta Ailerons (DA)	7129	6	Torgo
Delta Elevators (DE)	9517	6	Torgo
Analyzing Categorical Data (AN)	4052	7	Keel
Kinematics (KI)	8192	8	Torgo
Pumadyn (PM)	8192	8	Torgo
California Housing (CH)	20460	8	Keel
Abalone (AB)	4177	9	Keel
MV Artificial Domain (MV)	40768	10	Keel
House_16H (HO)	22784	16	Keel
Elevators (EL)	16559	18	Keel
Computer activity (CA)	8192	21	Keel
Ailerons (AI)	13750	40	Keel

For each dataset and for each algorithm, we carried out a five-fold cross-validation and executed 6 trials for each fold with different seeds for the random function generator (30 trials in total). The values used in the experiments for the parameters of PAES–RCS and PAES–RL can be found in Antonelli *et al.* (2013b). In particular, the archive size, the number of fuzzy sets for each variable, the minimum and maximum numbers of rules were the same for both PAES–RCS and PAES–RL.

We executed 50,000 and 300,000 fitness evaluations of PAES–RCS and PAES–RL, respectively. In the comparison, we also considered the results generated by PAES–RL after 50,000 fitness evaluations. We denoted PAES–RL executed for 50,000 and 300,000 evaluations as PAES–RL50 and PAES–RL300, respectively.

To compare PAES–RCS with PAES–RL we adopted the epsilon dominance and the hypervolume. The aim of this analysis was to show that PAES–RCS, though performing only 50,000 fitness evaluations, achieved Pareto front approximations comparable with the ones achieved by PAES–RL300, thus confirming the effectiveness of the RCS approach in speeding up the convergence. Further, the solutions were also compared in terms of accuracy and complexity by using the FIRST, MEDIAN, and LAST solutions.

Table 18.2 shows the results of the non-parametric statistical tests executed on the epsilon dominance and the hypervolume: for each indicator and for each MOEFS, we show the Iman and Davenport *p-value* and the Friedman rank.

For both the indicators, the Iman and Davenport statistical hypothesis of equivalence is rejected and so statistical differences among the three MOEFSs are detected. Thus, we applied the Holm *post hoc* procedure considering PAES–RL300 as control algorithm (associated with the lowest rank and in bold in the Table). For both the indicators, we observed that the statistical hypothesis of equivalence was rejected for PAES–RL50, but not for PAES–RCS.

By analyzing the results of the statistical tests, we deduced that PAES–RL needs a larger number of fitness evaluations to converge to Pareto front approximations comparable to the ones achieved by PAES–RCS after 50,000 evaluations. On the other hand, these results can be explained by analyzing the different sizes of the search spaces handled by the two MOEFSs. Indeed, PAES–RCS selects rules and conditions of these rules from an initial set of candidate rules generated by the Wang and Mendel algorithm: thus, rules are learned in a very constrained space. Unlike PAES–RCS, PAES–RL learns the rules by exploring a space consisting of all the possible valid combinations of propositions which can be generated from the linguistic values defined on the universes of the input and output variables. This space rapidly becomes difficult to manage with the increase of the number of input variables.

Table 18.2: Results of the statistical tests on epsilon dominance and hypervolume among PAES–RL50, PAES–RCS, and PAES–RL300.

	Epsilon dominance				
	Algorithm	*Friedman Rank*	*Iman and Davenport p-value*		*Hypothesis*
	PAES–RL50	2.75			
	PAES–RCS	1.916	4.19E-04		Rejected
	PAES–RL300	1.333			
		Holm Post hoc Procedure			
i	*Algorithm*	*z-value*	*p-value*	*alpha/i*	*Hypothesis*
2	PAES–RL50	3.47	5.20E-04	0.025	Rejected
1	PAES–RCS	1.429	1.53E-01	0.05	Not Rejected
	Hypervolume				
	Algorithm	*Friedman Rank*	*Iman and Davenport p-value*		*Hypothesis*
	PAES–RL50	2.667			
	PAES–RCS	1.917	3.91E-03		Rejected
	PAES–RL300	1.417			
		Holm Post hoc Procedure			
i	*Algorithm*	*z-value*	*p-value*	*alpha/i*	*Hypothesis*
2	PAES–RL50	3.061	2.20E-03	0.025	Rejected
1	PAES–RCS	1.224	2.21E-01	0.05	Not Rejected

To evaluate the generalization capabilities of the FRBSs on the Pareto front approximation, we considered the accuracy of the three representative solutions. In Figures 18.11 and 18.12, we plot the mean values of the MSE/2 and the complexity measured in terms of total rule length for the FIRST, MEDIAN, and LAST solutions for all the datasets, on both the training and test sets. We observe that PAES–RL300 generates more complex solutions than PAES–RL50 and PAES–RCS, except for datasets with a high number of input variables, namely EL, CA, and AI. For almost all the datasets the Pareto front approximations generated by PAES–RL50 are dominated by the Pareto front approximations generated by both PAES–RL300 and PAES–RCS, thus highlighting that PAES–RCS generates better trade-off solutions than PAES–RL, both on training and test sets, when the same number of fitness evaluations are performed.

In order to assess if there exist statistical differences among the MSE/2 corresponding to the representative solutions generated by PAES–RCS and the two versions of PAES–RL, we applied non-parametric statistical tests by combining all the datasets: for each approach and for each of the three representative solutions we generated a distribution consisting of the mean values of the MSE/2 on the test set. Table 18.3 shows the results of the statistical tests. For all the three solutions, the Iman and Davenport test rejected the statistical hypothesis of equivalence. Then,

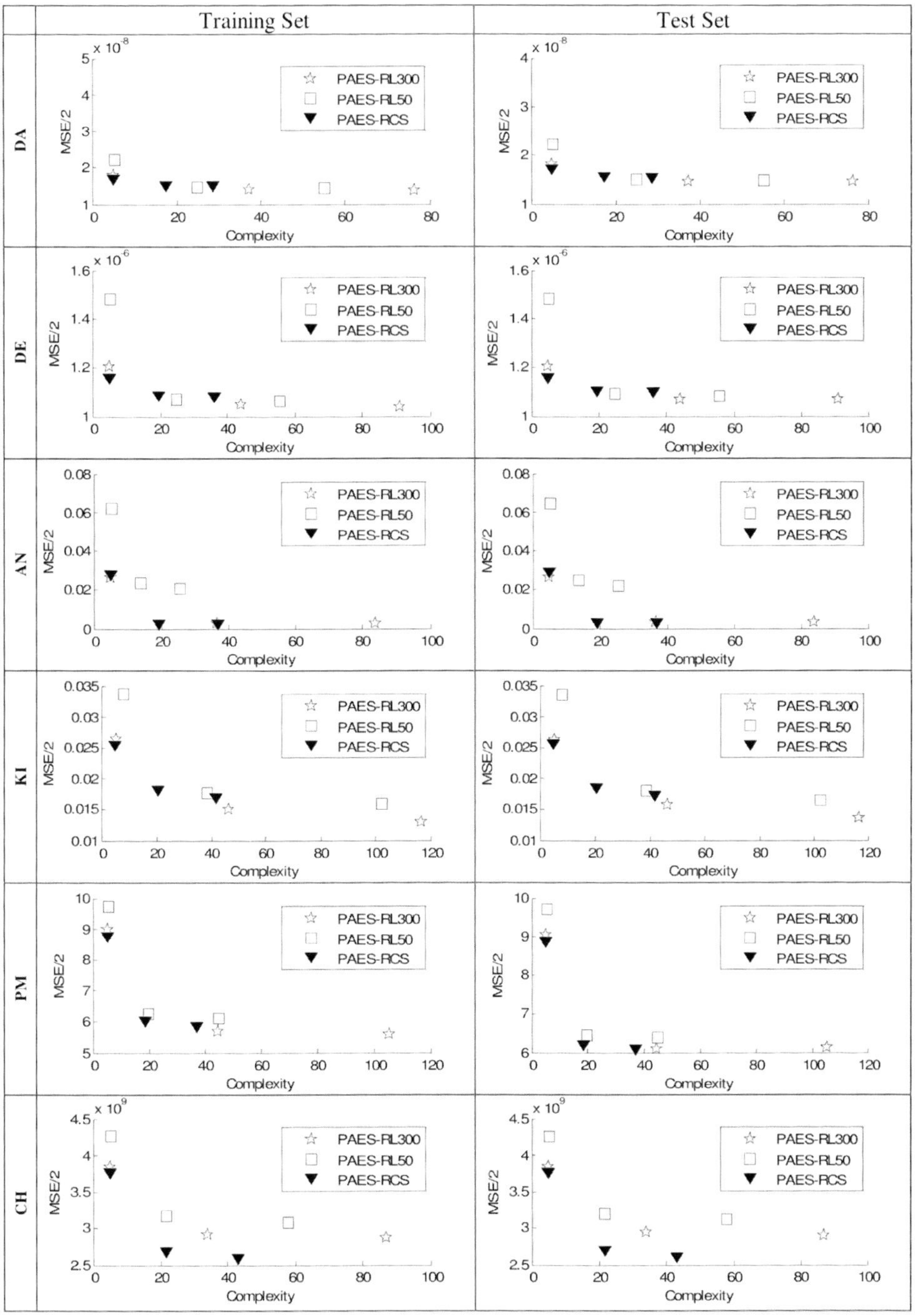

Figure 18.11: Plots of the FIRST, MEDIAN, and LAST solutions onto the Complexity-MSE/2 plane (first six datasets).

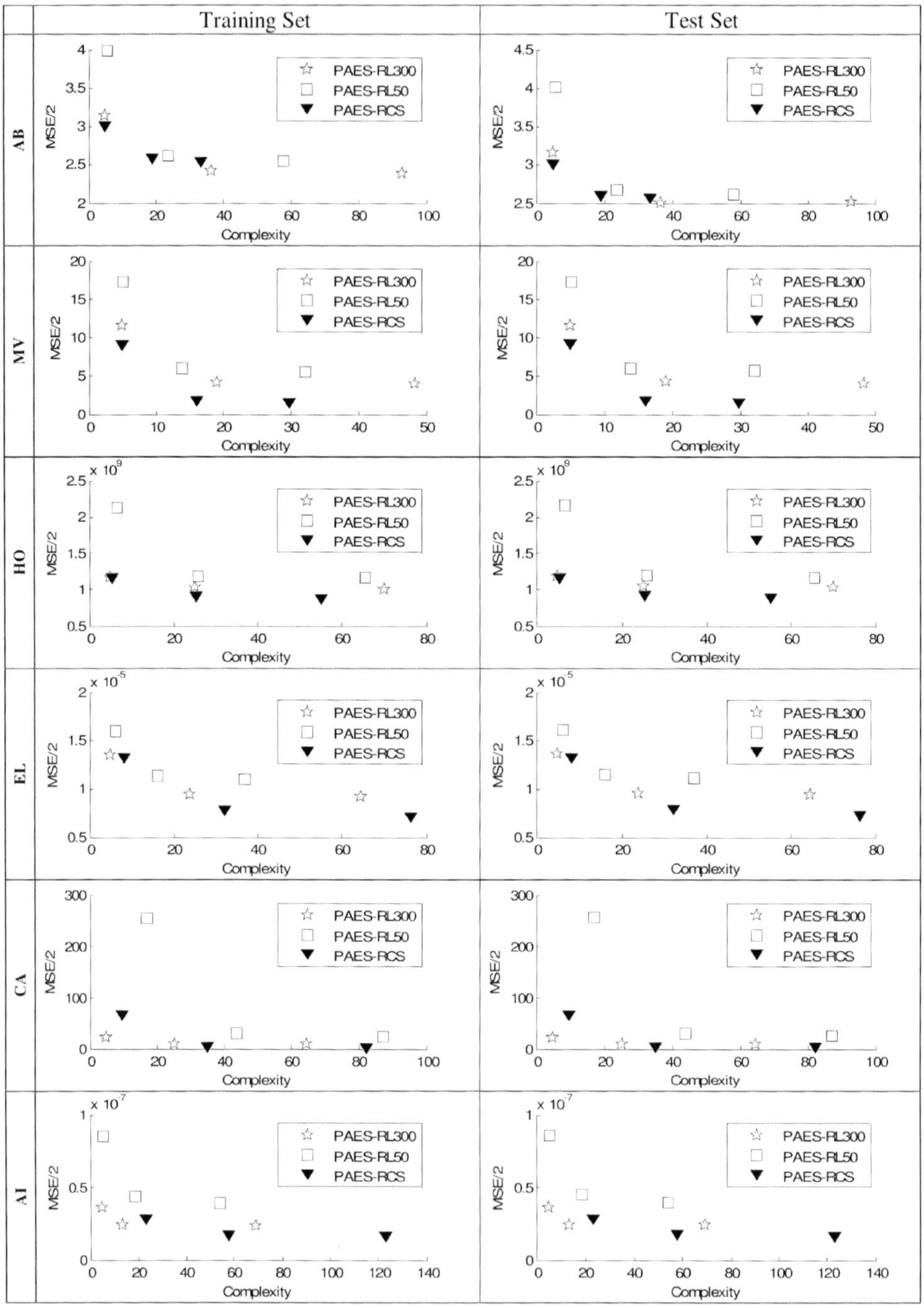

Figure 18.12: Plots of the FIRST, MEDIAN, and LAST solutions onto the Complexity-MSE/2 plane (last six datasets).

Table 18.3: Results of the statistical tests on the FIRST, MEDIAN, and LAST solutions applied to the test sets for PAES–RL50, PAES–RCS, and PAES–RL300.

	FIRST				
	Algorithm	*Friedman Rank*	*Iman and Davenport p-value*		*Hypothesis*
	PAES–RL50	2.75			
	PAES–RCS	1.667	2.33E-03		Rejected
	PAES–RL300	1.583			
		Holm Post hoc Procedure			
i	*Algorithm*	*z-value*	*p-value*	*alpha/i*	*Hypothesis*
2	PAES–RL50	2.858	4.27E-03	0.025	Rejected
1	PAES–RCS	0.204	8.38E-01	0.05	Not Rejected
	MEDIAN				
	Algorithm	*Friedman Rank*	*Iman and Davenport p-value*		*Hypothesis*
	PAES–RL50	2.75			
	PAES–RCS	1.749	1.78E-03		Rejected
	PAES–RL300	1.5			
		Holm Post hoc Procedure			
i	*Algorithm*	*z-value*	*p-value*	*alpha/i*	*Hypothesis*
2	PAES–RL50	3.061	2.20E-03	0.025	Rejected
1	PAES–RCS	0.612	5.40E-01	0.05	Not Rejected
	LAST				
	Algorithm	*Friedman Rank*	*Iman and Davenport p-value*		*Hypothesis*
	PAES–RL50	3			
	PAES–RCS50	1.167	3.71E-10		Rejected
	PAES–RL300	1.833			
		Holm Post hoc Procedure			
i	*Algorithm*	*z-value*	*p-value*	*alpha/i*	*Hypothesis*
2	PAES–RL50	4.49	7.10E-06	0.025	Rejected
1	PAES–RL300	1.632	1.03E-01	0.05	Not Rejected

the Holm *post hoc* procedure was performed by considering as control algorithms PAES–RL300 for the FIRST and MEDIAN solutions and PAES–RCS for the LAST solutions. For all the three solutions, the statistical hypothesis of equivalence was rejected only for PAES–RL50. Thus, we concluded that PAES–RL300 and PAES–RCS result to be statistically equivalent in terms of MSE/2.

The results on the test set confirm that PAES–RCS after 50,000 fitness evaluations generates on average solutions with MSE/2 similar to the ones generated by PAES–RL after 300,000 evaluations and that the MSE/2 of the solutions achieved by PAES–RL after 50,000 fitness evaluations are not statistically equivalent to the ones obtained by PAES–RCS and PAES–RL300.

18.6.2. *Example of MOEFSs Application to Classification Problems with Imbalanced Datasets*

In Antonelli *et al.* (2013a), we have proposed the application of a multi-objective evolutionary learning scheme for generating FRBCs for imbalanced datasets. In particular, the RB and the membership function parameters of a set of FRBCs are concurrently learned by optimizing the sensitivity, the specificity, and the complexity. We recall that imbalanced datasets are characterized by classification categories not equally represented. These datasets are particularly interesting since lots of real world classification problems are often associated with data samples which consist of a large percentage of normal examples (negative classes) and a small percentage of atypical or relevant examples (positive classes).

The proposed MOEFS, denoted as PAES-3obj in Antonelli *et al.* (2013a), for imbalanced datasets is based on $(2 + 2)$M-PAES and exploits a chromosome C composed of two parts (C_{RB}, C_{DB}), where C_{RB} and C_{DB} are shown, respectively, in Figures 18.4 and 18.8. The MOEFS concurrently optimizes three objectives, namely *TPR*, *FPR*, calculated as in Equation (17), and complexity, expressed in terms of total rule length.

We compared the results achieved by PAES-3obj with the ones achieved by two recent single-objective evolutionary fuzzy classifiers (EFCs) appropriately designed for imbalanced datasets. The first EFC (Villar *et al.*, 2012) performs an evolutionary database learning with an embedded rule-base generation. The second EFC (Lopez *et al.*, 2013) builds a hierarchical FRBC: first, a genetic programming algorithm is used to learn the rule-base and then a post-process, which includes a genetic rule selection and a membership function parameters tuning, is applied to the generated FRBC. We denote these two comparison approaches as GA-FS + GL and GP-COACH-H, respectively. We recall that both the comparison approaches rebalance the training set using a state-of-the-art oversampling method, namely SMOTE (Chawla *et al.*, 2002).

We evaluated the performance of the three algorithms on the 22 classification datasets used in Villar *et al.* (2012) and extracted from the KEEL repository (available at http://sci2s.ugr.es/keel/datasets.php). We used a five-fold cross validation as in Villar *et al.* (2012) and in Lopez *et al.* (2013). As shown in Table 18.4, the datasets are characterized by different numbers of input variables (from 7 to 13) and input/output instances (from 184 to 4174), and by different values of the imbalance ratio (IR). The IR is defined as the ratio between the number of instances of the majority and minority classes.

In order to analyze the results of PAES-3obj, each three-dimensional Pareto front approximation was projected onto the FPR–TPR plane: each FRBC of the Pareto front approximation was represented as a point corresponding to its pair (FPR, TPR). These pairs give origin to the so-called ROC curve [Fawcett (2006)].

Table 18.4: Datasets used in the experiments for classification problems.

Dataset	# Instances	# Variables	IR
Abalone19	4174	8	128.87
Abalone9vs18	731	8	16.68
*E.coli*0137vs26	281	7	39.15
*E.coli*4	336	7	13.84
Glass016vs2	192	9	10.29
Glass016vs5	184	9	19.44
Glass2	214	9	10.39
Glass4	214	9	15.47
Glass5	214	9	22.81
Page-blocks13vs2	472	10	15.85
Shuttle0vs4	1829	9	13.87
Shuttle2vs4	129	9	20.5
Vowel0	988	13	10.1
Yeast05679vs4	528	8	9.35
Yeast1289vs7	947	8	30.56
Yeast1458vs7	693	8	22.1
Yeast1vs7	459	8	13.87
Yeast2vs4	514	8	9.08
Yeast2vs8	482	8	23.1
Yeast4	1484	8	28.41
Yeast5	1484	8	32.78
Yeast6	1484	8	39.15

We recall that the ROC analysis is typically adopted to compare different binary classifiers with each other. In particular, one classifier in the ROC space is better than (dominates) another if it is located more North–West (higher TPR and/or lower FPR) than the other. For this reason, in order to select a set of potentially optimal FRBCs, we extracted the non-dominated solutions obtained on the training set in the FPR–TPR plane and used only these solutions for plotting the ROC curve. Further, to evaluate the overall quality of our approach, we calculated the AUC.

As regards GA-FS + GL and GP-COACH-H, they do not generate a set of FRBCs characterized by different values of TPR and FPR but they just provide one classifier with its associated sensitivity and specificity. In this case, the ROC curve is generated by connecting the point corresponding to the unique FRBC to $(0, 0)$ and $(1, 1)$, respectively. The corresponding AUC is computed as in Equation (18).

Table 18.5 shows, for each dataset, the average values of the AUCs computed on the test set for the solutions generated by GA-FS + GL, GP-COACH-H, and PAES-3obj. We point out that the ROC curve on the test set is obtained by connecting the points selected in the training set. For each dataset, the values of the highest AUCs are shown in bold. We observe that in most of the datasets, the solutions generated by PAES-3obj are associated with the highest values of AUC. Further, the solutions

Table 18.5: Average values of the AUC computed on the test set.

Dataset	GA-FS + GL	GP-COACH-H	PAES-3obj
Abalone19	0.699	0.594	**0.727**
Abalone9-18	0.628	0.780	**0.811**
*E.coli*0137vs26	0.790	**0.898**	0.892
*E.coli*4	0.860	**0.934**	0.909
glass016vs2	0.626	0.646	**0.662**
glass016vs5	0.867	0.871	**0.885**
Glass2	**0.729**	0.609	0.705
Glass4	0.853	0.793	**0.864**
Glass5	0.755	0.856	**0.898**
Page-Blocks13vs4	0.937	0.884	**0.951**
shuttle0vs4	**0.999**	0.996	0.996
shuttle2vs4	0.992	**1.000**	0.937
Vowel0	0.928	**0.946**	0.903
Yeast05679vs4	0.793	0.785	**0.835**
Yeast1289vs7	**0.750**	0.696	0.688
Yeast1458vs7	0.641	0.588	**0.645**
yeastB1vs7	0.754	0.681	**0.775**
Yeast2vs4	0.884	0.897	**0.944**
Yeast2vs8	0.710	0.731	**0.814**
Yeast4	0.835	0.813	**0.868**
Yeast5	0.935	0.928	**0.952**
Yeast6	0.870	0.880	**0.888**
Mean	0.811	0.809	**0.843**

generated by GA-FS + GL and GP-COACH-H are characterized, on average, by similar values of AUC.

To statistically validate the previous observations, we applied non-parametric statistical tests for multiple comparisons among the three algorithms by combining all the datasets. Table 18.6 shows the results of the non-parametric statistical tests. With a significance level lower than 0.05, we observed that the Iman and Davenport statistical hypothesis of equivalence is rejected and so statistical differences among the three algorithms were detected. Thus, we applied the Holm post-hoc procedure considering the PAES-3obj as control algorithm (associated with the lowest rank and in bold in the Table). The statistical hypothesis of equivalence can be rejected for both GA-FS + GL and GP-COACH-H, thus confirming that PAES-3obj outperforms, in terms of AUC on the test set, the other algorithms.

The main advantage of PAES-3obj is that, unlike GA-FS + GL and GP-COACH-H, the training set does not need to be re-balanced by using the SMOTE oversampling algorithm. This advantage stands out especially when dealing with datasets characterized by a large number of instances and a high IR. Indeed, the

Table 18.6: Results of the non-parametric statistical tests on the AUC computed on the test set.

	Algorithm	*Friedman rank*	*Iman and Davenport p-value*		*Hypothesis*
	GA-FS + GL	2.272			
	GP-COACH-H	2.227	0.0126		Rejected
	PAES-3obj	1.499			
			Holm post-hoc procedure		
i	*Algorithm*	*z-value*	*p-value*	*alpha/i*	*Hypothesis*
2	GA-FS + GL	2.562	0.0103	0.025	Rejected
1	GP-COACH-H	1.809	0.0158	0.05	Rejected

Table 18.7: Average values of the complexity and number of rules for GA-FS + GL and PAES-3obj.

	GA-FS + GL		**PAES-3obj (Min)**		**PAES-3obj (Max)**	
Dataset	#Rules	Comp	#Rules	Comp	#Rules	Comp
Abalone19	7.40	14.80	2.70	8.30	12.87	66.60
Abalone9-18	4.40	12.32	2.60	8.03	12.10	59.70
*E.coli*0137vs26	4.20	10.08	2.43	3.17	7.63	24.93
*E.coli*4	58.20	162.96	2.33	3.53	6.67	25.00
Glass016vs2	3.60	10.80	2.93	8.73	11.00	58.43
Glass016vs5	4.00	12.00	2.10	2.57	5.00	14.97
Glass2	8.20	24.60	2.93	8.73	8.87	44.27
Glass4	8.40	26.88	2.83	6.60	7.20	30.30
Glass5	5.20	15.60	2.43	4.37	5.77	19.47
Page-Blocks13vs4	6.60	21.12	2.63	7.80	6.53	34.17
shuttle0vs4	14.80	32.56	2.00	2.00	3.27	10.70
shuttle2vs4	4.20	12.60	2.00	2.00	2.10	2.13
Vowel0	4.40	22.88	2.30	8.77	8.37	58.97
Yeast05679vs4	9.40	20.68	2.47	6.60	11.33	53.60
Yeast1289vs7	13.80	41.40	3.00	10.10	11.60	56.07
Yeast1458vs7	3.80	8.36	2.73	8.73	11.00	55.80
yeast1vs7	6.80	19.04	2.53	6.60	10.93	47.77
Yeast2vs4	2.20	6.60	2.57	6.17	8.83	40.90
Yeast2vs8	5.00	27.00	2.53	5.80	8.57	40.43
Yeast4	6.40	17.92	2.23	5.47	10.50	51.67
Yeast5	4.80	14.40	3.00	8.67	9.33	44.13
Yeast6	5.00	14.00	3.40	10.70	11.40	55.37
Mean	8.67	24.94	2.58	6.52	8.68	40.70

oversampling of the minority class becomes computationally expensive, the size of the dataset almost doubles and, consequently, the learning time increases.

As an example of the FRBCs that can be generated by using PAES-3obj, we extracted the solution with the highest AUC from the Pareto front approximation

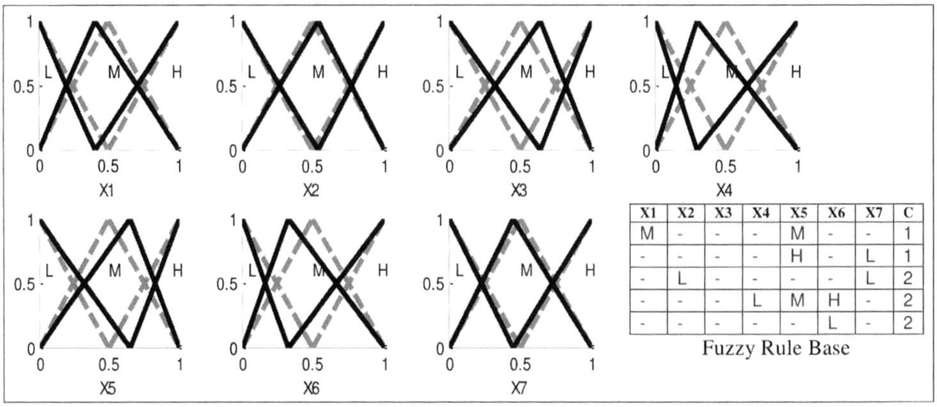

X1	X2	X3	X4	X5	X6	X7	C
M	-	-	-	M	-	-	1
-	-	-	-	H	-	L	1
-	L	-	-	-	-	L	2
-	-	-	L	M	H	-	2
-	-	-	-	-	L	-	2

Figure 18.13: An example of database and rule-base generated by PAES-3obj.

of a specific fold of the *E.coli*4 dataset. In Figure 18.13, we show the overall KB composed by the linguistic fuzzy partitions, associated with the input variables, and the fuzzy RB. In this figure, we represent the initial and the optimized fuzzy partitions by gray dashed lines and solid black lines, respectively. We denote as L, M, and H, the labels of the fuzzy sets which represent, respectively, the low, medium and high levels of each linguistic variable universe. Further, "1" and "2" are the labels of, respectively, the minority and the majority classes, and "-" represents the "don't care" condition.

We observe that, even though the optimized fuzzy partitions are slightly different from the initial ones, they continue to be interpretable (order, coverage and distinguishability are maintained). As regards the RB, we note that it is characterized by a reduced number of rules and conditions in the rules, thus ensuring a very high readability of the final RB.

18.7. Conclusions and Current Research Trends

In this chapter, we have presented the main features of MOEFSs, which have been proposed in the last years for both classification and regression problems. In particular, we have discussed the chromosome coding, mating operators, objective functions, and multi-objective evolutionary algorithms that have been used in most of these systems. Further, we have shown how the results of MOEFSs can be analyzed and compared. Finally, we have discussed some experimental results obtained by applying MOEFSs to both regression and classification datasets. Although MOEFSs can be considered as a mature research area, there still exist some challenges which have to be investigated. One of the most critical aspects, which limits the use of MOEFSs, is the effort needed for their execution. This effort is strongly affected by the computation of the fitness, especially when the dataset is large. To reduce the computational cost, some solutions have been investigated such as employing parallel evolutionary algorithms, exploiting fitness approximation (Cococcioni *et al.*, 2011) and adopting instance selection techniques (Antonelli *et al.*, 2012a; Fazzolari *et al.*, 2013b). Another critical aspect is to manage high-dimensional datasets since the search space increases with the number of features. To limit this drawback, feature selection during the evolutionary process and ad-hoc modified MOEAs have being explored (Alcalá *et al.*, 2011). Finally, classical MOEAs, which have been used so far in MOEFSs, are not suitable for managing more than three objectives. Since interpretability is now evaluated by using a number of indexes, which can be used as different objectives in the optimization process, appropriate algorithms recently proposed in the multi-objective evolutionary framework for dealing with a large number of objectives will have to be investigated and experimented.

References

Alcalá, R., Alcalá-Fdez, J. and Herrera, F. (2007). A proposal for the genetic lateral tuning of linguistic fuzzy systems and its interaction with rule selection. *IEEE T. Fuzzy Syst.*, 15(4), pp. 616–635.

Alcalá, R., Ducange, P., Herrera, F., Lazzerini, B. and Marcelloni, F. (2009). A multiobjective evolutionary approach to concurrently learn rule and data bases of linguistic fuzzy-rule-based systems. *IEEE T. Fuzzy Syst.*, 17(5), pp. 1106–1122.

Alcalá, R., Gacto, M. J., Herrera, F. and Alcalá-Fdez, J. (2007). A multi-objective genetic algorithm for tuning and rule selection to obtain accurate and compact linguistic fuzzy rule-based systems. *Int. J. Uncertain. Fuzz.*, 15(5), pp. 539–557.

Alcalá, R., Gacto, M. J. and Herrera, F. (2011). A fast and scalable multiobjective genetic fuzzy system for linguistic fuzzy modeling in high-dimensional regression problems. *IEEE T. Fuzzy Syst.*, 19(4), pp. 666–681.

Alonso, J. M., Magdalena, L. and González-Rodríguez, G. (2009). Looking for a good fuzzy system interpretability index: An experimental approach. *Int. J. Approx. Reason.*, 51(1), pp. 115–134.

Antonelli, M., Ducange, P., Lazzerini, B. and Marcelloni, F. (2009). Multi-objective evolutionary learning of granularity, membership function parameters and rules of Mamdani fuzzy systems, *Evol. Intell.*, 2(1–2), pp. 21–37.

Antonelli, M., Ducange, P., Lazzerini, B. and Marcelloni, F. (2011a). Learning concurrently data and rule bases of Mamdani fuzzy rule-based systems by exploiting a novel interpretability index. *Soft Comput.*, 15(10), pp. 1981–1998.

Antonelli, M., Ducange, P., Lazzerini, B. and Marcelloni, F. (2011b). Learning knowledge bases of multi-objective evolutionary fuzzy systems by simultaneously optimizing accuracy, complexity and partition integrity. *Soft Comput.*, 15(12), pp. 2335–2354.

Antonelli, M., Ducange, P. and Marcelloni, F. (2012a). Genetic training instance selection in multi-objective evolutionary fuzzy systems: A co-evolutionary approach. *IEEE T. Fuzzy Syst.*, 20(2), pp. 276–290.

Antonelli, M., Ducange, P. and Marcelloni, F. (2012b). Multi-objective evolutionary rule and condition selection for designing fuzzy rule-based classifiers. In *2012 IEEE International Conference on Fuzzy Systems* (*FUZZ-IEEE*), pp. 1–7.

Antonelli, M., Ducange, P., Marcelloni, F. and Segatori, A. (2013a). Evolutionary fuzzy classifiers for imbalanced datasets: An experimental comparison. In *2013 Joint IFSA World Congress and NAFIPS Annual Meeting*, pp. 13–18.

Antonelli, M., Ducange, P. and Marcelloni, F. (2013b). An efficient multi-objective evolutionary fuzzy system for regression problems. *Int. J. Approx. Reason.*, 54(9), pp. 1434–1451.

Bleuler, S., Laumanns, M., Thiele, L. and Zitzler, E. (2003). Pisa a platform and programming language independent interface for search algorithms. In Fonseca, C., Fleming, P., Zitzler, E., Thiele, L. and Deb, K. (eds.), *Evolutionary Multi-Criterion Optimization*, Vol. 2632, *Lect. Notes Comput. Sci.* Berlin, Heidelberg: Springer, pp. 494–508.

Botta, A., Lazzerini, B., Marcelloni, F. and Stefanescu, D. C. (2009). Context adaptation of fuzzy systems through a multi-objective evolutionary approach based on a novel interpretability index. *Soft Comput.*, 13(5), pp. 437–449.

Casillas, J., Martínez, P. and Benítez, A. (2009). Learning consistent, complete and compact sets of fuzzy rules in conjunctive normal form for regression problems. *Soft Comput.*, 13(5), pp. 451–465.

Chawla, N. V., Bowyer, K. W., Hall, L. O. and Kegelmeyer, W. P. (2002). Smote: Synthetic minority over-sampling technique. *J. Artif. Intell. Res.*, 16, pp. 321–357.

Cococcioni, M., Ducange, P., Lazzerini, B. and Marcelloni, F. (2007). A Pareto-based multi-objective evolutionary approach to the identification of Mamdani fuzzy systems. *Soft Comput.*, 11(11), pp. 1013–1031.

Cococcioni, M., Lazzerini, B. and Marcelloni, F. (2011). On reducing computational overhead in multi-objective genetic Takagi–Sugeno fuzzy systems. *Appl. Soft Comput.*, 11(1), pp. 675–688.

Coello, C. A. C., Lamont, G. B. and Van Veldhuisen, D. A. (2007). *Evolutionary Algorithms for Solving Multi-Objective Problems*. Springer.

Cordon, O., del Jesus, M. J. and Herrera, F. (1999). A proposal on reasoning methods in fuzzy rule-based classification systems. *Int. J. Approx. Reason.*, 20(1), pp. 21–45.

Cordón, O. (2011). A historical review of evolutionary learning methods for Mamdani-type fuzzy rule-based systems: Designing interpretable genetic fuzzy systems. *Int. J. Approx. Reason.*, 52(6), pp. 894–913.

Deb, K., Pratap, A., Agarwal, S. and Meyarivan, T. (2002). A fast and elitist multiobjective genetic algorithm: NSGA-II. *IEEE T. Evol. Comput.*, 6(2), pp. 182–197.

de Oliveira, J. (1999). Semantic constraints for membership function optimization. *IEEE T. Syst. Man Cy. A*, 29(1), pp. 128–138.

Ducange, P., Lazzerini, B. and Marcelloni, F. (2010). Multi-objective genetic fuzzy classifiers for imbalanced and cost-sensitive datasets. *Soft Comput.*, 14(7), pp. 713–728.

Ducange, P. and Marcelloni, F. (2011). Multi-objective evolutionary fuzzy systems. In Fanelli, A., Pedrycz, W. and Petrosino, A. (eds.), *Fuzzy Logic and Applications*, Vol. 6857, *Lect. Notes Comput. Sci.*, Berlin, Heidelberg: Springer, pp. 83–90.

Fawcett, T. (2006). An introduction to ROC analysis. *Pattern Recogn. Lett.*, 27(8), pp. 861–874.

Fazzolari, M., Alcalá, R., Nojima, Y., Ishibuchi, H. and Herrera, F. (2013a). A review of the application of multiobjective evolutionary fuzzy systems: Current status and further directions. *IEEE T. Fuzzy Syst.*, 21(1), pp. 45–65.

Fazzolari, M., Giglio, B., Alcalá, R., Marcelloni, F. and Herrera, F. (2013b). A study on the application of instance selection techniques in genetic fuzzy rule-based classification systems: Accuracy-complexity trade-off. *Know.-Based Syst.*, 54, pp. 32–41.

Friedman, M. (1937). The use of ranks to avoid the assumption of normality implicit in the analysis of variance. *J. Am. Stat. Assoc.*, 32(200), pp. 675–701.

Gacto, M. J., Alcalá, R. and Herrera, F. (2009). Adaptation and application of multi-objective evolutionary algorithms for rule reduction and parameter tuning of fuzzy rule-based systems. *Soft Comput.*, 13(5), pp. 419–436.

Gacto, M. J., Alcalá, R. and Herrera, F. (2010). Integration of an index to preserve the semantic interpretability in the multiobjective evolutionary rule selection and tuning of linguistic fuzzy systems. *IEEE T. Fuzzy Syst.*, 18(3), pp. 515–531.

Gacto, M. J., Alcalá, R. and Herrera, F. (2011). Interpretability of linguistic fuzzy rule-based systems: An overview of interpretability measures. *Inform. Sci.*, 181(20), pp. 4340–4360.

Guillaume, S. (2001). Designing fuzzy inference systems from data: An interpretability-oriented review. *IEEE T. Fuzzy Syst.*, 9(3), pp. 426–443.

Herrera, F. and Martínez, L. (2000). A 2-tuple fuzzy linguistic representation model for computing with words. *IEEE T. Fuzzy Syst.*, 8(6), pp. 746–752.

Holm, S. (1979). A simple sequentially rejective multiple test procedure. *Scand. J. Stat.*, 6(2), pp. 65–70.

Horn, J., Nafpliotis, N. and Goldberg, D. E. (1994). A niched Pareto genetic algorithm for multiobjective optimization. In *Proc. First IEEE C. Evol. Computat.*, pp. 82–87.

Iman, R. L. and Davenport, J. M. (1980). Approximations of the critical region of the fbietkan statistic. *Common Stat.*, 9(6), pp. 571–595.

Ishibuchi, H., Murata, T. and Türksen, I. B. (1997). Single-objective and two-objective genetic algorithms for selecting linguistic rules for pattern classification problems. *Fuzzy Set. Syst.*, 89(2), pp. 135–150.

Ishibuchi, H., Nakashima, T. and Murata, T. (2001). Three-objective genetics-based machine learning for linguistic rule extraction. *Inform. Sci.*, 136(1–4), pp. 109–133.

Ishibuchi, H., Nakashima, T. and Nii, M. (2004). *Classification and Modeling with Linguistic Information Granules: Advanced Approaches to Linguistic Data Mining (Advanced Information Processing)* Secaucus, NJ, USA: Springer-Verlag.

Ishibuchi, H. and Nojima, Y. (2007). Analysis of interpretability-accuracy tradeoff of fuzzy systems by multiobjective fuzzy genetics-based machine learning. *Int. J. Approx. Reason.*, 44(1), pp. 4–31.

Ishibuchi, H. and Yamamoto, T. (2004). Fuzzy rule selection by multi-objective genetic local search algorithms and rule evaluation measures in data mining. *Fuzzy Set. Syst.*, 141(1), pp. 59–88.

Klir, G. J. and Yuan, B. (1995). *Fuzzy Sets and Fuzzy Logic*. New Jersey: Prentice Hall.

Knowles, J. D. and Corne, D. W. (2000). Approximating the nondominated front using the Pareto archived evolution strategy. *Evol. Comput.*, 8(2), pp. 149–172.

Lopez, V., Fernandez, A., del Jesus, M. J. and Herrera, F. (2013). A hierarchical genetic fuzzy system based on genetic programming for addressing classification with highly imbalanced and borderline data-sets. *Knowl.-Based Syst.*, 38, pp. 85–104.

Mencar, C. and Fanelli, A. (2008). Interpretability constraints for fuzzy information granulation. *Inform. Sci.*, 178(24), pp. 4585–4618.

Nguyen, C. H., Pedrycz, W., Duong, T. L. and Tran, T. S. (2013). A genetic design of linguistic terms for fuzzy rule based classifiers. *Int. J. Approx. Reason.*, 54(1), pp. 1–21.

Pulkkinen, P. and Koivisto, H. (2010). A dynamically constrained multiobjective genetic fuzzy system for regression problems. *IEEE T. Fuzzy Syst.*, 18(1), pp. 161–177.

Sheskin, D. (2003). *Handbook of Parametric and Nonparametric Statistical Procedures.* Chapman & Hall/CRC.

Villar, P., Fernandez, A., Carrasco, R. A. and Herrera, F. (2012). Feature selection and granularity learning in genetic fuzzy rule-based classification systems for highly imbalanced data-sets. *Int. J. Uncertain. Fuzz.*, 20(03), pp. 369–397.

Wang, L.-X. and Mendel, J. M. (1992). Generating fuzzy rules by learning from examples. *IEEE T. Syst. Man Cyb.*, 22(6), pp. 1414–1427.

Wilcoxon, F. (1945). Individual comparisons by ranking methods. *Biometrics*, 1, pp. 80–83.

Zadeh, L. (1965). Fuzzy sets. *Inform. Control*, 8(3), pp. 338–353.

Zar, J. (1999). *Biostatistical Analysis.* Upper Saddle River, NJ: Prentice-Hall.

Zhou, S.-M. and Gan, J. Q. (2008). Low-level interpretability and high-level interpretability: A unified view of data-driven interpretable fuzzy system modelling. *Fuzzy Set. Syst.*, 159(23), pp. 3091–3131.

Zitzler, E., Laumanns, M. and Bleuler, S. (2004). A tutorial on evolutionary multiobjective optimization. In *Metaheuristics for Multiobjective Optimisation*, pp. 3–37. Springer.

Zitzler, E., Laumanns, M. and Thiele, L. (2001). SPEA2: Improving the strength pareto evolutionary algorithm for multiobjective optimization. In Giannakoglou, K. C., Tsahalis, D. T., Périaux, J., Papailiou, K. D. and Fogarty, T. (eds.), *Evolutionary Methods for Design Optimization and Control with Applications to Industrial Problems.* International Center for Numerical Methods in Engineering, pp. 95–100.

Zitzler, E., Thiele, L., Laumanns, M., Fonseca, C. and da Fonseca, V. (2003). Performance assessment of multiobjective optimizers: An analysis and review. *IEEE T. Evol. Comput.*, 7(2), pp. 117–132.

Chapter 19

Bio-Inspired Optimization of Interval Type-2 Fuzzy Controllers

Oscar Castillo

This chapter presents a general framework for designing interval type-2 fuzzy controllers (FCs) based on bio-inspired optimization techniques. The problem of designing optimal type-2 FCs for complex nonlinear plants under uncertain environments is of crucial importance in achieving good results for real-world applications. Traditional approaches have been the use of genetic algorithms (GAs) or trial and error approaches; however results tend to be not optimal or require very large design times. More recently, bio-inspired optimization techniques, like ant colony optimization (ACO) or particle swarm intelligence, have also been tried on optimal design of FCs. In this chapter, we show how the use of bio-inspired optimization techniques can be used to obtain results that outperform traditional approaches in the design of optimal type-2 FCs.

19.1. Introduction

We describe in this chapter, new methods for building intelligent systems using type-2 fuzzy logic and bio-inspired optimization techniques. Bio-inspired optimization includes techniques, such as particle swarm optimization (PSO), ant colony optimization (ACO) and genetic algorithms (GAs), have been applied in numerous optimization problems. In this paper, we are extending the use of fuzzy logic to a higher order, which is called type-2 fuzzy logic (Castillo and Melin, 2008; Mendel, 2000). Combining type-2 fuzzy logic with bio-inspired optimization techniques, we can build powerful hybrid intelligent systems that can use the advantages that each technique offers in solving complex control problems.

Fuzzy logic is an area of soft computing that enables a computer system to reason with uncertainty (Zadeh, 1975). A fuzzy inference system consists of a set of if-then rules defined over fuzzy sets (Castillo and Melin, 2008; Mendel, 2000). Fuzzy sets generalize the concept of a traditional set by allowing the membership degree to be any value between 0 and 1. This corresponds, in the real world, to many situations where it is difficult to decide in an unambiguous manner if something belongs or not to a specific class. Fuzzy expert systems, for example, have been applied with some success to problems of decision, control, diagnosis and classification, just because they can manage the complex expert reasoning involved in these areas of application. The main disadvantage of fuzzy systems is that they cannot adapt to changing situations. For this reason, it is a good idea to combine fuzzy logic with neural networks or GAs, because either one of these last two methodologies could give adaptability to the fuzzy system (Castro *et al.*, 2009; Wang *et al.*, 2004). On the other hand, the knowledge that is used to build these fuzzy rules is uncertain. Such uncertainty leads to rules whose antecedents or consequents are uncertain, which translates into uncertain antecedent or consequent membership functions (Hagras, 2004; Mendel, 2000). Type-1 fuzzy systems, like the ones mentioned above, whose membership functions are type-1 fuzzy sets, are unable to directly handle such uncertainties. Type-2 fuzzy sets are fuzzy sets whose membership grades themselves are type-1 fuzzy sets; they are very useful in circumstances where it is difficult to determine an exact membership function for a fuzzy set (Biglarbegian *et al.*, 2011; Castillo *et al.*, 2008a, 2008b; Melin and Castillo, 2004, 2007).

Uncertainty is an inherent part of intelligent systems used in real-world applications (Bingül and Karahan, 2011; Castillo *et al.*, 2007). The use of new methods for handling incomplete information is of fundamental importance (Cazarez-Castro *et al.*, 2008; Dereli *et al.*, 2011; Martinez-Marroquin *et al.*, 2009; Starczewski, 2009; Yager, 1980). Type-1 fuzzy sets used in conventional fuzzy systems cannot fully handle the uncertainties present in intelligent systems (Cervantes and Castillo, 2010; Chaoui and Gueaieb, 2008). Type-2 fuzzy sets that are used in type-2 fuzzy systems can handle such uncertainties in a better way because they provide us with more parameters (Castillo *et al.*, 2012; Galluzzo and Cosenza, 2010; Hsiao *et al.*, 2008). This chapter deals with the design of intelligent systems using interval type-2 fuzzy logic for minimizing the effects of uncertainty produced by the instrumentation elements, environmental noise, etc. Experimental results include simulations of feedback control systems for nonlinear plants using type-1 and type-2 fuzzy logic controllers (FLCs); a comparative analysis of the systems' response is performed, with and without the presence of uncertainty (Martinez *et al.*, 2009, 2010). The main contribution of the chapter is the proposed approach for the design of type-2 FLCs using bio-inspired optimization algorithms (Astudillo *et al.*, 2010; Castillo *et al.*, 2012).

We describe the use of ACO for the problem of finding the optimal intelligent controller for an autonomous wheeled mobile robot, in particular for the problem of tuning a fuzzy controller (FC) of Sugeno type. In our case study the controller has four inputs, each of them with two membership functions and we consider the interpolation point for every pair of membership function as the main parameter and their individual shape as secondary ones in order to achieve the tuning of the FC by using an ACO algorithm (Martinez-Marroquin *et al.*, 2009). Simulation results show that using ACO and coding the problem with just three parameters instead of six, allows us to find an optimal set of membership function parameters for the fuzzy control system with less computational effort needed (Castillo *et al.*, 2012).

This chapter also describes the application of the optimization algorithm for particle swarm known by its acronym as PSO, used to adjust the parameters of membership functions of a FLC to find the optimal intelligent control for a wheeled autonomous mobile robot. Results of several simulations show that the PSO is able to optimize the type-1 and type-2 FLC for this specific application (Martinez *et al.*, 2010). We use the PSO method to find the parameters of the membership functions of a type-2 FLC in order to minimize the state error for nonlinear systems. PSO is used to find the optimal type-2 FLC to achieve regulation of the output and stability of the closed-loop system (Martinez *et al.*, 2009). For this purpose, we change the values of the cognitive, social and inertia variables in the PSO. Simulation results, with the optimal FLC implemented in Simulink, show the feasibility of the proposed approach.

In general, the above mentioned applications of type-2 fuzzy logic in intelligent control are representative of the state of art in the area. However, we also have to mention that there exist applications of type-2 fuzzy logic in pattern recognition (Huang *et al.*, 2009), time series prediction (Castro *et al.*, 2009), and classification (Dereli *et al.*, 2011), which have been successful in the real world, but are not the main concern in this chapter. There have also been important theoretical advances on type-2 fuzzy logic that have enable more efficient processing and type reduction (Mendel, 2000; Starczewski, 2009; Yager, 1980), which have helped obtaining solutions to real world problems (Kim *et al.*, 2010; Koca *et al.*, 2011; Poornaselvan *et al.*, 2008; Sudha and Vijaya Santhi, 2011; Wagner and Hagras, 2007a, 2007b; Wu and Tan, 2004, 2006).

19.2. Design of Interval Type-2 FCs

Uncertainty is an inherent part of intelligent systems used in real-world applications (Wagner and Hagras, 2007a; Wu and Tan, 2006). The use of new methods for handling incomplete information is of fundamental importance (Castillo and Melin, 2008; Mendel, 2000). Type-1 fuzzy sets used in conventional fuzzy systems cannot fully handle the uncertainties present in intelligent systems. Type-2 fuzzy sets that are used in type-2 fuzzy systems can handle such uncertainties in a better way because they provide us with more parameters (Biglarbegian *et al.*, 2011; Castro *et al.*, 2007). This section deals with the design of intelligent systems using interval type-2 fuzzy logic for minimizing the effects of uncertainty produced by the instrumentation elements, environmental noise, etc. Experimental results include simulations of feedback control systems for nonlinear plants using type-1 and type-2 FLCs; a comparative analysis of the systems' response is performed, with and without the presence of uncertainty (Castillo *et al.*, 2012).

19.2.1. *Introduction to the Design*

Uncertainty affects decision-making and appears in a number of different forms. The concept of information is fully connected with the concept of uncertainty. The most fundamental aspect of this connection is that the uncertainty involved in any problem solving situation is a result of some information deficiency, which may be incomplete, imprecise, fragmentary, not fully reliable, vague, contradictory, or deficient in some other way. Uncertainty is an attribute of information. The general framework of fuzzy reasoning allows handling much of this uncertainty; fuzzy systems employ type-1 fuzzy sets, which represent uncertainty by numbers in the range [0, 1]. When something is uncertain, like a measurement, it is difficult to determine its exact value, and of course type-1 fuzzy sets make more sense than using sets. However, it is not reasonable to use an accurate membership function for something uncertain, so in this case what we need is another type of fuzzy sets, those which are able to handle these uncertainties, the so called type-2 fuzzy sets. So, the amount of uncertainty in a system can be reduced by using type-2 fuzzy logic because it offers better capabilities to handle linguistic uncertainties by modeling vagueness and unreliability of information (Castillo and Melin, 2008; Mendel, 2000).

In this section, we deal with the application of interval type-2 fuzzy control to nonlinear dynamic systems (Juang and Hsu, 2009b; Juang *et al.*, 2009; Mohammadi *et al.*, 2010). It is a well-known fact, that in the control of real systems, the instrumentation elements (instrumentation amplifier, sensors, digital to analog, analog to digital converters, etc.) introduce some sort of unpredictable values in the information that has been collected (Castillo *et al.*, 2012). So, the controllers designed under idealized conditions tend to behave in an inappropriate manner. Since, uncertainty is inherent in the design of controllers for real world applications; we are presenting how to deal with this problem using type-2 FLC, to reduce the effects of imprecise information (Mendel, 2000). We are supporting this statement with experimental results, qualitative observations, and quantitative measures of errors. For quantifying the errors, we utilized three widely used performance criteria, these are: Integral of square error (ISE), integral of the absolute value of the error (IAE), and integral of the time multiplied by the absolute value of the error (ITAE).

19.2.2. *Fuzzy Logic Systems (FLSs)*

In this section, a brief overview of type-1 and type-2 fuzzy systems is presented. This overview is considered as necessary to understand the basic concepts needed to understand the methods and algorithms presented later in the paper (Castillo and Melin, 2008; Mendel, 2000).

19.2.2.1. *Type-1 FLSs*

In the 40s and 50s, many researchers proved that dynamic systems could be mathematically modeled using differential equations. In these works we have the foundations of the Control Theory, which in addition with the Transform Theory (Laplace's Theory), provided an extremely powerful means of analyzing and designing control systems. These theories were developed until the 70s, when the area was called Systems Theory to indicate its definitiveness.

Soft computing techniques have become an important research topic, which can be applied in the design of intelligent controllers. These techniques have tried to avoid the abovementioned drawbacks, and they allow us to obtain efficient controllers, which utilize the human experience in a more natural form than the conventional mathematical approach. In the cases in which a mathematical representation of the controlled system is difficult to obtain, the process operator has the knowledge, the experience to express the relationships existing in the process behavior.

A FLS, described completely in terms of type-1 fuzzy sets is called a type-1 FLS. It is composed by a knowledge base, which comprises the information given by the process operator in form of linguistic control rules, a fuzzification interface, which has the effect of transforming crisp data into fuzzy sets, and inference system, which uses the fuzzy sets in conjunction with the knowledge base to make inferences by means of a reasoning method. Finally, a defuzzification interface, which translates the fuzzy control action so obtained to a real control action using a defuzzification method.

In this section, the implementation of the FC in terms of type-1 fuzzy sets, has two input variables, which are the error $e(t)$, the difference between the reference signal and the output of the process, as well as the error variation $\Delta e(t)$,

$$e(t) = r(t) - y(t), \tag{1}$$

$$\Delta e(t) = e(t) - e(t-1), \tag{2}$$

so the control system can be represented as in Figure 19.1.

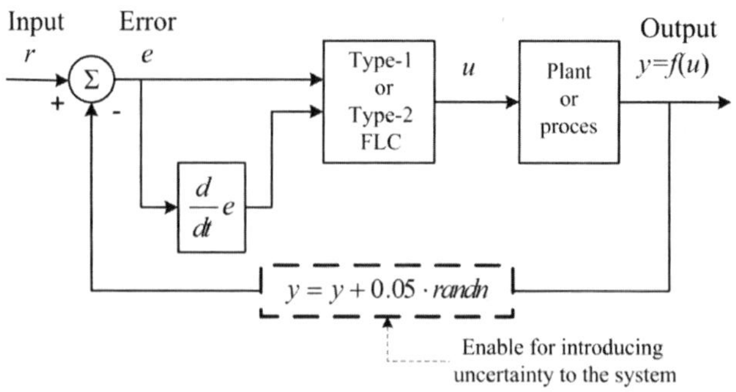

Figure 19.1: System used for obtaining the experimental results for control.

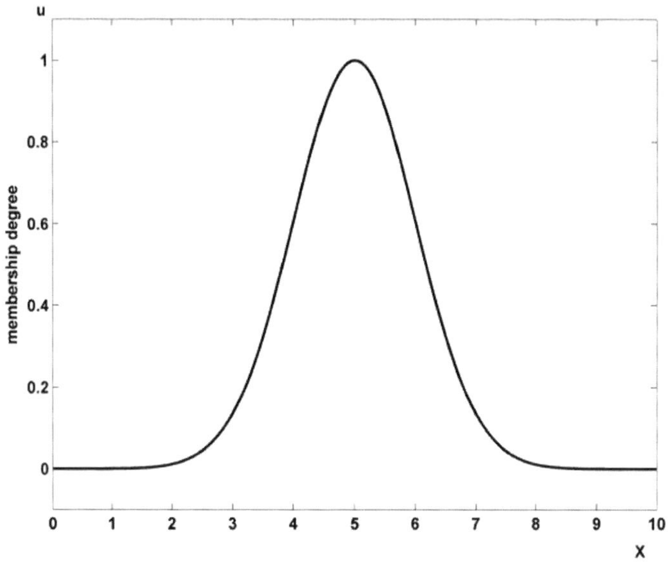

Figure 19.2: Type-1 membership function.

19.2.2.2. *Type-2 FLSs*

If for a type-1 membership function, as in Figure 19.2, we blur it to the left and to the right, as illustrated in Figure 19.3, then a type-2 membership function is obtained. In this case, for a specific value x', the membership function (u'), takes on different values, which are not all weighted the same, so we can assign an amplitude distribution to all of those points.

Doing this for all $x \in X$, we create a three-dimensional membership function — a type-2 membership function — that characterizes a type-2 fuzzy set. A type-2 fuzzy set $\tilde{A}$, is characterized by the membership function:

$$\tilde{A} = \{((x, u), \mu_{\tilde{A}}(x, u)) | \forall x \in X, \forall u \in J_x \subseteq [0, 1]\}, \tag{3}$$

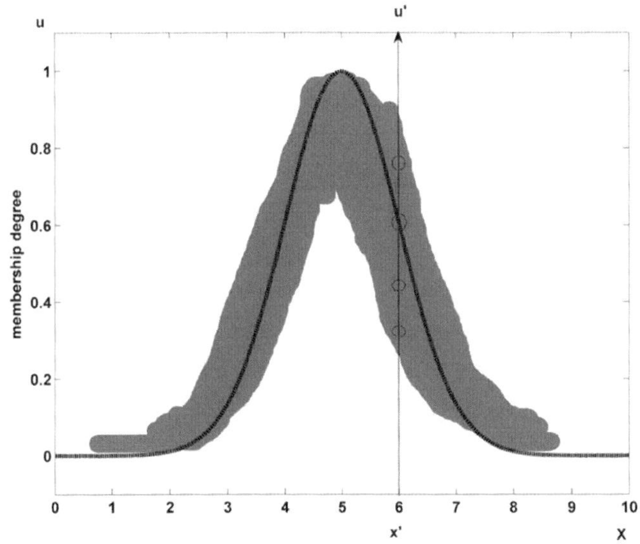

Figure 19.3: Blurred type-1 membership function.

in which $0 \leq \mu_{\tilde{A}}(x, u) \leq 1$. Another expression for $\tilde{A}$ is

$$\tilde{A} = \int_{x \in X} \int_{u \in J_x} \frac{\mu_{\tilde{A}}(x, u)}{(x, u) J_x} \subseteq [0, 1], \tag{4}$$

where $\int\int$ denotes the union over all admissible input variables x and u. For discrete universes of discourse $\int$ is replaced by $\sum$ (Mendel, 2000). In fact $J_x \subseteq [0, 1]$ represents the primary membership of x, and $\mu_{\tilde{A}}(x, u)$ is a type-1 fuzzy set known as the secondary set. Hence, a type-2 membership grade can be any subset in [0, 1], the primary membership, and corresponding to each primary membership, there is a secondary membership (which can also be in [0, 1]) that defines the possibilities for the primary membership. Uncertainty is represented by a region, which is called the footprint of uncertainty (FOU). If $\mu_{\tilde{A}}(x, u) = 1, \forall u \in J_x \subseteq [0, 1]$ then we have an interval type-2 membership function, as shown in Figure 19.4. The uniform shading for the FOU represents the entire interval type-2 fuzzy set and it can be described in terms of an upper membership function $\bar{\mu}_{\tilde{A}}(x)$ and a lower membership function $\underline{\mu}_{\tilde{A}}(x)$.

A FLS described using at least one type-2 fuzzy set is called a type-2 FLS. Type-1 FLSs are unable to directly handle rule uncertainties, because they use type-1 fuzzy sets that are certain. On the other hand, type-2 FLSs, are very useful in circumstances where it is difficult to determine an exact membership function, and there are measurement uncertainties.

It is known that type-2 fuzzy sets enable modeling and minimizing the effects of uncertainties in rule-based FLS. Unfortunately, type-2 fuzzy sets are more difficult

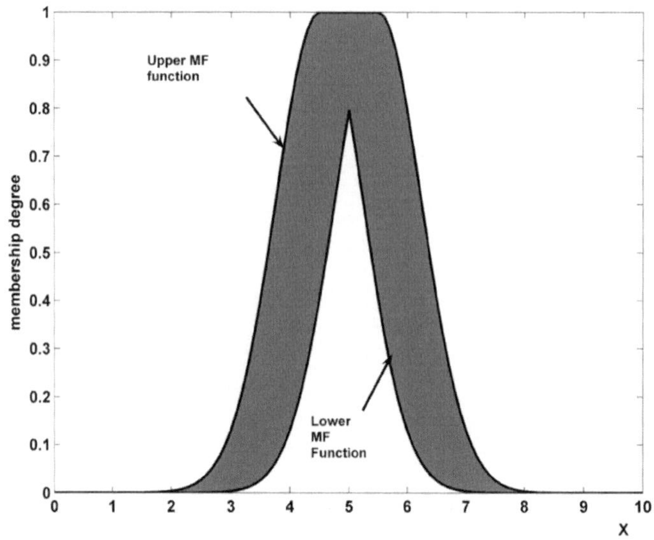

Figure 19.4: Interval type-2 membership function.

to use and understand than type-1 fuzzy sets; hence, their use is not widespread yet. As a justification for the use of type-2 fuzzy sets, are mentioned at least four sources of uncertainties not considered in type-1 FLSs:

1. The meanings of the words that are used in the antecedents and consequents of rules can be uncertain (words mean different things to different people).
2. Consequents may have histogram of values associated with them, especially when knowledge is extracted from a group of experts who do not all agree.
3. Measurements that activate a type-1 FLS may be noisy and therefore uncertain.
4. The data used to tune the parameters of a type-1 FLS may also be noisy.

All of these uncertainties translate into uncertainties about fuzzy set membership functions. Type-1 fuzzy sets are not able to directly model such uncertainties because their membership functions are totally crisp. On the other hand, type-2 fuzzy sets are able to model such uncertainties because their membership functions are themselves fuzzy. A type-1 fuzzy set is a special case of a type-2 fuzzy set; its secondary membership function is a subset with only one element, unity.

A type-2 FLS is again characterized by IF-THEN rules, but its antecedent or consequent sets are now of type-2. Type-2 FLSs, can be used when the circumstances are too uncertain to determine exact membership grades such as when the training data is corrupted by noise. Similar to a type-1 FLS, a type-2 FLS includes a fuzzifier, a rule-base, fuzzy inference engine, and an output processor, as we can see in Figure 19.5. The output processor includes type-reducer and defuzzifier; it

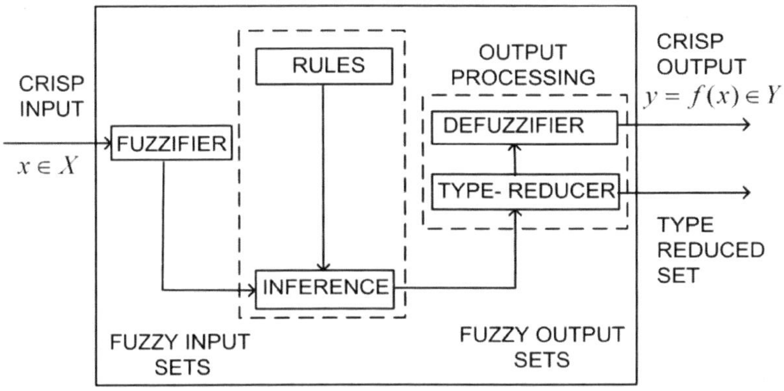

Figure 19.5: Type-2 FLS.

generates a type-1 fuzzy set output (from the type-reducer) or a crisp number (from the defuzzifier). Now, we will explain each of the blocks of Figure 19.5.

19.2.2.2.1. Fuzzifier

The fuzzifier maps a crisp point $\mathbf{x} = (\mathrm{x}_1, \ldots, \mathrm{x}_\mathrm{p})^\mathrm{T} \in X_{1\times}X_{2\times\cdots\times}X_p \equiv \mathbf{X}$ into a type-2 fuzzy set $\tilde{A}_x$ in $\mathbf{X}$, interval type-2 fuzzy sets in this case. We will use type-2 singleton fuzzifier, in a singleton fuzzification, the input fuzzy set has only a single point on non-zero membership. $\tilde{A}_x$ is a type-2 fuzzy singleton if $\mu_{\tilde{A}_x}(x) = 1/1$ for $\mathbf{x} = \mathbf{x}'$ and $\mu_{\tilde{A}_x}(x) = 1/0$ for all other $\mathbf{x} \neq \mathbf{x}'$.

19.2.2.2.2. Rules

The structure of rules in a type-1 FLS and a type-2 FLS is the same, but in the latter the antecedents and the consequents will be represented by type-2 fuzzy sets. So for a type-2 FLS with p inputs $x_1 \in X_1, \ldots, x_p \in X_p$ and one output $y \in Y$, multiple input single output (MISO), if we assume there are M rules, the lth rule in the type-2 FLS can be written as follows:

$$R^l : \text{ IF } x_1 \text{ is } \tilde{F}_1^l \text{ and } x_p \text{ is } \tilde{F}_p^l, \qquad \text{THEN } y \text{ is } \tilde{G}^l \; l = 1, \ldots, M. \tag{5}$$

19.2.2.2.3. Inference

In the type-2 FLS, the inference engine combines rules and gives a mapping from input type-2 fuzzy sets to output type-2 fuzzy sets. It is necessary to compute the join $\sqcup$, (unions) and the meet $\prod$ (intersections), as well as extended sup-star compositions (sup star compositions) of type-2 relations. If $\tilde{F}_1^l \times \cdots \times \tilde{F}_p^l = \tilde{A}^l$, Equation (5) can be rewritten as

$$R^l : \tilde{F}_1^l \times \cdots \times \tilde{F}_p^l \to \tilde{G}^l = \tilde{A}^l \to \tilde{G}^l \quad l = 1, \ldots, M. \tag{6}$$

R^l is described by the membership function $\mu_{R^l}(\mathbf{x}, y) = \mu_{R^l}(x_1, \ldots, x_p, y)$, where

$$\mu_{R^l}(\mathbf{x}, y) = \mu_{\tilde{A}^l \to \tilde{G}^l}(\mathbf{x}, y), \tag{7}$$

can be written as:

$$\begin{aligned}\mu_{R^l}(\mathbf{x}, y) &= \mu_{\tilde{A}^l \to \tilde{G}^l}(\mathbf{x}, y) = \mu_{\tilde{F}_1^l}(x_1) \prod \cdots \prod \mu_{\tilde{F}_p^l}(x_p) \prod \mu_{\tilde{G}^l}(y) \\ &= \left[\prod_{i=1}^{p} \mu_{\tilde{F}_i^l}(x_i)\right] \prod \mu_{\tilde{G}^l}(y).\end{aligned} \tag{8}$$

In general, the p-dimensional input to R^l is given by the type-2 fuzzy set $\tilde{A}_x$ whose membership function is

$$\mu_{\tilde{A}_x}(\mathbf{x}) = \mu_{\tilde{x}_1}(x_1) \prod \cdots \prod \mu_{\tilde{x}p}(x_p) = \prod_{i=1}^{p} \mu_{\tilde{x}i}(x_i), \tag{9}$$

where $\tilde{X}_i (i = 1, \ldots, p)$ are the labels of the fuzzy sets describing the inputs. Each rule R^l determines a type-2 fuzzy set $\tilde{B}^l = \tilde{A}_x \circ R^l$ such that:

$$\mu_{\tilde{B}^l}(y) = \mu_{\tilde{A}_x \circ R^l} = \sqcup_{x \in \mathbf{X}} \left\lfloor \mu_{\tilde{A}_x}(\mathbf{x}) \prod \mu_{R^l}(\mathbf{x}, y) \right\rfloor \quad y \in Y \quad l = 1, \ldots, M. \tag{10}$$

This equation is the input/output relation in Figure 19.5 between the type-2 fuzzy set that activates one rule in the inference engine and the type-2 fuzzy set at the output of that engine.

In the FLS we used interval type-2 fuzzy sets and meet under product t-norm, so the result of the input and antecedent operations, which are contained in the firing set $\prod_{i=1}^{p} \mu_{\tilde{F}_{i_i}}(x_i^{'} \equiv F^l(\mathbf{x}')$, is an interval type-1 set,

$$F^l(\mathbf{x}') = \left[\underline{f}^l(\mathbf{x}'), \bar{f}^l(\mathbf{x}')\right] \equiv \left[\underline{f}^l, \bar{f}^l\right], \tag{11}$$

where

$$\underline{f}^l(\mathbf{x}') = \underline{\mu}_{\tilde{F}_1^l}(x_1^{'}) * \cdots * \underline{\mu}_{\tilde{F}_p^l}(x_p^{'}) \tag{12}$$

and

$$\bar{f}^l(\mathbf{x}') = \bar{\mu}_{\tilde{F}_1^l}(x_1^{'}) * \cdots * \bar{\mu}_{\tilde{F}_p^l}(x_p^{'}), \tag{13}$$

where * is the product operation.

19.2.2.2.4. Type reducer

The type-reducer generates a type-1 fuzzy set output, which is then converted in a crisp output through the defuzzifier. This type-1 fuzzy set is also an interval set, for the case of our FLS we used center of sets (COSs) type reduction, $Y_{\cos}$ which is expressed as

$$Y_{\cos}(\mathbf{x}) = [y_l, y_r] = \int_{y^1 \in [y_l^1, y_r^1]} \cdots \int_{y^M \in [y_l^M, y_r^M]} \times \int_{f^1 \in [\underline{f}^1, \bar{f}^1]} \cdots \int_{f^M \in [\underline{f}^M, \bar{f}^M]} \frac{1}{\frac{\sum_{i=1}^{M} f^i y^i}{\sum_{i=1}^{M} f^i}}. \tag{14}$$

This interval set is determined by its two end points, y_l and y_r, which corresponds to the centroid of the type-2 interval consequent set $\tilde{G}^i$,

$$C_{\tilde{G}^i} = \int_{\theta_1 \in J_{y1}} \cdots \int_{\theta_N \in J_{yN}} \frac{1}{\frac{\sum_{i=1}^{N} y_i \theta_i}{\sum_{i=1}^{N} \theta_i}} = [y_l^i, y_r^i], \tag{15}$$

before the computation of $Y_{\cos}$ ($\mathbf{x}$), we must evaluate Equation (15), and its two end points, y_l and y_r. If the values of f_i and y_i that are associated with y_l are denoted f_l^i and y_l^i, respectively, and the values of f_i and y_i that are associated with y_r are denoted f_r^i and y_r^i, respectively, from Equation (14), we have

$$y_l = \frac{\sum_{i=1}^{M} f_l^i y_l^i}{\sum_{i=1}^{M} f_l^i}, \tag{16}$$

$$y_r = \frac{\sum_{i=1}^{M} f_r^i y_r^i}{\sum_{i=1}^{M} f_r^i}. \tag{17}$$

19.2.2.2.5. Defuzzifier

From the type-reducer we obtain an interval set $Y_{\cos}$, to defuzzify it we use the average of y_l and y_r, so the defuzzified output of an interval singleton type-2 FLS is

$$y(\mathbf{x}) = \frac{y_l + y_r}{2}. \tag{18}$$

In this paper, we are simulating the fact that the instrumentation elements (instrumentation amplifier, sensors, digital to analog, analog to digital converters, etc.) are introducing some sort of unpredictable values in the collected information. In the case of the implementation of the type-2 FLC, we have the same characteristics as in type-1 FLC, but we used type-2 fuzzy sets as membership functions for the inputs and for the output.

19.2.2.3. *Performance criteria*

For evaluating the transient closed-loop response of a computer control system we can use the same criteria that normally are used for adjusting constants in proportional integral derivative (PID) controllers. These are:

1. ISE.

$$\mathrm{ISE} = \int_0^\infty [e(t)]^2 dt. \tag{19}$$

2. IAE.

$$\mathrm{IAE} = \int_0^\infty |e(t)| dt. \tag{20}$$

3. ITAE.

$$\mathrm{ITAE} = \int_0^\infty t|e(t)| dt. \tag{21}$$

The selection of the criteria depends on the type of response desired, the errors will contribute different for each criterion, so we have that large errors will increase the value of ISE more heavily than to IAE. ISE will favor responses with smaller overshoot for load changes, but ISE will give longer settling time. In ITAE, time appears as a factor, and therefore, ITAE will penalize heavily errors that occur late in time, but virtually ignore errors that occur early in time. Designing using ITAE will give us the shortest settling time, but it will produce the largest overshoot among the three criteria considered. Designing considering IAE will give us an intermediate result, in this case, the settling time will not be so large than using ISE or so small than using ITAE, and the same applies for the overshoot response. The selection of a particular criterion is depending on the type of desired response.

19.3. Optimization of FCs using ACO

In this section, we describe the application of a simple ACO (S-ACO) as a method of optimization for membership functions' parameters of a FLC in order to find the optimal intelligent controller for an Autonomous Wheeled Mobile Robot (Castillo *et al.*, 2012). Simulation results show that ACO outperforms a GA in the optimization of FLCs for an autonomous mobile robot (Castillo *et al.*, 2012).

19.3.1. *Introduction*

Nowadays, fuzzy logic is one of the most used methods of computational intelligence and with the best future; this is possible thanks to the efficiency and simplicity of Fuzzy Systems since they use linguistic terms similar to those that human beings use (Zadeh, 1975).

The complexity for developing fuzzy systems can be found at the time of deciding which are the best parameters of the membership functions, the number of rules or even the best granularity that could give us the best solution for the problem that we want to solve (Castillo and Melin, 2008).

A solution for the above mentioned problem is the application of evolutionary algorithms for the optimization of fuzzy systems (Castillo *et al.*, 2008a; Cervantes and Castillo, 2010; Cordon *et al.*, 2004; Martinez *et al.*, 2009; Wagner and Hagras, 2007a; Wu and Tan, 2006). Evolutionary algorithms can be a useful tool since its capabilities of solving nonlinear problems, well-constrained or even NP-hard problems. However, recently there have also been proposals of new optimization techniques based on biological or natural phenomena that have achieved good results in real world problems, for example, ACO, the bat algorithm, firefly algorithm, chemical optimization, and others (Astudillo *et al.*, 2010).

This section describes the application of one recent bio-inspired algorithms, such as the ACO (Juang and Hsu, 2009b) as a method of optimization of the parameters of the membership functions of the FLC in order to find the best intelligent controller for an Autonomous Wheeled Mobile Robot (Castillo *et al.*, 2012; Martinez-Marroquin *et al.*, 2009).

19.3.2. *S-ACO Algorithm*

ACO is a probabilistic technique that can be used for solving problems that can be reduced to finding good path along graphs. This method is inspired on the behavior presented by ants in finding paths from the nest or colony to the food source (Juang and Hsu, 2009b).

The S-ACO is an algorithmic implementation that adapts the behavior of real ants to solutions of minimum cost path problems on graphs (Poornaselvan *et al.*, 2008). A number of artificial ants build solutions for a certain optimization problem and exchange information about the quality of these solutions making allusion to the communication systems of the real ants.

Let us define the graph $G = (V, E)$, where V is the set of nodes and E is the matrix of the links between nodes. G has $n_G = |V|$ nodes. Let us define L^K as the number of hops in the path built by the ant k from the origin node to the destiny node. Therefore, it is necessary to find:

$$Q = \{q_a, \ldots, q_f \,|q_1 \in C\}, \tag{22}$$

where Q is the set of nodes representing a continuous path with no obstacles; $q_a, \ldots, q_f$ are former nodes of the path and C is the set of possible configurations of the free space. If $x^k(t)$ denotes a Q solution in time t, $f(x^k(t))$ expresses the quality of the solution. The general steps of S-ACO are as follows:

- Each link (i, j) is associated with a pheromone concentration denoted as τ_{ij}.
- A number $k = 1, 2, \ldots, n_k$ are placed in the nest.
- On each iteration all ants build a path to the food source (destiny node). For selecting the next node a probabilistic equation is used:
- Remove cycles and compute each route weight $f(x^k(t))$. A cycle could be generated when there are no feasible candidates nodes, that is, for any i and any k, $N_i^k = \emptyset$; then the predecessor of that node is included as a former node of the path.
- Pheromone evaporation is calculated with equation:

$$\tau_{ij}(t) \leftarrow (1 - \rho)\tau_{ij}(t), \tag{23}$$

  where $\rho \in [0, 1]$ is the evaporation rate value of the pheromone trail. The evaporation is added to the algorithm in order to force the exploration of the ants, and avoid premature convergence to sub-optimal solutions. For $\rho = 1$ the search becomes completely random.
- The update of the pheromone concentration is realized using equation:

$$\tau_{ij}(t + 1) = \tau_{ij}(t) + \sum^{n_k} \Delta\tau_{ij}^k(t), \tag{24}$$

  where $\Delta\tau_{ij}^k$ is the amount of pheromone that an ant k deposits in a link ij in a time t.
- Finally, the algorithm can be ended in three different ways:
  - When a maximum number of epochs has been reached.
  - When it has been found an acceptable solution, with $f(x_k(t)) < \varepsilon$.
  - When all ants follow the same path.

19.3.3. *Problem Statement*

The model of the robot considered in this paper is a unicycle mobile robot, that consists of two driving wheels mounted of the same axis and a front free wheel (Castillo *et al.*, 2012; Castro *et al.*, 2007b; Martinez *et al.*, 2009; Martinez-Marroquin *et al.*, 2009).

A unicycle mobile robot is an autonomous, wheeled vehicle capable of performing missions in fixed or uncertain environments. The robot body is symmetrical around the perpendicular axis and the center of mass is at the geometrical center of the body. It has two driving wheels that are fixed to the axis that passes through C and one passive wheel prevents the robot from tipping over as it moves on a plane.

In what follows, it is assumed that motion of the passive wheel can be ignored in the dynamics of the mobile robot presented by the following set of equations:

$$M(q)\dot{\vartheta} + C(q, \dot{q})\dot{\vartheta} + D\vartheta = \tau + F_{ext}(t), \tag{25}$$

where $q = (x, y, \theta)^T$ is the vector of the configuration coordinates; $\vartheta = (v, w)^T$ is the vector of linear and angular velocities; $\tau = (\tau_1, \tau_2)$ is the vector of torques applied to the wheels of the robot where τ_1 and τ_2 denote the torques of the right and left wheel respectively (Figure 19.6); $F_{ext} \in \mathbb{R}^2$ uniformly bounded disturbance vector; $M(q) \in \mathbb{R}^{2\times 2}$ is the positive-definite inertia matrix; $C(q, \dot{q})\vartheta$ is the vector of centripetal and Coriolis forces; and $D \in \mathbb{R}^{2\times 2}$ is a diagonal positive-definite damping matrix.

Furthermore, the Equation (25) has the following non-holonomic constraint:

$$\dot{y}\cos\theta - \dot{x}\sin\theta = 0, \tag{26}$$

which corresponds to a no-slip wheel condition preventing the robot from moving sideways (Chaoui and Gueaieb, 2008).

The control objective is to design a FLC of τ that ensures:

$$\lim_{t\to\infty} \|q_d(t) - q(t)\| = 0, \tag{27}$$

for any continuously, differentiable, bounded desired trajectory $q_d \in \mathbb{R}^3$ while attenuating external disturbances.

19.3.4. *Fuzzy Logic Control Design*

In order to satisfy the control objective it is necessary to design a FLC for the real velocities of the mobile robot. To do that, a Takagi–Sugeno FLC was designed, using linguistic variables in the input and mathematical functions in the output. The error of the linear and angular velocities (v_d, w_d respectively), were taken as inputs variables, while the right (τ_1) and left (τ_2) torques as outputs. The membership functions used on the input are trapezoidal for the negative (N) and positive (P), and a triangular was used for the zero (C) linguistic terms. The interval used for this FC is $[-50, 50]$ (Castro *et al.*, 2007b).

The rule set of the FLC contains nine rules, which governs the input–output relationship of the FLC and this adopts the Takagi–Sugeno style inference engine, and it is used with a single point in the outputs, this mind that the outputs are constant values, obtained using weighted average defuzzification procedure. In Table 19.1, we present the rule set whose format is established as follows:

$$\text{Rule}\,i\text{: if } e_v \text{ is } G_1 \text{ and } e_w \text{ is } G_2 \text{ then } F \text{ is } G_3 \text{ and } N \text{ is } G_4$$

where $G_1, \ldots, G_4$ are the fuzzy set associated to each variable $I = 1, 2, \ldots, 9$.

Table 19.1: Fuzzy rules set.

e_v/e_w	N	Z	P
N	N/N	N/Z	N/P
Z	Z/N	Z/Z	Z/P
P	P/N	P/Z	P/P

Table 19.2: Parameters of the membership functions.

MF Type	Point	Minimal value	Maximal value
Trapezoidal	a	−50	−50
	b	−50	−50
	c	−15	−5.1
	d	−1.5	−0.5
Triangular	a	−5	−1.8
	b	0	0
	c	1.8	5
Trapezoidal	a	0.5	1.5
	b	5.1	15
	c	50	50
	d	50	50
Constant (N)	a	−50	−50
Constant (C)	a	0	0
Constant (P)	a	50	50

To find the best FLC, we used a S-ACO to find the parameters of the membership functions. Table 19.2 shows the parameters of the membership functions, the minimal and maximum values in the search range for the S-ACO algorithm to find the best FLC.

It is important to remark that values shown in Table 19.2 are applied to both inputs and both outputs of the FLC.

19.3.5. *ACO Architecture*

The S-ACO algorithm was applied for the optimization of the membership functions for the FLC. For developing the architecture of the algorithm it was necessary to follow the next steps:

1. Marking the limits of the problem in order to eliminate unnecessary complexity.
2. Representing the architecture of the FLC as a graph that artificial ants could traverse.

Table 19.3: Parameters of membership functions included in S-ACO search.

MF type	Point	Minimal value	Maximal value
Trapezoidal	c	−15	−5.1
	d	−1.5	−0.5
Triangular	a	−5	−1.8
	c	1.8	5
Trapezoidal	a	0.5	1.5
	b	5.1	15

Table 19.4: Number of possible values of the parameters of membership functions.

MF Type	Point	Combinations
Trapezoidal	c	100
	d	15
Triangular	a	33
	c	33
Trapezoidal	a	15
	b	100

3. Achieving an adequate handling of the pheromone but permitting the algorithm to evolve by itself.

19.3.5.1. *Limiting the problem and graph representation*

One of problems found on the development of the S-ACO algorithm was to make a good representation of FLC. First we reduced the number of elements that the method needed to find by deleting the elements whose minimal value and maximal values are the same (see Table 19.2) and therefore if they were included they will not change any way. Table 19.3 shows the parameters of the membership functions included in the search.

The next step was to represent those parameters shown in Table 19.3; to that, was necessary to discretize the parameters in a range of possible values in order to represent every possible value as a node in the graph of search. The level of discretization between minimal and maximal value was of 0.1 (by example: $-1.5, -1.4, -1.3, \ldots, -0.5$).

Table 19.4 shows the number of possible values that each parameter can take.

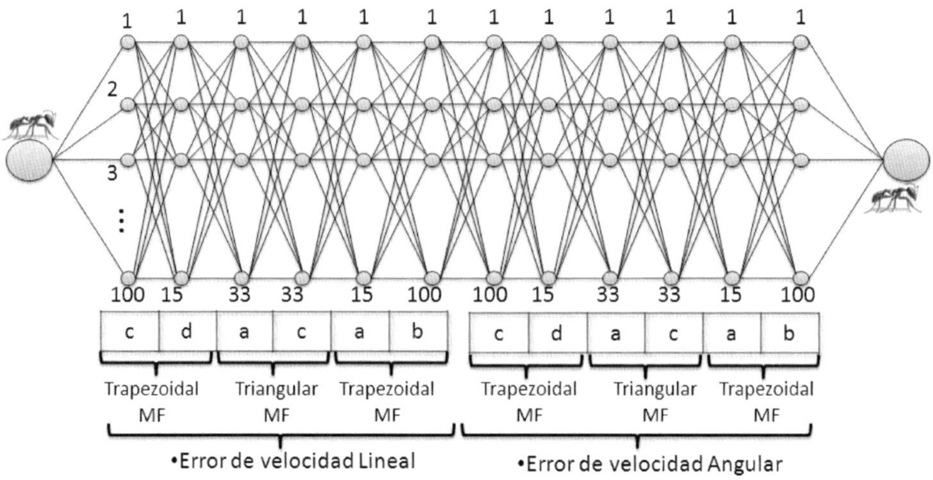

Figure 19.6: S-ACO search graph.

Figure 19.6 shows the search graph for the proposed S-ACO algorithm, the graph can be viewed as a tree where the root is the nest and the last node is the food source.

19.3.6. *Simulation Results*

Table 19.5 shows the results of the FLC, obtained varying the values of maximum iterations and number of artificial ants, where the highlighted row shows the best result obtained with the method. Figure 19.10 shows the evolving of the method.

A trajectory tracking controller has been designed based on the dynamics and kinematics of the autonomous mobile robot through the application of ACO for the optimization of membership functions for the FLC with good results obtained after simulations.

19.4. Optimization of FCs using PSO

This section describes the application of the optimization algorithm for particle swarm known by its acronym as PSO (Engelbrecht, 2005), used to adjust the parameters of membership functions of a FLC to find the optimal intelligent control for a wheeled autonomous mobile robot (Martinez *et al.*, 2010). Results of several simulations show that the PSO is able to optimize the type-1 and type-2 FLC for this specific application (Castillo *et al.*, 2012).

This section describes the application of particle swarm algorithm (PSO) as a method of optimizing the parameters of membership functions of the proposed FLC in order to find the best intelligent controller for an autonomous mobile robot.

Table 19.5: S-ACO results of simulations for FLC optimization.

Iterations	Ants	α	ρ	Average error	Time
20	10	0.2	Random	1.5589	00:01:30
20	10	0.2	Random	1.451	00:01:34
25	10	0.2	Random	1.5566	00:01:46
25	10	0.2	Random	1.4767	00:01:51
25	10	0.2	Random	1.4739	00:02:05
25	10	0.2	Random	1.6137	00:02:08
25	10	0.2	Random	1.6642	00:01:54
25	100	0.2	Random	1.3484	00:20:30
25	100	0.2	Random	1.3413	00:18:44
25	100	0.2	Random	1.3360	00:18:31
25	100	0.2	Random	1.2954	00:18:32
25	100	0.2	Random	1.4877	00:18:41
25	100	0.2	Random	1.2391	00:18:31
10	15	0.2	Random	1.6916	00:01:14
10	15	0.2	Random	1.4256	00:01:09
40	65	0.2	Random	1.2783	00:19:17
40	65	0.2	Random	1.4011	00:19:45
40	65	0.2	Random	1.2216	00:19:33
40	65	0.2	Random	1.2487	00:19:49
50	70	0.2	Random	1.3782	00:26:09
50	70	0.2	Random	1.0875	00:27:35
50	70	0.2	Random	1.4218	00:33:45
50	70	0.2	Random	1.475	01:08:48
25	80	0.2	Random	1.4718	00:14:55
25	80	0.2	Random	1.4212	00:15:00
25	80	0.2	Random	1.3221	00:14:52
25	80	0.2	Random	1.1391	00:15:41
50	80	0.2	Random	1.2148	00:28:43
62	**50**	**0.2**	**Random**	**1.0322**	**00:24:49**
50	80	0.2	Random	1.1887	00:29:55
50	80	0.2	Random	1.2158	00:29:56
60	90	0.2	Random	1.3493	00:41:56
60	90	0.2	Random	1.3060	00:39:48
60	90	0.2	Random	1.3161	00:40:00

19.4.1. *PSO Algorithm*

Optimizer by clouds or swarm of particles (PSO) is a relatively new technique that is slowly taking rise and recognition as an effective and efficient algorithm (Engelbrecht, 2005). While PSO algorithm shares similarities with other evolutionary computation techniques while also differs in certain respects and needs no evolution operators such as crossover and mutation (Cordon *et al.*, 2004).

PSO emulates the swarm behavior of insects, a herd of grazing animals, a cloud of birds, a host of fish in these swarms or clouds that made the search for food in a collaborative manner. Each member of a swarm adapts its search patterns, learning from his own experience and experiences of other members, i.e., taking into account their cognitive beliefs and social beliefs.

These phenomena are discussed in the algorithm and the mathematical models are built on the method for updating the positions of each particle.

In the PSO algorithm, a member in the swarm, called a particle, represents a possible solution is a point in the search space. The global optimum is considered as the location of food, the problem would be implemented as the optimal solution found. Each particle has a fitness value and a speed to adjust the flying direction according to the best.

The general formula [Equation (28)] for determining the motion of particles which are presented below, is shown in two parts the cognitive and social part of which are crucial to identify the type of algorithm that is being implemented in our case we used the Full GBEST i.e., both C_1 and C_2 must have values greater than 0 but less than 4, respectively.

$$V_{id} = V_{id}(t+1) + C_1 r_{id}(t)[Y_{id}(t) - X_{id}(t)] + C_2 r_2(t)[Y_{id}(t) - X_{id}(t)]. \quad (28)$$

There is another formula [Equation (33)] that is critical for the update of each particle, this assesses the current position of the particle and the previous position to choose which is the most appropriate to find the result more quickly this position is recalculated at each new iterations that is the algorithm.

$$X_i(t+1) = X_i(t) + V_i(t+1). \quad (29)$$

19.4.2. *Design of the FC*

As determined by one of the most used and effective techniques to solve control problems is to use fuzzy systems to meet the control objective, so it is necessary to design a FC for the actual speed of the mobile robot. In this research work, a type inference systems using Takagi–Sugeno type fuzzy system in order both 1 and 2, the use of linguistic variables in the input and output functions is applied. The error of linear and angular velocities (respectively) was taken as input variables, while the left and right pairs are taken as outputs. The membership functions used in the entry are trapezoidal for negative (N) and positive (P), and a triangle was used to zero (C) linguistic terms. Figure 19.7 shows the input and output variables used, these are used for both types of fuzzy logic (1 and 2).

The FLC has nine rules, which are adapted to the style of Takagi–Sugeno controller, so the output has a single point, so the results are constants values

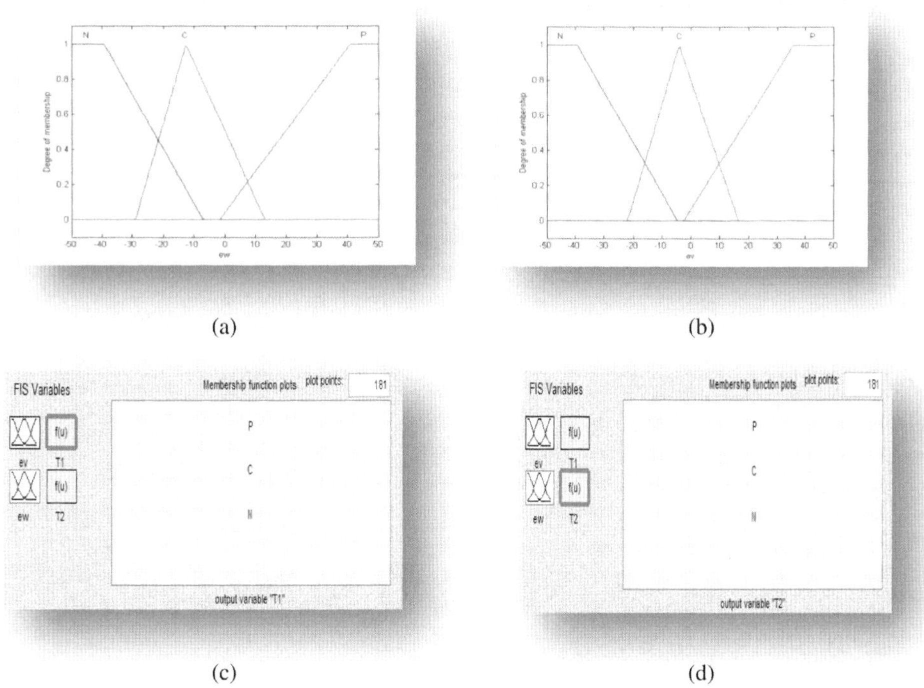

Figure 19.7: Variable input/output: (a) error of the linear velocity (ev). (b) Angular velocity error (ew). (c) Exit fee (τ1). (d) Exit left (τ2).

(P, C, N), which are obtained through a procedure using a weighted average defuzzification by:

ϖ R1: If Vangular is C and VLinear is C, then τ 1 is C and τ 2 is C
ϖ R2: If Vangular is C and VLinear is P, then τ 1 is C and τ 2 is P
ϖ R3: If Vangular is C and VLinear is N, then τ 1 is C and τ 2 is N
ϖ R4: If Vangular is P and VLinear is C, then τ 1 is P and τ 2 is C
ϖ R5: If Vangular is and P VLinear is P, then τ 1 is P and τ 2 is P
ϖ R6: If VLinear is P and Vangular is N, then τ 1 is P and τ 2 is N
ϖ R7: If VLinear is N and Vangular is C, then τ 1 is N and τ 2 is C
ϖ R8: If VLinear is N and Vangular is P, then τ 1 is N and τ 2 is P
ϖ R9: If Vangular VLinear is N and is N, then τ 1 is N and τ 2 is N.

The linguistic terms of input variables are shown in the first row and column of Table 19.6, the rest of the content corresponds to the linguistic terms of output variables.

Table 19.6: FLC rules.

Ev/ew	N	C	P
N	N/N	N/C	N/P
C	C/N	C/C	C/P
P	P/N	P/C	P/P

Table 19.7: Results for PSO using the constriction coefficient for type-1.

Experiment No.	Iterations	Swarm	Coefficient constriction	Average error	Runtime
1	50	50	1.0	0.0606	00:20:05
2	100	200	1.0	0.2670	02:44:53
3	100	100	1.0	0.0301	01:49:55
4	100	150	1.0	0.0315	01:54:31
5	100	50	1.0	0.0266	03:16:34
6	**100**	**57**	**1.0**	**0.0211**	**00:41:38**
7	100	300	1.0	0.0276	04:04:54
8	100	80	1.0	0.0527	01:03:45
9	150	80	1.0	0.0260	01:35:17
10	300	150	1.0	0.0307	04:30:16
11	500	200	1.0	0.0529	39:56:23
12	200	90	1.0	0.0345	01:54:59
13	150	100	1.0	0.0496	01:36:37
14	100	53	1.0	0.0230	00:39:29

19.4.3. *Results of the Simulations*

This section presents the results of proposed controller to stabilize the autonomous mobile robot. The evaluation is done through computer simulation done in MATLAB® and Simulink® (Wagner and Hagras, 2007b).

Table 19.7 shows the results of the FLC, obtained by varying the values of maximum iterations and the number of particles, where the highlighted row shows the best result obtained with the method.

As you can see, the above results are acceptable for type-1 FLC obtaining a final result of 0.0211 using 57 particles and 100 iterations in a time of 47 minutes and 38 seconds for this experiment, but as previously mentioned were also simulations with type-2, taking into account the same parameters and conditions of Takagi–Sugeno controller, the results of these simulations are presented below in Table 19.8.

The above results are acceptable for type-2 fuzzy logic control because we obtain a final result of 0.0500 using 380 particles and 300 iterations in a time of seven hours 55 minutes and 08 seconds for this experiment, which cannot be considered high due to the complexity of the problem.

Table 19.8: Results of PSO using the constriction coefficient for type-2.

Experiment no.	Iterations	Swarm	Coefficient constriction	Average error	Runtime
1	100	150	1.0	0.0659	02:20:31
2	100	200	1.0	0.0675	02:56:21
3	100	250	1.0	0.0666	03:05:31
4	200	150	1.0	0.0663	03:55:06
5	200	200	1.0	0.0651	04:07:14
6	200	250	1.0	0.0642	04:20:10
7	200	300	1.0	0.0536	04:54:43
8	200	350	1.0	0.0554	05:12:09
9	250	350	1.0	0.0600	05:38:20
10	300	300	1.0	0.0531	06:12:57
11	300	350	1.0	0.0503	07:30:28
12	**300**	**380**	**1.0**	**0.0500**	**07:55:08**
13	350	400	1.0	0.0501	08:10:15
14	350	450	1.0	0.0503	08:59:01
15	400	300	1.0	0.0502	12:31:11

Table 19.9: Comparison of results of the PSO algorithm for type-1 and type-2.

	Iterations	Swarm	Average error	Runtime
PSO with type-1 fuzzy logic	100	57	0.0211	00:41:38
PSO with type-2 fuzzy logic	300	380	0.0050	07:55:08

The type-2 FCs were implemented with the type-2 fuzzy logic toolbox that was developed previously by our research group (Castro *et al.*, 2007a, 2007b).

With the results of the experiments shown in Table 19.9, we can determine that for this particular problem the optimized type-2 FLC clearly outperform its type-1 counterpart.

The trajectory tracking controller is designed based on the dynamics and kinematics of mobile autonomous robot through the application of PSO for the optimization of membership functions of FC, both type-1 and type-2 with the good results obtained after simulations.

19.5. Conclusions

This chapter has presented a general framework for designing interval type-2 FCs based on bio-inspired optimization techniques. A trajectory tracking controller has been designed based on the dynamics and kinematics of the autonomous mobile robot through the application of ACO for the optimization of membership functions for the FLC with good results obtained after simulations. Also, a trajectory tracking controller is designed based on the dynamics and kinematics of mobile autonomous robot through the application of PSO for the optimization of membership functions of the FC for both type-1 and type-2 with the good results obtained after simulations. As future work we plan to test other bio-inspired optimization techniques, like the bat or firefly algorithms for this particular robotic application and in other different kind of applications.

References

Astudillo, L., Melin, P. and Castillo, O. (2010). A new optimization method based on a paradigm inspired by nature. *Stud. Comput. Intell.*, 312, pp. 277–283.

Biglarbegian, M., Melek, W. W. and Mendel, J. M. (2011). Design of novel interval type-2 fuzzy controllers for modular and reconfigurable robots: Theory and experiments. *IEEE Trans. Ind. Electron.*, 58, pp. 1371–1384.

Bingül, Z. and Karahan, O. (2011). A fuzzy logic controller tuned with PSO for 2 DOF robot trajectory control. *Expert Syst. Appl.*, 38, pp. 1017–1031.

Castillo, O., Martinez, A. I. and Martinez, A. C. (2007). Evolutionary computing for topology optimization of type-2 fuzzy systems. *Adv. Soft Comput.*, 41, pp. 63–75.

Castillo, O. and Melin, P. (2008). *Type-2 Fuzzy Logic: Theory and Applications*. Heidelberg, Germany: Springer-Verlag.

Castillo, O., Huesca, G. and Valdez, F. (2008a). Evolutionary computing for topology optimization of type-2 fuzzy controllers. *Stud. Fuzziness Soft Comput.*, 208, pp. 163–178.

Castillo, O., Aguilar, L. T., Cazarez-Castro, N. R. and Cardenas, S. (2008b). Systematic design of a stable type-2 fuzzy logic controller. *Appl. Soft Comput. J.*, 8, pp. 1274–1279.

Castillo, O., Martinez-Marroquin, R., Melin, P., Valdez, F. and Soria, J. (2012). Comparative study of bio-inspired algorithms applied to the optimization of type-1 and type-2 fuzzy controllers for an autonomous mobile robot. *Inf. Sci.*, 192, pp. 19–38.

Castro, J. R., Castillo, O. and Melin, P. (2007a). An interval type-2 fuzzy logic toolbox for control applications. *Proc. FUZZ-IEEE 2007*. London, UK, pp. 1–6.

Castro, J. R., Castillo, O. and Martinez, L. G. (2007b). Interval type-2 fuzzy logic toolbox. *Eng. Lett.*, 15(1), p. 14.

Castro, J. R., Castillo, O., Melin, P., Martinez, L. G., Escobar, S. and Camacho, I. (2007c). Building fuzzy inference systems with the interval type-2 fuzzy logic toolbox. *Adv. Soft Comput.*, 41, pp. 53–62.

Castro, J. R., Castillo, O., Melin, P. and Rodriguez-Diaz, A. (2009). A hybrid learning algorithm for a class of interval type-2 fuzzy neural networks. *Inf. Sci.*, 179, pp. 2175–2193.

Cazarez-Castro, N. R., Aguilar, L. T. and Castillo, O. (2008). Hybrid genetic-fuzzy optimization of a type-2 fuzzy logic controller. *Proc. Eighth Int. Conf. Hybrid Intell. Syst., HIS 2008*. Barcelona, Spain, pp. 216–221.

Cervantes, L. and Castillo, O. (2010). Design of a fuzzy system for the longitudinal control of an F-14 airplane. *Stud. Comput. Intell.*, 318, pp. 213–224.

Chaoui, H. and Gueaieb, W. (2008). Type-2 fuzzy logic control of a flexible-joint manipulator. *J. Intell. Robot. Syst.: Theory Appl.*, 51, pp. 159–186.

Cordon, O., Gomide, F., Herrera, F., Hoffmann, F. and Magdalena, L. (2004). Ten years of genetic fuzzy systems: Current framework and new trends. *Fuzzy Sets Syst.*, 141, pp. 5–31.

Dereli, T., Baykasoglu, A., Altun, K., Durmusoglu, A. and Turksen, I. B. (2011). Industrial applications of type-2 fuzzy sets and systems: A concise review. *Comput. Ind.*, 62, pp. 125–137.

Engelbrecht, A. P. (2005). *Fundamentals of Computational Swarm Intelligence*. England: Wiley.

Galluzzo, M. and Cosenza, B. (2010). Adaptive type-2 fuzzy logic control of a bioreactor. *Chem. Eng. Sci.*, 65, pp. 4208–4221.

Hagras, H. (2004). Hierarchical type-2 fuzzy logic control architecture for autonomous mobile robots. *IEEE Trans. Fuzzy Syst.*, 12, pp. 524–539.

Hsiao, M., Li, T. H. S., Lee, J. Z., Chao, C. H. and Tsai, S. H. (2008). Design of interval type-2 fuzzy sliding-mode controller. *Inf. Sci.*, 178, pp. 1686–1716.

Huang, H. C., Chu, C. M. and Pan, J. S. (2009). The optimized copyright protection system with genetic watermarking. *Soft Comput.*, 13, pp. 333–343.

Juang, C.-F. and Hsu, C.-H. (2009a). Reinforcement ant optimized fuzzy controller for mobile-robot wall-following control. *IEEE Trans. Ind. Electron.*, 56, pp. 3931–3940.

Juang, C.-F. and Hsu, C.-H. (2009b). Reinforcement interval type-2 fuzzy controller design by online rule generation and Q-value-aided ant colony optimization. *IEEE Trans. Syst., Man, Cybern., Part B Cybern.*, 39, pp. 1528–1542.

Juang, C.-F., Hsu, C.-H. and Chuang, C.-F. (2009). Reinforcement self-organizing interval type-2 fuzzy system with ant colony optimization. *Proc. IEEE Int. Conf. Syst., Man, Cybern.*, San Antonio, pp. 771–776.

Kim, W.-D., Jang, H.-J. and Oh, S.-K. (2010). The design of optimized fuzzy cascade controller: focused on type-2 fuzzy controller and HFC-based genetic algorithms. *Trans. Korean Inst. Electr. Eng.*, 59, pp. 972–980.

Koca, G. O., Akpolat, Z. H. and Özdemir, M. (2011). Type-2 fuzzy sliding mode control of a four-bar mechanism. *Int. J. Model. Simul.*, 31, pp. 60–68.

Martinez, R., Castillo, O. and Aguilar, L. T. (2009). Optimization of interval type-2 fuzzy logic controllers for a perturbed autonomous wheeled mobile robot using genetic algorithms. *Inf. Sci.*, 179, pp. 2158–2174.

Martinez, R., Rodriguez, A., Castillo, O. and Aguilar, L. T. (2010). Type-2 fuzzy logic controllers optimization using genetic algorithms and particle swarm optimization. *Proc. IEEE Int. Conf. Granular Comput., GrC 2010*, San Jose, California, USA, pp. 724–727.

Martinez-Marroquin, R., Castillo, O. and Soria, J. (2009). Parameter tuning of membership functions of a type-1 and type-2 fuzzy logic controller for an autonomous wheeled mobile robot using ant colony optimization. *Proc. IEEE Int. Conf. Syst., Man, Cybern.* San Antonio, pp. 4770–4775.

Melin, P. and Castillo, O. (2004). A new method for adaptive control of nonlinear plants using type-2 fuzzy logic and neural networks. *Int. J. Gen. Syst.*, 33, pp. 289–304.

Melin, P. and Castillo, O. (2007). An intelligent hybrid approach for industrial quality control combining neural networks, fuzzy logic and fractal theory. *Inf. Sci.*, 177, pp. 1543–1557.

Mendel, J. M. (2000). Uncertainty, fuzzy logic, and signal processing. *Signal Process. J.*, 80, pp. 913–933.

Mohammadi, S. M. A., Gharaveisi, A. A. and Mashinchi, M. (2010). An evolutionary tuning technique for type-2 fuzzy logic controller in a nonlinear system under uncertainty. *Proc. 18th Iran. Conf. Electr. Eng., ICEE 2010*, Tehran, Iran, pp. 610–616.

Poornaselvan, K. J., Gireesh Kumar, T. and Vijayan, V. P. (2008). Agent based ground flight control using type-2 fuzzy logic and hybrid ant colony optimization to a dynamic environment. *Proc. First Int. Conf. Emerg. Trends Eng. Technol., ICETET 2008*, Nagpur, Maharashtra, India, pp. 343–348.

Starczewski, J. T. (2009). Efficient triangular type-2 fuzzy logic systems. *Int. J. Approx. Reason.*, 50, pp. 799–811.

Sudha, K. R. and Vijaya Santhi, R. (2011). Robust decentralized load frequency control of interconnected power system with generation rate constraint using type-2 fuzzy approach. *Int. J. Electr. Power Energy Syst.*, 33, pp. 699–707.

Wagner, C. and Hagras, H. (2007a). A genetic algorithm-based architecture for evolving type-2 fuzzy logic controllers for real world autonomous mobile robots. *Proc. IEEE Conf. Fuzzy Syst.*, London, UK.

Wagner, C. and Hagras, H. (2007b). Evolving type-2 fuzzy logic controllers for autonomous mobile robots. *Adv. Soft Comput.*, 41, pp. 16–25.

Wang, C.-H., Cheng, C.-S. and Lee, T.-T. (2004). Dynamical optimal training for interval type-2 fuzzy neural network (T2FNN). *IEEE Trans. Syst., Man, Cybern., Part B Cybern.*, 34(3), pp. 1462–1477.

Wu, D. and Tan, W.-W. (2004). A type-2 fuzzy logic controller for the liquid level process. *Proc. IEEE Conf. Fuzzy Systems*. Budapest, Hungary, pp. 953–958.

Wu, D. and Tan, W.-W. (2006). Genetic learning and performance evaluation of interval type-2 fuzzy logic controllers. *Eng. Appl. Artif. Intell.*, 19, pp. 829–841.

Yager, R. R. (1980). Fuzzy subsets of type II in decisions. *J. Cybern.*, 10, pp. 137–159.

Zadeh, L. A. (1975). The concept of a linguistic variable and its application to approximate reasoning. *Inf. Sci.*, 8, pp. 43–80.

Chapter 20

Nature-Inspired Optimization of Fuzzy Controllers and Fuzzy Models

Radu-Emil Precup and Radu-Codruţ David

This chapter deals with the nature-inspired optimal tuning of fuzzy controllers (FCs) and of fuzzy models. In the first part, the charged system search (CSS) algorithm, a novel nature-inspired optimization algorithm, is employed for the optimal tuning of Takagi–Sugeno proportional-integral (PI) FCs for nonlinear servo systems, minimizing the objective functions defined as the sum of time multiplied by squared error and the sum of output sensitivity function of the state sensitivity model with respect to process parametric variations; optimal fuzzy control systems with reduced parametric sensitivity are derived. The second part presents the simulated annealing (SA) algorithm, a representative nature-inspired optimization algorithm, which carries out the optimal tuning of Takagi–Sugeno fuzzy model parameters for anti-lock braking systems (ABS), derived on the basis of the modal equivalence principle by placing a set of linearized process models at several operating points in the rule consequents; the objective functions expressed as the root mean square of modeling errors are minimized. Both parts focus on performance improvements of fuzzy control systems and fuzzy models.

20.1. Introduction

The majority of fuzzy control applications uses fuzzy controllers (FCs) for direct feedback control or placed at the low level in hierarchical control system structures (Precup and Hellendoorn, 2011). However, fuzzy control can be used at the supervisory level, for example, in adaptive control system structures. Nowadays fuzzy control is no longer only used to directly express the knowledge on the process or, in other words, to carry out model-free fuzzy control. A fuzzy controller can be tuned from a fuzzy model obtained in terms of system identification techniques, and thus it can be viewed in the framework of model-based fuzzy control or in the framework of data-driven control (Hjalmarsson *et al.*, 1998; Radac *et al.*, 2011; Owens *et al.*, 2013; Hou and Wang, 2013; Formentin *et al.*, 2013a, 2013b).

The following categories of FCs are most often used:

- Mamdani FCs, referred to also as linguistic FCs, with either fuzzy consequents that represent type-I fuzzy systems (Sugeno, 1999) or singleton consequents which belong to type-II fuzzy systems. These FCs are usually used as direct closed-loop controllers.
- Takagi–Sugeno FCs, known also as type-III fuzzy systems especially when affine consequents are employed, and typically used as supervisory controllers.

A systematic way to meet the performance specifications of fuzzy control systems is the optimization in terms of optimization problems with variables represented by the parameters of FCs or fuzzy models. Nature-inspired algorithms can solve the optimization problems, and they ensure the optimal tuning of FCs and fuzzy models in order to meet the performance specifications expressed by adequately defined objective functions and constraints. The motivation for nature-inspired optimization algorithms in combination with fuzzy control and fuzzy modeling concerns their ability to cope with non-convex or non-differentiable objective functions due to controllers' structures and nonlinearities, and to process complexity, which can lead to multi-objective optimization problems.

The latest nature-inspired optimization algorithms applied to the parameter tuning of FCs include genetic algorithms (Onieva *et al.*, 2012; Das *et al.*, 2013; Pérez *et al.*, 2013), simulated annealing (SA) (Haber *et al.*, 2009; Jain *et al.*, 2011; Precup *et al.*, 2012a), particle swarm optimization (PSO) (Bingül and Karahan, 2011; Oh *et al.*, 2011; Precup *et al.*, 2013a), Gravitational Search Algorithms (GSAs) (Precup *et al.*, 2013a, 2013b; David *et al.*, 2013), Ant Colony Optimization (Kumaresan, 2011; Chang *et al.*, 2012; Lu and Liu, 2013), cross-entropy (Haber *et al.*, 2010), chemical optimization (Melin *et al.*, 2013), charged system search (CSS) algorithms (Precup *et al.*, 2014), harmony search (Wang *et al.*, 2013), etc., in several fuzzy control system structures. The appropriate tools specific to the analysis of fuzzy systems must be accounted for in all applications (Preitl and Precup, 1997; Batyrshin *et al.*, 2002; Škrjanc *et al.*, 2002; Baranyi *et al.*, 2003, 2013; Škrjanc and Blažič, 2005; Johanyák, 2010; Topalov *et al.*, 2011; Tikk *et al.*, 2011; Angelov and Yager, 2012, 2013; Obradović *et al.*, 2013; Feriyonika and Dewantoro, 2013).

Some popular applications on the nature-inspired optimal tuning of fuzzy models concern the optimization of the parameters in the rule antecedents and consequents of Takagi–Sugeno fuzzy models by SA (Almaraashi *et al.*, 2010), the SA-based tuning of the parameters of input membership functions (m.f.s) in fuzzy control systems for general nonlinear systems (Liu and Yang, 2000), chaotic time series (Yanara and Akyürek, 2011), ABS (David *et al.*, 2014), servo systems (Precup *et al.*, 2013c), and magnetic levitation systems (David *et al.*, 2012; Dragos *et al.*, 2013). A hybrid PSO-based algorithm is suggested for Takagi–Sugeno fuzzy model identification (Wang *et al.*, 2011). The input m.f.s of Takagi–Sugeno fuzzy models are also tuned by a combination of Island Model Parallel Genetic Algorithm and space search memetic algorithm (Ho and Garibaldi, 2013). The migration algorithms (Vaščák, 2012; Vaščák and Pal'a, 2012), the PSO-based optimization of linguistic fuzzy models (Chen *et al.*, 2012; Jiang *et al.*, 2012), the Variable string length Artificial Bee Colony algorithm (Su *et al.*, 2012), the genetic algorithms (Pedrycz and Song, 2012) and the chaotic GSA (Li *et al.*, 2013) give good results in fuzzy model optimization.

This chapter presents two original solutions for the optimal tuning of fuzzy control systems and fuzzy models. This methodology of parameter tuning is important as it represents a proficient approach to the design of optimal control systems with a reduced parametric sensitivity. The included digital and experimental results validate new important contributions, as the nature-inspired optimization algorithms provide simplified process models in the design and tuning of fuzzy control systems with reduced sensitivity in regards to the process parameters involved in the sensitivity models, and the relatively small number of tuning parameters used in the objective functions, which facilitate the design of low-cost optimal fuzzy control systems.

The next section gives aspects concerning the design and tuning of Mamdani and Takagi–Sugeno FCs with dynamics with focus on PI-FCs and the Takagi–Sugeno fuzzy models. Section 20.3 discusses the CSS algorithm-based optimal tuning of FCs for nonlinear servo systems. Section 20.4 presents the SA algorithm-based optimal tuning of the parameters of input m.f.s of Takagi–Sugeno fuzzy models for anti-lock braking systems (ABSs). The concluding remarks are highlighted in Section 20.5.

20.2. FCs and Fuzzy Models

20.2.1. *Structures and Design Methodology of FCs*

The FCs without dynamics offer nonlinear input–output static maps, which can be modified by the proper tuning of all parameters in the FC structure (the shapes and scaling factors of m.f.s, the rule-base, and the defuzzification method). The introduction of dynamics of integral and/or derivative type in the FC structure can be carried out on either the inputs or the outputs of the FC resulting in two versions of PI-FCs (Preitl and Precup, 1997):

- The PI-FC with integration of controller output (PI-FC-OI),
- The PI-FC with integration of controller input (PI-FC-II)

and both versions of PI-FCs, with the structures given in Figure 20.1, are type-2 fuzzy systems according to Sugeno and Kóczy (Sugeno, 1999; Kóczy, 1996).

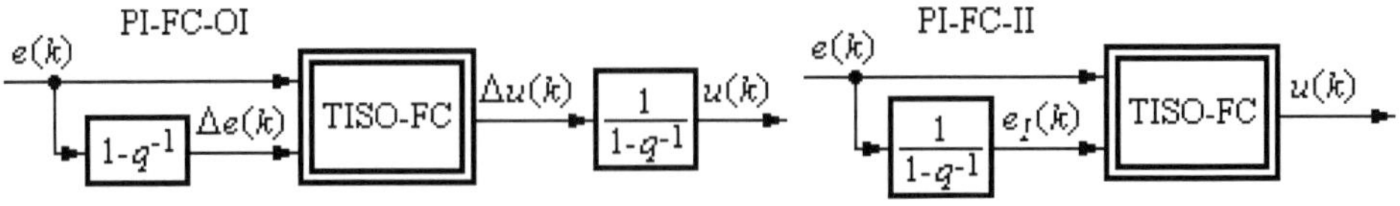

Figure 20.1: Structures of PI-FCs.

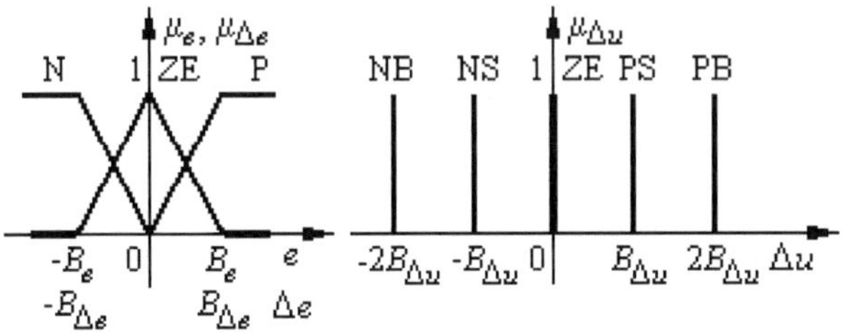

Figure 20.2: Input and output membership functions of Mamdani PI-FCs with integration on controller output.

As shown in Figure 20.1, the two PI-FCs are built around the two inputs-single output fuzzy controller (TISO-FC) without dynamics. The presentation is focused on PI-FCs as they can be easily extended to PI-derivative FCs (PID-FCs) and transformed in particular forms of proportional-derivative FCs (PD-FCs). In addition, the structures presented in Figure 20.1 can be processed such that to be extended to two-degree-of-freedom (2-DOF) FCs.

The dynamics of the PI-FC-OI is obtained by the numerical differentiation of the control error $e(k)$, which results in the increment of control error $\Delta e(k) = e(k) - e(k-1)$, and by the numerical integration of the increment of control signal $\Delta u(k) = u(k) - u(k-1)$ which leads to the control signal $u(k)$. The variable k in Figure 20.1 is the current discrete time index, and q indicates the forward time shift operator. The dynamics of the PI-FC-II is obtained by the numerical integration of $e(k)$, which gives the integral of control error $e_I(k) = e_I(k-1) + e(k)$. It is assumed here that the eventually nonlinear scaling factors of the input and output variables of TISO-FC are inserted in the controlled process.

The fuzzification in the TISO-FC block that belongs to PI-FC-OI is performed by means of the input m.f.s illustrated in Figure 20.2 for the Mamdani PI-FCs. The fuzzification in the TISO-FC that belongs to the PI-FC-II is performed by the same m.f.s as those of the PI-FC-OI, but the input variable $e_I(k)$ is used instead of $\Delta e(k)$, and the output variable $u(k)$ is used instead of $\Delta u(k)$. The relatively simple shapes of m.f.s presented in Figure 20.2 and their reduced numbers ensure the cost-effective implementation of the FCs. Other distributions of the membership functions can modify in a desired way the FC nonlinearities. The Takagi–Sugeno PI-FCs employ only the input m.f.s taken from Figure 20.2.

Both versions of Mamdani PI-FCs, namely the PI-FC-OI and the PI-FC-II, employ Mamdani's MAX-MIN compositional rule of inference assisted by the rule-base exemplified for the PI-FC-OI

$$\begin{aligned}
&\text{Rule 1: IF } e(k) \text{ IS N AND } \Delta e(k) \text{ IS P THEN } \Delta u(k) \text{ IS ZE},\\
&\text{Rule 2: IF } e(k) \text{ IS ZE AND } \Delta e(k) \text{ IS P THEN } \Delta u(k) \text{ IS PS},\\
&\text{Rule 3: IF } e(k) \text{ IS P AND } \Delta e(k) \text{ IS P THEN } \Delta u(k) \text{ IS PB},\\
&\text{Rule 4: IF } e(k) \text{ IS N AND } \Delta e(k) \text{ IS ZE THEN } \Delta u(k) \text{ IS NS},\\
&\text{Rule 5: IF } e(k) \text{ IS ZE AND } \Delta e(k) \text{ IS ZE THEN } \Delta u(k) \text{ IS ZE},\\
&\text{Rule 6: IF } e(k) \text{ IS P AND } \Delta e(k) \text{ IS ZE THEN } \Delta u(k) \text{ IS PS},\\
&\text{Rule 7: IF } e(k) \text{ IS N AND } \Delta e(k) \text{ IS N THEN } \Delta u(k) \text{ IS NB},\\
&\text{Rule 8: IF } e(k) \text{ IS ZE AND } \Delta e(k) \text{ IS N THEN } \Delta u(k) \text{ IS NS},\\
&\text{Rule 9: IF } e(k) \text{ IS P AND } \Delta e(k) \text{ IS N THEN } \Delta u(k) \text{ IS ZE}
\end{aligned} \tag{1}$$

and the center of gravity method for singletons is used for defuzzification. The inference engines of both versions of Takagi–Sugeno PI-FCs are based on the SUM and PROD operators assisted by the rule-base exemplified for the PI-FC-OI.

$$\begin{aligned}
&\text{Rule 1: IF } e(k) \text{ IS N AND } \Delta e(k) \text{ IS P THEN } \Delta u(k) = K_P^1[\Delta e(k) + \mu^1 e(k)],\\
&\text{Rule 2: IF } e(k) \text{ IS ZE AND } \Delta e(k) \text{ IS P THEN } \Delta u(k) = K_P^2[\Delta e(k) + \mu^2 e(k)],\\
&\text{Rule 3: IF } e(k) \text{ IS P AND } \Delta e(k) \text{ IS P THEN } \Delta u(k) = K_P^3[\Delta e(k) + \mu^3 e(k)],\\
&\text{Rule 4: IF } e(k) \text{ IS N AND } \Delta e(k) \text{ IS ZE THEN } \Delta u(k) = K_P^4[\Delta e(k) + \mu^4 e(k)],\\
&\text{Rule 5: IF } e(k) \text{ IS ZE AND } \Delta e(k) \text{ IS ZE THEN } \Delta u(k) = K_P^5[\Delta e(k) + \mu^5 e(k)],\\
&\text{Rule 6: IF } e(k) \text{ IS P AND } \Delta e(k) \text{ IS ZE THEN } \Delta u(k) = K_P^6[\Delta e(k) + \mu^6 e(k)],\\
&\text{Rule 7: IF } e(k) \text{ IS N AND } \Delta e(k) \text{ IS N THEN } \Delta u(k) = K_P^7[\Delta e(k) + \mu^7 e(k)],\\
&\text{Rule 8: IF } e(k) \text{ IS ZE AND } \Delta e(k) \text{ IS N THEN } \Delta u(k) = K_P^8[\Delta e(k) + \mu^8 e(k)],\\
&\text{Rule 9: IF } e(k) \text{ IS P AND } \Delta e(k) \text{ IS N THEN } \Delta u(k) = K_P^9[\Delta e(k) + \mu^9 e(k)]
\end{aligned} \tag{2}$$

and the weighted average method is employed for defuzzification.

The PI-FC structures and the rule-bases given in Equations (1) and (2) make these controllers behave like bumpless interpolators between separately designed PI controllers. The maximum number of such controllers is nine, and the following conditions ensure the interpolation between only two separately designed PI controllers in case of Takagi–Sugeno PI-FCs:

$$
\begin{aligned}
&K_P^1 = K_P^2 = K_P^4 = K_P^5 = K_P^6 = K_P^8 = K_P^9 = K_P, \\
&K_P^3 = K_P^7 = \eta\, K_P, \\
&\mu^1 = \mu^2 = \mu^3 = \mu^4 = \mu^5 = \mu^6 = \mu^7 = \mu^8 = \mu^9 = \mu.
\end{aligned} \tag{3}
$$

The unified design methodology consists of the following design steps for Mamdani and Takagi–Sugeno PI-FCs in their PI-FC-OI versions:

Step 1. The continuous-time design of the linear PI controller with the transfer function $C(s)$

$$C(s) = \frac{k_c(1 + sT_i)}{s} = k_C\left[1 + \frac{1}{(sT_i)}\right], \quad k_C = k_c T_i, \tag{4}$$

is carried out, leading to the controller gain k_c (or k_C) and to the integral time constant T_i.

Step 2. The sampling period T_s is set according to the requirements of quasi-continuous digital control. Tustin's method is then applied to discretize the continuous-time linear PI controller, and the recurrent equation of the incremental digital PI controller is

$$\Delta u(k) = K_P[\Delta e(k) + \mu e(k)], \tag{5}$$

where the expressions of the parameters K_P and μ in Equations (3) and (5) are

$$K_P = k_c\left(\frac{T_i - T_s}{2}\right), \quad \mu = \frac{2T_s}{(2T_i - T_s)}. \tag{6}$$

The parameter η, with typical values $0 < \eta < 1$, is introduced in Equation (3) to alleviate the overshoot of the fuzzy control system when both inputs have the same sign. Therefore, these PI-FCs can also be applied to the control of non-minimum phase systems with right half-plane zeros when such rule-bases produce the alleviation of the downshoot.

Step 3. The modal equivalence principle (Galichet and Foulloy, 1995) is applied to map the linear controller parameters onto the PI-FC ones. Therefore, the tuning condition for the Takagi–Sugeno PI-FC-OI is

$$B_{\Delta e} = \mu\, B_e \tag{7}$$

and the tuning conditions for the Mamdani PI-FC-OI is

$$B_{\Delta e} = \mu\, B_e, \quad B_{\Delta e} = K_P\, \mu\, B_e. \tag{8}$$

The tuning conditions for the Mamdani PI-FC-II (Preitl and Precup, 1997) are

$$B_{\Delta e} = \left(\frac{1}{\mu}\right) B_e, \quad B_{\Delta e} = K_P\, B_e \tag{9}$$

and the tuning condition for the Takagi–Sugeno PI-FC-II results as follows in a similar manner:

$$B_{\Delta e} = \left(\frac{1}{\mu}\right) B_e. \tag{10}$$

The value of the parameter B_e in Equations (7)–(10) must be set by the designer. This value can be set according to designer's experience, and the stability analysis of the fuzzy control system can be conducted with this regard. However, the systematic tuning of the parameter B_e will be ensured as follows as solutions to the optimization problems as this parameter will be one of the elements of the vector variable of the objective functions.

The PD-FCs are designed using the methodology for PI-FCs. The design is carried out in terms of the PD-FC structure obtained from the PI-FC-OI structure given in Figure 20.1 by dropping out the output integrator.

The PID-FC structure is presented in Figure 20.3, where the TISO-FC^{PD} block and the TISO-FC^{PI} block are identical to the TISO-FC block given in Figure 20.1, u_k^{PD} is the control signal of the PD controller, and Δu_k^{PI} is the increment of control signal calculated by the PI controller. The fuzzification is carried out by means of the input m.f.s exemplified in Figure 20.3 for the Takagi–Sugeno PID-FC, where $g \in \{PI, PD\}$. Figure 20.3 indicates that the PID-FC structure consists of a parallel connection of PD-FC and PI-FC.

The design of the PID-FC is carried out using the same methodology. However, the equivalence to the linear PID controller has to be ensured in terms of the manipulation (Precup *et al.*, 2008) of the input–output characterization of the linear PID controller which is transformed into the nonlinear parallel structure given in Figure 20.3. The transfer function of the linear PID controller is $C(s)$;

$$C(s) = k_C\left[1 + \frac{1}{(sT_i)} + sT_d\right] = \frac{k_c(1+sT_{c1})(1+sT_{c2})}{s},$$
$$k_c = \frac{k_C}{T_i}, \quad T_{c1,2} = \frac{T_i\left(1 \pm \sqrt{1-\frac{4T_d}{T_i}}\right)}{2}, \tag{11}$$

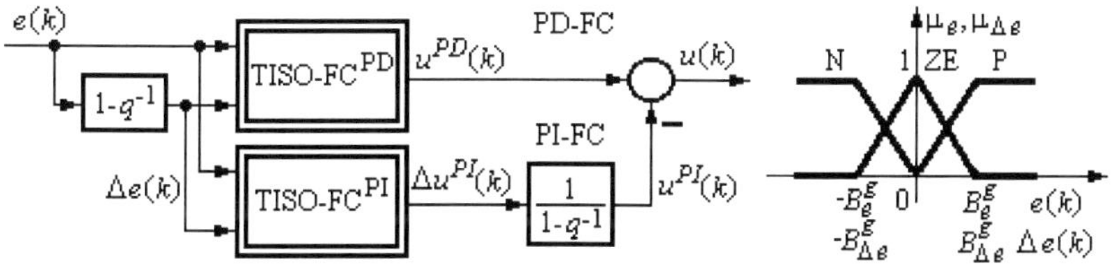

Figure 20.3: Structure and input membership functions of Takagi–Sugeno PID-FC.

where T_d is the derivative time constant and T_{c1} and T_{c2} are the controller time constants.

Setting the sampling period T_s, Tustin's method leads to the discrete-time PID controller with the transfer function $C(q^{-1})$

$$C(q^{-1}) = \frac{\rho_0 + \rho_1 q^{-1} + \rho_2 q^{-2}}{1 - q^{-1}},$$
$$\rho_0 = k_c\left(\frac{1 + T_d}{T_s}\right), \quad \rho_1 = -k_c\left(\frac{1 + 2T_d}{T_s} - \frac{T_s}{T_i}\right), \quad \rho_2 = k_c\frac{T_d}{T_s}. \tag{12}$$

The expression (12) is organized as the following parallel connection of a discrete-time PD controller and a discrete-time PI controller with the superscripts PD and PI, respectively, associated to Figure 20.3:

$$C(q^{-1}) = K_P^{PD}(1 - q^{-1} + \mu^{PD}) - \frac{K_P^{PI}(1 - q^{-1} + \mu^{PI})}{(1 - q^{-1})},$$
$$K_P^{PD} = \rho_2, \quad \mu^{PD} = -\frac{\rho_1}{\rho_2}, \quad K_P^{PI} = \rho_2 - \rho_1 - \rho_0, \tag{13}$$
$$\mu^{PI} = \frac{2\rho_2}{(\rho_2 - \rho_1 - \rho_0)}.$$

Therefore, it is justified to carry out the separate design of the PI-FC and of the PD-FC shown in Figure 20.3 using the same methodology.

The PI-FC can be involved in 2-DOF FCs by the fuzzification of some of the controller blocks in 2-DOF linear controllers in order to improve the control system performance. The 2-DOF PI-FCs exhibit performance improvements over the one-DOF FCs (Precup *et al.*, 2009; Preitl *et al.*, 2010a, 2010b), and similar controller structures can be formulated as state-feedback control systems.

The extensions of FCs to type-2 FCs prove additional performance improvement. The tuning of type-2 FCs is mainly based on optimization algorithms (Linda and Manic, 2011a, 2011b; Kayacan *et al.*, 2011; Castillo and Melin, 2012a, 2012b).

20.2.2. *Takagi–Sugeno Fuzzy Models*

The general rule-base of the continuous-time Takagi–Sugeno fuzzy model (of the process) consists of the rules (Takagi and Sugeno, 1985);

$$\begin{aligned}&\text{Rule } i\text{: IF } z_1(t) \text{ IS } T^i_{1,k_1} \text{ AND } z_2(t) \text{ IS } T^i_{2,k_2} \text{ AND} \ldots \text{AND } z_s(t) \text{ IS } T^i_{s,q_s}\\ &\qquad \text{THEN } y_m(t) = \varphi_i(\mathbf{x}(t)), \quad i = 1, \ldots, n_g,\end{aligned} \tag{14}$$

where t is the continuous time variable, n_R is the number of rules, $y_m(t)$ is the continuous-time Takagi–Sugeno fuzzy model output, the notations T^i_{1,k_1}, T^i_{2,k_2}, and

T^i_{s,k_s} are used for the linguistic terms of the input variables $z_1(t)$, $z_2(t)$, and $z_s(t)$, respectively, referred to also as scheduling variables, with the number and ranges of indices $k_1 = 1 \ldots f_1, k_2 = 1 \ldots f_2$, and $k_s = 1 \ldots f_s$, $\mathbf{x}(t) = [x_1(t)\, x_2(t) \ldots x_n(t)]^T$ is the input vector to the fuzzy model, namely an additional input vector which appears in the rule consequent and it can represent the state vector of the process, the superscript T indicates the matrix transposition, and the functions φ_i can be general arbitrary smooth functions, with particular forms as linear functions, affine functions or crisp models with dynamics including linear or nonlinear state-space models placed in the rule consequents. The discrete-time Takagi–Sugeno fuzzy model is similar to Equation (14), but the discrete time variable k is used instead of the continuous time variable t.

20.3. CSS Algorithm-Optimal Tuning of FCs for Nonlinear Servo Systems

The process is characterized by the following nonlinear continuous-time time-invariant single input–single output (SISO) state-space model which defines a general class of nonlinear servo systems:

$$m(t) = \begin{cases} -1, & \text{if } u(t) \le -u_b, \\ \dfrac{[u(t) + u_c]}{(u_b - u_c)}, & \text{if } -u_b < u(t) < -u_c, \\ 0, & \text{if } -u_c \le |u(t)| \le u_a, \\ \dfrac{[u(t) - u_a]}{(u_b - u_a)}, & \text{if } u_a < u(t) < u_b, \\ 1, & \text{if } u(t) \ge u_b, \end{cases}$$

$$\dot{\mathbf{x}}_P(t) = \begin{bmatrix} 0 & 1 \\ 0 & -\frac{1}{T_\Sigma} \end{bmatrix} \mathbf{x}_P(t) + \begin{bmatrix} 0 \\ \frac{k_P}{T_\Sigma} \end{bmatrix} m(t) + \begin{bmatrix} 1 \\ 0 \end{bmatrix} d(t), \tag{15}$$

$$y(t) = [1 \quad 0]\ \mathbf{x}_P(t),$$

where k_P is the process gain, T_Σ is the small time constant, the control signal u is a pulse width modulated duty cycle, and m is the output of the saturation and dead zone static nonlinearity specific to the actuator. The nonlinearity is modeled by the first equation in Equation (15), with the parameters u_a, u_b, and u_c fulfilling the conditions $0 < u_a < u_b, 0 < u_c < u_b$. The state-space model (15) includes the actuator and measuring element dynamics. The state vector $\mathbf{x}_P(t)$ is expressed as follows in (angular) position applications:

$$\mathbf{x}_P(t) = [x_{P,1}(t) \quad x_{P,2}(t)]^T = [\alpha(t) \quad \omega(t)]^T, \tag{16}$$

where $\alpha(t)$ is the angular position, $\omega(t)$ is the angular speed, and the controlled output is $y(t) = x_{P,1}(t) = \alpha(t)$.

The nonlinearity in (15) is neglected in the following simplified model of the process expressed as the transfer function $P(s)$:

$$P(s) = \frac{k_{EP}}{[s(1 + T_{\Sigma}s)]}. \tag{17}$$

This transfer function is considered for u as input and y as output. The equivalent process gain is k_{EP}:

$$k_{EP} = \begin{cases} \dfrac{k_P}{(u_b - u_c)}, & \text{if } -u_b < u(t) < -u_c, \\ \dfrac{k_P}{(u_b - u_a)}, & \text{if } u_a < u(t) < u_b. \end{cases} \tag{18}$$

Therefore, $P(s)$ can be used in the controller design and tuning in two cases out of the five cases concerning the nonlinearity in Equation (15).

The process models, Equations (15) and (17) can be employed in the control designs of servo systems in various applications accepting that the parameters k_P and T_{Σ} depend on the operating point. That is the reason why the design of control systems with a reduced parametric sensitivity with respect to k_P and T_{Σ} is justified. In this context, the minimization of the discrete-time objective function $J(\boldsymbol{\rho})$ ensures the sensitivity reduction with respect to the modifications of k_P or T_{Σ}:

$$J(\boldsymbol{\rho}) = \sum_{k=0}^{\infty} \{k|e(k)| + \gamma^2[\sigma(k)]^2\}, \tag{19}$$

where γ is the weighting parameter, $\boldsymbol{\rho}$ is the vector variable of the objective function and also the parameter vector of the FC, σ is the output sensitivity function defined in the state sensitivity model with respect to k_P or T_{Σ}, and the variables in the sum depend on $\boldsymbol{\rho}$.

The objective function $J(\boldsymbol{\rho})$ is referred to as the sum of absolute control errors multiplied by time and squared output sensitivity function. The output sensitivity function σ is introduced in Equation (19) because one of the goals of the FC controller design is to reduce the parametric variations effects of the controlled plant on the controlled output. Other objective functions can be defined to include the state sensitivity functions if the goal is to reduce the effects of the parametric variations of the controlled plant on the state variables.

The discrete-time objective function given in Equation (19) can be defined either directly or from continuous-time objective functions with the sampling period included in the consideration of the weighting parameter. The dynamic regimes with regard to step-type modifications of the reference and disturbance inputs should be considered.

Making use of Equation (19), the optimization problem which ensures the optimal design of the controllers resulting in fuzzy control system performance enhancement and a reduced parametric sensitivity, is defined as follows:

$$\boldsymbol{\rho}^* = \arg\min_{\boldsymbol{\rho} \in D_\rho} J(\boldsymbol{\rho}), \tag{20}$$

where $\boldsymbol{\rho}^*$ is the optimal value of the vector $\boldsymbol{\rho}$ and D_ρ is the feasible domain of $\boldsymbol{\rho}$. The stability of the fuzzy control system should first be taken into consideration when setting the domain D_ρ.

The PI controllers can cope with the process modeled in Equation (17) if they are inserted in 2-DOF linear control system structures (Precup *et al.*, 2009; Åström and Hägglund, 1995; Preitl and Precup, 1996, 1999). The transfer function of the PI controller is given in Equation (4). The PI controllers can be tuned by the extended symmetrical optimum (ESO) method (Preitl and Precup, 1996, 1999) to guarantee a desired tradeoff to the performance specifications (i.e., maximum values of control system performance indices) imposed to the control system using a single design parameter referred to as β, with the recommended values within $1 < \beta < 20$. The diagrams presented in Figure 20.4 can be used in setting the value of the design parameter β and, therefore, the tradeoff to the linear control system performance indices expressed as percent overshoot $\sigma_1[\%]$, normalized settling time $\hat{t}_s = t_s/T_\Sigma$, normalized rise time $\hat{t}_r = t_r/T_\Sigma$ and phase margin φ_m.

The PI tuning conditions specific to the ESO method ((Preitl and Precup, 1996, 1999) are

$$k_c = \frac{1}{\left(\beta\sqrt{\beta}k_{EP}T_\Sigma^2\right)}, \quad T_i = \beta T_\Sigma, \quad k_C = \frac{1}{\left(\sqrt{\beta}k_{EP}T_\Sigma\right)}. \tag{21}$$

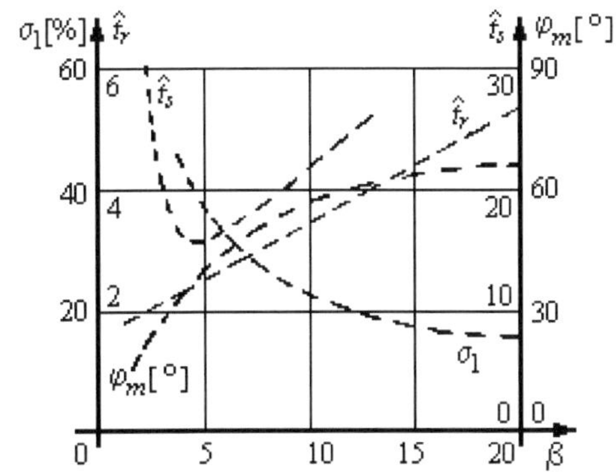

Figure 20.4: Linear control system performance indices versus the parameter β specific to the ESO method for the step-type modification of the reference input.

Figure 20.4 is important because both possible values of k_{EP} according to Equation (18) should be used in setting certain values of β, which ensure the fulfillment of the performance specifications imposed to the control system. A simple version of set-point filter which ensures the performance improvement of the linear control system by the cancellation of a zero in the closed-loop transfer function with respect to the reference input (Preitl and Precup, 1996, 1999) is

$$F(s) = \frac{1}{(1+\beta T_{\Sigma} s)}. \tag{22}$$

The PI-FCs are designed starting with the linear PI controllers such that to ensure the further improvement of the control system performance indices for the nonlinear process modeled in Equation (15). The presentation and the results will be focused on the Takagi–Sugeno PI-FC-OI, but the presentation for the Mamdani PI-FC-OI and for both versions of PI-FC-II is straightforward.

In the context of the previous section, the controller parameter vector, to be determined by the CSS algorithm that solves the optimization problem, Equation (20), is

$$\boldsymbol{\rho} = [\rho_1 \quad \rho_2 \quad \rho_3]^T = [\beta \quad B_e \quad \eta]^T \in \mathbf{R}^3. \tag{23}$$

The application of the CSS algorithm described as follows will give the optimal parameter vector $\boldsymbol{\rho}^*$

$$\boldsymbol{\rho}^* = \left[\rho_1^* \quad \rho_2^* \quad \rho_3^*\right]^T = \left[\beta^* \quad B_e^* \quad \eta^*\right]^T. \tag{24}$$

Equation (7) is next applied to obtain the optimal value of the last parameter of the PI-FC-OI, $B_{\Delta e}^*$. Equations (8), (9), and (10) are applied to obtain the optimal values of the parameters of other versions of PI-FCs.

20.3.1. *Application of CSS Algorithm*

The specific features of CSS algorithms concern the random determination of the initial positions of charged particles (CPs) and the initial velocities of CPs set to zero. Each CP has an associated magnitude of charge $q_{c,i}$ and as a result it creates an electrical field around its space. The magnitude of the charge is defined considering the quality of its solution as

$$q_{c,i} = \frac{(g_i - g_{best})}{(g_{best} - g_{worst})}, \quad i = 1, \ldots, N, \tag{25}$$

where g_{best} and g_{worst} are the so far best and the worst fitness of all CPs, g_i represents the objective function value or the fitness of ith CP, and N is the total number of CPs. The separation distance r_{ij} between two CPs is defined (Precup *et al.*, 2011) as

$$r_{ij} = \frac{(\|\mathbf{X}_i - \mathbf{X}_j\|)}{\left(\left\|\frac{(\mathbf{X}_i+\mathbf{X}_j)}{2} - \mathbf{X}_{best}\right\| + \varepsilon\right)}, \quad \mathbf{X}_o \in \mathbf{R}^{q_s}, \quad o \in \{i, j, best\}, \tag{26}$$

where q_s is the dimension of the search space, $\mathbf{X}_i$ and $\mathbf{X}_j$ are the position vectors of ith and jth CP, respectively, $\mathbf{X}_{best}$ is the position of the best current CP, ε, $\varepsilon > 0$, is a constant introduced to avoid singularities, and the Euclidean norm is considered in Equation (26).

The electric forces between any two CPs are used in increasing CSS algorithm's exploitation ability. The good CPs can attract the other CPs and the bad ones repel the others, proportional to their rank c_{ij} (Precup *et al.*, 2011; Kaveh and Talatahari, 2010a, 2010b, 2010c)

$$c_{ij} = \begin{cases} -1, & \text{if } g_i < g_j, \\ 1, & \text{otherwise}, \end{cases} \tag{27}$$

where the parameter c_{ij} determines the type and the degree of influence of each CP on the other CPs, considering their fitness apart from their charges.

The value of the resultant electrical force $\mathbf{F}_j$ acting on jth CP (Precup *et al.*, 2011) is

$$\mathbf{F}_j = q_j \sum_{i, i \neq j} \left(\frac{q_i r_{ij} i_1}{a^3} + \frac{q_i i_2}{r_{ij}^2} \right) c_{ij}(\mathbf{X}_i - \mathbf{X}_j), \quad (i_1, i_2) = \begin{cases} (0, 1), & \text{if } r_{ij} \geq a, \\ (1, 0), & \text{otherwise}, \end{cases} \tag{28}$$

where $i, j = 1 \ldots N$. Equation (28) shows that each CP is considered as a charged sphere with radius a having a uniform volume charge density.

The new position (vector) $\mathbf{X}_j(k_{iter} + 1)$ and velocity (vector) $\mathbf{V}_j(k_{iter} + 1)$ of each CP is determined (Precup *et al.*, 2014; Kaveh and Talatahari, 2010a, 2010b, 2010c) in terms of

$$\begin{aligned} \mathbf{X}_j(k_{iter} + 1) &= r_{j1} k_a \left(\frac{\mathbf{F}_j}{m_j}\right) (\Delta k)^2 + r_{j2} k_v \mathbf{V}_j(k_{iter}) \Delta k + \mathbf{X}_j(k_{iter}), \\ \mathbf{V}_j(k_{iter} + 1) &= \frac{\left[\mathbf{X}_j(k_{iter} + 1) - \mathbf{X}_j(k_{iter})\right]}{\Delta k}, \end{aligned} \tag{29}$$

where k_{iter} is the current iteration index which is dropped out at certain variables for the sake of simplicity, k_a is the acceleration parameter, k_v is the velocity parameter which controls the influence of the previous velocity, r_{j1} and r_{j2} are two random numbers uniformly distributed in the range $0 < r_{j1}, r_{j2} < 1$, m_j is the mass of jth CP which is set here as equal to $q_{c,j}$, and Δk is the time step set to 1.

The effect of the pervious velocity and the resultant force acting on a CP can be decreased or increased based on the values of k_a and k_v, respectively. Since k_a is the parameter related to the attracting forces; selecting a large value of k_a may cause a fast convergence and choosing a small value can increase the computational time. k_v controls the exploration process. The following modifications of k_a and k_v with respect to the iteration index are applied (Precup *et al.*, 2014):

$$k_a = 3\left(\frac{1 - k_{iter}}{k_{\max}}\right), \quad k_v = 0.5\left(\frac{1 + k_{iter}}{k_{\max}}\right), \tag{30}$$

where $k_{\max}$ is the maximum number of iterations.

The CSS algorithm consists of the following steps (Preitl and Precup, 1999):

Step A. Initialize the q_s = three-dimensional search space, the number of CPs N and randomly generate the CPs' position vector $\mathbf{X}_i \in \mathbf{R}^3$.

Step B. Evaluate the CPs' fitness using Equation (19) by simulations and/or experiments conducted with the fuzzy control system accounting for the following relationship that maps the CSS algorithm onto the optimization problem, Equation (20):

$$g_i = J(\boldsymbol{\rho}), \quad \mathbf{X}_i = \boldsymbol{\rho}, \quad i = 1 \dots N. \tag{31}$$

Step C. Update g_{best} and g_{worst}, and update $q_{c,i}$ using Equation (25) for $i = 1 \dots N$.

Step D. Compute the total force in different directions using Equations (26), (27) and (28), and update the CPs' velocities and positions using Equation (29).

Step E. Validate the obtained vector solution $\mathbf{X}_i$ in terms of checking the following inequality-type constraint which guarantees that the fuzzy control system with the obtained parameter vector $\boldsymbol{\rho} = \mathbf{X}_i$ ensures the convergence of the objective function (Precup *et al.*, 2011, 2014)

$$|y(t_f) - r(t_f)| \leq 0.001|r(t_f) - r(0)|, \tag{32}$$

where t_f is the final time moment, theoretically ∞ according to (19), but practically finite such that to capture all control system transients.

Step F. Increment k_{iter} and go to Step B until the maximum number of iterations is reached, i.e., $k_{iter} = k_{\max}$, and the optimal parameter vector will be that last position vector out of the N position vectors which offers the minimum value of objective (fitness) function, $\rho^* = \mathbf{X}_i$.

20.3.2. *Example Concerning a Laboratory Servo System*

The CSS algorithm has been applied to exemplify the optimal tuning of a Takagi–Sugeno PI-FC-OI in the position control of a laboratory servo system in terms of solving the optimization problem, Equation (20). The experimental setup is illustrated in Figure 20.5. An optical encoder is used for the measurement of the angle and a tacho-generator for the measurement of the angular speed. The speed can also be estimated from the angle measurements. The PWM signals proportional with the control signal are produced by the actuator in the power interface. The main features of the experimental setup (Precup *et al.*, 2012b; Radac *et al.*, 2012) are: rated amplitude of 24 V, rated current of 3.1 A, rated torque of 15 N cm, rated speed of 3000 rpm, and weight of inertial load of 2.03 kg. The nominal values of the parameters of the process model given in Equations (15) and (17), obtained by a least squares algorithm, are $u_a = 0.15$, $u_b = 1$, $u_c = 0.15$, $k_{P0} = k_{EP0} = 140$, and $T_{\Sigma 0} = 0.92\,\text{s}$, and the subscript 0 points out the nominal value of a certain parameter.

The steps A to F of the CSS algorithm have been applied, and the main results are presented as follows. The weighting parameters for the objective function defined in Equation (19) have been set to the values $\gamma^2 \in \{0, 0.142, 1.42, 14.2\}$ for the PI-FC tuning such that to ensure a reduced sensitivity with respect to k_P, and $\gamma^2 = \{0, 0.15885, 1.5885, 15.885\}$ for the PI-FC tuning such that to ensure a reduced sensitivity with respect to T_Σ, in order to reflect a ratio of $\{0, 0.1, 1, 10\}$ of the initial values of the two terms in the sum given in Equation (19).

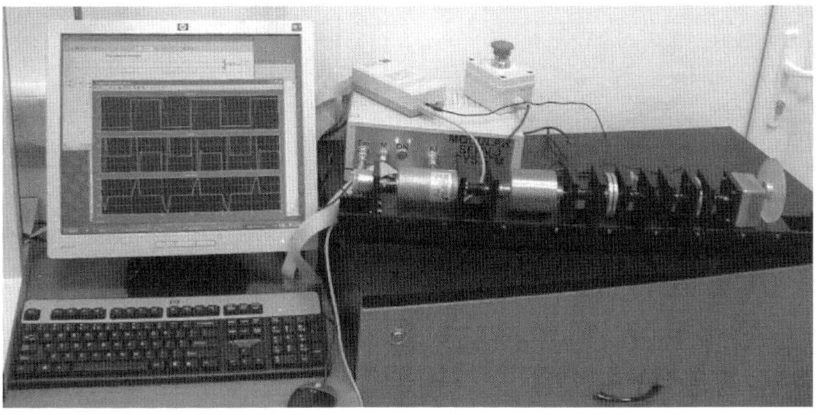

Figure 20.5: Servo system experimental setup in the Intelligent Control Systems Laboratory of the Politehnica University of Timisoara.

The variables of the objective function have been initialized taking into consideration the following boundaries which define the feasible domain of $\boldsymbol{\rho}$

$$D_\rho = \{\beta | 3 \leq \beta \leq 17\} \times \{B_e | 20 \leq B_e \leq 40\} \times \{\eta | 0.25 \leq \eta \leq 0.75\}. \quad (33)$$

The CSS algorithm implementation is assisted by running the required digital simulations of the fuzzy control system behavior with respect to $r = 40$ rad step-type modification of the reference input. This dynamic regime has been considered in relation with the optimization problem, Equation (20).

In order to ensure a good convergence of the CSS algorithm the following parameters have been chosen on the basis of numerous trial runs and previous experience: $N = 20$, k_a and k_v computed according to Equation (30). The maximum number of iterations used as stop criterion of the CSS algorithm has been set to $k_{\max} = 100$. In order to reduce the complexity of the algorithm the volume charged density for each CP has been considered unitary, namely $a = 1$. In addition, $\varepsilon = 10^{-4}$ has been set in Equation (26).

The sampling period has been set to $T_s = 0.01$ s, which is acceptable for quasi-continuous digital control. The state sensitivity models of the fuzzy control systems with respect to k_P and T_Σ must be derived (Precup *et al.*, 2013a; David *et al.*, 2013) because they are involved in the step B of the CSS algorithm.

The optimal controller parameters and the minimum objective function values with respect for the sensitivity reduction with respect to k_P and T_Σ are summarized in Table 20.1 and in Table 20.2, respectively. The data contained by these tables demonstrate the algorithm's convergence to the optimum as they were obtained

Table 20.1: Weighting parameter, controller parameters for the CSS algorithm-based tuning of PI-FC-OI with a reduced sensitivity with respect to k_P.

γ^2	$B^*_{\Delta e}$	B^*_e	η^*	β^*	k^*_c	T^*_i	$J(\rho^*)$
0	0.084519	40	0.75	5.14965	0.003421	4.73768	155252
0.142	0.084497	40	0.75	5.15098	0.003421	4.7389	354007
1.42	0.081739	40	0.75	5.32457	0.003365	4.8986	2149610
14.2	0.022529	20	0.25	9.65464	0.002499	8.88227	19379100

Table 20.2: Weighting parameter, controller parameters for the CSS algorithm-based tuning of PI-FC-OI with a reduced sensitivity with respect to T_Σ.

γ^2	$B^*_{\Delta e}$	B^*_e	η^*	β^*	k^*_c	T^*_i	$J(\rho^*)$
0	0.084519	40	0.75	5.14965	0.003421	4.73768	155252
0.15885	0.084735	40	0.75	5.13651	0.003426	4.72559	380819
1.5885	0.084982	40	0.75	5.12164	0.003431	4.7119	2419410
15.885	0.020722	20	0.25	10.4964	0.002396	9.65673	21711500

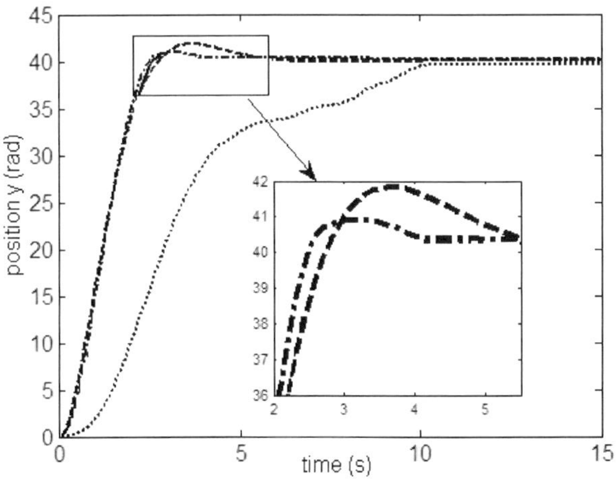

Figure 20.6: Real-time experimental results of control systems with initial PI controller (dotted), initial Takagi–Sugeno PI-FC-OI (dashed) and non-adaptive CSS algorithm-based tuned Takagi–Sugeno PI-FC-OI (dash-dotted).

after repeated algorithm reiterations. All iterations have involved the evaluation of the minimum objective function using the position of each agent. All results are given as average values taken for the best five runs of the algorithm.

Figure 20.6 illustrates the experimental results for three controller architectures, i.e., a linear control system with PI controller tuned by the ESO method for $\beta = 4$, a fuzzy control system with Takagi–Sugeno PI-FC-OI obtained from the PI controller by the modal equivalence principle, with the parameters $B_e = 40$, $\eta = 0.75$, and $B_{\Delta e} = 0.1$, and a fuzzy control system with Takagi–Sugeno PI-FC-OI tuned by the CSS algorithm. These experimental results illustrate the performance improvement offered by the CSS algorithm in the dynamic regime characterized by the $r = 40$ rad step-type modification of the reference input.

The comparisons of nature-inspired optimization algorithms can be carried out by means of several performance indices. Two such indices are the convergence speed defined as the number of evaluations of the objective functions until finding their minimum values (Precup *et al.*, 2013a), and the number of evaluations per iteration (David *et al.*, 2013). As these two indices point out how fast a solution is found, they can miss other relevant information on the overall solution's quality. This limitation can be mitigated by another second performance index, namely the accuracy rate, defined as the standard deviation reported to the average of the solutions (Precup *et al.*, 2014). Nevertheless, complexity analyses of the algorithms can be conducted. The results of the comparisons of the performance indices should be presented as average values for several runs of the algorithms in order to alleviate the impact of the random parameters in the algorithms.

20.4. Simulated Algorithm-Based Optimal Tuning of Input Membership Function Parameters of Takagi–Sugeno Fuzzy Models for ABS

The continuous-time state-space model of the ABS laboratory equipment is derived from the first-principle process model (David *et al.*, 2014)

$$\begin{aligned} J_1\dot{x}_1 &= F_n r_1 \mu(\lambda) - d_1 x_1 - M_{10} - M_1, \\ J_2\dot{x}_2 &= -F_n r_2 \mu(\lambda) - d_2 x_2 - M_{20}, \end{aligned} \tag{34}$$

where λ is the longitudinal slip (the wheel slip), J_1 and J_2 are the inertia moments of wheels, x_1 and x_2 are the angular velocities, d_1 and d_2 are the friction coefficients in wheels' axes, M_{10} and M_{20} are the static friction torques that oppose the normal rotation, M_1 is the brake torque, r_1 and r_2 are the radii of wheels, F_n is the normal force that the upper wheel pushes upon the lower wheel, $\mu(\lambda)$ is the friction coefficient, and $\dot{x}_1$ and $\dot{x}_2$ are the wheels' angular accelerations. The identification by experiment-based measurements leads to the following process parameter values (David *et al.*, 2014) that correspond to the experimental setup illustrated in Figure 20.7:

$$\begin{gathered} r_1 = r_2 = 0.99\,\text{m}, \quad F_n = 58.214\,\text{N}, \quad J_1 = 7.53 \cdot 10^{-3}\,\text{kg}\,\text{m}^2, \\ J_2 = 25.6 \cdot 10^{-3}\,\text{kg}\,\text{m}^2, \quad d_1 = 1.1874 \cdot 10^{-4}\,\text{kg}\,\text{m}^2/\text{s}, \\ d_2 = 2.1468 \cdot 10^{-4}\,\text{kg}\,\text{m}^2/\text{s}, \quad M_{10} = 0.0032\,\text{N}\,\text{m}, \quad M_{20} = 0.0925\,\text{N}\,\text{m}. \end{gathered} \tag{35}$$

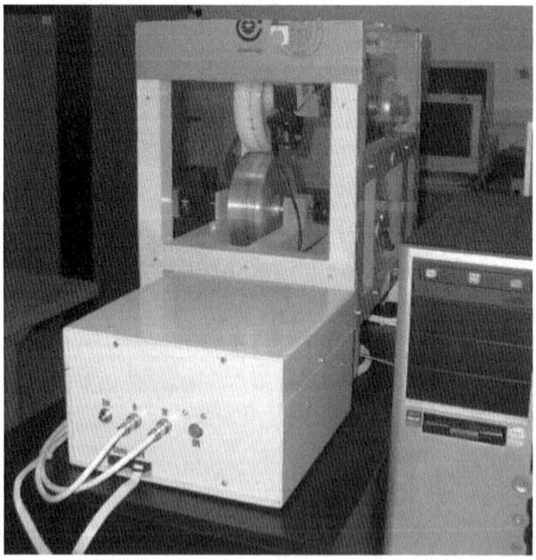

Figure 20.7: ABS experimental setup in the Intelligent Control Systems Laboratory of the Politehnica University of Timisoara.

The wheel slip and the nonlinear term $S(\lambda)$ are expressed as

$$\begin{aligned} \lambda &= \frac{(r_2 x_2 - r_1 x_1)}{(r_2 x_2)}, \quad x_2 \neq 0, \\ S(\lambda) &= \frac{\mu(\lambda)}{\{L[\sin\varphi - \mu(\lambda)\cos\varphi]\}}, \quad \tan\phi \neq \mu(\lambda), \end{aligned} \tag{36}$$

where $L = 0.37\,\text{m}$ is the arm's length which fixes the upper wheel and $\phi = 65.61°$ is the angle between the normal direction in wheels' contact point and the direction of L.

The state-space equations of the nonlinear process specific to ABS (David *et al.*, 2014) are

$$\begin{aligned} \dot{x}_1 &= S(\lambda)(c_{11}x_1 + c_{12}) + c_{13}x_1 + c_{14} + (c_{15}S(\lambda) + c_{16})s_1 M_1, \\ \dot{x}_2 &= S(\lambda)(c_{21}x_1 + c_{22}) + c_{23}x_2 + c_{24} + c_{25}S(\lambda)s_1 M_1, \\ \dot{M}_1 &= c_{31}(b(u) - M_1), \end{aligned} \tag{37}$$

where u is the control signal applied to the actuator, i.e., the DC motor which drives the upper wheel, and the actuator's nonlinear model is highlighted in the third equation. The expressions of the parameters in Equation (37) (David *et al.*, 2014; Radac *et al.*, 2009) are

$$\begin{aligned} &c_{11} = \frac{r_1 d_1}{J_1}, \quad c_{12} = \frac{(M_{10} + M_g) r_1}{J_1}, \quad c_{13} = -\frac{d_1}{J_1}, \quad c_{14} = -\frac{M_{10}}{J_1}, \\ &c_{15} = \frac{r_1}{J_1}, \quad c_{16} = -\frac{1}{J_1}, \quad c_{21} = -\frac{r_2 d_1}{J_2}, \quad c_{22} = -\frac{(M_{10} + M_g) r_2}{J_2}, \\ &c_{23} = -\frac{d_2}{J_2}, \quad c_{24} = -\frac{M_{20}}{J_2}, \quad c_{25} = -\frac{r_2}{J_2}. \end{aligned} \tag{38}$$

The variable λ is considered as the controlled output of the process specific to ABS, and the notation $y = \lambda$ will be used in this context. The state variable x_1 is substituted from Equation (37) in the model, Equation (38), and the continuous-time state-space equations of the process specific to ABS (David *et al.*, 2014) is transformed into

$$\dot{\mathbf{x}} = \begin{bmatrix} z_1(\lambda, x_2) & 0 & z_3(\lambda, x_2) \\ 0 & z_{40}(\lambda) & z_5(\lambda) \\ 0 & 0 & -c_{31} \end{bmatrix} \mathbf{x} + \begin{bmatrix} 0 \\ 0 \\ c_{31} \end{bmatrix} b(u) + \mathbf{d}(\lambda, x_2), \tag{39}$$

where the state vector is

$$\mathbf{x} = [\lambda \quad x_2 \quad M_1]^T, \tag{40}$$

$z_1(\lambda, x_2)$, $z_3(\lambda, x_2)$, $z_{40}(\lambda)$, and $z_5(\lambda)$ are nonlinear functions, and $\mathbf{d}(\lambda, x_2)$ is the disturbance input vector.

The approach to the SA-based optimal tuning of the parameters of input m.f.s of Takagi–Sugeno fuzzy models for ABS is expressed in terms of the following steps presented as follows and based on the modal equivalence principle (Galichet and Foulloy, 1995). This approach is different to the sector nonlinearity approach (Ohtake *et al.*, 2001), but the SA algorithm can be applied after the initial Takagi–Sugeno fuzzy models are obtained by the sector nonlinearity approach.

Step 1. Set the structure of the Takagi–Sugeno fuzzy model, that means the number of operating points which is equal to the number of rules n_R of the Takagi–Sugeno fuzzy model, the number of input linguistic terms of the variables λ, x_2 and M_1, the shapes of the m.f.s of the input linguistic terms, the operators in the inference engine, and the defuzzification method. The SUM and PROD operators in the inference engine, and the weighted average defuzzification method are applied for this process.

Step 2. Linearize the continuous-time state-space equations of the process, Equation (37) and the output equation which is the first equation in Equation (36) at n_R important operating points. This yields in n_R linearized continuous-time local process models. The local process models are placed in the rule consequents of the continuous-time Takagi–Sugeno fuzzy model, and they are related to the modal values of the input m.f.s which are exactly the coordinates of the operating points in terms of the modal equivalence principle (Galichet and Foulloy, 1995). The complete rule-base of the continuous-time Takagi–Sugeno fuzzy model is the following particular form of the continuous-time Takagi–Sugeno fuzzy model, Equation (14):

$$\begin{aligned}&\text{Rule } i: \text{IF } \lambda(t) \text{ IS } T^i_{\lambda,l} \text{ AND } x_2(t) \text{ IS } T^i_{x_2,p} \text{ AND } M_1(t) \text{ IS } T^i_{M_1,q}\\ &\text{THEN} \begin{cases} \dot{\mathbf{x}}(t) = \mathbf{A}_i\mathbf{x}(t) + \mathbf{B}_i u(t) \\ y_m(t) = \mathbf{C}_i\mathbf{x}(t) \end{cases}, \quad i = 1 \ldots n_R,\end{aligned} \tag{41}$$

where $T^i_{v,l}$, $T^i_{v,p}$, and $T^i_{v,q}$ are the linguistic terms $T_{\lambda,l}$, $T_{x_2,p}$, and $T_{M_1,q}$ of the input variables (scheduling variables) $\lambda(t)$, $x_2(t)$, and $M_1(t)$, respectively, with the recommended numbers of linguistic terms and of ranges of indices $l = 1 \ldots 5$, $p \in \{1, 2\}$ and $q = 1$, $v \in \{\lambda, x_2, M_1\}$, and the matrices $\mathbf{A}_i$, $\mathbf{B}_i$, and $\mathbf{C}_i$ in the rule consequents have appropriate dimensions.

Step 3. Set the sampling period T_s and discretize the n_R models in the rule consequents of the Takagi–Sugeno fuzzy model, Equation (41) accepting the zero-order hold. The complete rule-base of the discrete-time Takagi–Sugeno fuzzy model is

$$\begin{aligned}&\text{Rule } i : \text{IF } \lambda(k) \text{ IS } T^i_{\lambda,l} \text{ AND } x_2(k) \text{ IS } T^i_{x_2,p} \text{ AND } M_1(k) \text{ IS } T^i_{M_1,q}\\ &\text{THEN} \begin{cases} \mathbf{x}(k+1) = \mathbf{A}_{d,i}\mathbf{x}(k) + \mathbf{B}_{d,i}u(k) \\ y_m(k) = \mathbf{C}_{d,i}\mathbf{x}(k) \end{cases}, \quad i = 1 \ldots n_R,\end{aligned} \tag{42}$$

where $y_m(k)$ is the discrete-time Takagi–Sugeno fuzzy model output, and the matrices $\mathbf{A}_{d,i}$, $\mathbf{B}_{d,i}$, and $\mathbf{C}_{d,i}$ in the rule consequents have appropriate dimensions exemplified as follows.

The recommended value of the sampling period is $T_s = 0.01\,\text{s}$ which accounts for the process dynamics (Precup *et al.*, 2012c). The disturbance input vector is neglected in Equations (41) and (42) for the sake of simplicity and for dealing with models which are close to real-world applications.

Step 4. Define the optimization problem that leads to optimal Takagi–Sugeno fuzzy models

$$\begin{aligned}&\boldsymbol{\rho}^* = \arg\min_{\boldsymbol{\rho}\in D} J(\boldsymbol{\rho}),\\ &J(\boldsymbol{\rho}) = \sqrt{\frac{1}{N}\sum_{k=1}^{N}(y(k,\boldsymbol{\rho}) - y_m(k,\boldsymbol{\rho}))^2} = \sqrt{\frac{1}{N}\sum_{k=1}^{N}(e_m(k,\boldsymbol{\rho}))^2},\end{aligned} \tag{43}$$

where $\boldsymbol{\rho}$ is the parameter vector of the Takagi–Sugeno fuzzy model and also the vector variable of the objective function $J(\boldsymbol{\rho})$, $\boldsymbol{\rho}^*$ is the optimal parameter vector of the Takagi–Sugeno fuzzy model and the solution to Equation (43), $y(k,\boldsymbol{\rho})$ is the process output at kth sampling interval, $y_m(k,\boldsymbol{\rho})$ is the fuzzy model output, the modeling error is

$$e_m(k,\boldsymbol{\rho}) = y(k,\boldsymbol{\rho}) - y_m(k,\boldsymbol{\rho}), \tag{44}$$

D is the feasible domain of $\boldsymbol{\rho}$ and N is the length of the discrete time horizon. The elements of the vector $\boldsymbol{\rho}$ are a part of the parameters of the input m.f. parameters. $J(\boldsymbol{\rho})$ in Equation (43) is the root mean square error (RMSE) between the model output (the wheel slip) of the Takagi–Sugeno fuzzy model and of the real-world process.

Step 5. Apply the SA algorithm described in the next section to solve the optimization problem, Equation (43) that leads to the vector $\boldsymbol{\rho}^*$. The elements of the vector $\boldsymbol{\rho}^*$ are the optimal input m.f. parameters, and they belong to the optimal Takagi–Sugeno fuzzy model.

20.4.1. *Application of SA Algorithm*

The operating mechanism of SA algorithms uses a probabilistic framework to accept the solution on the basis of the analogy with the temperature decrease in metallurgy (Kirkpatrick *et al.*, 1983; Geman and Geman, 1984). Considering the initial solution represented by the vector $\boldsymbol{\zeta} \in \mathbf{R}^{q_s}$ (q_s is the dimension of the search space) with the fitness value $g(\boldsymbol{\zeta})$ of the fitness function (i.e., of the objective function) g, $g : \mathbf{R}^{q_s} \to \mathbf{R}$, the new probable solution is represented by the vector $\boldsymbol{\psi} \in \mathbf{R}^{q_s}$ which is chosen such that to belong to the vicinity of $\boldsymbol{\zeta}$. In order to make the SA algorithm more computationally efficient, two additional iteration indices are defined (Precup *et al.*, 2013a), namely the success rate s_r and the rejection rate r_r. The success rate s_r aims the acceleration of the cooling process by forcing a jump in temperature when the minimum value of the fitness function changes for a preset number of times at the same temperature level. The rejection rate r_r is proposed as an alternative index for the convergence of the algorithm, and it is reset only when small values of the fitness function are found and not when the temperature cools.

The steps of the SA algorithm applied in the step 5 of the optimal tuning approach are:

Step A. Generate the initial solution, i.e., conduct the following operations: generate a random initial solution $\boldsymbol{\zeta}$ and calculate its fitness value $g(\boldsymbol{\zeta})$, set the minimum temperature $\theta_{\min}$, using the notation k_{iter} for the current iteration index, initialize the maximum allowed number of iterations $k_{\max}$ for each temperature step, the maximum accepted success rate $s_{r\max}$, the maximum accepted rejection rate $r_{r\max}$, and the minimum accepted value of the fitness function $g_{\min}$, set the initial temperature θ_0, i.e., the temperature $\theta_{k_{iter}}$ for $k_{iter} = 0$, and set the initial rejection rate $r_r = 0$.

Step B. Set the initial value of the iteration index $k_{iter} = 0$ and the initial success rate $s_r = 0$.

Step C. Generate a new probable solution $\boldsymbol{\psi}$ in the vicinity of $\boldsymbol{\zeta}$ by disturbing $\boldsymbol{\zeta}$, and calculate its fitness value $g(\boldsymbol{\psi})$.

Step D. Accept or not the new solution by means of the change of fitness expressed as the difference $\Delta g_{\psi\zeta}$

$$\Delta g_{\psi\zeta} = g(\boldsymbol{\psi}) - g(\boldsymbol{\zeta}). \tag{45}$$

If $\Delta g_{\psi\zeta} \le 0$, accept $\boldsymbol{\zeta} = \boldsymbol{\psi}$ as the new vector solution. Otherwise, set the random parameter q_k, $0 \le q_k \le 1$, and calculate the probability p_ψ of $\boldsymbol{\psi}$ to be the next solution

$$p_\psi = \exp\left(\frac{-\Delta g_{\psi\zeta}}{\theta_{k_{iter}}}\right). \tag{46}$$

If $p_\psi > q_k$, $\boldsymbol{\zeta} = \boldsymbol{\psi}$ is the new solution.

Step E. If the new solution is accepted, then update the new solution and g, increment k_{iter} and reset $r_r = 0$. Otherwise, increment r_r. If r_r has reached its maximum value $r_{r\,\max}$, go to step I; otherwise, continue with the next step.

Step F. Increment s_r. If s_r has reached its maximum value $s_{r\,\max}$, continue with the next step; otherwise, increment k_{iter}. If k_{iter} has reached its maximum value $k_{\max}$, continue with the next step; otherwise, go to step C.

Step G. The temperature is decreased in terms of the temperature decrement rule, referred to also as the cooling schedule, which gives the next temperature $\theta_{k_{iter}+1}$

$$\theta_{k_{iter}+1} = \alpha_{cs}\theta_{k_{iter}}, \tag{47}$$

where $\alpha_{cs} = \text{const}, \quad \alpha_{cs} < 1$.

Step H. If $\theta_{k_{iter}} > \theta_{\min}$ or $g(\boldsymbol{\zeta}) > g_{\min}$, go to step C. Otherwise, continue with the next step.

Step I. Validate the obtained vector solution $\boldsymbol{\zeta}$ by checking the following inequality-type constraint which guarantees that the Takagi–Sugeno fuzzy model with the obtained model parameters $\boldsymbol{\rho} = \boldsymbol{\zeta}$ ensures the convergence of the objective function:

$$|y(N, \boldsymbol{\rho}) - y_m(N, \boldsymbol{\rho})| \leq \varepsilon_y |y(N, \boldsymbol{\rho}) - y(1, \boldsymbol{\rho})|, \tag{48}$$

where the value $\varepsilon_y = 0.001$ is recommended for a 2% settling time, and it is taken from the optimal tuning of Takagi–Sugeno FCs (Precup *et al.*, 2013a, 2013b; David *et al.*, 2013).

Step J. The algorithm is stopped, and the last validated vector solution $\boldsymbol{\zeta}$ is the solution to the optimization problem, Equation (43).

This SA algorithm is mapped onto the optimization problem, Equation (43) by means of the following relations between the parameter vectors $\boldsymbol{\zeta}$ and $\boldsymbol{\psi}$ in the SA algorithm and the parameter vector $\boldsymbol{\rho}$ in the optimization problem:

$$\boldsymbol{\psi} = \boldsymbol{\rho}, \quad \boldsymbol{\zeta} = \boldsymbol{\rho} \tag{49}$$

and between the fitness function g in the SA algorithm and the objective function J in the optimization problem:

$$g(\boldsymbol{\psi}) = J(\boldsymbol{\rho}), \quad g(\boldsymbol{\zeta}) = J(\boldsymbol{\rho}). \tag{50}$$

In this context, the last new solution found will be the vector solution $\boldsymbol{\rho}^*$ to the optimization problem, Equation (43):

$$\boldsymbol{\rho}^* = \boldsymbol{\zeta}. \tag{51}$$

20.4.2. *Example Concerning a Laboratory ABS*

The optimal tuning approach has been applied to obtain optimal Takagi–Sugeno fuzzy models of the laboratory ABS. A part of the results and of the implementation details related to the Takagi–Sugeno fuzzy model characterized by $n_R = 3$ is presented as follows.

The largest domains of variation of the state variables in all ABS operating regimes are $0 \le \lambda \le 1.1$, $0 \le x_2 \le 180$, and $0 \le M_1 \le 11$. As pointed out in the step 2, the first input (scheduling) variable, λ, uses five linguistic terms, $T_{\lambda,l}, l = 1 \ldots 5$. The triangular m.f.s of these linguistic terms are

$$\mu_{LT_{\lambda,l}} : [0, 1.1] \to [0, 1],$$

$$\mu_{LT_{\lambda,l}}(\lambda) = \begin{cases} 0, & \lambda < a_{\lambda,l}, \\ 1 + \dfrac{(\lambda - b_{\lambda,l})}{(b_{\lambda,l} - a_{\lambda,l})}, & a_{\lambda,l} \le \lambda < b_{\lambda,l}, \\ 1 - \dfrac{(\lambda - b_{\lambda,l})}{(c_{\lambda,l} - b_{\lambda,l})}, & b_{\lambda,l} \le \lambda < c_{\lambda,l}, \\ 0, & \lambda \ge c_{\lambda,l}, \end{cases} \quad a_{\lambda,l} < b_{\lambda,l} < c_{\lambda,l}, \ l = 1 \ldots 5. \tag{52}$$

The parameters $a_{\lambda,l}, l = 1 \ldots 5$ and $c_{\lambda,l},\ l = 1 \ldots 5$, are the feet of the triangular m.f.s, they are variable and they belong to the vector variable $\boldsymbol{\rho}$ of the objective function, and the parameters $b_{\lambda,l}, l = 1 \ldots 5$, which stand for the modal values of the m.f.s, are fixed and they take the values $b_{\lambda,1} = 0.1$, $b_{\lambda,2} = 0.2$, $b_{\lambda,3} = 0.4$, $b_{\lambda,4} = 0.8$, and $b_{\lambda,5} = 1$. The second input variable, x_2, uses two linguistic terms, $T_{x_2,p},\ p \in \{1, 2\}$, with the triangular m.f.s of type, Equation (52). The parameters $a_{x_2,p},\ p \in \{1, 2\}$, and $c_{x_2,p}$, $p \in \{1, 2\}$, are the feet of the triangular m.f.s, they are variable and they belong to $\boldsymbol{\rho}$, and the parameters $b_{x_2,p}$, $p \in \{1, 2\}$, are fixed and they take the values $b_{x_2,1} = 50$ and $b_{x_2,2} = 150$. The third input variable, M_1, uses one linguistic term, $T_{M_1,1}$, with the triangular m.f. of type, Equation (52). The parameters $a_{M_1,1}$ and $c_{M_1,1}$, which represent the feet of the triangular m.f.s, are variable and they belong to $\boldsymbol{\rho}$, and the parameter $b_{M_1,1}$ is fixed, $b_{M_1,1} = 10$. Therefore, the parameter vector $\boldsymbol{\rho}$ of the Takagi–Sugeno fuzzy model that will be obtained by the application of the SA algorithm is

$$\begin{aligned} \boldsymbol{\rho} = [&a_{\lambda,1} \ \ c_{\lambda,1} \ \ a_{\lambda,2} \ \ c_{\lambda,2} \ \ a_{\lambda,3} \ \ c_{\lambda,3} \ \ a_{\lambda,4} \ \ c_{\lambda,4} \ \ a_{\lambda,5} \ \ c_{\lambda,5} \\ &a_{x_2,1} \ \ c_{x_2,1} \ \ a_{x_2,2} \ \ c_{x_2,2} \ \ a_{M_1,1} \ \ c_{M_1,1} \end{aligned} \tag{53}$$

and the feasible domain in Equation (43) is

$$\begin{aligned} D = &[-0.01, 0.01] \times [0.15, 0.25] \times [0.05, 0.15] \times [0.35, 0.45] \times [0.15, 0.25] \\ &\times [0.75, 0.85] \times [0.35, 0.45] \times [0.95, 1.05] \times [0.75, 0.85] \times [1.05, 1.15] \end{aligned}$$

$$\times [-0.1, 0.1] \times [130.9, 170.1] \times [40, 60] \times [170, 190] \times [-0.5, 0.5] \times [10.5, 11.5] \in \mathbf{R}^{16}. \tag{54}$$

Setting the sampling period $T_s = 0.01$ s, the control signal u applied to the laboratory ABS has been generated as two weighted sums (one for training and one for validation) of pseudo-random binary signals. $N = 10000$ data points have been used in the training, and $N = 25000$ data points have been used for validation. The variation of u versus time is presented in Figure 20.8 that gives the input data for validation (testing). The state-space model matrices in the rule consequents of the rules 1 and 10 of the Takagi–Sugeno fuzzy model, Equation (42) are

$$\begin{aligned}
\mathbf{A}_{d,1} &= \begin{bmatrix} 0.9441 & -0.0025 & 0.0194 \\ -1.0335 & 1.0012 & -0.0601 \\ 0 & 0 & 0.8157 \end{bmatrix}, \quad \mathbf{B}_{d,1} = \begin{bmatrix} 0.0021 \\ -0.0059 \\ 0.1843 \end{bmatrix}, \\
& \qquad \mathbf{C}_{d,1} = [1 \ \ 0 \ \ 0], \\
\mathbf{A}_{d,10} &= \begin{bmatrix} 1.0041 & -0.0003 & 0.0069 \\ -0.3192 & 1 & -0.0519 \\ 0 & 0 & 0.8157 \end{bmatrix}, \quad \mathbf{B}_{d,10} = \begin{bmatrix} 0.0007 \\ -0.0054 \\ 0.1843 \end{bmatrix}, \\
& \qquad \mathbf{C}_{d,10} = [1 \ \ 0 \ \ 0].
\end{aligned} \tag{55}$$

The first set of experimental results is presented in Figure 20.9 as the outputs of the real-world process (the ABS laboratory equipment) and of the initial

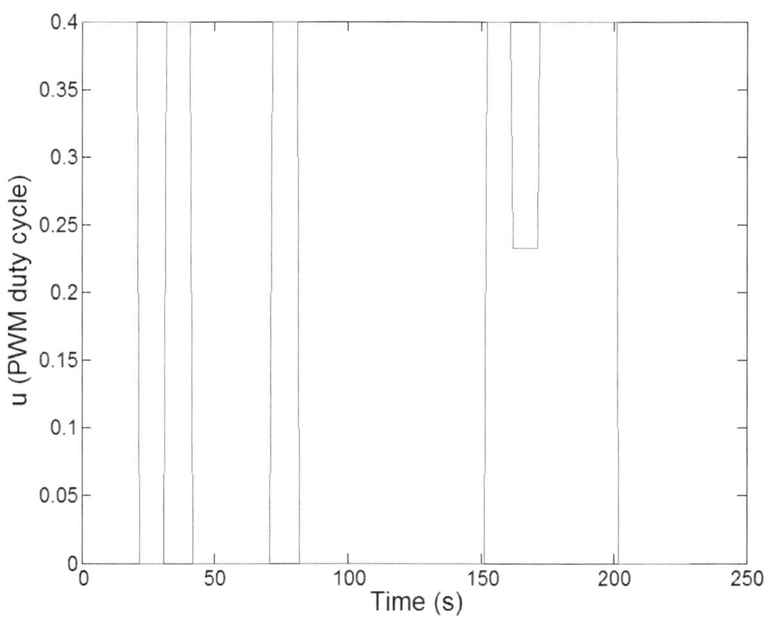

Figure 20.8: Control signal versus time used in the validation (testing) data.

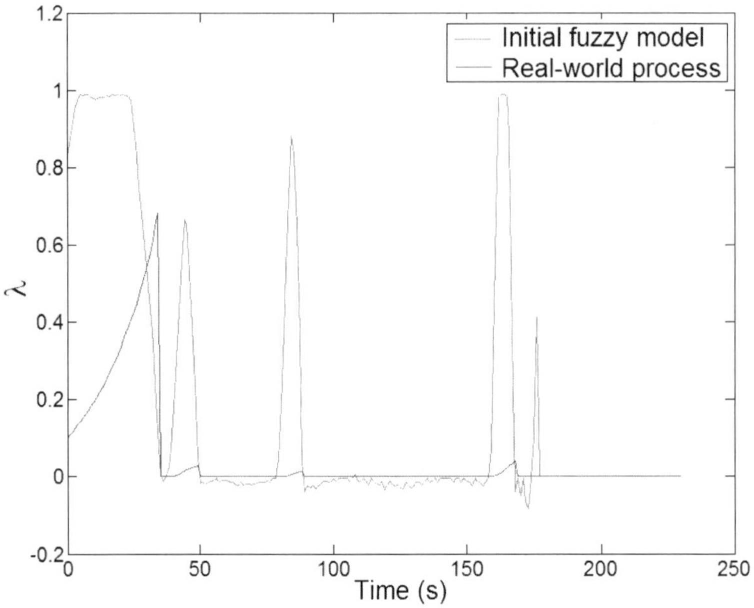

Figure 20.9: Real-time experimental results: Wheel slip λ versus time for the initial Takagi–Sugeno fuzzy model and for the real-world process considering the validation dataset.

Takagi–Sugeno fuzzy model before the application of SA algorithm, i.e., with the parameter vector $\boldsymbol{\rho}$

$$\boldsymbol{\rho} = \begin{bmatrix}0 & 0.2 & 0.1 & 0.4 & 0.2 & 0.8 & 0.4 & 1 & 0.8 & 1.1 & 0 & 150 & 50 & 180 & 0 & 11\end{bmatrix}^T. \tag{56}$$

The results presented in Figure 20.9 for the validation dataset illustrate the large difference between the Takagi–Sugeno fuzzy model and the real-world process, and they justify the need for the optimal tuning of the parameters of Takagi–Sugeno fuzzy models.

The maximum success and rejection rates in the SA algorithm have been set to $r_{r\max} = 100$ and to $s_{r\max} = 50$. A limit of $k_{\max} = 80$ iterations for each temperature step has been imposed. The SA algorithm has been stopped after reaching a final temperature of $\theta_{80} = 0.093246$. The initial temperature has been set to $\theta_0 = 1$, and the minimum temperature has been set to $\theta_{\min} = 10^{-8}$. The value of the parameter in the temperature decrement rule has been set to $\alpha_{cs} = 0.8$. The minimum accepted value of the fitness function (i.e., of the objective function) has been set to $g_{\min} = 10^{-4}$.

The final solution obtained by the SA algorithm is

$$\boldsymbol{\rho}^* = [0.0086 \quad 0.1614 \quad 0.09901 \quad 0.4067 \quad 0.2295 \quad 0.8471 \quad 0.4019 \quad 0.9578 \\ 0.847 \quad 1.12 \quad 0.02202 \quad 169 \quad 59.85 \quad 180.5 \quad -0.3227 \quad 11.04]^T, \tag{57}$$

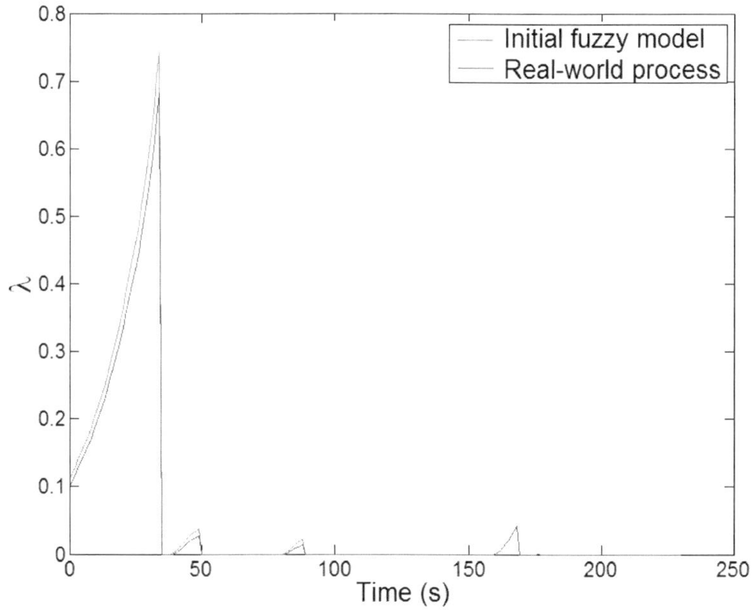

Figure 20.10: Real-time experimental results: Wheel slip λ versus time for the Takagi–Sugeno fuzzy model after optimization by the SA algorithm and for the real-world process considering the validation dataset.

and it corresponds to the final value $J(\boldsymbol{\rho}^*) = 0.74989$ of the objective function that shows a decrease from the initial value $J(\boldsymbol{\rho}) = 0.95373$.

The second set of experimental results is presented in Figure 20.10 as the output of the real-world process and of the Takagi–Sugeno fuzzy model after the application of the SA algorithm [i.e., with the parameter vector $\boldsymbol{\rho}^*$ given in Equation (57)], for the validation dataset. Figure 20.10 shows that the performance of the Takagi–Sugeno fuzzy model is improved by the application of the SA algorithm which optimizes the input m.f. parameters because reduced modeling errors are obtained.

The aspects concerning the comparisons of nature-inspired optimization algorithms presented in Section 20.3 are applied to the comparison of the SA algorithm with other algorithms as well. Once again we recommend the presentation of the results of the comparisons of the performance indices as average values for several runs of the algorithms; this offers fair comparisons because the impact of the random parameters in the algorithms is alleviated.

20.5. Conclusions and Outlook

This chapter has presented aspects concerning the nature-inspired optimization of FCs and fuzzy models. The presentation has been focused on Takagi–Sugeno and

Mamdani PI-FCs which are rather general as the presented design methodology can easily be applied to PD-FCs and extended to PID-FCs.

Once the optimization problems are defined, the nature-inspired optimization algorithms can be applied to get the optimal tuning of the parameters of FCs and fuzzy models. The chapter has given the exemplification of two such algorithms, the SA and the CSS. The results can be extended with no major difficulties to other algorithms. We advise the reduction of the number of parameters tuned by the nature-inspired algorithms in order to have a reasonable dimension of the search space which will offer an efficient search for the optimal solution.

The major shortcoming of nature-inspired algorithms in optimal design and tuning is represented by the large number of evaluations of the objective functions. This can be solved by the inclusion of gradient information that can be included from data-driven approaches.

Acknowledgments

This work was supported by a grant of the Romanian National Authority for Scientific Research, CNCS–UEFISCDI, Project No. PN-II-ID-PCE-2011-3-0109, and by a grant in the framework of the Partnerships in priority areas — PN II program of the Romanian National Authority for Scientific Research ANCS, CNDI–UEFISCDI, project number PN-II-PT-PCCA-2011-3.2-0732. The authors would like to thank M.Sc. Ramona-Bianca Grad and Dr. Mircea-Bogdan Rădac for their precious support in the experimental part.

References

Almaraashi, M., John, R., Coupland, S. and Hopgood, A. (2010). Time series forecasting using a TSK fuzzy system tuned with simulated annealing. In *Proc. 2010 IEEE Int. Conf. Fuzzy Syst.* (*FUZZ-IEEE 2010*). Barcelona, Spain, pp. 1–6.

Angelov, P. and Yager, R. (2012). A new type of simplified fuzzy rule-based systems. *Int. J. Gen. Syst.*, 41, pp. 163–185.

Angelov, P. and Yager, R. (2013). Density-based averaging — A new operator for data fusion. *Inf. Syst.*, 222, pp. 163–174.

Åström, K. J. and Hägglund, T. (1995). *PID Controllers Theory:Design and Tuning*. North Carolina, US: Instrument Society of America, Research Triangle Park.

Baranyi, P., Tikk, D., Yam, Y. and Patton, R. J. (2003). From differential equations to PDC controller design via numerical transformation. *Comput. Ind.*, 51, pp. 281–297.

Baranyi, P., Yam, Y. and Varlaki, P. (2013). *TP Model Transformation in Polytopic Model-Based Control*. Boca Raton, FL: Taylor & Francis.

Batyrshin, I., Kaynak, O. and Rudas, I. J. (2002). Fuzzy modeling based on generalized conjunction operations. *IEEE Trans. Fuzzy Syst.*, 10, pp. 678–683.

Bingül, Z. and Karahan, O. (2011). A fuzzy logic controller tuned with PSO for 2 DOF robot trajectory control. *Expert Syst. Appl.*, 38, pp. 1017–1031.

Castillo, O. and Melin, P. (2012a). A review on the design and optimization of interval type-2 fuzzy controllers. *Appl. Soft Comput.*, 12, pp. 1267–1278.

Castillo, O. and Melin, P. (2012b). Optimization of type-2 fuzzy systems based on bio-inspired methods: A concise review. *Inf. Sci.*, 205, pp. 1–19.

Chang, Y.-H., Tao, C.-W., Lin, H.-W. and Taur, J.-S. (2012). Fuzzy sliding-mode control for ball and beam system with fuzzy ant colony optimization. *Expert Syst. Appl.*, 39, pp. 3624–3633.

Chen, D., Wang, J., Zou, F., Zhang, H. and Hou, W. (2012). Linguistic fuzzy model identification based on PSO with different length of particles. *Appl. Soft Comput.*, 12, pp. 3390–3400.

Das, S., Pan, I. and Das, S. (2013). Fractional order fuzzy control of nuclear reactor power with thermal-hydraulic effects in the presence of random network induced delay and sensor noise having long range dependence. *Energy Convers. Manage.*, 68, pp. 200–218.

David, R.-C., Dragos, C.-A., Bulzan, R.-G., Precup, R.-E., Petriu, E. M. and Radac, M.-B. (2012). An approach to fuzzy modeling of magnetic levitation systems. *Int. J. Artif. Intell.*, 9, pp. 1–18.

David, R.-C., Precup, R.-E., Petriu, E. M., Radac, M.-B. and Preitl, S. (2013). Gravitational search algorithm-based design of fuzzy control systems with a reduced parametric sensitivity. *Inf. Sci.*, 247, pp. 154–173.

David, R.-C., Grad, R.-B., Precup, R.-E., Radac, M.-B., Dragos, C.-A. and Petriu, E. M. (2014). An approach to fuzzy modeling of anti-lock braking systems. In Snášel, V., Krömer, P., Köppen, M. and Schaefer, G. (eds.), *Advances in Intelligent Systems and Computing, Vol. 223*. Cham, Heidelberg, New York, Dordrecht, London: Springer-Verlag, pp. 83–93.

Dragos, C.-A., Precup, R.-E., David, R.-C., Preitl, S., Stinean, A.-I. and Petriu, E. M. (2013). Simulated annealing-based optimization of fuzzy models for magnetic levitation systems. In *Proc. 2013 Joint IFSA World Congr. NAFIPS Annu. Meet.* Edmonton, AB, Canada, pp. 286–291.

Feriyonika and Dewantoro, G. (2013). Fuzzy sliding mode control for enhancing injection velocity performance in injection molding machine. *Int. J. Artif. Intell.*, 10, pp. 75–87.

Formentin, S., Karimi, A. and Savaresi, S. M. (2013a). Optimal input design for direct data-driven tuning of model-reference controllers. *Autom.*, 49, pp. 1874–1882.

Formentin, S., van Heusden, K. and Karimi, A. (2013b). A comparison of model-based and data-driven controller tuning. *Int. J. Adapt. Control Signal Process.* doi: 10.1002/acs.2415.

Galichet, S. and Foulloy, L. (1995). Fuzzy controllers: Synthesis and equivalences. *IEEE Trans. Fuzzy Syst.*, 3, pp. 140–148.

Geman, S. and Geman, D. (1984). Stochastic relaxation, Gibbs distribution and the Bayesian restoration in images. *IEEE Trans. Pattern Anal. Mach. Intell.*, 6, pp. 721–741.

Haber, R. E., Haber-Haber, R., Jiménez, A. and Galán, R. (2009). An optimal fuzzy control system in a network environment based on simulated annealing. An application to a drilling process. *Appl. Soft Comput.*, 9, pp. 889–895.

Haber, R. E., del Toro, R. M. and Gajate, A. (2010). Optimal fuzzy control system using the cross-entropy method. A case study of a drilling process. *Inf. Sci.*, 180, pp. 2777–2792.

Hjalmarsson, H., Gevers, M., Gunnarsson, S. and Lequin, O. (1998). Iterative feedback tuning: theory and applications. *IEEE Control Syst. Mag.*, 18, pp. 26–41.

Ho, D. T. and Garibaldi, J. M. (2013). An improved optimisation framework for fuzzy time-series prediction. In *Proc. 2013 IEEE Int. Conf. Fuzzy Syst.* (*FUZZ-IEEE 2013*). Hyderabad, India, pp. 1–8.

Hou, Z.-S. and Wang, Z. (2013). From model-based control to data-driven control: Survey, classification and perspective. *Inf. Sci.*, 235, pp. 3–35.

Jain, R., Sivakumaran, N. and Radhakrishnan, T. K. (2011). Design of self tuning fuzzy controllers for nonlinear systems. *Expert Syst. Appl.*, 38, pp. 4466–4476.

Jiang, H., Kwong, C. K., Chen, Z. and Ysim, Y. C. (2012). Chaos particle swarm optimization and T-S fuzzy modeling approaches to constrained predictive control. *Expert Syst. Appl.*, 39, pp. 194–201.

Johanyák, Z. C. (2010). Student evaluation based on fuzzy rule interpolation. *Int. J. Artif. Intell.*, 5, pp. 37–55.

Kaveh, A. and Talatahari, S. (2010a). A novel heuristic optimization method: charged system search. *Acta Mech.*, 213, pp. 267–289.

Kaveh, A. and Talatahari, S. (2010b). Optimal design of truss structures via the charged system search algorithm. *Struct. Multidisp. Optim.*, 37, pp. 893–911.

Kaveh, A. and Talatahari, S. (2010c). A charged system search with a fly to boundary method for discrete optimum design of truss structures. *Asian J. Civ. Eng.* (*Build. Housing*), 11, pp. 277–293.

Kayacan, E., Oniz, Y., Aras, A. C., Kaynak, O. and Abiyev, R. (2011). A servo system control with time-varying and nonlinear load conditions using type-2 TSK fuzzy neural system. *Appl. Soft Comput.*, 11, pp. 5735–5744.

Kirkpatrick, S., Gelatt, C. D. Jr. and Vecchi, M. P. (1983). Optimization by simulated annealing. *Science*, 220, pp. 671–680.

Kóczy, L. T. (1996). Fuzzy IF-THEN rule models and their transformation into one another. *IEEE Trans. Syst., Man, Cybern., Part A: Syst. Humans*, 26, pp. 621–637.

Kumaresan, N. (2011). Optimal control for stochastic linear quadratic singular periodic neuro Takagi–Sugeno (T–S) fuzzy system with singular cost using ant colony programming. *Appl. Math. Model.*, 35, pp. 3797–3808.

Li, C., Zhou, J., Xiao, J. and Xiao, H. (2013). Hydraulic turbine governing system identification using T-S fuzzy model optimized by chaotic gravitational search algorithm. *Eng. Appl. Artif. Intell.*, 26, pp. 2073–2082.

Linda, O. and Manic, M. (2011a). Interval type-2 fuzzy voter design for fault tolerant systems. *Inf. Sci.*, 181, pp. 2933–2950.

Linda, O. and Manic, M. (2011b). Uncertainty-robust design of interval type-2 fuzzy logic controller for delta parallel robot. *IEEE Trans. Ind. Inf.*, 7, pp. 661–670.

Liu, G. and Yang, W. (2000). Learning and tuning of fuzzy membership functions by simulated annealing algorithm. In *Proc. 2000 IEEE Asia-Pac. Conf. Circuits Syst.* (*APCCAS 2000*). Tianjin, China, pp. 367–370.

Lu, H.-C. and Liu, H.-K. (2013). Ant colony fuzzy neural network controller for cruising vessel on river. *Appl. Ocean Res.*, 42, pp. 43–54.

Melin, P., Astudillo, L., Castillo, O., Valdez, F. and Garcia, M. (2013). Optimal design of type-2 and type-1 fuzzy tracking controllers for autonomous mobile robots under perturbed torques using a new chemical optimization paradigm. *Expert Syst. Appl.*, 40, pp. 3185–3195.

Obradović, D., Konjović, Z., Pap, E. and Rudas, I. J. (2013). Linear fuzzy space-based road lane model and detection. *Knowl.-Based Syst.*, 38, pp. 37–47.

Oh, S.-K., Jang, H.-J. and Pedrycz, W. (2011). A comparative experimental study of type-1/type-2 fuzzy cascade controller based on genetic algorithms and particle swarm optimization. *Expert Syst. Appl.*, 38, pp. 11217–11229.

Ohtake, H., Tanaka, K. and Wang, H. O. (2001). Fuzzy modeling via sector nonlinearity concept. In *Proc. Joint 9th IFSA World Congr. 20th NAFIPS Int. Conf.* Vancouver, BC, Canada, 1, pp. 127–132.

Onieva, E., Milanés, V., Villagrá, J., Pérez, J. and Godoy, J. (2012). Genetic optimization of a vehicle fuzzy decision system for intersections. *Expert Syst. Appl.*, 39, pp. 13148–13157.

Owens, D. H., Freeman, C. T. and Thanh, V. D. (2013). Norm-optimal iterative learning control with intermediate point weighting: theory, algorithms, and experimental evaluation. *IEEE Trans. Control Syst. Technol.*, 21, pp. 999–1007.

Pedrycz, W. and Song, M. (2012). A genetic reduction of feature space in the design of fuzzy models. *Appl. Soft Comput.*, 12, pp. 2801–2816.

Pérez, J., Milanés, V., Godoy, J., Villagrá, J. and Onieva, E. (2013). Cooperative controllers for highways based on human experience. *Expert Syst. Appl.*, 40, pp. 1024–1033.

Precup, R.-E., Preitl, S., Tar, J. K., Fodor, J., Ursache, I.-B. and Clep, P. A. (2008). Low-cost fuzzy logic approach to ship course control. In *Proc. 50th Int. Symp. ELMAR-2008*. Zadar, Croatia, 2, pp. 423–426.

Precup, R.-E., Preitl, S., Petriu, E. M., Tar, J. K., Tomescu, M. L. and Pozna, C. (2009). Generic two-degree-of-freedom linear and fuzzy controllers for integral processes. *J. Franklin Inst.*, 346, pp. 980–1003.

Precup, R.-E. and Hellendoorn, H. (2011). A survey on industrial applications of fuzzy control. *Comput. Ind.*, 62, pp. 213–226.

Precup, R.-E., David, R.-C., Petriu, E. M. and Preitl, S. (2011). Optimal fuzzy controllers tuned by charged system search algorithms. In *Proc. 2011 Online Conf. Soft Comput. Ind. Appl.* (*WSC 16*). pp. 1–10.

Precup, R.-E., David, R.-C., Petriu, E. M., Preitl, S. and Radac, M.-B. (2012a). Fuzzy control systems with reduced parametric sensitivity based on simulated annealing. *IEEE Trans. Ind. Electron.*, 59, pp. 3049–3061.

Precup, R.-E., David, R.-C., Petriu, E. M., Preitl, S. and Radac, M.-B. (2012b). Novel adaptive gravitational search algorithm for fuzzy controlled servo systems. *IEEE Trans. Ind. Inf.*, 8, pp. 791–800.

Precup, R.-E., Spataru, S. V., Radac, M.-B., Petriu, E. M., Preitl, S., Dragos, C.-A. and David, R.-C. (2012c). Experimental results of model-based fuzzy control solutions for a laboratory antilock braking system. In Hippe, Z. S., Kulikowski, J. L. and Mroczek, T. (eds.), *Advances in Intelligent and Soft Computing*, Vol. 99. Berlin, Heidelberg: Springer-Verlag, pp. 223–234.

Precup, R.-E., David, R.-C., Petriu, E. M., Radac, M.-B., Preitl, S. and Fodor, J. (2013a). Evolutionary optimization-based tuning of low-cost fuzzy controllers for servo systems. *Knowl.-Based Syst.*, 38, pp. 74–84.

Precup, R.-E., David, R.-C., Petriu, E. M., Preitl, S. and Radac, M.-B. (2013b). Fuzzy logic-based adaptive gravitational search algorithm for optimal tuning of fuzzy controlled servo systems. *IET Control Theory Appl.*, 7, pp. 99–107.

Precup, R.-E., Radac, M.-B., Petriu, E. M., Dragos, C.-A. and Preitl, S. (2013c). Simulated annealing approach to fuzzy modeling of servo systems. In *Proc. 2013 IEEE Int. Conf. Cybern.* (*CYBCONF 2013*). Lausanne, Switzerland, pp. 267–272.

Precup, R.-E., David, R.-C., Petriu, E. M., Preitl, S. and Radac, M.-B. (2014). Novel adaptive charged system search algorithm for optimal tuning of fuzzy controllers. *Expert Syst. Appl.*, 41, pp. 1168–1175.

Preitl, S. and Precup, R.-E. (1996). On the algorithmic design of a class of control systems based on providing the symmetry of open-loop Bode plots, Buletinul Stiintific al U.P.T.*Trans. Autom. Control Comput. Sci.*, 41(55), pp. 47–55.

Preitl, S. and Precup, R.-E. (1997). *Introducere in Conducerea Fuzzy a Proceselor*. Bucharest, Romania: Editura Tehnica.

Preitl, S. and Precup, R.-E. (1999). An extension of tuning relations after symmetrical optimum method for PI and PID controllers. *Autom.*, 35, pp. 1731–1736.

Preitl, S., Precup, R.-E. and Preitl, Z. (2010a). Aspects concerning the tuning of 2-DOF fuzzy controllers. In *Proc. 10th Triennial Int. SAUM Conf. Syst., Autom. Control Measurements* (*SAUM 2010*). Niš, Serbia, pp. 210–219.

Preitl, S., Precup, R.-E., Dragos, C.-A. and Radac, M.-B. (2010b). Tuning of 2-DOF fuzzy PI (D) controllers. Laboratory applications. In *Proc. 11th IEEE Int. Symp. Comput. Intell. Inf.* (*CINTI 2010*). Budapest, Hungary, pp. 237–242.

Radac, M.-B., Precup, R.-E., Preitl, S., Tar, J. K. and Burnham, K. J. (2009). Tire slip fuzzy control of a laboratory anti-lock braking system. In *Proc. Eur. Control Conf. 2009* (*ECC 2009*). Budapest, Hungary, pp. 940–945.

Radac, M.-B., Precup, R.-E., Petriu, E. M. and Preitl, S. (2011). Application of IFT and SPSA to servo system control. *IEEE Trans. Neural Netw.*, 22, pp. 2363–2375.

Radac, M.-B., Precup, R.-E., Petriu, E. M., Cerveneak, B.-S., Dragos, C.-A. and Preitl, S. (2012). Stable iterative correlation-based tuning algorithm for servo systems. In *Proc. 38th Annu. Conf. IEEE Ind. Electron. Soc.* (*IECON 2012*). Montreal, QC, Canada, pp. 2500–2505.

Škrjanc, I., Blažič, S. and Matko, D. (2002). Direct fuzzy model-reference adaptive control. *Int. J. Intell. Syst.*, 17, pp. 943–963.

Škrjanc, I. and Blažič, S. (2005). Predictive functional control based on fuzzy model: Design and stability study. *J. Intell. Robot. Syst.*, 43, pp. 283–299.

Su, Z.-G., Wang, P.-H., Shen, J., Zhang, Y.-F. and Chen, L. (2012). Convenient T–S fuzzy model with enhanced performance using a novel swarm intelligent fuzzy clustering technique. *J. Process Control*, 22, pp. 108–124.

Sugeno, M. (1999). On stability of fuzzy systems expressed by fuzzy rules with singleton consequents. *IEEE Trans. Fuzzy Syst.*, 7, pp. 201–224.

Takagi, T. and Sugeno, M. (1985). Fuzzy identification of systems and its applications to modelling and control. *IEEE Trans. Syst., Man, Cybern.*, 15, pp. 116–132.

Tikk, D., Johanyák, Z. C., Kovács, S. and Wong, K. W. (2011). Fuzzy rule interpolation and extrapolation techniques: Criteria and evaluation guidelines. *J. Adv. Comput. Intell. Intell. Inf.*, 15, pp. 254–263.

Topalov, A. V., Oniz, Y., Kayacan, E. and Kaynak, O. (2011). Neuro-fuzzy control of antilock braking system using sliding mode incremental learning algorithm. *Neurocomputing*, 74, pp. 1883–1893.

Vaščák, J. (2012). Adaptation of fuzzy cognitive maps by migration algorithms. *Kybernetes*, 41, pp. 429–443.

Vaščák, J. and Pal'a, M. (2012). Adaptation of fuzzy cognitive maps for navigation purposes by migration algorithms. *Int. J. Artif. Intell.*, 8, pp. 20–37.

Wang, H., Zhao, L., Du, W. and Qian, F. (2011). A hybrid method for identifying T–S fuzzy models. In *Proc. 2011 Eighth Int. Conf. Fuzzy Syst. Knowl. Discov.* (*FSKD 2011*). Shanghai, China, 1, pp. 11–15.

Wang, L., Yang, R., Pardalos, P. M., Qian, L. and Fei, M. (2013). An adaptive fuzzy controller based on harmony search and its application to power plant control. *Int. J. Electr. Power Energy Syst.*, 53, pp. 272–278.

Yanara, T. A. and Akyürek, Z. (2011). Fuzzy model tuning using simulated annealing. *Expert Syst. Appl.*, 38, pp. 8159–8169.

Chapter 21

Genetic Optimization of Modular Neural Networks for Pattern Recognition with a Granular Approach

Patricia Melin

In this chapter, we propose a multi-objective hierarchical genetic algorithm (HGA) for modular neural network (MNN) optimization. A granular approach is used due to the fact that the dataset is divided into granules or sub modules. The main objective of this method is to know the optimal number of sub modules or granules, but also allow the optimization of the number of hidden layers, number of neurons per hidden layer, error goal and learning algorithms per module. The proposed approach is based on a Micro GA and was tested for a pattern recognition application. Simulation results show that the proposed MNN approach offers advantages over existing neural network (NN) models

21.1. Introduction

Hybrid intelligent systems are computational systems that integrate different intelligent techniques. Examples of these techniques are modular neural networks (MNN) and genetic algorithms (GAs). Hybrid intelligent systems are now being used to support complex problem solving and decision-making in a wide variety of tasks. Hybrid intelligent systems allow the representation and manipulation of different types and forms of data and knowledge, which may come from various sources. In this chapter, these techniques are combined using a granular approach. It was decided to apply the proposed method to pattern recognition to test the approach with complex problems.

There are many works that combine different techniques and they have demonstrated that the integration of different intelligent techniques provide good results, such as in Hidalgo *et al.* (2009); Melin *et al.* (2009, 2010, 2011, 2012); Mendoza *et al.* (2009a, 2009b); Sánchez and Melin (2010).

This chapter is organized as follows: Section 21.2 contains the basic concepts used in this research work, Section 21.3 contains the general architecture of the proposed method, Section 21.4 presents experimental results and in Section 21.5, the conclusions of this work are presented.

21.2. Basic Concepts

In this section, we present a brief overview of the basic concepts used in this research work.

21.2.1. *Modular Neural Networks*

Neural networks (NNs) can be used to extract patterns and detect trends that are too complex to be noticed by either humans or other computer techniques [24]. The MNNs are comprised of modules. The idea on which this kind of learning structure is based on the divide-and-conquer paradigm: The problem should be divided into smaller sub problems that are solved by experts (modules) and their partial solutions should be integrated to produce a final solution (Azamm, 2000; Khan *et al.*, 2009; Santos *et al.*, 2006). A module can be a sub-structure or a learning sub-procedure of the whole network (Auda and Kamel, 1999).

The results of the different applications involving MNNs lead to the general evidence that the use of MNNs implies a significant learning improvement comparatively to a single NN and especially to the back-propagation NN. Each NN works independently in its own domain. Each of the NNs is build and trained for a specific task (Melin and Castillo, 2005).

21.2.2. *Multi-Objective HGA*

A Genetic algorithm (GA) is an optimization and search technique based on the principles of genetics and natural selection (Haupt and Haupt, 2004; Mitchell, 1998; Segovia *et al.*, 2002). GAs are non-deterministic methods that employ crossover and mutation operators for deriving offspring. GAs work by maintaining a constant-sized population of candidate solutions known as individuals (chromosomes) (Coley, 1999; Huang and Wechsler, 1999; Nawa *et al.*, 1999).

Introduced in Tang *et al.* (1998), a HGA is a type of GA is that for some complex systems, which cannot be easily represented, this type of GA can be a better choice. The complicated chromosomes may provide a good new way to solve the problem (Wang *et al.*, 2002; Worapradya and Pratishthananda, 2004).

Multi-objective optimization (MO) seeks to optimize the components of a vector-valued cost function. Unlike single objective optimization, the solution to this problem is not a single point, but a family of points known as the Pareto-optimal set. Each point in this surface is optimal in the sense that no improvement can be achieved in one cost vector component that does not lead to degradation in at least one of the remaining components (Fonseca and Fleming, 1993).

There are three general approaches to MO. The first is to combine the individual objective functions into a single composite function (Aggregating functions). The second is to use Population-based approaches and the third is to use Pareto-based approaches. A Pareto optimal set is a set of solutions that are non-dominated with respect to each other. Pareto optimal sets can be of varied sizes, but the size of the Pareto set increases with the increase in the number of objectives (Abraham *et al.*, 2005).

In this work, the multi-objective GA is based on a Micro genetic algorithm, proposed in Coello Coello *et al.* (2007); Coello Coello and Toscano Pulido (2005). Two main characteristics of this kind of genetic algorithm are that it works with a small population and has a re-initialization process.

21.2.3. *Granular Computing*

Granular computing is often defined as an umbrella term to cover many theories, methodologies, techniques, and tools that make use of granules in complex problem solving. Granular computing is a new term for the problem solving paradigm and may be viewed more on a philosophical rather than technical level (Yao, 2000, 2004, 2005a, 2007).

Granular computing has begun to play important roles in bioinformatics, e-Business, security, machine learning, data mining, high-performance computing and wireless mobile computing in terms of efficiency, effectiveness, robustness and uncertainty (Bargiela and Pedrycz, 2006; Yao, 2005b; Yu and Pedrycz, 2009).

A granule may be interpreted as one of the numerous small particles forming a larger unit. The philosophy of thinking in terms of levels of granularity, and its implementation in more concrete models, would result in disciplined procedures that help to avoid errors and to save time for solving a wide range of complex problems. At least three basic properties of granules are needed: internal properties reflecting the interaction of elements inside a granule, external properties revealing its interaction with other granules and, contextual properties showing the relative existence of a granule in a particular environment (Yao, 2001).

21.3. General Architecture of the Proposed Method

The proposed method combines MNNs and fuzzy logic as response integrators. In particular, it can be used for pattern recognition. This proposed method is able to use some datasets, for example to use "N" biometric measures to identify someone and the data of each biometric measure would be divided into different numbers of sub

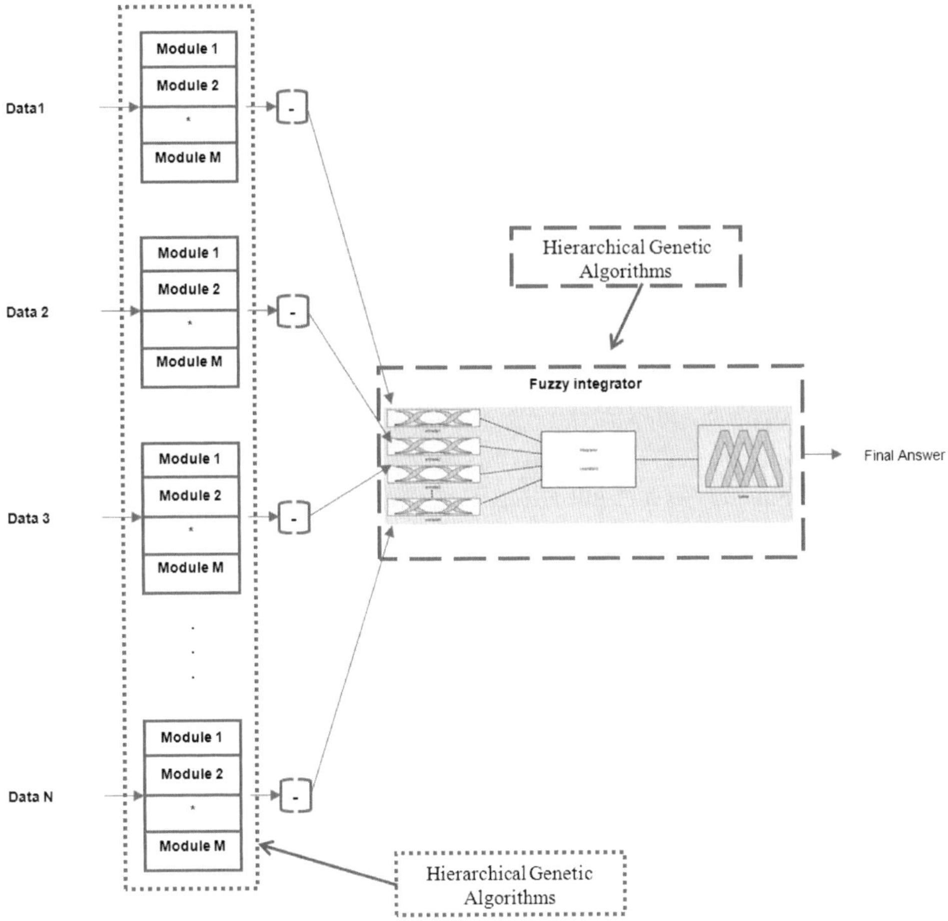

Figure 21.1: The general architecture of the proposed method.

modules. The general architecture of the proposed method is shown in Figure 21.1. For joining the different responses of each biometric measure fuzzy integration is used. The proposed method also performs the optimization of the MNNs (as number of layers, goal error, number of neurons, etc.) and the different parameters of the fuzzy integrator.

21.3.1. *Architecture of the Proposed Method for the MNN*

The proposed method for MNN consists in changing the number of modules and the data per module, for example in the case of human recognition; it means that there will be different number of persons in each sub module. The number of sub modules can be established by a genetic algorithm, but at this moment the number

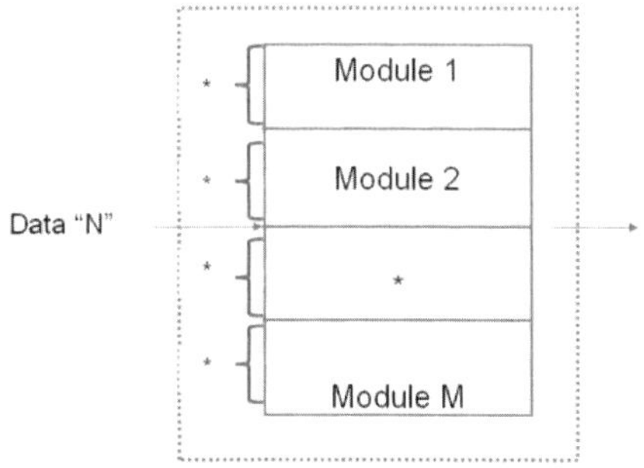

Figure 21.2: The architecture of proposed method for the MNN.

is established randomly. The architecture of the proposed method for the modular neural network is shown in Figure 21.2.

This method also chooses randomly which images will be used for training, but first the percentage of images for training is established (at this moment that percentage is defined randomly).

21.3.2. *Description of the Multi-Objective HGA for MNN Optimization*

With the purpose of knowing the optimal number of modules and the percentage of data for training, it is proposed the use of a genetic algorithm that allows the optimization of these parameters and others as the number of hidden layers, number of neurons per hidden layer, error goal and learning algorithms per module.

Figure 21.3 shows the chromosome, which was proposed for optimization of the neural networks.

The way in which the multi-objective HGA works is illustrated and described in more detail below.

First, a random population is generated. This random population is divided in two parts: a non-replaceable and replaceable portion. The non-replaceable portion never changes during the evolution, this helps to provide diversity. The replaceable portion experiences changes after certain condition is satisfied, this condition is called nominal convergence.

The working population at the beginning is taken (with a certain probability) from both portions of the main population. During each cycle, the MOHGA uses conventional genetic operators.

The external memory is initially empty, in each cycle the non-dominated vectors found are saved in that memory, logically a comparison is performed between the new vectors found and vectors already stored.

The MOHGA has two kinds of convergence. The first is the usually used (for example when it has the maximum number of cycle or generations, or when the value desired of one objective function is obtained). The second is called Nominal

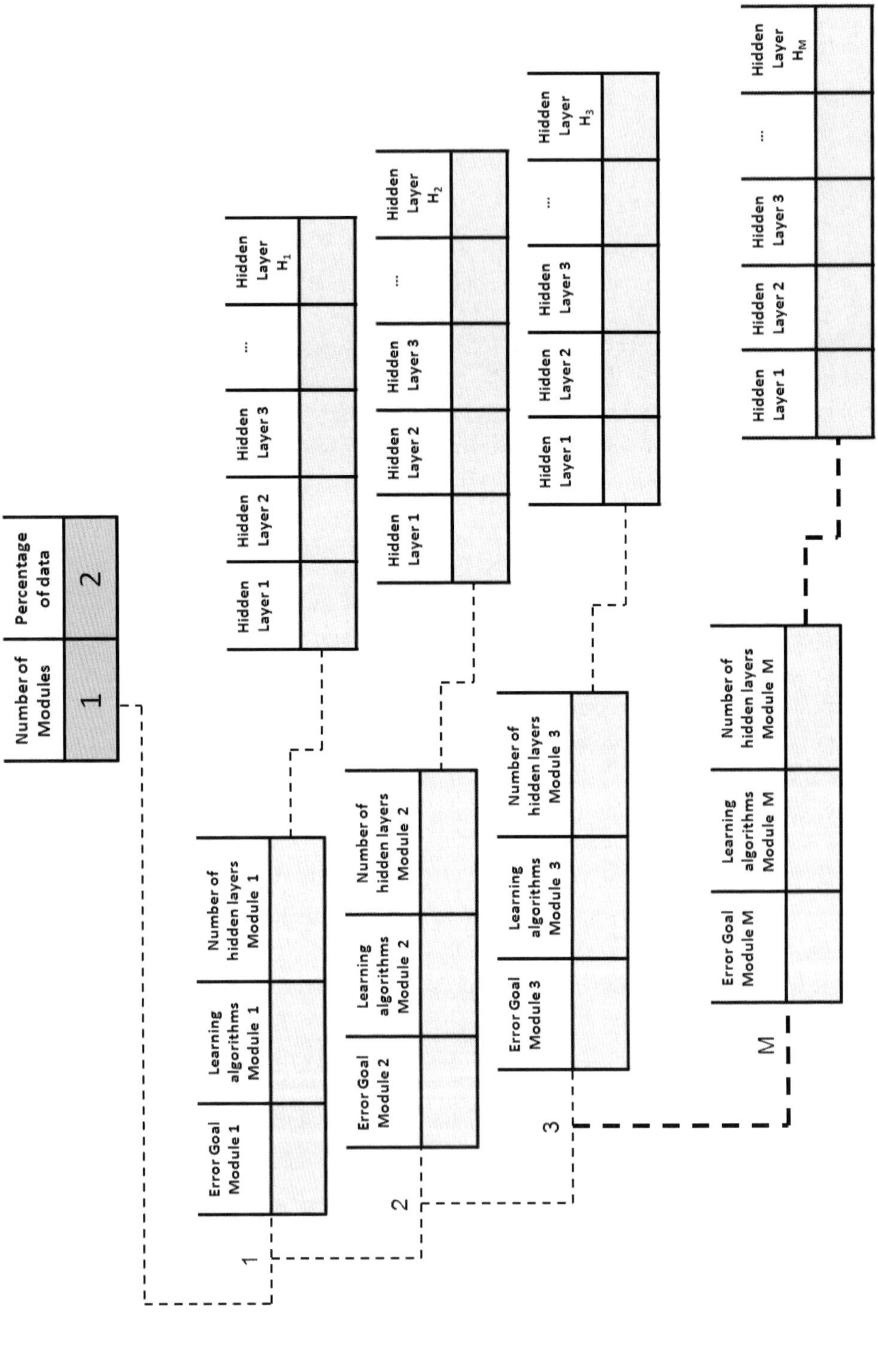

Figure 21.3: The chromosome of the multi-objective HGA for the MNN.

Convergence, in this case is established each five generations, here two non-dominated vectors are taken of the external memory and these are compared with two vectors of the Replaceable portion, if the two vectors taken of the replaceable portion are dominated by the others, those vector are replaceable for the two vectors of the external memory, then the working population is re-initialized.

21.3.3. *Objective Functions*

In order to not only get the network that provides us with the lowest error of recognition another objective function is set, and so we not only obtain the best network with the lowest error of recognition, but also obtain a modular neural network that uses the lowest percentage of data for the training phase. The objective functions are defined below:

$$\text{Min } f_1 = \sum_{i=1}^{m}\left(\sum_{j=1}^{n_m}\frac{x_j}{n_m}\right), \tag{1}$$

$$\text{Min } f_2 = \textbf{percentage of data}. \tag{2}$$

21.3.4. *Databases*

The databases used in this work are described below in more detail.

21.3.4.1. *Ear database*

We used a database of the University of Science and Technology of Beijing (USTB, 2009). The database consists of 77 people that contain four images per person (one ear), the image dimensions are 300 × 400 pixels, and the format is BMP.

The persons are students and teachers from the department of Information Engineering. Two images with angle variation and one with illumination variation are used.

21.3.4.2. *Voice database*

In the case of voice, the database consists of 10 voice samples (of 77 persons), WAV format. The persons are students from the Tijuana Institute of Technology. The word that they said in Spanish was "ACCESAR". To pre-process the voice the Mel Frequency Cepstral Coefficients were used.

21.4. Experimental Results

In this section, the results obtained in this work are presented. It was decided to use the database already described above. For the integration of responses the winner takes all method was used.

21.4.1. *Non-Optimized Results*

In this test the images percentage and the images, which would be used for training, were established randomly. The non-optimized results of the modular neural network are shown below.

21.4.1.1. *Non-optimized results of ear*

The best five results for the ear are shown in Table 21.1. In this test, it can be noticed that when the number of data per module is varied the rate of recognition varies.

It can be noticed that in the training # 4, that when the images 2, 3, and 4 are used a rate of recognition of 100% is obtained.

21.4.1.2. *Non-optimized results of voice*

The best five results for the voice are shown in Table 21.2. In this test, we can notice that when the number of data per module is varied the rate of recognition varies.

It can be noticed that in the training # 3, that when the voices 1, 3, 5, 7, 8 and 10 are used, a rate of recognition of 96.75% using eight sub modules is obtained.

21.4.2. *Optimized Results*

These tests make use of the multi-objective HGA, this MOHGA allows the optimization of parameters of the modular neural network, such as number of sub

Table 21.1: The best results for the ear (non-optimized).

Training	Images for training	Persons per module	Recognition rate
1	(1, 3, and 4)	Module # 1 (1 to 6) Module # 2 (7 to 14) Module # 3 (15 to 77)	67.53% (52/77)
2	(2 and 4)	Module # 1 (1 to 38) Module # 2 (39 to 70) Module # 3 (71 to 77)	77.92% (120/154)
3	(1 and 3)	Module # 1 (1 to 9) Module # 2 (10 to 44) Module # 3 (45 to 77)	83.11% (128/154)
4	(2, 3, and 4)	Module # 1 (1 to 40) Module # 2 (41 to 50) Module # 3 (51 to 77)	100% (77/77)
5	(2 and 3)	Module # 1 (1 to 23) Module # 2 (24 to 47) Module # 3 (48 to 77)	93.50% (144/154)

Table 21.2: The best results for voice (non-optimized).

Training	Images for training	Persons per module	Recognition rate
1	53% (1, 3, 6, 7, and 9)	Module # 1 (1 to 22) Module # 2 (23 to 57) Module # 3 (58 to 77)	278/385 72.20%
2	48% (1, 2, 5, 6, and 7)	Module # 1 (1 to 39) Module # 2 (40 to 68) Module # 3 (69 to 77)	260/385 67.53%
3	35% (2, 5, 8, and 9)	Module # 1 (1 to 36) Module # 2 (37 to 68) Module # 3 (69 to 77)	401/462 86.79%
4	46% (3, 5, 6, 7, and 10)	Module # 1 (1 to 40) Module # 2 (41 to 67) Module # 3 (68 to 77)	347/385 90.12%
5	59% (1, 3, 5, 7, 8, and 10)	Module # 1 (1 to 7) Module # 2 (8 to 39) Module # 3 (40 to 77)	298/308 96.75%

Table 21.3: Main parameters of the MOHGA.

Memory size	Non-replaceable memory	Replaceable memory	Working memory	Pareto optimal	Duration
50	25	25	5	7	12:48:08

modules, percentage of data for training, number of hidden layers, number of neurons per hidden layer, error goal and learning algorithms per module.

21.4.2.1. *Optimized results of the ear*

The main parameters used in this evolution are shown in Table 21.3 and the Pareto optimal set found for the ear are shown in Figure 21.4.

The solutions found in the Pareto optimal set are shown in Table 21.4, and the best architecture is shown in Table 21.5.

The solutions that have a recognition rate greater than 97% are taken, and of the resulting set, the solution with lower percentage of data is the best for us.

21.4.2.2. *Optimized results of the voice*

The main parameters used in this evolution are shown in Table 21.6.

The solutions found in the Pareto optimal set are shown in Table 21.7, and the best architecture is shown in Table 21.8.

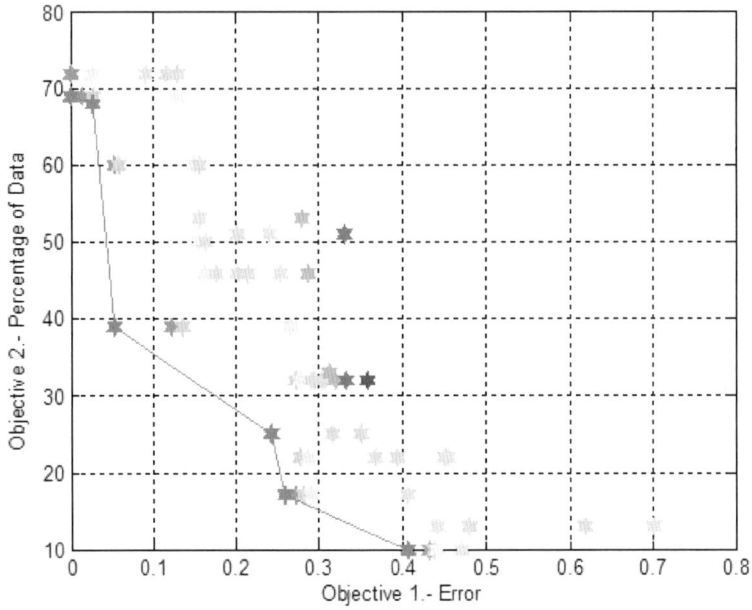

Figure 21.4: Pareto optimal set for the evolution of the ear.

Table 21.4: The best results for the ear (Pareto optimal set).

Solution	No. of modules	% of data	Total rec. (%)	Error
1	5	69	100	0
2	6	68	97.40	0.0260
3	5	39	94.80	0.0519
4	5	25	75.75	0.2424
5	9	17	74.02	0.2597
6	9	17	74.02	0.2597
7	5	10	59.30	0.4069

Table 21.5: The best result of the ear (optimized).

No. of mod.	% and images	No. hidden layers and num. of neurons	Persons per module	Rec. rate	Error
5	69%	3(173,135,44)	Module # 1 (1 to 6)	77/77	0
	(2, 3, and 4)	2(153,120)	Module # 2 (7 to 13)	100%	
		4(72,184,96,116)	Module # 3 (14 to 27)		
		2(197,166)	Module # 4 (28 to 53)		
		3(164,22,94)	Module # 5(54 to 77)		

Table 21.6: Main parameters of the MOHGA.

Memory size	Non-replaceable memory	Replaceable memory	Working memory	Pareto optimal	Duration
50	25	25	5	9	01:51:12

Table 21.7: The best results for voice (Pareto optimal).

Solution	No. of modules	% of data	Total rec. (%)	Error
1	5	79	98.05	0.0195
2	9	49	97.40	0.0260
3	9	44	96.96	0.0303
4	5	38	95.88	0.0411
5	10	19	89.44	0.1055
6	10	19	89.44	0.1055
7	7	17	83.76	0.1623
8	7	7	74.45	0.2554
9	6	4	73.73	0.2626

Table 21.8: The best result of the voice (optimized).

No. of mod.	% and voices	No. hidden layers and No. of neurons	Persons per module	Rec. rate	Error
9	49%	4 (57,144,128,83)	Module # 1(1 to 14)	375/385	0.0260
	(1, 3, 8, 9 and 10)	4 (156,189,158,193)	Module # 2(15 to 35)	97.40%	
		5(123,105,169,110,105)	Module # 3(36 to 46)		
		1(89)	Module # 4(47 to 50)		
		3(78,143,62)	Module # 5(51 to 53)		
		2(101,38)	Module # 6(54 to 55)		
		4(22,60,91,173)	Module # 7(56 to 64)		
		4(81,128,139,118)	Module # 8(65 to 72)		
		4(145,28,187,32)	Module # 9(73 to 77)		

The solutions that have a recognition rate greater than 97% are taken, and of the resulting set, the solution with lower percentage of data is the best for us.

21.5. Conclusions

A new method for designing modular neural networks with a granular approach was proposed. The main goal of this work was providing the modular neural networks with the following characteristics: allow changing the number of modules, data per module, and percentage of data for training, all of that with the goal of obtaining a better rate of recognition.

A multi-objective HGA was developed for optimization of some parameters of the model of modular neural networks, these parameters are the number of modules, percentage of data for training, goal error per module, number of hidden layers per module and their respective neurons. This MOHGA is able to obtain the best modular neural network with the lowest error of recognition and that uses the lowest percentage of data for the training phase.

In this work when the tests with the ear are compared, a significant difference does not exist, because the database has few images per person, but if we compare the non-optimized versus the optimized test in the case of the voice, we can notice that with less data a good recognition rate is obtained.

References

Abraham, A., Jain, L. and Goldberg R. (2005). *Evolutionary Multiobjective Optimization, First Edition*. Heidelberg, Germany: Springer.

Auda, G. and Kamel, M. S. (1999). Modular neural networks, a survey. *Int. J. Neural Syst.*, 9(2), pp. 129–151.

Azamm, F. (2000). *Biologically Inspired Modular Neural Networks*. Ph.D. thesis. Blacksburg, Virginia: Virginia Polytechnic Institute and State University.

Bargiela, A. and Pedrycz, W. (2006). The roots of granular computing. *IEEE Int. Conf. Granular Comput. (GrC), 2006*, San Jose, California, USA, pp. 806–809.

Coello Coello, C. A., Lamont, G. B. and van Veldhuizen, D. A. (2007). *Evolutionary Algorithms for Solving Multi-Objective Problems, Second Edition*. Heidelberg, Germany: Springer.

Coello Coello, C. A. and Toscano Pulido, G. (2001). A micro-genetic algorithm for multiobjective optimization. In Coello, C. A. and Corne, D. W. (eds.), *Evolutionary Multiobjective Optimization 2001. Lecture Notes in Computer Science*, 1993, pp. 126–140.

Coley, A. (1999). *An Introduction to Genetic Algorithms for Scientists and Engineers, Har/Dskt Edition*. Singapore: WSPC.

Database Ear Recognition Laboratory from the University of Science & Technology Beijing (USTB). Found on the Web page: http://www.ustb.edu.cn/resb/en/index.htm asp (Accessed 21 September 2009).

Fonseca, C. M. and Fleming, P. J. (1993). Genetic algorithms for multiobjective optimization: formulation, discussion and generalization. *Int. Conf. Genetic Algorithms (ICGA 1993)*, San Mateo, USA, pp. 416–423.

Haupt, R. and Haupt, S. (2004). *Practical Genetic Algorithms, Second Edition*. New York: Wiley-Interscience, pp. 42–43.

Hidalgo, D., Castillo, O. and Melin, P. (2009). Type-1 and type-2 fuzzy inference systems as integration methods in modular neural networks for multimodal biometry and its optimization with genetic algorithms. *Inf. Sci.*, 179(13), pp. 2123–2145.

Huang, J. and Wechsler, H. (1999). Eye location using genetic algorithm. *Second Int. Conf. Audio Video-Based Biometric Person Authentic., 1999*, Corfel, Greece, pp. 130–135.

Khan, A., Bandopadhyaya, T. and Sharma, S. (2009). Classification of stocks using self-organizing map. *Int. J. Soft Comput. Appl.*, 4, pp. 19–24.

Melin, P. and Castillo, O. (2005). *Hybrid Intelligent Systems for Pattern Recognition Using Soft Computing: An Evolutionary Approach for Neural Networks and Fuzzy Systems, First Edition*. Heidelberg, Germany: Springer, pp. 119–122.

Melin, P., Kacprzyk, J. and Pedrycz, W. (2009). *Bio-Inspired Hybrid Intelligent Systems for Image Analysis and Pattern Recognition*. Heidelberg, Germany: Springer.

Melin, P., Mendoza, O. and Castillo, O. (2010). An improved method for edge detection based on interval type-2 fuzzy logic. *Expert Syst. Appl.*, 37(12), pp. 8527–8535.

Melin, P., Mendoza, O. and Castillo, O. (2011). Face recognition with an improved interval type-2 fuzzy logic Sugeno integral and modular neural networks. *IEEE Trans. Syst., Man, Cybern., Part A*, 41(5), pp. 1001–1012.

Melin, P., Sánchez, D. and Castillo, O. (2012). Genetic optimization of modular neural networks with fuzzy response integration for human recognition. *Inf. Sci.*, 197, pp. 1–19.

Mendoza, O., Melin, P. and Castillo, O. (2009a). Interval type-2 fuzzy logic and modular neural networks for face recognition applications. *Appl. Soft Comput.*, 9(4), pp. 1377–1387.

Mendoza, O., Melin, P. and Licea, G. (2009b). A hybrid approach for image recognition combining type-2 fuzzy logic, modular neural networks and the Sugeno integral. *Inf. Sci.*, 179(13), pp. 2078–2101.

Mitchell, M. (1998). *An Introduction to Genetic Algorithms, Third Edition*. Colorado: Bradford.

Nawa, N., Takeshi, F., Hashiyama, T. and Uchikawa, Y. (1999). A study on the discovery of relevant fuzzy rules using pseudobacterial genetic algorithm. *IEEE Trans. Ind. Electron.*, 46(6), pp. 1080–1089.

Sánchez, D. and Melin, P. (2010). Modular neural network with fuzzy integration and its optimization using genetic algorithms for human recognition based on iris, ear and voice biometrics. In Patricia, M., Janusz, K. and Witold, P. (eds.), *Soft Computing for Recognition Based on Biometrics Studies in Computational Intelligence, First Edition*. Heidelberg, Germany: Springer, pp. 85–102.

Santos, J. M., Alexandre, L. A. and Marques de Sá, J. (2006). Modular neural network task decomposition via entropic clustering. *Sixth Int. Conf. Intell. Sys. Design Appl., ISDA (1) 2006*, Jinan, China, pp. 1067–1072.

Segovia, J., Szczepaniak, P. S. and Niedzwiedzinski, M. (2002). *E-Commerce and Intelligent Methods, First Edition*. Heidelberg, Germany: Physica-Verlag, p. 181.

Tang, K. S., Man, K. F., Kwong, S. and Liu, Z. F. (1998). Minimal fuzzy memberships and rule using hierarchical genetic algorithms. *IEEE Trans. Ind. Electron.*, 45(1), pp. 162–169.

Wang, C., Soh, Y. C., Wang, H. and Wang, H. (2002). A hierarchical genetic algorithm for path planning in a static environment with obstacles. *Can. Conf. Electr. Comput. Eng. 2002, IEEE CCECE 2002*, 3, Niagara Falls, Canada, pp. 1652–1657.

Worapradya, K. and Pratishthananda, S. (2004). Fuzzy supervisory PI controller using hierarchical genetic algorithms. *Fifth Asian Control Conf., 2004*, 3, Taipei, Taiwan, pp. 1523–1528.

Yao, J. T. (2005a). Information granulation and granular relationships. *Proc. 2005 IEEE Conf. Granular Comput. (GrC)*, San Jose, California, USA, pp. 326–329.
Yao, J. T. (2007). A ten-year review of granular computing. *Proc. Third IEEE Int. Conf. Granular Comput. (GrC), 2007*, San Jose, California, USA, pp. 734–739.
Yao, Y. Y. (2000). Granular computing: basic issues and possible solutions. *Proc. Fifth Joint Conf. Inf. Sci.*, 2000, pp. 186–189.
Yao, Y. Y. (2001). On modeling data mining with granular computing. *25th Int. Comput. Softw. Appl. Conf. (COMPSAC 2001)*, Taipei, Taiwan, pp. 638–649.
Yao, Y. Y. (2004). A partition model of granular computing. *Lect. Notes Comput. Sci.*, 3100, Heidelberg, Germany, pp. 232–253.
Yao, Y. Y. (2005b). Perspectives of granular computing. *IEEE Int. Conf. Granular Comput. (GrC) 2005*, San Jose, California, USA, pp. 85–90.
Yu, F. and Pedrycz, W. (2009). The design of fuzzy information granules: Tradeoffs between specificity and experimental evidence. *Appl. Soft Comput.*, 9(1), pp. 264–273.

Chapter 22

Hybrid Evolutionary-, Constructive- and Evolving Fuzzy Neural Networks

Michael J. Watts and Nikola Kasabov

The term "evolving" in its most general form means "changing through time", "developing", or "unfolding". In this chapter, we will describe several ways in which this concept has been applied to artificial neural networks (ANNs), i.e., evolutionary, constructive, evolving, and their hybrid combinations. The chapter presents a review of various methods, systems and their applications developed in the last 20 or so years and also points to new directions for the development of evolving ANN (EANN). It makes a clear distinction between evolutionary ANN, where the whole ANN is optimized with the use of heuristic driven evolutionary algorithms (EA) that are population, generation based, and the constructive EANN which develop their structure and functionality using incremental learning methods, even though they may use EA for some parameter optimization if necessary. A type of constructive ANN, called evolving connectionist system (ECoS) is presented in more detail in another chapter of the handbook.

22.1. Introduction

There are several well-known problems associated with conventional artificial neural network (ANN, also called connectionist systems). Difficulties such as selecting the topology of a network, the training algorithm and parameters used, the amount of knowledge an ANN can store, and their limited adaptability over time, all place constraints on the real world performance of connectionist structures.

The topology of an ANN will have a distinct effect upon its quality. The input features used are of critical importance. Including redundant or irrelevant features of the input space will cause the network to learn very slowly, if at all, and will require a larger network in order to handle the unnecessarily complex input space.

Conversely, omitting important features will make learning in the network almost impossible. Statistical analysis can help make these decisions, but has a problem handling unending (continuous) data streams.

The number of hidden nodes in a feed-forward network is of great concern to an ANN practitioner. Although it has been established that a feed-forward ANN with sufficient hidden neurons can approximate any continuous function (Kolmogorov, 1957; Cybenko, 1989), the number of neurons needed is unknown. Again, it is a balancing act between having too few, which will make learning impossible due to a lack of connections within which to store knowledge, and having too many, which makes over-learning almost inevitable. The final architectural problem with ANN is the connectivity of the neurons. Some connections after training will probably be less relevant than others: their presence may cause confusion and inefficiency in the network.

Selection of the training parameters is a multi-parameter optimization problem: too low a learning rate means that the network will train slowly, but with less chance of becoming stuck in a local minimum. Too high a learning rate will speed the training process, but increases the chances of it being stuck in a local minimum. An additional danger is that a high learning rate will lead to over-training, or over-fitting, on the training data. The momentum parameter of the algorithm must also be chosen with care: if the momentum is too low, then it will not serve its purpose of smoothing the network's trajectory across the error surface. If it is too high, then the network may overshoot the global minimum. Some work has also been done on dynamically calculating the training parameters as learning is underway (Moreira and Fiesler, 1995; Schiffmann *et al.*, 1994).

ANN are limited in dynamic adaptation. Catastrophic forgetting is the term used to describe what happens when an ANN previously trained on one dataset is further trained on another (McCloskey and Cohen, 1989). Although the ANN is usually able to learn the new dataset quite adequately, it is likely to forget the previous dataset. This causes problems when the ANN must be used in a so-called "online learning" application, which requires new data to be continuously accommodated: the new data will be handled, but the old data will be forgotten.

Although there are now many variants of back-propagation training in existence, they all suffer from a lack of training speed (Fahlman, 1988). Back-propagation requires the repeated presentation of the entire training set, usually hundreds or thousands of times before an acceptable result is obtained. Although some back-propagation derived algorithms are usually much faster (e.g., quickprop (Fahlman, 1988)), these still require the repetitive presentation of the training set.

Most of these problems are search problems: we must search for the near-optimal topology of an ANN; we must search for the near-optimal parameters when training the ANN. There are, therefore, three main approaches to optimizing the structure of ANN:

(a) Using evolutionary algorithms (EAs) for the optimization of the whole ANN; we call these evolutionary ANN (Section 22.2).
(b) Using a constructive algorithm. We call these constructive ANN (Section 22.3).
(c) Using improved constructive algorithms for the ANN to self-organize and adapt its structure, functionality and to accumulate new knowledge across multiple datasets and problems. This is the case of evolving connectionist systems (ECoS, Section 22.4). As a partial case ECoS can use EA for the optimization of some of their parameters if necessary, but the main emphasis is on the learning and adaptation methods that are brain-like methods.

In this chapter, we assume that the reader is already familiar with the basic principles of ANN and gradient-descent based ANN training. We also assume that the reader is familiar with the principles of EA, especially genetic algorithms (GA), evolutionary programming (EP) and evolution strategies (ES).

22.2. Evolutionary ANN

EA are search algorithms inspired by natural selection and biological evolution. Attempts to solve the search problems in ANN using the search abilities of EA have brought the two areas of ANN and EA together with pioneering work by D. Fogel and later by X. Yao.

While methods of combining EA and ANN continue to be an active area of research, most of the work in this field has been directed towards evolving the architecture of the ANN, its parameters, and its connection weights.

The type of EA used varies according to the application. GA are very widely used, but this raises issues with representation of the ANN as a chromosome, and in how the chromosomes (genotype) are mapped to the final ANN (the phenotype). EP has also been used, especially when evolving the connection weights of the ANN. This avoids the problems with mapping from genotype to phenotype, as the mutation evolutionary operator in EP works directly on the phenotype. This does, however, require finding a suitable method of mutation for the problem at hand.

Whichever EA is used, the fitness of each individual ANN within a population must be evaluated. This is usually derived from some measure of the performance of the ANN, which is often measured as the accuracy over a particular dataset, or how well it solves a particular problem. Care must be taken when selecting the fitness measure, as the EA may become stuck in an evolutionary dead-end if the fitness measure is not carefully designed to avoid it. An incautiously designed fitness function can also cause the EA to over-optimize the ANN on one aspect of the problem at the expense of other aspects.

22.2.1. *Evolving the Architecture of ANN*

As discussed above, the topology of an ANN has an enormous effect on its performance. Many researchers have investigated using EA for solving this problem. There are two general ways in which ANN topology can be evolved: directly, where the structure and connectivity of the ANN are encoded directly into the EA; and indirectly, where the EA evolves parameters of the ANN structure, which are then processed to create the final ANN. The fitness of the individuals is taken as some measure of the performance of the ANN, usually some measure of the error over a training dataset.

The most straight-forward approach used is to evolve through an EA the number of neurons in each layer. In Arena *et al.* (1993), each chromosome in the genetic algorithm was treated as a two-dimensional matrix, with each cell row representing the presence or absence of one node of the network. During evaluation, the number of nodes present in each layer was counted and an appropriate multilayer perceptron (MLP) architecture created. If no nodes were present in a row, then that layer was not included in the phenotype. Crossover was implemented as the exchange of a sub matrix from each parent. This method was tested on the optimization of a complex nonlinear system and was shown to be effective at determining a near optimal topology for the MLP. This was a direct encoding approach.

A similar two-dimensional chromosome approach can also be used, where the connectivity of the neurons is being evolved. The values of the alleles represented the presence or absence of a connection between neurons. Neurons that had no connections were removed from the ANN.

A different approach was taken in Schiffman *et al.* (1993). Here both of the previous concepts were combined, and the length of the chromosome determined the number of nodes present, as well as the connectivity of the nodes. This approach to ANN design was tested on a medical classification problem, that of identifying thyroid disorders, and provided networks that were both smaller and more accurate than manually designed ANNs. These examples were again direct encoding schemas.

A simpler, but indirect, approach was used in Watts and Kasabov (1998) to optimize the structure of a Fuzzy Neural Network (FuNN, Kasabov *et al.*, 1997). FuNN have fuzzy membership functions attached to each input and output neuron, as well as hidden neurons that represent fuzzy rules. Watts and Kasabov used a simple GA to evolve the number of fuzzy MF for each input and output, as well as the number of hidden neurons. They also directly selected which input variables were used, that is, the GA simultaneously evolved the optimal feature set as well as the optimal FuNN structure.

Note, however, that all the above methods optimize an ANN, after which the ANN becomes a fixed-topology ANN, which is a significant limit for the dynamic adaptation of the ANN. That is, the EA optimizes the ANN to the dataset used in the evaluation function, it does not allow it to adapt to any other datasets.

22.2.2. *Evolving the Training Parameters of ANN*

In addition to the selection of an ANN's topology, it is also possible to use EA to select the training parameters for the network. In these applications the EA evolves the learning parameters of the ANN, and the fitness criterion is the performance of the ANN after training.

In Choi and Bluff (1995) a GA was used to select the training parameters for the back-propagation training of an MLP. In this work, the chromosome encoded the learning rate, momentum, sigmoid parameter and number of training epochs to be used for the back-propagation training of the network. This technique was tested with several different datasets, including bottle classification data, where a glass bottle is classified as either being suitable for reuse or suitable for recycling and breast cancer data, which classifies tissue samples as malignant or benign. For each of the test datasets, the genetically derived network outperformed those networks whose control parameters were manually set, often by a significant margin. However, this approach still suffers from the inherent limitations of back-propagation training.

22.2.3. *Evolving the Connection Weights of ANN*

While gradient-descent methods such as back-propagation are powerful and useful for many applications, there are certain situations in which they will fail. As error-driven learning algorithms, back-propagation requires an error function that is continuous and differentiable, yet there are many real-world applications in which this is not the case. Back-propagation is also a local learning algorithm, that is, the change in connection weights moves the network from one point of the problem space to another nearby point. This means that the ANN can easily become trapped in local minima and fail to find the global optimum. Thus, for some problems EA training may be the only way in which to guarantee convergence and it becomes more efficient to train the ANN via EA. There are also some esoteric architectures of ANN (see below) that can only be feasibly trained via a search algorithm such as EA.

When evolving the connection weights of ANN, each individual in the EA population represents one set of connection weights. During the evaluation phase of the EA each individual is decoded into an ANN and the performance of the ANN is evaluated. Exactly how the ANN is evaluated depends entirely on the application being attempted. The simplest approach is to propagate an input dataset through the candidate ANN, and compare its outputs with the target outputs, that is, compute an error value, where the fitness of the individual is inversely proportional to the error. In these applications the EA is serving as a supervized learning algorithm. This, however, requires a set of known output values which might not be available or even be appropriate for the problem. The advantages of avoiding local minima, however, remain. An example of this approach was breast cancer detection from mammograms (Fogel *et al.*, 1997). Here, EP was used to evolve the connection weights of a MLP whose inputs were certain features of a mammogram. The evaluation function was a simple count of the number of examples that were correctly classified as cancer or not-cancer. While backpropagation was not successful at solving this problem, EP was able to produce a network with greater than 98% accuracy. Other examples of this approach are detecting sea mines from sonar returns (Porto *et al.*, 2005) and screening compounds for their anti-HIV activity (Ma *et al.*, 2006). In each of these examples, the EP algorithm works directly on the MLP, as opposed to a string of values as with GA. Changes are evolved to the connection weights. The changes to the weights are normally distributed around a mean of zero and selection was via a tournament process. The winner of each tournament was the MLP that had the highest evaluation, which was usually the lowest mean-squared error.

An interesting application of EP to MLP was evaluating potential future moves on a checkers board (Chellapilla and Fogel, 2001). The input to the MP was an encoded representation of the positions of pieces on a checkers board, and the output was an evaluation of the "goodness" of the pieces' distributions, that is, an evaluation of how advantageous the positions were to the player. The evaluation function used for this application was quite interesting. Since it was not feasible to evaluate the mean-squared error for this problem (such a measure would anyway be quite meaningless for this application) the candidate MLP played several games of checkers against other MLP, and the software chose the move that gave the best future board configuration. The games themselves were run using a simple checkers engine which would search through possible moves and future board configurations based on the current positions of pieces. The candidate MLP assessed the value of each configuration. MLP which assessed the values of configurations better won more games in the tournaments and were used as the basis of the next generation. MLP which were not so good lost more games and were eliminated. This approach worked well enough that the system was able to earn a "Master" rating on an online checkers system. A similar approach was later adapted to playing chess (Fogel *et al.*, 2004) where the system again achieved a "Master" rating.

An early example of GA-based training of non-MLP ANN was de Garis (1990, 1992). The networks used in these experiments were fully self-connected, synchronous networks. These networks are basically impossible to train via gradient descent and cannot learn using any approach other than EA. These "GenNets" were used to attempt tasks that were time dependent, such as controlling the walking action of a pair of stick legs. With this problem the inputs to the network were the current angle and angular velocity of the "hip" and "knee" joints of each leg. The outputs were the future angular acceleration of each of the joints. Both the inputs and outputs for this problem were time dependent. Conventional training methods proved to be incapable of solving this problem, while GenNets solved it very easily. Other applications of GenNets involved creating "production rule" GenNets, which duplicated the function of a production rule system. These were then inserted into a simulated artificial insect and used to process inputs from sensor GenNets. The outputs of the production rule GenNets sent signals to other GenNets to execute various actions, i.e., eat, flee, mate etc.

A similarly structured recurrent network was used in Fukuda *et al.* (1997), to attempt a similar problem. The application area in this research was using the genetically trained network to control a physical biped robot. Not only was the robot able to walk along flat and sloped surfaces, it was able to generalize its behavior to deal with surfaces it had not encountered in training. Comparison of the results gained from the genetically trained network to those trained by other methods showed that not only did the genetically trained network train more efficiently than the others; it was also able to perform much better than the others.

22.2.4. *Problems with Evolutionary ANN*

There are several problems in training ANN with EA. Firstly, the way in which connection weight values are encoded in GA chromosomes is an issue. Most GA use binary encoding, but to accurately represent connection weights to a high precision requires a large number of bits per connection weight. Too many bits per weight leads to very long chromosomes, which are inefficient, while too few bits means that there will not be sufficient precision to find the optimal weight values.

While an EA can solve the problem of selecting the training parameters of an ANN, the problem of selecting the parameters for the EA remain. While EA are generally more robust to parameter selection than ANN, incorrect selection of parameters such as population size can mean that the EA takes too long to run (for too many individuals) or does not have enough genetic diversity to solve the problem (for too few individuals).

A substantial problem with using EA to optimize ANN is that it is slow. No matter what is being optimized, every candidate ANN must be evaluated. This can involve running backpropagation training over a complete training dataset, or putting each ANN through a tournament with several other ANN. Since there are usually many thousands of ANN evaluated in a single run of an EA, this adds up to a substantial amount of time. Even today, with the fast processors available, the amount of time taken to optimize an ANN using an EA can be prohibitive for large datasets.

Another significant problem with evolving the connection weights of ANN using GA is the so-called permutation problem (Hancock, 1992). Assume we have an ANN with three hidden neurons, where each of the hidden neurons is fully connected to each of the input neurons, and each connection has a unique weight value. The order in which these hidden neurons appear in the ANN does not affect the performance of the network at all; in fact every permutation of the neurons yields exactly the same output values. Yet the order in which the connection weights appear in an artificial chromosome does matter, as they will be treated as completely unique individuals by the GA. This makes crossover operations very inefficient at finding new solutions.

Finally, while EA can solve problems with topology and parameter section, and can select connection weights, they cannot solve the problem of limited dynamic adaptation. This is when further data related to the problem appears and cannot be learned by the ANN without forgetting what it has previously learned. This is a fundamental limit of fixed-topology ANN. This limit is the motivation for constructive neural networks, which are described in the next section.

22.3. Constructive ANN

The problems with evolutionary ANN described thus far all spring from the fixed nature of traditional algorithms: once architecture has been selected for the ANN, it is not possible or not easy to alter it. This means that additional knowledge cannot be accommodated, as is needed in life-long learning applications, due to the constant number of connections within which the knowledge of the ANN is stored.

If the topology of the network can be determined automatically, then the problem of adaptation in the evolutionary ANN becomes less significant. This is the motivation behind so-called constructive ANN, where the network is constructed by the training algorithm, during training. Instead of starting with an ANN of fixed topology, a constructive algorithm starts with a minimal network and progressively adds neurons and connections as needed by the training algorithm. This is the other meaning of "evolving": while constructive algorithms do not follow the principles of EA, they are evolving as the ANN changes and adapts through time. That is, the network "evolves" by altering its structure as data is presented to it.

This helps with the topology determination process, as most constructive algorithms will stop adding neurons when such additions no longer improve performance. The learning algorithms applied to constructive networks are called constructive learning algorithms.

Constructive algorithms began as an extension of the backpropagation of errors training algorithms operating on the well-known MLP. One of the earliest constructive algorithms proposed, was the Dynamic Node Creation algorithm (Ash, 1989). As constructive algorithms matured, they started to move away from the backpropagation algorithm in favor of other training methods, and started to modify the MLP architecture to a greater degree than just expanding its hidden layer. Two examples of this kind of algorithm are the Tiling algorithm (Mézard and Nadal, 1989) and the Upstart algorithm (Frean, 1990). The Cascade Correlation algorithm (Fahlman and Lebiere, 1990) abandoned the MLP structure completely, but still used a form of backpropagation to set the connection weights. The final group of constructive algorithms is described here and is quite different from their predecessors: These are the Resource Allocating Network (RAN; Platt, 1991); the evolutionary nearest-neighbor MLP (NN-MLP; Zhao and Higuchi, 1996); and the grow and learn (GAL) network (Alpaydin, 1994). They generally have little in common with the architectures of previous ANN algorithms, and use a method of training specific to their architecture.

22.3.1. *Resource Allocating Networks*

The RAN was proposed in Platt (1991) as a way of quickly loading knowledge into a network without over-training. It is a two neuron layer network, where the first layer represents input space regions and the second layer represents the output function being modeled. The first layer neurons use Gaussian functions. The parameters of each Gaussian function represent a specific region of the input space: each neuron in that layer calculates its activation based on how close its region is to the presented input vector, and will thus respond most strongly to inputs from that region. The output layer performs a weighted sum over the outputs of the input layer neurons, and adds a constant vector that is independent of the input vector. Figure 22.1 shows a RAN network.

A RAN learns via two different mechanisms: the first adds Gaussian units according to the novelty of the input examples presented. The second modifies the connection weights according to the error of the network. The network begins with no stored patterns. As training examples are presented, both the distance between the existing Gaussian units and the input vector, and the difference between the actual and desired output vectors, are measured. If they are above a certain threshold, a new node is added. The Gaussian parameters of the new node are set so that its maximum response is for the current, novel example, with its width being proportional to its distance from the nearest existing node. The connections to the output layer are set to the difference between the network output and the desired output. If a new unit is not added, then the existing connections to the output layer are modified via a

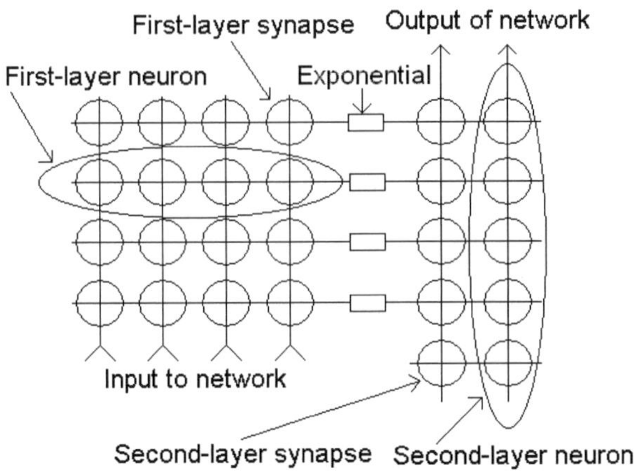

Figure 22.1: A RAN.

simple gradient descent algorithm so that the error of the network is reduced. As training progresses, the threshold values decay towards a set value: this means that the knowledge stored in the network will become more and more finely represented.

22.3.2. *Nearest Neighbor MLP*

The NN-MLP is a connectionist implementation of the nearest-neighbor classifier algorithm (Gates, 1972). In this architecture, each hidden layer neuron corresponds to a training example, with the incoming connection weight vector of the neuron being equal to the example vector it represents. Activation of the hidden neurons is calculated in the following manner: the distance between the incoming weight vector and the current example vector is calculated, and this measure is subtracted from a counter value embedded in each hidden neuron. When the value of this counter reaches zero, the neuron fires, outputting a value of one. When a neuron fires, it inhibits all other neurons that belong to the same class from firing. An output neuron will fire when any of its inputs is one. The simplest way of constructing a NN-MLP is to create one hidden neuron for each example in the training set. This, however, will lead to a very large hidden layer, with all of the problems of efficiency and generalization accuracy that entails.

A means of constructing parsimonious NN-MLP was proposed in Zhao and Higuchi (1996). This algorithm is designed to find the minimum number of hidden neurons needed to accurately model the training dataset. The algorithm is called the $R4$-Rule, for the four separate procedures employed in it: Recognition, Remembrance, Reduction, and Review. Recognition is the process by which training examples are matched to hidden neurons. Of interest in this phase are two parameters associated with each neuron, the class label of the neuron, denoted as λ, and its importance, denoted as ρ. A hidden neuron n will fire if all three of the following conditions are true:

— It belongs to the same class as the training example (that is, $\lambda_n = \lambda_x$).
— The incoming connection weight vector of n is closer to x than any others.
— The ρ value is the largest. The values of λ_n and ρ_n are set automatically during training: whenever n is a winner, the value of ρ_n is increased. If it is a loser (it matches the first two conditions given above but has a lower ρ value) then ρ_n is decreased.

Remembrance involves evaluating the performance of the network across the dataset. If a large number of recognition errors occur, then new hidden neurons will be added to the network. As opposed to adding a single hidden neuron for each misclassified example, only one hidden neuron is added for each misclassified class. This reduces the number of neurons added to the network. If the recognition rate is high, then hidden neurons can be removed.

Reduction prunes neurons from the network when their values get very low. Only a single neuron is removed every time the reduction procedure is carried out. This is to stabilize the learning process. If the removal of the neuron causes classification errors then the reduction process is undone.

Review adjusts the connection weights of the network, and is carried out whenever a neuron is added or deleted. It is a supervized learning process, and adjusts the connection weights of the network to be closer to x.

These four steps and the relationships between them are shown in Figure 22.2.

22.3.3. *GAL Networks*

GAL networks were proposed by Alpaydin (1994). They are three neuron layer binary classification networks that expand their structure as required to

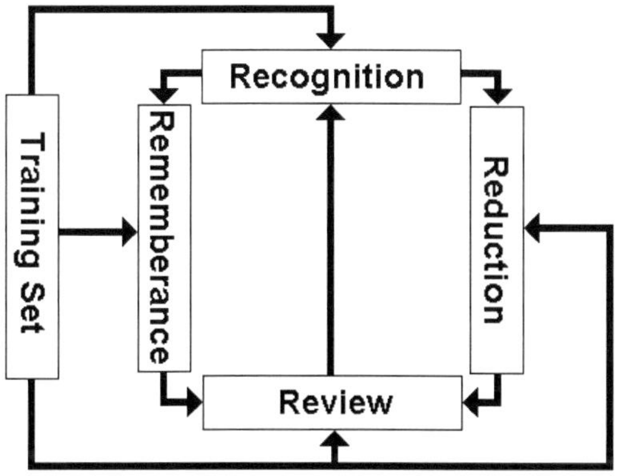

Figure 22.2: The R4 algorithm.

accommodate new training examples. The first neuron layer is the input layer: initially, this is the only layer that exists in the network. The second layer of neurons is the exemplar layer, which represents the memorized training examples. The third layer is called the class layer. The neurons in this layer represent the classes that the network is learning to distinguish. A vector is propagated through the input layer to each neuron in the exemplar layer. There, the distance between the input vector and the incoming connection weight vector is calculated, with Euclidean distance being the most commonly used distance measure. The exemplar neuron with the least distance between the input vector and its incoming connection weight vector is the winner and is allowed to activate. The winner will emit a value of one, while all other exemplar neurons will stay quiescent. The exemplar neuron layer to class neuron layer connection weights identify which class neuron will activate for each exemplar neuron.

Training of a GAL network occurs one example at a time. If the current example is correctly classified (that is, the correct class neuron is activated) then no changes are made to the network. If the current example is misclassified, then a new exemplar neuron is added. When a new exemplar neuron is added, its incoming connection weights are set to the current input vector, so that it will activate the most strongly if that example is seen again. The outgoing connections of the new exemplar are set so that the desired class neuron activates. If the class is new (not represented by the network) then a new class neuron is added also.

During the course of training, some of the exemplar neurons may become redundant. This is because newer exemplars may sit closer to the boundaries of the classes being learned than the existing exemplars. To deal with these redundant neurons, sleep learning of GAL networks was developed. First, an exemplar neuron is randomly identified. Its incoming connection weight vector is extracted, and used as an input vector. The input vector is then propagated through the network to identify the desired output class for that neuron. Then, the vector is again propagated through the network with the current exemplar neuron disabled. If the network still correctly classifies the example, then the current exemplar is redundant and can be removed. This process can be repeated as many times as desired. Since this procedure can lead to an increase in error for the GAL network, it is often necessary to repeat the training/sleep learning process several times.

A GAL network will always have a winning exemplar neuron. This means that there will always be one class neuron that activates, whether it is the right class or not. To deal with this, the top two activated exemplars are found (the "best two" exemplars) and their corresponding classes identified. If the two classes are different, then no class neuron will activate. If they are the same, then that class will be the winner. This has the effect of giving the network the capacity to reject an example as unclassifiable.

The basic GAL learning algorithm does not modify the connection weights. The only modification to the network is via the addition and deletion of neurons. This has some disadvantages, such as sensitivity to noise and a tendency to memorize the training set at the expense of generalization. Fine-tuning of GAL can overcome this problem to some extent, by modifying the input to exemplar connection weights. This modification is done according to Equation (1).

$$W_{i,e}(t+1) = W_{i,e}(t) + \alpha(P_i - W_{i,e}(t)), \tag{1}$$

where

$W_{i,e}(t)$ is the connection weight from input i to exemplar e,
α is a learning rate term, that is usually set to decay as learning progresses, and
P_i is element i of the current training vector $\mathbf{P}$.

The intent of this modification is to move the winning exemplar neurons weight vector towards the statistical mean of that class. It is noted (Alpaydin, 1994, p. 407) that "a large number of iterations will be necessary" to tune the GAL network. GAL is limited to classification problems. However, it is able to continue to learn additional datasets after the completion of the initial training cycle. Also, the removal of redundant neurons through sleep learning will protect it from over-training. Although the training algorithm is iterative, the algorithm itself is quite simple. If the number of training iterations were kept to a minimum, then GAL could be expected to be very efficient.

22.3.4. *Problems with Constructive Algorithms*

This section has presented a sample of the constructive algorithms in existence. While there are many others, this sample covers the major principles employed and illustrates the drawbacks of these algorithms. The major problem that is suffered by most, especially the older, backpropagation trained MLP derived algorithms, is that they are limited to learning a single dataset, a problem that is shared by ANN evolved with EA. This is a major limitation, as one of the major advantages of constructive networks is that they can continue to adapt to new data throughout their lifetime. Another significant problem is that some constructive algorithms are only suitable for classification, for example GAL (Kwok and Yeung, 1999).

22.4. ECoS

ECoS networks have several advantages over other constructive algorithms. Firstly, they are not limited to a particular application domain; they can be applied to both classification and function approximation. Secondly, they do not require multiple presentations of the training dataset, as is the case with some of the constructive algorithms in existence, such as RAN and GAL. Finally, they are able to continue learning and are not restricted to learning a single training set as other constructive algorithms are.

ECoS is a class of constructive ANN architectures with a learning algorithm that modifies the structure of the network as training examples are presented. Although the seminal ECoS architecture was the Evolving Fuzzy Neural Network (EFuNN), several other architectures have been developed that utilize the ECoS algorithm. These include the minimalist Simple Evolving Connectionist System (SECoS) and the Dynamic Evolving Neural-Fuzzy Inference System (DENFIS).

ECoS was designed around the following principles (Kasabov, 1998):

(1) The ECoS training algorithm is designed with the intention that all the algorithm can learn from the data is learned in the first training pass (one-pass learning). Additional exposure to the training data is not necessary.
(2) ECoS are intended to be used in an online learning application. This means that new data will be constantly and continuously coming into the system, and that this data must be learned by the network without forgetting the old. The general ECoS architecture and learning algorithm allows an ECoS network to accommodate this new data without a catastrophic forgetting of the old.
(3) The manner in which neurons are added to an ECoS means that some training examples are stored, initially, verbatim within the structure of the network. These examples are then either modified (refined) by exposure to further examples, or, depending upon the training parameters used, remain the same and can be later retrieved.

The advantages of ECoS are that they avoid the problems associated with traditional connectionist structures such as MLP (Kasabov, 1998; Kasabov *et al.*, 2003): They are hard to over-train, due to the constructive nature of their learning algorithm; they learn quickly, as the learning algorithm is a one-pass algorithm, that is, it requires only a single presentation of the dataset; and they are far more resistant to catastrophic forgetting than most other models, as new training data is represented by adding new neurons, rather than accommodating the additional data in the existing neurons. ECoS networks also have several advantages over other constructive algorithms. Firstly, they are not limited to a particular application domain; they can be applied to both classification and function approximation. Secondly, they do not require multiple presentations of the training dataset, as is the case with some of the constructive algorithms in existence, such as RAN (Platt, 1991) and GAL (Alpaydin, 1994). Finally, they are able to continue learning and are not restricted to learning a single training set as are other constructive algorithms.

22.4.1. *ECoS Architecture and Learning*

The first ECoS network was EFuNN (Kasabov, 1998), from which a generalized constructive ANN architecture and training algorithm was derived. An ECoS network is a multiple neuron layer, constructive ANN. An ECoS network will always have at least one "evolving" neuron layer. This is the constructive layer, the layer that will grow and adapt itself to the incoming data, and is the layer with which the learning algorithm is most concerned. The meaning of the connections leading into this layer, the activation of this layer's neurons and the forward propagation algorithms of the evolving layer all differ from those of classical connectionist systems such as MLP. For the purposes of this chapter, the term "input layer" refers to the neuron layer immediately preceding the evolving layer, while the term "output layer" means the neuron layer immediately following the evolving layer. This is irrespective of whether or not these layers are the actual input or output layers of the network proper. For example, in Figure 22.3, which shows a generic ECoS structure, the "input layer" could be the input layer proper of the network (as with SECoS networks) or it could be a neuron layer that processes the actual input values for presentation to the evolving layer (as with EFuNN networks). By the same token, the "output layer" could be the actual output layer of the network (as it is with SECoS) or a neuron layer that further processes the outputs of the evolving layer (as with EFuNN). The connection layers from the input neuron layer to the evolving neuron layer and from the evolving layer to the output neuron layer are fully connected.

The activation A_n of an evolving layer neuron n is determined by Equation (2).

$$A_n = 1 - D_n, \tag{2}$$

where D_n is the distance between the input vector and the incoming weight vector for that neuron. Since ECoS evolving layers are fully connected, it is possible to

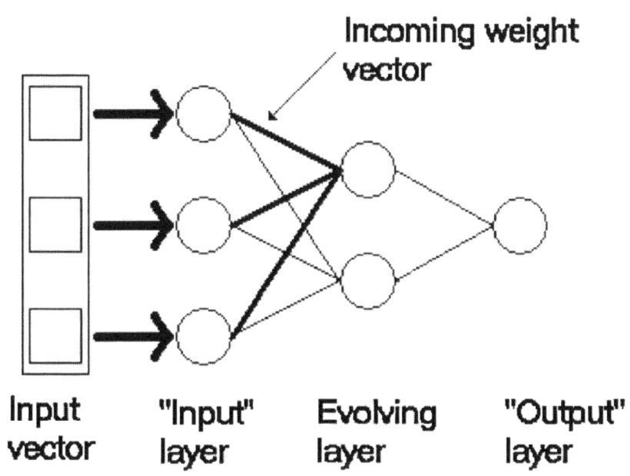

Figure 22.3: General ECoS architecture.

measure the distance between the current input vector and the incoming weight vector of each evolving-layer neuron. Although the distance can be measured in any way that is appropriate for the inputs, this distance function must return a value in the range of zero to unity. For this reason, most ECoS algorithms assume that the input data will be normalized, as it is far easier to formulate a distance function that produces output in the desired range if it is normalized to the range zero to unity.

Whereas most ANN propagate the activation of each neuron from one layer to the next, ECoS evolving layers propagate their activation by one of two alternative strategies. The first of these strategies, entitled OneOfN propagation, involves only propagating the activation of the most highly activated ("winning") neuron. The second strategy, Many of N propagates the activation values of those neurons with an activation value greater than the activation threshold A_{thr}.

The ECoS learning algorithm is based on accommodating new training examples within the evolving layer, by either modifying the weight values of the connections attached to the evolving layer neurons, or by adding a new neuron to that layer. The algorithm employed is described below.

- For each input vector **I** and its associated desired output vector $\mathbf{O_d}$
  - Propagate **I** through the network,
  - Find the most activated evolving layer neurons j and its activation A,
  - If $A_j < S_{\mathrm{thr}}$ then,
    - Add a neuron,
  - Else
    - Find the errors E between $\mathbf{O_d}$ and the output activations A_o,
    - If $E > E_{\mathrm{thr}}$ then,
      - Add a neuron,
    - Else
      - Update the connections to the winning evolving layer neuron j.

The addition of neurons to the evolving layer is driven by the novelty of the current training example: if the current example is particularly novel (it is not adequately represented by the existing neurons) then a new neuron will be added. Four parameters are involved in this algorithm: the sensitivity threshold S_{thr}, the error threshold E_{thr}, and the two learning rates η_1 and η_2. The sensitivity threshold and error threshold both control the addition of neurons and when a neuron is added, its incoming connection weight vector is set to the input vector **I**, and its outgoing weight vector is set to the desired output vector $\mathbf{O_d}$. The sensitivity and error thresholds are measures of the novelty of the current example. If the current example causes a low activation (that is, it is novel with respect to the existing neurons) then the sensitivity threshold will cause a neuron to be added that represents that example. If the example does not trigger the addition of a neuron via the sensitivity threshold, but the output generated by that example results in an output error that is greater than the error threshold (that is, it had a novel output), then a neuron will be added.

22.4.2. *Evolving Fuzzy Neural Network*

EFuNN were proposed by Kasabov (1998c). They are fuzzy neural networks developed within the ECoS framework, that is, they are FuNNs (Kasabov *et al.*, 1997) that have been modified to take into account the principles of ECoS. The distance measure used in EFuNN is the normalized fuzzy distance, as defined in Equation (3).

$$D_n = \frac{\frac{1}{2}\left(\sum_{i=1}^{c} \left|\boldsymbol{I}_i - \boldsymbol{W}_{i,n}\right|\right)}{\sum_{i=1}^{c} \boldsymbol{W}_{i.n}}, \tag{3}$$

where

c is the number of condition neurons,
I is the input vector, and
W is the input to condition layer weight matrix.

The learning algorithm is only slightly different from the general ECoS learning algorithm, in that the weight values for the incoming and outgoing connections of a new neuron are the fuzzified input and output values: there must therefore be two additional steps performed the fuzzification of the current input and desired output vectors, before insertion of the new neuron.

22.4.3. *Simple Evolving Connectionist System*

The SECoS was proposed (Watts and Kasabov, 2000) as a minimalist implementation of the ECoS algorithm. SECoS were first introduced in Watts (1999b) and more fully developed in Watts and Kasabov (2000). Lacking the fuzzification and defuzzification mechanisms of EFuNN, the SECoS model was created for several reasons. Firstly, they are a simpler alternative to EFuNN. Since they lack the fuzzification and defuzzification structures of EFuNN, SECoS are much simpler to implement: with fewer connection matrices and a smaller number of neurons, there is much less processing involved in simulating a SECoS network. They are also much easier to understand and analyze: while EFuNN expands the dimensionality of the input and output spaces with its fuzzy logic elements, SECoS deals with the input and output space “as is”. Therefore, rather than dealing with a fuzzy problem space, SECoS deals with the problem space directly. Each neuron that is added to the network during training represents a point in the problem space, rather than a point in the expanded fuzzy problem space. Secondly, for some situations, fuzzified inputs are not only unnecessary but harmful to performance, as they lead to an increase in the number of evolving layer neurons. Binary datasets are particularly vulnerable to this, as fuzzification does nothing but increase the dimensionality of the input data. By removing the fuzzification and defuzzification capabilities, it is proposed that the adaptation advantages of EFuNN are retained while eliminating the disadvantages of fuzzification, specifically by eliminating the need to select the number and parameters of the input and output membership functions.

A SECoS has only three layers of neurons, the input layer, with linear transfer functions, an evolving layer with distance-based neuron activation functions, and an output layer with a simple saturated linear activation function. The distance function used in the evolving layer is the normalized Manhattan distance, as shown in Equation (4).

$$D_n = \frac{\sum_{i=1}^{c} |\mathbf{I}_c - \mathbf{W}_c|}{\sum_{i=1}^{x} |\mathbf{I}_c + \mathbf{W}_c|}, \tag{4}$$

where

c is the number of input neurons in the SECoS,
I is the input vector,
W is the input to evolving layer weight matrix.

The learning algorithm is the same as that used by EFuNN. However, in SECoS the input vector is the actual crisp input vector, while the desired outputs vector is the unmodified desired output vector.

22.4.4. *Dynamic Evolving Fuzzy Inference System (DENFIS)*

DENFIS was developed by Kasabov and Song (2002). While EFuNN and SECoS apply supervised clustering of the input–output data, the co-ordinates of the cluster centers being represented as connection weights (input and output respectively) of the evolving (hidden) neurons, DENFIS evolves the hidden nodes through unsupervised clustering of the input examples and then evolves a function to approximate the data in each cluster as a local output model. This function can be a linear regression, a Takagi–Sugeno function of any order, a nonlinear model such as another ANN, etc.

DENFIS is a time-series prediction model that can work successfully for online, real time prediction problems (Kasabov *et al.*, 2003; Kasabov, 2007).

22.4.5. *Applications of ECoS*

ECoS have been applied to many different application areas. The first of these is automatic speech recognition. In Kasabov (1999), EFuNNs were applied to spoken phoneme recognition. EFuNNs were again applied to this problem in Watts (1999a), and were shown to be both accurate and highly adaptable. The efficiency of SECoS networks in this application area was demonstrated in Watts and Kasabov (2000), where a comparison with MLP showed that they were faster training, more adaptable and more accurate than MLP. Speech recognition via whole word recognition has also been done using ECoS networks. EFuNNs were used in Ghobakhlou *et al.* (2000), while SECoS were adopted in Ghobakhlou and Seesink (2001), for speech-control of a robot, and in Ghobakhlou and Kasabov (2003), for control of a home-automation system.

Bioinformatics is another area where ECoS have been applied. Prediction of RNA initiation sites, that is, sites on RNA strands where protein transcription begins, was accomplished in Futschik *et al.* (1999). Comparisons between EFuNN and MLP were carried out, and EFuNN was found to be able to detect unique RNA patterns that other methods could not. EFuNN was used to model gene regulatory networks in Kasabov *et al.* (2000). The data for the model were gene expression levels captured from micro-arrays. Useful rules describing the development of the cells through time were discovered. Using EFuNN, the work in Futschik *et al.* (2003) identified cancer tissues from gene expression in micro arrays and used rule extraction to identify cancer genes. No comparison with other algorithms was done, but this was not an issue because knowledge discovery via rule extraction was the goal of the work. Useful rules were extracted from the trained EFuNN. A review of bioinformatics and neuroinformatics application of ECoS can be found in Kasabov (2008a; 2008b; 2007; 2014).

Clinical and micro array genetic data was combined using EFuNN in Futschik *et al.* (2003; 2003b) to generate patient prognoses, where the outcomes were either that the patient would die, or the patient would recover. A multi-modular approach was used, where clinical data was modeled by one module and genetic data by another. The reported accuracies of EFuNN were higher than those reported by earlier researchers (87.5% as opposed to 77.6%).

Another bio-medical application of EFuNN was presented in Leichter *et al.* (2001). In this paper, an EFuNN was used to classify the stimulus received by a subject based on the electrical activity of the brain, as read by an EEG. Although the purpose of the paper was to demonstrate an independent component analysis (ICA) based approach to de-noising the EEG data, EFuNN was found to be accurate.

ECoS networks have been shown to be well-suited to image and video processing. Classifying motion vector patterns, or the changes from one frame to the next in an MPEG video stream was the application in Koprinska and Kasabov (1999). The task was to classify a frame from a compressed video stream as one of six classes: static, panning, zooming, object motion, tracking, and dissolve. This work compared the performance of EFuNN against the LVQ algorithm (Kohonen, 1997), as well as analyzing the effect of varying the number of membership functions on performance.

The performance of MLP and EFuNN were compared in Sorwar *et al.* (2001), where the application was the classification of images of textures. EFuNN was found to be more accurate and to have a much lower computational load than MLP. The lower computational load presumably came about from EFuNNs faster training algorithm.

Horticultural applications of image processing were the subject of Elder (2000); Woodford (2001, 2008a); Woodford *et al.* (2004). The problem dealt with here was classification of pest damage on apple tree leaves. This involved presenting full color images to an EFuNN that then had to identify which of three insect pests — Codling Moth, Leafroller, and Appleleaf Curling Midge — had caused the damage in the image. EFuNN were found to be more accurate at classifying images than k-means, MLP and SVM.

The ability to extract fuzzy rules was also considered to be an advantage in this application area. EFuNN were used to classify images of handwritten digits in Ng *et al.* (2004), where an extensive exploration of the parameters of the EFuNN and the problem itself was carried out. Accuracies ranged from 94–99%, showing how effective EFuNN was for this problem.

In the area of computer network security, ECoS have been shown to be very useful. In Abraham and Jain (2005); Abraham *et al.* (2005) EFuNN were used for network intrusion detection, where they achieved a detection accuracy of 100%. Incoming network packets were analyzed by EFuNN in Chavan *et al.* (2004) to determine whether or not the packets represented an attack. A comparison with MLP showed that the rapid adaptation capability of EFuNN made it the better choice for this application.

The flexibility of ECoS networks have led to them being applied to many other application areas. In Kasabov and Fedrizzi (1999) the task was to predict the New Zealand stock market index the SE40. Comparison of the results of EFuNN with a FuNN showed that EFuNN was both more accurate and more adaptable than FuNN. EFuNN were also applied to predicting the SE40 in Wang (2001), although no comparison with other models was presented. The NASDAQ-100 stock index was modeled in Abraham *et al.* (2001a), where an EFuNN was used to predict whether or not stocks were going to go up or down. The results were described in the paper as "promising", although no comparison with other predictive methods was reported.

EFuNN was used in Abraham *et al.* (2001b; 2001c) to predict rainfall in the southern Indian state of Kerala, and a similar application, modeling rainfall in Switzerland, was presented in Woodford (2005; 2008b), where the goal was to learn more about the rainfall phenomenon by extracting fuzzy rules from EFuNN.

EFuNN was again used in de Moraes and dos Santos Machado (2005) for online evaluation of trainee performance in a virtual reality training task. A comparison with MLP showed that EFuNN was marginally more accurate (98.6% compared with 95.6%).

The problem of detecting abnormal behavior by the occupants of an intelligent environment was addressed in Rivera-Illingworth *et al.* (2005), where they used a SECoS network to integrate the data from 18 different sensors in a single room. While the accuracy of SECoS was equivalent to other methods that were investigated, the fast training speed and adaptability of SECoS made it more useful.

Time-delay neural networks and EFuNN were used to classify the outputs of an artificial nose in Zanchettin and Ludermir (2004), where it was shown that EFuNN was faster and more accurate.

Many applications of DENFIS were reported for superior time series prediction when compared to other ANN and AI methods (Kasabov, 2007).

In every case where ECoS networks were compared with conventional ANN such as MLP, the ECoS networks were shown to have better accuracy, to train faster, and to adapt better. ECoS networks have therefore been shown to be a useful family of algorithms with wide-ranging applications. Other authors have further developed, modified and improved these techniques for various applications (see Kasabov (2007, 2014)).

22.4.6. *Evolutionary Optimization of ECoS*

Although ECoS networks are able to avoid many of the problems associated with other constructive algorithm, there is still scope for optimization using EA. The goal when optimizing ECoS is to achieve a network that is accurate (whether over training or testing datasets) and is parsimonious, that is, that has the minimum number of evolving-layer neurons necessary to achieve the first criterion. Firstly, the parameters must be optimized to the problem at hand; Secondly for datasets with a large number of features, feature selection is helpful in achieving a smaller ECoS; Thirdly, as online pattern-based learning algorithms, the order in which the initial training vectors are presented will also influence the performance of the ECoS.

There are two different modes in which an ECoS network may be optimized, online and offline. Online optimization is carried out while the ECoS is training, that is, while neurons are being added and connection weights modified. Conversely, offline optimization is carried out outside of the training process.

ES were used to optimize the parameters online in both Watts and Kasabov (2001) and Chan and Kasabov (2004). While Watts and Kasabov (2001) used a simple (1+1) ES to optimize all four basic training parameters for each training example, Chan and Kasabov (2004) used a (μ, λ) ES to optimize the learning rates only, with respect to a sliding window of data where the window was moved though the training data stream. A similar windowing-of-data approach was used in Kasabov *et al.* (2003), although in this case a GA was used instead of an ES. The GA optimized all learning parameters and the fitness was evaluated as a function of the error over the training data window.

GA were used for offline optimization of both training parameters and the order of training examples in (Watts and Kasabov, 2002; Watts, 2004). The fitness function in this case was based on minimizing both the error over the provided dataset, and the overall change in the size of the evolving layer of the ECoS. A similar approach was taken in Minku and Ludermir (2005), although the order of the training examples was not optimized. A GA was also used for offline optimization of the training parameters in Kasabov and Song (2002), where the fitness function was based entirely on the error over the training dataset. A co-evolutionary GA was used to evolve ensembles of EFuNN in Minku and Ludermir (2006), where data was first clustered, and each cluster split into a training and a testing dataset. The GA optimized an individual EFuNN over each training and testing set, where the optimization was with respect to the accuracy and size of the network. The overall result was that the ensemble performed better than a single EFuNN trained over the entire dataset.

An unusual approach to offline optimization was reported in Arnott (2000). In this work, a GA was used to optimize the fuzzy rules and membership functions that were extracted from a trained EFuNN. The modified rules and MF were then re-inserted into the EFuNN for testing. Thus, the GA was really optimizing a fuzzy system, although the close-coupling between EFuNN and their associated rules and MF made it a useful approach.

22.5. Conclusions and Further Directions

This chapter presented an historic review of some of the methods, systems and applications of hybrid evolving ANN, including: evolutionary ANN, constructive ANN, and some ECoS methods and applications. More methods and applications of ECoS are presented in the next chapter of this volume. ECoS is an area of computational intelligence that is further developing with new methods being proposed every year, many of them based on more brain-inspired and nature inspired techniques. These are the evolving spiking neural networks (eSNN), the evolving neurogenetic systems and the quantum inspired ECoS.

References

Abraham, A. and Jain, R. (2005). Soft computing models for network intrusion detection systems. In *Classification and Clustering for Knowledge Discovery*. Berlin, Heidelberg: Springer, pp. 191–207.

Abraham, A., Jain, R., Sanyal, S. and Han, S. Y. (2005). SCIDS: A soft computing intrusion detection system. In *Distributed Computing — IWDC* 2004. Berlin, Heidelberg: Springer, pp. 252–257.

Abraham, A., Nath, B. and Mahanti, P. K. (2001a). Hybrid intelligent systems for stock market analysis. In *Computational Science — ICCS* 2001. Berlin, Heidelberg: Springer, pp. 337–345.

Abraham, A., Philip, N. S. and Joseph, K. B. (2001b). Will we have a wet summer? Soft computing models for long term rainfall forecasting. In *15th European Simulation Multi conference* (*ESM* 2001), *Modelling and Simulation*, pp. 1044–1048.

Abraham, A., Steinberg, D. and Philip, N. S. (2001c). Rainfall forecasting using soft computing models and multivariate adaptive regression splines. *IEEE SMC Trans., Special Issue on Fusion of Soft Computing and Hard Computing in Industrial Applications*.

Alpaydin, E. (1994). GAL: Networks that grow when they learn and shrink when they forget. *Int. J. Pattern Recogn.*, 8(1), pp. 391–414.

Arena, P., Caponetto, R., Fortuna, L. and Xibilia, M. G. (1993). M.L.P. optimal topology via genetic algorithms. In *Artificial Neural Nets and Genetic Algorithms*, New York: Springer-Verlag Wien, pp. 670–674.

Arnott, R. (2000). Application of a genetic algorithm to optimise EFuNN rule sets. *Technical report*, Department of Information Science, University of Otago, New Zealand.

Ash, T. (1989). Dynamic node creation in backpropagation networks. *Connect. Sci.*, 1(4), pp. 365–375.

Chavan, S., Shah, K., Dave, N., Mukherjee, S., Abraham, A. and Sanyal, S. (2004). Adaptive neuro-fuzzy intrusion detection systems. In *Proc. Int. Conf. Info. Tech.: Coding Comp.* (*ITCC*04), pp. 70–75.

Chan, Z. S. and Kasabov, N. (2004). Evolutionary computation for online and offline parameter tuning of evolving fuzzy neural networks. *Int. J. Comput. Intelligence Ap.*, 4(03), pp. 309–319.

Chellapilla, K. and Fogel, D. B. (2001). Evolving an expert checkers playing program without using human expertise. *IEEE T Evolut. Comput.*, 5(4), pp. 422–428.

Choi, B. and Bluff, K. (1995). Genetic optimisation of control parameters of a neural network. In Kasabov, N. K. and Coghill, G. (eds.), *Artificial Neural Networks and Expert Systems*. IEEE Computer Society Press, pp. 174–177.

Cybenko, G. (1989). Approximation by super positions of sigmoidal function. *Math. Control Signal*, 2, pp. 303–314.

de Garis, H. (1990). Genetic programming: Evolution of a time dependent neural network module which teaches a pair of stick legs to walk. In *Proc. Ninth European Conf. Artificial Intelligence*. Stockholm, Sweden.

de Garis, H. (1992). Artificial nervous systems: The genetic programming of production-rule-GenNet circuits. In *Proc. Int. Joint Conf. Neural Networks*. Beijing, China.

de Moraes, R. M. and dos Santos Machado, L. (2005). Evaluation system based on EFuNN for online training evaluation in virtual reality. In *CIARP* 2005, *LNCS* 3773.

Fahlman, S. E. (1988). An empirical study of learning speed in back-propagation networks. *Technical Report*CMU-CS-88-162, Department of Computer Science, Carnegie-Mellon University.

Fahlman, S. E. and Lebiere, C. (1990). The cascade-correlation learning architecture. In Touretzky, D. S. (ed.), *Advances in Neural Information Processing Systems* 2, Morgan Kaufman Publishers, pp. 524–532.

Fogel, D. B., Wasson, E. C., Boughton, E. M. and Porto, V. W. (1997). A step toward computer-assisted mammography using evolutionary programming and neural networks. *Cancer Lett.*, 119(1), pp. 93–97.

Fogel, D. B., Hays, T. J., Hahn, S. H. and Quon, J. (2004). A self-learning evolutionary chess program. *P. IEEE*, 92(12), pp. 1947–1954.

Fontanari, J. and Meir, R. (1991). Evolving a learning algorithm for the binary perceptron. *Networks*, 2, pp. 353–359.

Frean, M. (1990). The upstart algorithm: A method for constructing and training feedforward neural networks. *Neural Comput.*, 2(2), pp. 198–209.

Futschik, M., Schreiber, M., Brown, M. and Kasabov, N. (1999). Comparative studies of neural network models for mRNA analysis. In *ISMB* 1999, Heidelberg, p. 43.

Futschik, M. E., Reeve, A. and Kasabov, N. (2003). Evolving connectionist systems for knowledge discovery from gene expression data of cancer tissue. *Artif. Intell. Med.*, 28, pp. 165–189.

Futschik, M. E., Sullivan, M., Reeve, A. and Kasabov, N. (2003). Modular decision system and information integration for improved disease outcome prediction. In *Proc. ECCB*'2003, pp. 13–15.

Futschik, M. E., Sullivan, M., Reeve, A. and Kasabov, N. (2003). Prediction of clinical behaviour and treatment for cancers. *OMJ Applied Bioinformatics*, 2(3), pp. S53–S58.

Fukuda, T., Komata, Y. and Arakawa, T. (1997). Recurrent neural networks with self-adaptive GAs for biped locomotion robot. In *Proc. Int. Conf. Neural Networks ICNN'* 97. IEEE Press, Houston.

Ghobakhlou, A. and Kasabov, N. (2003). A methodology for adaptive speech recognition systems and a development environment. In *Proc. Artif. Neural Networks Neural Information Processing ICANN/ICONIP* 2003 *Int. Conf.* Istanbul, Turkey, pp. 316–319.

Ghobakhlou, A. and Seesink, R. (2001). An interactive multi modal system for mobile robotic control. In *Proc. Fifth Biannual Conf. Artif. Neural Networks and Expert Systems* (*ANNES*2001), pp. 93–99.

Ghobakhlou, A., Watts, M. J. and Kasabov, N. (2000). Online expansion of output space in evolving fuzzy neural networks. In *Proc. ICONIP* 2000, Taejon, Korea, Vol. 2, pp. 891–896.

Hancock, P. J. (1992). Genetic algorithms and permutation problems: A comparison of recombination operators for neural net structure specification. In *International Workshop on Combinations of Genetic Algorithms and Neural Networks, COGANN*-92, IEEE, pp. 108–122.

Kasabov, N., Kozma, R., Kilgour, R., Laws, M., Taylor, J., Watts, M. and Gray, A. (1997). A methodology for speech data analysis and a framework for adaptive speech recognition using fuzzy neural networks. In Kasabov, N., Kozma, R., Ko, K., O'Shea, R., Coghill, G. and Gedeon, T. (eds.), *Progress in Connectionist-Based Information Systems*. Singapore: Springer.

Kasabov, N. (1998). The ECoS framework and the ECO learning method for evolving connectionist systems. *J Adv. Comput. Intell.*, 2(6), pp. 195–202.

Kasabov, N. (1998). Evolving fuzzy neural networks — algorithms, applications and biological motivation. In Yamakawa, T. and Matsumoto, G. (eds.), *Methodologies for the Conception, Design and Application of Soft Computing*. World Scientific, Vol. 1, pp. 271–274.

Kasabov, N. (1999). Evolving connectionist systems: A theory and a case study on adaptive speech recognition. In *International Joint Conference on Neural Networks, IJCNN'99*. Vol. 5, pp. 3002–3007.

Kasabov, N., Erzegovezi, L., Fedrizzi, M., Beber, A. and Deng, D. (2000). Hybrid intelligent decision support systems and applications for risk analysis and prediction of evolving economic clusters in Europe. In N. Kasabov, (ed.), *Future Directions for Intelligent Information Systems and Information Sciences*. Springer Verlag, pp. 347–372.

Kasabov, N. and Fedrizzi, M. (1999). Fuzzy neural networks and evolving connectionist systems for intelligent decision making. In *Proc. Eighth Int. Fuzzy Systems Association World Congress*, Taiwan, pp. 30–35.

Kasabov, N., Kim, J., Watts, M. J. and Gray, A. R. (1997). FuNN/2 — a fuzzy neural network architecture for adaptive learning and knowledge acquisition. *Inform. Sciences*, 101(3), pp. 155–175.

Kasabov, N. and Song, Q. (2000). Dynamic evolving neuro-fuzzy inference system (DENFIS): Online learning and application for time-series prediction. In *Proc. Sixth Int. Conf. Soft Computing. Fuzzy Logic Systems Institute*, Iizuka, Japan, pp. 696–702.

Kasabov, N. and Song, Q. (2002). GA — parameter optimisation of evolving connectionist systems for classification and a case study from bioinformatics. In *Proc. Ninth Int. Conf. on Neural Information Processing, ICONIP'02*. IEEE, Vol. 2, pp. 602–605.

Kasabov, N., Song, Q. and Nishikanawa, I. (2003). Evolutionary computation for dynamic parameter optimisation of evolving connectionist systems for online prediction of time series with changing dynamics. In *Proc. Int. Joint Conf. on Neural Networks*. IEEE, Vol. 1, pp. 438–443.

Kasabov, N. (2001). Brain-like functions in evolving connectionist systems for on-line, knowledge-based learning. In Kitamura, T. (ed.), *What should be Computed to Understand and Model Brain Function, Volume* 3 *of FLSI Soft Computing Series*. World Scientific, pp. 77–113.

Kasabov, N. (2003). *Evolving Connectionist Systems: Methods and Applications in Bioinformatics, Brain Study and Intelligent Machines*. Springer.

Kasabov, N. (2007). *Evolving Connectionist Systems, Second Edition*. Springer.

Kasabov, N. (2008). Evolving intelligence in humans and machines: integrative connectionist systems approach, feature article. *IEEE CIS Magazine*, August, 2008, Vol. 3, No. 3, pp. 23–37.

Kasabov, N. (2008). Adaptive modelling and discovery in bioinformatics: The evolving connectionist approach. *Int. J. Intell. Syst.*, 23, pp. 545–555.

Kasabov, N. (ed.) (2014). *The Springer Handbook of Bio-/Neuroinformatics*. Springer, p. 1230.

Kermani, B. G., Schiffman, S. S. and Nagle, H. T. (1999). Using neural networks and genetic algorithms to enhance performance in an electronic nose. *IEEE T. Bio-med. Eng.*, 46(4), pp. 429–439.

Kohonen, T. (1997). *Self-Organizing Maps, Second Edition*. Springer.

Kolmogorov, A. (1957). On the representation of continuous functions of many variables by superposition of continuous functions of one variable and addition. *Dokl. Akad. Nauk. USSR*, 114, pp. 953–956. (In Russian)

Koprinska, I. and Kasabov, N. (1999). An application of evolving fuzzy neural network for compressed video parsing. In *ICONIP/ANZIIS/ANNES'99 Workshop*. Dunedin, New Zealand, pp. 96–102.

Kwok, T.-Y. and Yeung, D.-Y. (1999). Constructive algorithms for structure learning in feedforward neural networks for regression problems. *IEEE T. Neural Networ.*

Leichter, C. S., Cichocki, A. and Kasabov, N. (2001). Independent component analysis and evolving fuzzy neural networks for the classification of single trial EEG data. In *Proc. Fifth Biannual Conf. Artif. Neural Networks and Expert Systems* (*ANNES* 2001), pp. 100–105.

Ma, C. Y., Wong, S. W., Hecht, D. and Fogel, G. B. (2006). Evolved neural networks for high throughput anti-HIV ligand screening. In *IEEE Congress on Evolutionary Computation, CEC* 2006. IEEE, pp. 2734–2741.

McCloskey, M. and Cohen, N. (1989). Catastrophic interference in connectionist networks: The sequential learning project. *Psychol. Learn. Motiv.*, 24, pp. 109–164.

Mézard, M. and Nadal, J.-P. (1989). Learning in feedforward layered networks: The tiling algorithm. *J. Phys. A*, 22, pp. 2191–2203.

Minku, F. L. and Ludermir, T. B. (2005). Evolutionary strategies and genetic algorithms for dynamic parameter optimization of evolving fuzzy neural networks. In *The 2005 IEEE Congress on Evolutionary Computation*, IEEE. Vol. 3, pp. 1951–1958.

Minku, F. L. and Ludermir, T. B. (2006). EFuNNs ensembles construction using a clustering method and a coevolutionary genetic algorithm. In *IEEE Congress on Evolutionary Computation, CEC* 2006, IEEE, pp. 1399–1406.

Moreira, M. and Fiesler, E. (1995). Neural networks with adaptive learning rate and momentum terms. *Technical Report* 95-04, Institut Dalle D'Intelligence Artificielle Perceptive.

Ng, G. S., Murali, T., Shi, D. and Wahab, A. (2004). Application of EFuNN for the classification of handwritten digits. *Int. J. Comput, Systems Signals*, 5(2), pp. 27–35.

Platt, J. (1991). A resource-allocating network for function interpolation. *Neural Comput.*, 3(2), pp. 213–225.

Porto, V. W., Fogel, D. B., Fogel, L. J., Fogel, G. B., Johnson, N. and Cheung, M. (2005). Classifying sonar returns for the presence of mines: evolving neural networks and evolving rules. In 2005 *IEEE Symp. Comput. Intell. Homeland Security and Personal Safety*. IEEE Press, Piscataway, NJ, pp. 123–130.

Rivera-Illingworth, F., Callaghan, V. and Hagras, H. (2005). A neural network agent based approach to activity detection in AmI environments. In *IEEE International Workshop, Intelligent Environments* 2005 (*IE*05). Colchester, UK.

Schiffmann, W., Joost, M. and Werner, R. (1994). Optimization of backpropagation algorithm for training multiplayer perceptrons. *Technical Report*, Institute of Physics, University of Koblenz.

Schiffmann, W., Joost, M. and Werner, R. (1993). Application of genetic algorithms to the construction of topologies for multilayer perceptrons. In Albrecht, R., Reeves, C. R. and Steele, N. (eds.), *Artificial Neural Nets and Genetic Algorithms*. New York: Springer-Verlag Wien, pp. 675–682.

Sorwar, G., Abraham, A. and Dooley, L. S. (2001). Texture classification based on DCT and soft computing. In *The Tenth IEEE Int. Conf. on Fuzzy Systems*, Vol. 3, pp. 545–548.

Wang, X. (2001). "On-line" time series prediction system — EFuNN-T. In *Proc. Fifth Biannual Conf. Artif. Neural Networks and Expert Systems* (*ANNES* 2001). pp. 82–86.

Watts, M. J. (1999a). An investigation of the properties of evolving fuzzy neural networks. In *Proc. ICONIP'99*. Perth, Australia, pp. 217–221.

Watts, M. J. (1999b). Evolving connectionist systems for biochemical applications. In Kasabov, N. and Ko, K. (eds.), *Emerging Knowledge Engineering and Connectionist-based Systems* (Proc. *ICONIP/ANZIIS/ANNES'99 Workshop "Future directions for intelligent systems and information sciences"*, Dunedin, 22–23 November 1999). Dunedin, New Zealand: University of Otago Press, pp. 147–151.

Watts, M. J. and Kasabov, N. (2000). Simple evolving connectionist systems and experiments on isolated phoneme recognition. In *Proc. First IEEE Conf. Evolutionary Computation and Neural Networks*. IEEE Press, San Antonio, pp. 232–239.

Watts, M. and Kasabov, N. (2001). Dynamic optimisation of evolving connectionist system training parameters by pseudo-evolution strategy. In *Proc.* 2001 *Congress Evolutionary Computation*. IEEE. Vol. 2, pp. 1335–1342.

Watts, M. and Kasabov, N. (2002). Evolutionary optimisation of evolving connectionist systems. In *Computational Intelligence, Proc. World on Congress on* (Vol. 1, pp. 606–610). IEEE.

Watts, M. J. (2004). *Evolving Connectionist Systems: Characterisation, Simplification, Formalisation, Explanation and Optimisation*. Doctoral dissertation.

Woodford, B. J. (2005). Rule extraction from spatial data using local learning techniques. In *Proc. SIRC* 2005 — *The Seventeenth Annual Colloquium of the Spatial Information Research Centre*. University of Otago, Dunedin, New Zealand.

Woodford, B. J. (2001). Comparative analysis of the EFuNN and the Support Vector Machine models for the classification of horticulture data. In *Proc. Fifth Biannual Conf. Artif. Neural Networks and Expert Systems* (*ANNES* 2001).

Woodford, B. J. (2008a). Evolving neurocomputing systems for horticulture applications. *J. Appl Soft Comput.*, 8, pp. 564–578.

Woodford, B. J. (2008b). Rule extraction from spatial data using an entropy-based fuzzy neural network. In Whigham, P. A., Drecki, I. and Moore, A. (eds.), *Proc. Twentieth Annual Colloquium of the Spatial Information Research Centre and GEOCOMP* (*SIRC'* 2008). The University of Auckland, Auckland, New Zealand, pp. 55–66.

Woodford, B. J., Deng, D. and Benwell, G. L. (2004). A wavelet-based neuro-fuzzy system for data mining small image sets. In Hogan, J., Montague, P., Purvis, M. and Steketee,

C. (eds.), *Australasian Workshop on Data Mining and Web Intelligence* (*DMWI*2004). University of Otago, Dunedin, New Zealand, pp. 139–144.

Zanchettin, C. and Ludermir, T. B. (2004). Evolving fuzzy neural networks applied to odor recognition in an artificial nose. In *Proc.* 2004 *IEEE Int. Joint Conf. on Neural Networks*, Vol. 1, pp. 675–680.

Zhao, Q. and Higuchi, T. (1996). Evolutionary learning of nearest-neighbour MLP. *IEEE T. Neural Networ.*, 7(3), pp. 762–767.

Part V

Applications

Chapter 23

Applications of Computational Intelligence to Decision-Making: Modeling Human Reasoning/Agreement

Simon Miller, Christian Wagner and Jonathan Garibaldi

Computational Intelligence provides valuable approaches and tools for the modeling of human reasoning and decision making. In this chapter, we look at how Computational Intelligence methods can be employed in decision-making problems where information from humans (e.g., survey data) is available. Specifically, we explore an example of modeling cyber security expert decision making using a combination of evolutionary algorithms and aggregation operators as well as generating type-1/type-2 fuzzy sets directly from data to enable comparisons between real world objects such as restaurants. For each of these cases, we show how CI techniques can provide powerful and practical tools for delivering decision support. Throughout, we highlight the capacity of the respective Computational Intelligence methods to capture and model key aspects of human reasoning such as the integration of multiple relevant aspects in challenging cyber security decisions and the often significant uncertainty associated with survey responses.

23.1. Introduction

In this chapter, we will look at how computational intelligence (CI) methods can be employed in decision-making problems where modeling human reasoning or agreement is required. To explore this subject, two examples will be used:

(1) Evolving Ordered Weighted Average (OWA) operators that model the decision-making processes of cyber-security experts.
(2) Similarity based applications that employ type-1 and General type-2 Fuzzy agreement models created from interval survey data.

In each of these examples we will show how CI techniques can provide powerful and practical tools for aiding human decision-making problems. The focus of the case studies included here is the use of CI techniques with survey data. A set of real-world surveys is used to demonstrate how CI techniques including evolutionary algorithms (EAs) and fuzzy logic can be utilized to capture the reasoning processes of human experts, and model the object human perception of concepts and words.

23.2. Case Study: Evolving OWA Operators to Model Cyber-Security Experts' Decision-Making

In this example, we will show how EAs can be employed to design OWA operators that model the decision-making processes of cyber-security experts.

23.2.1. *Background*

This section will provide an overview of the scenario, and describe the methods that have been employed.

Cyber-crime has become an increasing concern over recent years. This has been brought about by the constantly growing number of every day activities that are conducted online, for example, banking, shopping and e-government, and the availability of software and hardware that aids would-be attackers, reducing the need for technical knowledge. As a result, the field of cyber-security has rapidly grown in order to address concerns about the security of information systems, and the sensitive data that they hold. An important part of an organization's cyber-security provision is the assessment of security offered by proposed new information systems, while they are still in the design phase. This activity can inform systems designers about where there are weaknesses in their systems, and whether the level of security offered is appropriate for the consequences of a successful attack.

Primarily, cyber-security experts carry out security assessments of proposed systems, as often, this is the only way they can be achieved. However, assessing the security provided by a proposed system is a large and difficult task, and often there are a limited number of cyber-security professionals who are capable of carrying out the job.

In this example, we will consider how the load on cyber-security experts can be reduced, through creating models of parts of their expertise that can be used as decision aids during security assessments. This is achieved using a combination of EAs and OWAs to model some of the reasoning used by experts during an assessment.

23.2.2. *The Scenario*

The case study that we will be using is a decision-making exercise that was conducted at GCHQ — the UK Government's signals intelligence and information assurance agency. In the exercise a group of 39 cyber-security experts took part in a survey about the difficulty of technical attacks, and compromising or bypassing security components. The experts were drawn from a wide variety of backgrounds and included software architects, technical security consultants, penetration testers, vulnerability researchers, and specialist systems evaluators. All of the experts involved were highly experienced in their field, and accustomed to how UK government information systems are typically constructed and operated.

During the exercise, the experts were presented with a scenario created by GCHQ technical experts. The scenario was a proposal for a new government system that included details of the architecture of the system, some potential attacks on the system and the (security) components it was made up of. In reality, assessing such systems is an extremely in-depth task that requires a great deal of information. To address this, the experts were told to assume that the software and hardware used, and the frequency of software updates were typical of the government systems that they came across in their day-to-day work.

Figure 23.1 shows an example of the technical attacks that experts were shown. The diagram shows details of the system, the components of the system, and describes the path that an attacker would need to follow in order to successfully complete the attack. This attack involves an email with a malicious attachment containing an exploit, enabling the attacker to compromise the recipient's PC, and launch an ongoing attack on the system.

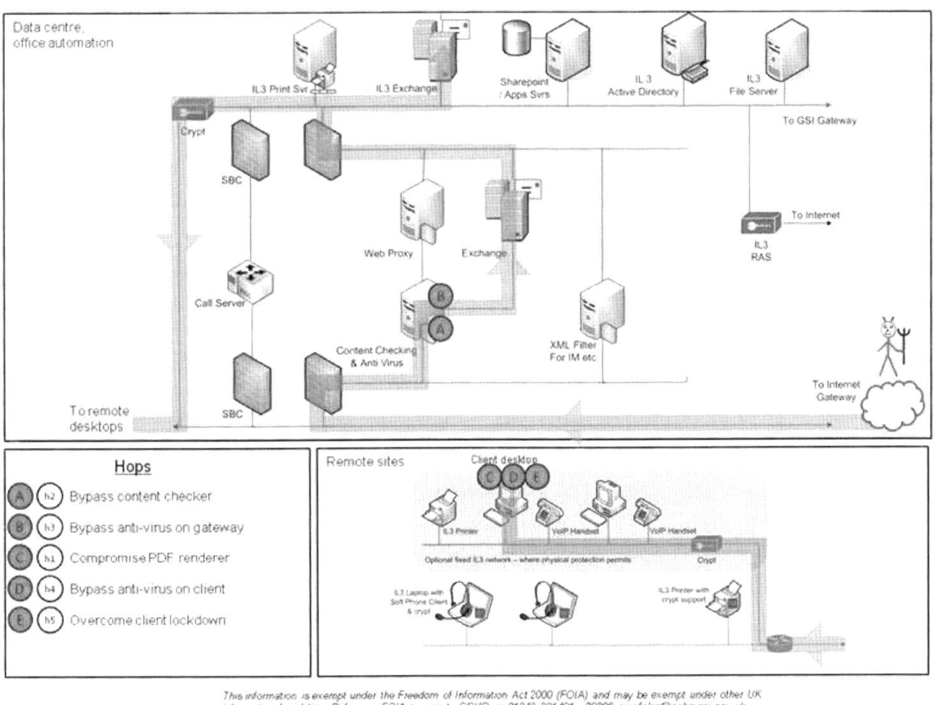

Figure 23.1: Example technical attack from scenario.

In order to complete the example attack shown in Figure 23.1, five components need to be either compromised or bypassed:

(1) Gateway Content Checker.
(2) Gateway Anti-virus.
(3) PDF renderer.
(4) Client Anti-virus.
(5) Client Access Controls.

23.2.3. *The Survey*

In total, the experts were shown 10 attacks on the proposed system. A survey was then conducted entailing two distinct types of activity:

(1) Ranking the 10 technical attacks in order of how difficult they are to successfully complete without being detected.
(2) Rating the difficulty of compromising or bypassing the 26 security components that make up the 10 attacks.

Ranking the attacks was simply a case of placing them in order from easiest to hardest. This method of eliciting difficulty allows experts to perform a series of pair-wise comparisons in order to establish an order of difficulty, e.g., "How does attack *a* compare with attack *b*?" is it easier or harder? Making distinctions in this way can facilitate the process of identifying salient attacks, as giving an abstract rating can sometimes prove difficult. A different type of survey was used to elicit the difficulties of compromising/bypassing each of the 26 security components. Experts were asked, "Overall, how difficult would it be for an attacker to successfully compromise/bypass this component without being noticed?", and they gave a rating between 0 (very easy) and 100 (very hard). This type of questioning allows experts to give an indication of the absolute difference in difficulty between security components, unlike ranking, which provides an intuitive way to obtain an ordering but elicits no information about the degree of difference between attacks.

Once this data has been collected from the experts, we have two levels of information:

(1) Rankings of attacks.
(2) Ratings of the overall difficulty of compromising/bypassing specific security components that make up attacks.

In this example, we will look at how the overall difficulty of specific components contributes to the difficulty of attacks they form part of, and which components are most important when ranking attacks. This is achieved through the use of OWAs to derive attack rankings from overall difficulty ratings.

Table 23.1: Attacks with constituent components.

Attack	Components
1	2,3,1,4,5
2	6,7,6,8,4
3	9
4	10,11,4,5
5	12,13,2,3,14,15,4,5
6	16,16,17,4,5
7	6,18,4,5
8	19,20,21
9	22,23,24
10	25,26,1,4,5

Each of the 26 components belongs to one or more of the 10 attacks, Table 23.1 shows which components belong to each attack. Note that some components are duplicated in a single attack, this is because a particular attack may involve bypassing/compromising the same type of component more than once, for example, an attacker may have to compromise multiple firewalls to reach a target.

In practice, a system is only as secure as its weakest element, i.e., the easiest way in. Identifying which are the weakest aspects of a system, i.e., the easiest ways of attacking it, is thus a highly relevant component of system security assessment, though obviously it does not provide all of the answers. Using this data we demonstrate how technical attack rankings can be derived from the component ratings through aggregation, and compare them with the actual rankings provided by the experts. This is particularly useful in real world assessment, as the method provides the potential for highlighting the most salient attacks for a new system using a database of pre-rated components, reducing the burden on expert resources.

23.2.4. *Ordered Weighted Averages*

The concept of exploring the relationships between the overall difficulty of components, and the difficulty of attacks came after discussion with technical experts from GCHQ in which a hypothesis was raised. When we asked about how they decide how difficult an attack is, we were told that each component of the attack is assessed, estimating how difficult it would be to bypass/compromise. Then, the difficulty of an attack is based chiefly on the most difficult component, with the remaining components carrying less weight in order of difficulty.

In order to explore this, and simulate the process of creating attack ratings and rankings by aggregating assessments of security components, we use OWA operators (Yager, 1988). An OWA is an operator that allows us to assign weights to objects based upon their position in an ordering (e.g., a difficulty ranking), as opposed to a traditional weighted average in which weights are assigned to specific objects. Equation (1) describes the process, where n is the number of weights/objects. The OWA consists of a set of weights (w) that add up to 1, and a set of objects that we wish to apply the operator to. In this case study the objects are the security components, or more specifically, the experts' assessments of the security components. To perform the operation we first sort the objects into order, for our security components this means sorting them by difficulty in descending order. Once the objects have been placed into an ordering (o), we apply each of the weights to each of the objects in turn, the first weight is multiplied by the first object and so on. This allows us to specify a weight to apply to the most difficulty component to compromise, the second most difficult, and so on. Once all of the weights have been applied to the objects, the sum of the results is calculated. In practice, if the first weight is close to 1, the resulting operator will close to a maximum operator, if the final weight is close to 1, the operator will be close to a minimum operator, between these extremes lie an almost infinite number of operators.

$$OWA_w(a) = \sum_{i=1}^{n} w_i o_i. \tag{1}$$

Table 23.2 shows the values provided by one expert for each of the components of attack 1 (2,3,1,4,5).

The OWA can then be applied to this set of values to produce an overall score for attack 1. For example, if we wanted to choose an OWA operator that gives more weight to the most difficult hop, our weights could be $w = 0.33, 0.27, 0.20, 0.13, 0.07$. To apply these to the expert's ratings $a = 25.00, 40.00, 20.50, 40.00, 70.00$, we first sort them by difficulty rating producing the following ordering: $o = 70.00, 40.00, 40.00, 25.00, 20.50$. We can then compute the OWA by multiplying each weight by the corresponding element in the ordering as shown in Equation (1), where n is equal to the number of weights/components. In this case a value of 46.59 is produced; the mean value is 39.10, showing that this OWA operator has given more weight to higher values of difficulty.

Table 23.2: Expert's 'overall' interval means for attack 1.

Component	Interval Mean
1	25.00
2	40.00
3	20.50
4	40.00
5	70.00

This procedure can be repeated for each of the attacks, using a given OWA operator. The result is a set of difficulty values for each of the attacks, that can be used to rank them from most to least difficult. Finally, the derived ranking can be compared with the actual ranking given by an expert to validate the OWA operator in question. In this case study we will use an EA to find suitable OWA weights for creating attack ratings.

23.2.5. *Evolutionary Algorithms*

EAs are a popular method of optimization for problems with very large solution spaces (see Chapter **14**). The most widely used EA method, the genetic algorithm (GA) is a heuristic search technique inspired by evolutionary biology. Selection, crossover, and mutation are applied to a population of individuals representing solutions in order to find a near-optimal solution. The GA is able to find suitable solutions to a problem, while evaluating a small fraction of the solution space. For problems with an extremely large solution space, this is essential.

Here, we will employ an EA to search a large number of possible OWA operators for the purpose of aggregating security component ratings to create ratings/rankings of specific technical attacks. The purpose of this is two-fold:

(1) To discover suitable OWA operators for creating ratings/rankings of attacks using assessments of security components.
(2) As the EA is unrestricted, the resulting weighting will also confirm/contradict our hypothesis that the most difficult component is the most important when ranking attacks, and will give a guide to how much importance can be assigned to each component.

For this case study the EA is implemented as follows:

Solutions are represented using a vector of weights. The maximum number of components in an attack is eight, therefore eight weights are used in solutions. For those attacks that do not have eight components, their component ratings are padded out with zeros so that there are eight. This avoids the potential for attacks that have fewer components being judged as being more difficult, purely because their weightings are concentrated on fewer components. An attack with more components should be more difficult than an equivalent attack with fewer components.

The *initial solution* is created by generating seven random points on a line from 0 to 1. The weights are the distances between zero, each point and 1. This ensures that the weights will add up to 1.

Fitness is determined by comparing each individual's actual attack ranking with the attack ranking derived from their component ratings using an OWA. Spearman's Rho is used to measure correlation between the rankings, producing a value between -1 (perfect negative correlation), 0 (no correlation), and 1 (perfect positive correlation). Error is calculated by subtracting each Spearman's Rho value from 1, so a perfect positive correlation will result in an error of zero. The mean squared error (MSE) over all individuals provides a metric for assessing the performance of a particular set of weights.

In *parent selection,* individuals are sorted by fitness and random individuals are chosen from the population using absolute values over a normal distribution forming a complementary cumulative distribution. That is to say, it is more likely that a lower numbered (and therefore fitter) individual will be chosen, though it is possible for any individual to be chosen.

In *Elitism*, the best individuals from each generation are copied into the next generation. This ensures that the best individual in a generation cannot be worse than the best in the preceding generation.

Mutation is achieved by selecting two weights from a solution, increasing one by a small amount and decreasing the other by the same amount. If either weighting becomes invalid (>1 or <0) another two elements are selected. This method ensures that the weights still add up to 1 after perturbation.

A single point *crossover* is used that takes two parents and creates a child consisting of the first half of the first parent, and the second half of the second parent. To make sure that the weights add up to 1, they are normalized. This allows us to preserve the characteristics of each parent, while maintaining a valid set of weights.

23.2.6. *Evolving OWAs*

The next step is to conduct a series of tests with the EA to determine appropriate proportions for the genetic operators and population/generations. Configurations have been chosen to result in a similar number of evaluations.

Experiments have been conducted on three groups of individuals: "odd" (i.e., the 1st, 3rd, 5th, ... individuals), "even" (i.e., the 2nd, 4th, 6th, ... individuals) and "all" individuals. The reason for this is that after tuning the weights with 50% of the overall group, we can then test these weights to see how they perform on unseen individuals in the remaining 50% of the group. The group containing all individuals will give an indication of the best that can be found using the selected search algorithms for the entire group.

23.2.7. *Results*

Table 23.3 shows the configurations tested, Table 23.4 provides the best results for each group and Table 23.5 describes the OWAs discovered. For each of these tests a population of 250 individuals is used over 250 generations, with 1% elitism.

Table 23.3: EA: Test set 1.

Test	Copy	Cross.	Mut.
1	0.00	0.20	0.79
2	0.20	0.20	0.59
3	0.40	0.20	0.39
4	0.60	0.20	0.19
5	0.79	0.20	0.00
6	0.50	0.00	0.49
7	0.30	0.40	0.29
8	0.20	0.60	0.19
9	0.10	0.80	0.09
10	0.00	0.99	0.00

Table 23.4: EA: Test set 1 — best results.

Test	Mean Sp.	MSE
Even		
3	0.6866	0.1425
Odd		
1	0.5713	0.2543
All		
1	0.6159	0.2069
2	0.6159	0.2069

Table 23.5: EA: Test set 1 — best OWAs.

	Best Weights							
Test	1	2	3	4	5	6	7	8
Even								
3	0.8985	0.0059	0.0311	0.0102	0.0065	0.0258	0.0037	0.0184
Odd								
1	0.7872	0.0185	0.1242	0.0505	0.0111	0.0032	0.0029	0.0024
All								
1	0.9582	0.0028	0.0242	0.0003	0.0057	0.0029	0.0002	0.0056
2	0.9621	0.0017	0.0221	0.0003	0.0045	0.0059	0.0009	0.0025

For all groups, the earlier tests result in the best solutions, when there is a small amount of crossover and large proportion of mutation. The copy operator does not appear to have much influence on the results, though this may be because the best individuals from each population are automatically copied to the next generation through elitism.

23.2.7.1. *Test set 2 — population and generations*

The best configuration from the previous set of tests for each group was used with a variety of generations/population combinations. Table 23.6 provides the configurations tested, Table 23.7 provides the results and Table 23.7 describes the best OWAs discovered. In the previous tests on the "all" group two configurations were tied for the lowest MSE. Both configurations were used in this set of tests, the (best) result shown in Tables 23.4 and 23.7 was achieved using the setup from test 2 in the previous set of tests.

In these tests there is less variation in the results, as we might expect, altering the configuration has more of an effect on the results than changing the ratio of populations to generations. All of the solutions found with the EA have a large bias towards the most difficult component, with very little weight being attributed to the remaining components.

23.2.7.2. *Alternate group weightings*

The next stage examines how the best weights for one group perform on the other. Table 23.9 shows the results of applying the best weights from the "odd" and "even" groups on the alternate group.

The results show that while the results are relatively good, suggesting that the OWAs found are robust, they are not as good as those seen in the previous tests with

Table 23.6: EA: Test set 2.

Test	Gens.	Pop.
11	50	1250
12	100	625
13	200	315
14	300	210
15	400	155
16	500	125

Table 23.7: EA: Test set 2 — best results.

Test	Mean Sp.	MSE
Even		
12	0.6885	0.1421
13	0.6866	0.1421
Odd		
13	0.5732	0.2519
16	0.5733	0.2519
All		
15	0.6165	0.2080

Table 23.8: EA: Test set 2 — best OWAs.

	Best Weights							
Test	1	2	3	4	5	6	7	8
Even								
12	0.8907	0.0011	0.0323	0.0120	0.0070	0.0174	0.0035	0.0359
13	0.8899	0.0044	0.0297	0.0126	0.0078	0.0242	0.0030	0.0284
Odd								
13	0.7858	0.0223	0.1285	0.0471	0.0115	0.0031	0.0015	0.0002
16	0.7854	0.0246	0.1248	0.0479	0.0117	0.0033	0.0001	0.0021
All								
15	0.9456	0.0022	0.0296	0.0006	0.0068	0.0011	0.0086	0.0055

Table 23.9: EA: Application of best weights to alternate group.

Test	Mean Sp.	MSE
Best 'even' weights applied to 'odd'		
12	0.5228	0.3013
13	0.5146	0.3118
Best 'odd' weights applied to 'even'		
13	0.5915	0.2381
16	0.5947	0.2337

Table 23.10: EA: Extended tests.

Max Sp.	**Min Sp.**	**Mean Sp.**	**Std. Dev. Sp.**
0.6200	0.6104	0.6150	0.0022
Max MSE	**Min MSE**	**Mean MSE**	**Std. Dev. MSE**
0.2137	0.2057	0.2092	0.0020

the same weights. It is reasonable to expect some reduction in performance, as the OWAs have been tuned to be specific to each group, that they still produce good aggregations indicates that it is likely that OWAs tuned on a sample of data can be applied to unseen data with good results.

23.2.7.3. *Extended test*

Finally, the best result from the "all" group is replicated 30 times with differing random seeds to give an idea of the variation in results. Table 23.10 shows the results of using the best weights from the "all" group over 30 tests, including the mean Spearman's Rho, mean MSE, and the standard deviation.

The results of the extended test show that the results are relatively stable. There is little difference between the maximum and minimum MSE (0.0080), and looking at the individual sets of weights it can be seen that they are all very similar. All solutions produced in this extended run of tests placed a weight greater than 0.92 on the first (most difficult) component.

23.2.8. *Summary*

In this section a series of EAs have been used to search for OWA operators, for the purpose of aggregating ratings of hops (security components) into ratings of AVs. It has been shown that EAs are able to find OWA operators that provide a robust method of deriving ratings and rankings of attacks from hop difficulty ratings.

What this tells us is that aggregating hop ratings is an appropriate method of rating and ranking specific attacks, and that given a database of ratings of generic hops (as was used in these experiments) unseen attacks can be rated. This provides the facility for systems designers to undertake what if? scenarios to estimate the effects of altering or adding/removing components to/from a proposed system.

Further to this we have also seen that the EAs, which are led solely by MSE, always find OWAs that place at least 92% of the weight on the most difficult hop. This lends weight to our hypothesis that the most difficult hop is the most important when rating the difficulty of an attack, and that the remaining hops carry little weight. The use of a combination of EAs and OWAs can be applied to any problem in which we want to find out the relative importance of sub-decisions (e.g., the level of security offered by specific components) in the process of making an overall decision (e.g., the difficulty of completing an entire attack).

23.3. Case Study: Using Interval Valued Survey Data in Similarity Based Applications of Type-1 and Type-2 Fuzzy Agreement Models

In this case study we will show how interval valued survey data can be modeled using type-1 (T1) and general type-2 fuzzy sets (GT2FSs) with an approach called the interval agreement approach (IAA) (Miller *et al.*, 2012), and how the resulting models can be employed in similarity based applications that aim to produce linguistic descriptions of objects (in this case, pubs and restaurants), and to compare objects with one another.

23.3.1. *Background*

Fuzzy logic sets (see Chapter **1**) are a useful and popular method of modeling the opinions and perceptions of groups of people. A lot of the work in this area has concentrated on the creation of fuzzy set (FS)-based models for words and/or concepts (e.g., (Wagner *et al.*, 2015; Miller *et al.*, 2012; Mendel and Wu, 2010; Coupland *et al.*, 2010 and Liu and Mendel, 2007)). The aim is to accurately capture the meaning people associate with words/concepts using FSs in order to be able to perform computation and reasoning based on these modelled words/concepts. Type-2 fuzzy sets (T2FSs) have been highlighted as particularly suitable for this approach as their additional degree of freedom in comparison to type-1 fuzzy sets (T1FSs) allow them to more accurately capture the distribution of uncertainty within a given set. This in turn enables complex modelling of variation and uncertainty in the meaning of words.

Capturing data directly from individuals on an area of interest is an important, and often the only, means of eliciting information and knowledge which is commonly strongly subjective. Once the data have been collected, the combined opinions of a group (and sub-groups) can be represented in models allowing for analysis of, and reasoning with, the consolidated knowledge that has been acquired.

23.3.2. *The Scenario*

The case study we will be using for this section focuses on survey exercises in which participants were asked to give their opinions of aspects of pubs and restaurants, and how they perceive words in specific contexts. With the data collected during the surveys, fuzzy models are produced using an approach called the IAA (Miller *et al.*, 2012) and the resulting models are used in two example similarity-based applications.

23.3.3. *The Survey*

Data collected during two survey exercises are used in this case study. The first consisted of two questionnaires, one asked participants to rate a series of local pubs/bars according to a number of concepts such as *Ambience* and *Service*. For each pub (e.g., *Rose and Crown*), participants were asked a series of six questions (e.g., "*How would you rate the service in the Rose and Crown?*"). In the other questionnaire, participants were asked to rate words in the context of specific concepts. For example, one of contexts presented to participants was *ambience in a pub*. They were then asked to rate the words *negative*, *neutral*, and *positive* in this context. The participants provided word-ratings for all 18 words (six concepts, with three words describing each). Words were chosen to elicit responses appropriate for each specific concept, e.g., *Delicious* for *Quality of Beer* or *Cheap* for *Cost of Beer.*

The second survey was conducted at the University of Nottingham, UK with a small group of six staff and students on two separate occasions, approximately eight weeks apart. On each occasion participants were asked to rate a series of concepts relating to the same 20 local restaurants. For example, questions included "*How polite are the staff*" and "*Overall, how would you rate this eating place?*".

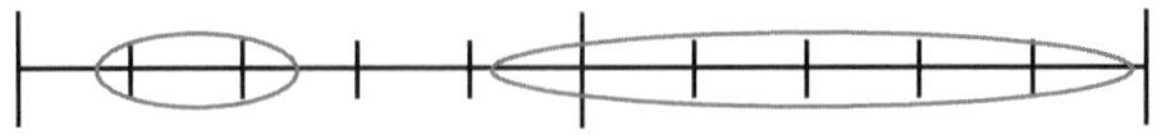

Figure 23.2: Interval responses, where "a" is a less uncertain response and "b" is a more uncertain response.

In both surveys a method of eliciting opinion was used that employed a design based on ellipses leading to intervals, i.e., where participants can express their uncertainty about a given response through specifying an ellipse/interval. The width of the interval denotes the participant's certainty in their answer, a narrow interval is used when they are sure where on the scale the answer lies, and a wider one where they are less certain. Figure 23.2 provides examples of more and less uncertain responses.

23.3.4. *The Interval Agreement Approach*

The IAA (Miller *et al.*, 2012; Wagner *et al.*, 2015) is a method of constructing T2 and GT2FSs using interval valued survey data like that used in this example. The IAA consists of two possible steps.

(1) The combination of multiple interval valued data to create T1FSs.
(2) The combination of T1FSs from step 1, to create GT2FSs.

For example, if we have multiple surveys of the same group (i.e., we have repeated a survey with the same participants) then we may use step 1 to produce a T1FS for each participant that models the opinions (over time) incorporating each of the responses an individual has given. The degree of membership to each of the T1FS models represents the intra-user agreement, that is, how much agreement there is over multiple surveys for the same person. Then, in the second step, we could combine the T1FS models to create a GT2FS. In this set, as before, the primary domain captures the agreement that the users have with themselves over repeated surveys. The secondary domain represents the inter-user agreement, that is, the level of agreement between multiple users. The GT2FSs capture both the intra- and inter-user agreement in two distinct domains.

Alternatively, if we only have one survey for each participant for example, we might use step 1 to model the inter-user agreement between a group of people for a specific survey. In this example, we will use both of these approaches for the two surveys we have conducted.

23.3.5. *Similarity Measures*

Similarity measures are methods that are used in (fuzzy) set theory to compare crisp, T1 and T2FSs.

23.3.6. *Similarity Measures for Crisp and T1 Fuzzy Sets*

In traditional (crisp) set theory, similarity measures have long been a useful tool allowing the comparison of sets in terms of their likeness. With the advent of FS theory, naturally, there was a desire to realize the important concept of similarity using FSs. A well-accepted and popular method used to measure similarity in both crisp and FS theory is the Jaccard similarity coefficient (Jaccard, 1908) which can be defined for crisp sets (CSs) as the cardinality of the intersection of two sets, divided by the cardinality of the union of the two sets as shown in Equation (2). For T1FSs, Equation (2) can be expressed as Equation (3). The result is a value $\in [0, 1]$ representing how similar A is to B, with 1 indicating that they are identical and 0 meaning that they are disjoint.

$$S_J^{CS}(A, B) = \frac{A \cap B}{A \cup B}, \tag{2}$$

$$S_J^{FS}(A, B) = \frac{\sum_{i=1}^{N} \min(\mu_A(x_i), \mu_B(x_i))}{\sum_{i=1}^{N} \max(\mu_A(x_i), \mu_B(x_i))}. \tag{3}$$

23.3.7. *Similarity Measures for T2FSs*

A number of methods have been proposed for measuring the similarity of interval T2FSs (IT2FSs) (e.g., Bustince, 2000; Gorzalczany, 1987; Wu and Mendel, 2008 and Zeng and Li, 2006) and GT2FSs (e.g., Mitchell, 2005 and Yang and Lin, 2009). In Nguyen and Kreinovich (2008) and Wu and Mendel (2009) the Jaccard similarity coefficient is extended for use with IT2FSs. Equation (4) shows how the extended Jaccard similarity coefficient is defined in Wu and Mendel (2009) where S_J^{IT2FS} is the extended Jaccard similarity function, and $\tilde{A}$ and $\tilde{B}$ are IT2FSs.

$$S_J^{IT2FS}(\tilde{A}, \tilde{B}) = \frac{\int_X \min(\bar{\mu}_{\tilde{A}}(x), \bar{\mu}_{\tilde{B}}(x))dx + \int_X \min(\underline{\mu}_{\tilde{A}}(x), \underline{\mu}_{\tilde{B}}(x))dx}{\int_X \max(\bar{\mu}_{\tilde{A}}(x), \bar{\mu}_{\tilde{B}}(x))dx + \int_X \max(\underline{\mu}_{\tilde{A}}(x), \underline{\mu}_{\tilde{B}}(x))dx}. \tag{4}$$

It can be seen that in this case, the upper and lower membership functions are used to determine the similarity of two IT2FSs. As the IAA approach generates both T1 and GT2FSs, we employ the Jaccard similarity for consistency. For T1FSs we use the Jaccard method described in Equation (3), and for GT2FSs we employ an extended form of the IT2 Jaccard similarity measure described in Wu and Mendel (2009) which we introduced in McCulloch *et al.* (2013). Equation (5) shows how Equation (4) can be expressed for GT2FSs as a weighted average of the Jaccard similarity for IT2FSs.

$$S_J^{zGT2FS}(\tilde{A}, \tilde{B}) = \frac{\sum_{i=1}^{I} z_i S_J^{IT2FS}(\tilde{A}_i, \tilde{B}_i)}{\sum_{i=1}^{I} z_i}, \tag{5}$$

where $\tilde{A}$ and $\tilde{B}$ are GT2FSs, I is the number of zSlices Wagner *et al.*, 2010, i.e., the IT2FSs that make up the GT2FS, i indicates a particular zSlice and z_i is the secondary degree of membership at each zLevel. Using this method we are able to compare perceptions of concepts/words, which will enable us to create linguistic profiles of pubs/restaurants, and make comparisons between them.

23.3.8. *Similarity Based Applications of Fuzzy Word and Concept Models*

Using the interval valued data collected during the surveys, T1 and GT2 fuzzy models created using the IAA, and similarity measures, we now demonstrate two practical applications.

(1) Creating linguistic descriptions for pubs based on the similarity of models of specific concepts (aspects) that relate to them to models of words that can be used to describe those concepts. For example, we can compute if a given pub's ambience is perceived as *negative*, *neutral*, or *positive* where both the labels and the pub-ratings are represented with fuzzy models.
(2) Comparing restaurants. For example, an individual may say "*My favorite restaurant is x, which restaurants are most like x*", or, in an unfamiliar place, the system may be used to recommend restaurants that share characteristics with a user's preferred restaurants in her/his home town. This is achieved by comparing fuzzy models of the user's preferred restaurant(s) with models of other restaurants using the similarity measure described previously.

23.3.9. *Comparing Concepts and Words*

In this application two sets of fuzzy models are created using the IAA.

(1) Word models describing a set of three adjectives for each of a set of six categories, namely: *Ambience*, *Service*, *Variety of Beer*, *Quality of Beer*, *Cost of Beer*, and *Overall rating.*
(2) Concept models of the six concepts for a series of 13 venues (pubs) in the center of Nottingham, UK.

Both models are created with the IAA using data collected during a single survey exercise with 18 local residents that employed two questionnaires, one for the rating of the words used to describe concepts of pubs in general and one for rating the actual aspects of individual pubs. The reason that we asked participants to rate the perception of words with regard to specific categories is that it is important that each word is evaluated separately in each context. Words may be perceived differently depending upon the context they are being used in.

Once the data had been collected, the IAA was used to create T1FSs representing each descriptive word and each concept for each pub. In this application the degree of membership represents the inter-user variation, that is, it shows the agreement between users over where the word lies on the scale. Figure 23.3a shows an example of the T1FS models of the *Ambience* concept for two pubs; *Trip to Jerusalem* and the *Joseph Else*. The figure shows that there concept is a significant difference in how the concept *Ambience* has been rated for each pub; the rating for the *Trip to Jerusalem* is superior to the rating for the *Joseph Else*. From a technical perspective, we can note that the fuzzy models resulting from the IAA are non-convex and non-normal. The non-convexity is a direct result of the IAA which does not remove outliers (by design). The non-normality is a result of the agreement operation, which results in wider and less *high* FSs for lower levels of agreement (overlap) of constituent

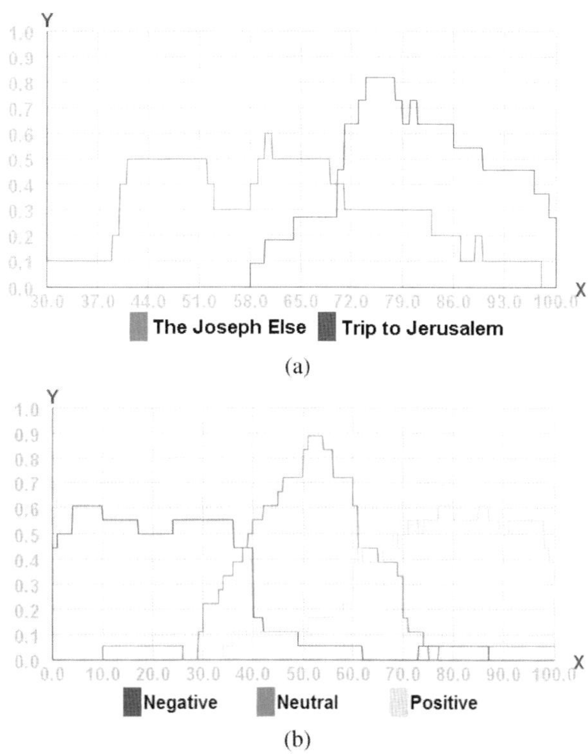

Figure 23.3: T1 FSs produced with the IAA for (a) the concept of *Ambience* in *Trip to Jerusalem* and *Joseph Else* and (b) the word models associated with the concept *Ambience*.

intervals and higher FSs with a narrower support where there is greater overlap. Thus, the resulting FSs directly reflect the agreement and discord on the given concept in the given context across participants. While it may be tempting at first glance to normalize the sets, the fact that there is no perfect agreement across all participants means that the model for the word/concept should *not* be completely true (i.e., 1) anywhere.

Figure 23.3b shows an example of the T1FS word models for *Negative*, *Neutral*, and *Positive* in the context of *Ambience* in a pub. As with the concept models, the resulting FSs clearly indicate agreement and discord amongst participants.

In the context of the application, it is worth noting that the word models can easily change, for example, with a more demanding audience, different intervals may be elicited. Also, different words may provide (more) meaningful results, for example, one could build models for the concept of *music volume* with individual word models, e.g., *low*, *ok*, *loud*, *unbearable*. Again, different audiences are likely to provide very different ratings for the words resulting in different user-centric mappings (similarities) between concepts (pubs/venues) and the given words.

Next, we will look at the outputs of the described application.

23.3.10. *Relating Concepts to Words — Results*

Once a set of word models and a set of concept models has been produced, we can compare the ratings of the concepts (e.g., *Service* in pub x) to the contextual word models of adjectives used to describe the same concept (e.g., *poor*, *acceptable*, or *excellent* service). The results of this will show us which word model most closely matches the concept models for each pub, allowing us to ask is pub x's *Service* most similar to *poor*, *acceptable*, or *excellent* service? We will then use the similarity values to generate a linguistic description of the pub which is specific to the individual/group of individuals surveyed.

Figure 23.4 shows three example profiles detailing the similarity between the type-1 fuzzy models of each concept for each pub and the T1 fuzzy word models representing the positive, neutral, and negative labels associated with each concept. In Figure 23.4, we can see that the concept models produced for *Trip to Jerusalem* have a high degree of similarity to the word models that represent positive labels for each question. A more evenly balanced response is shown for the *Ropewalk*, and the *Joseph Else* has a set of concept models that most closely match the neutral word models associated with each question.

Table 23.11 provides linguistic descriptions of each concept for each of the venues in Figure 23.4. Words have been selected by taking the word model that has the maximum similarity to each concept for each venue. The linguistic descriptions are clearly representative of the profiles previously shown (Figure 23.4), however in

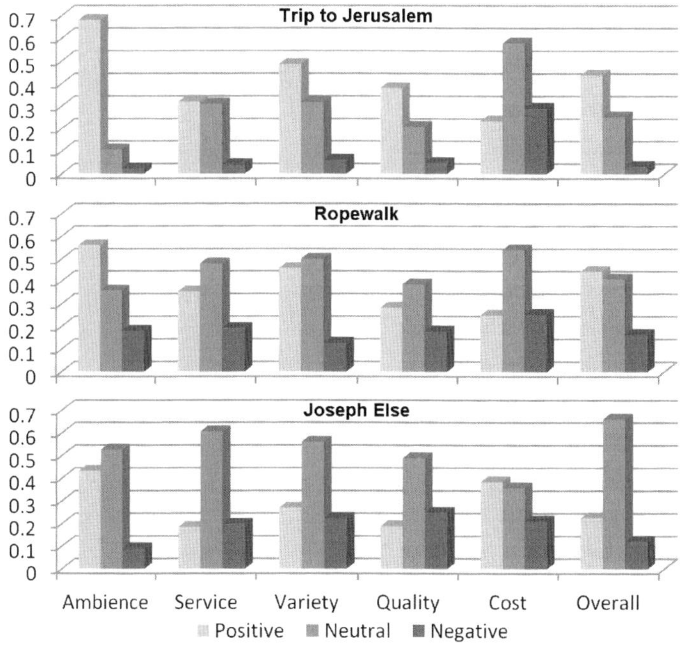

Figure 23.4: Similarity profiles for Trip to Jerusalem, Ropewalk and Joseph Else.

Table 23.11: Numeric example — Data.

Concept	Trip to Jerusalem	Ropewalk	Joseph Else
Ambience	Positive	Positive	Neutral
Service	Excellent	Acceptable	Acceptable
Variety of Beer	Wide	Wide	Reasonable
Quality of Beer	Delicious	Acceptable	Acceptable
Cost of Beer	Cheap	Cheap	Reasonable
Overall	Excellent	Acceptable	Acceptable

some cases, taking the maximum may not provide as much information as one would like. For example, the concept *Cost* for *The Ropewalk* produces very close similarity values when compared with the word models *reasonable* and *cheap.* By taking the maximum, we discard the information that it has a (relatively) high similarity with *reasonable.* To address this, we could use qualifiers for each term (e.g., *quite or very*). Defining qualifiers could potentially involve a similar methodology to that used to produce the word models.

The column charts in Figure 23.5 illustrate two examples of the similarity between the word models associated with an individual concept (e.g., *positive, neutral*, and *negative*) and the concept models (e.g., *Ambience* of the pubs) generated from the survey. The Ambience chart shows that for most venues the

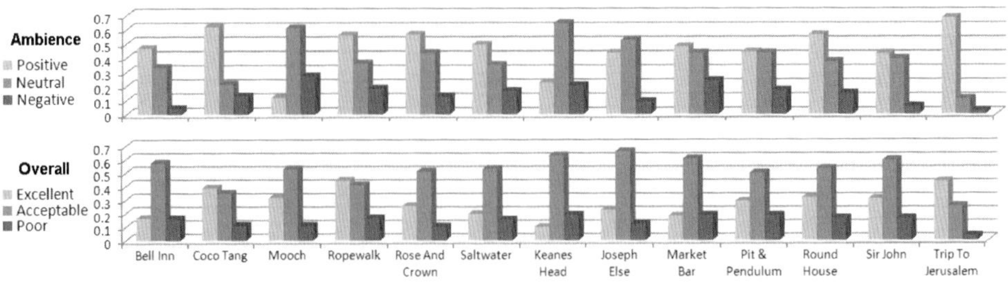

Figure 23.5: Similarity profiles for *ambience* and *overall rating* of pubs.

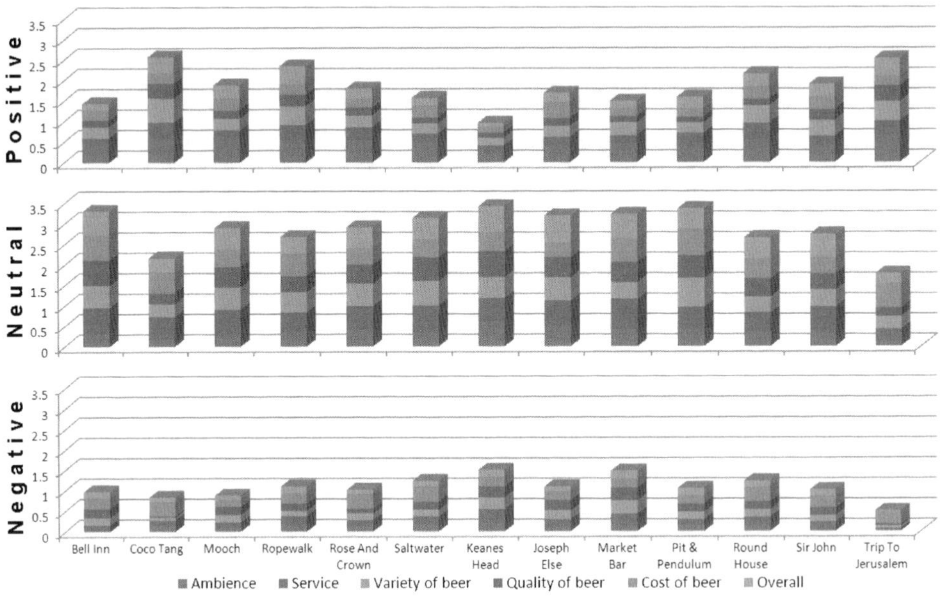

Figure 23.6: Total similarity of each pub with *Positive*, *Neutral*, and *Negative* word groups.

concept model produced for the *Ambience* question is most similar to the fuzzy word model for *positive* ambience. The results are slightly more varied for the *overall* concept which shows a stronger bias toward the *acceptable* label.

Figure 23.6 contains three column charts, each showing the total similarity of the concept models for each venue to *groupings* of the *positive*, *neutral*, and *negative* word models associated with each concept. As all concepts were rated with three words, we grouped the words describing *positive* ratings, the words describing *neutral* ratings and the words describing *negative* ratings in the top, middle, and bottom *rows* respectively. In each chart the columns are divided, showing the contribution each concept has to the overall total similarity for each pub/word group. It is immediately obvious that very few of the venues had greatest similarity with the *negative* word group models associated with each concept. For most venues the strongest similarities are with the *neutral* labels. Overall, this representation quickly summarizes the desirability of the different pubs (e.g., height of column in positive section) and visualizes which aspects (ambience, service, etc.) have contributed to this height/rating and how much.

23.3.11. *Comparing Concept Models Over Multiple Survey Iterations*

For the second application we use data collected in a survey conducted twice at the University of Nottingham, UK. Repeated surveying of the same group of participants allows us to derive not only models of the variation between people, but also models of the variation within an individual over time, i.e., the stability of their interpretation of a concept. Participants perceptions of concepts may change over time as their experience grows, or simply because their mood alters. Capturing the intra-user uncertainty is useful for extracting the *core* meaning of a concept. In this application we demonstrate how GT2FS models created with the IAA and interval valued survey data can be used to measure the similarity of (aspects of) restaurants.

The survey was conducted with a small group of six staff and students on two separate occasions approximately eight weeks apart. On each occasion participants were asked to rate a series of concepts relating to the same 20 local restaurants. For example, questions included "*How polite are the staff?*" and "*Overall, how would you rate this eating place?*". Ratings were provided using intervals as detailed in Section 23.3.3.

For the purposes of this case study, we focus on a subset of the data that includes data provided by all participants, over both surveys, to the question "*Overall, how would you rate this restaurant?*" for three of the restaurants. Though it uses only a portion of the available data, the example demonstrates how GT2FSs created using IAA can be used in conjunction with similarity measures to quantify the similarity of aspects of an item of interest.

As seen in Section 23.3.4, the first step is to create T1FSs. In this example, we use the T1FSs to represent data for each survey separately, capturing the data for each concept, for each survey and for each restaurant. Like the previous application, the membership degree for the T1 sets represents the amount of inter-user agreement on the concept of *overall quality* of each restaurant. Once each restaurant has two T1 fuzzy sets, one generated from each survey, these are combined in step 2 to create a general type-2 fuzzy set for each restaurant. The GT2FS represents inter-user agreement/uncertainty in the primary degree of membership and intra-user agreement/uncertainty in the secondary degree of membership.

The three GT2FSs for this example representing the concept of *Overall Quality* can be seen in Figure 23.7. The difference between the zSlices (the IT2FSs that make up the GT2FS) indicates how the ratings changed from one survey to the next,

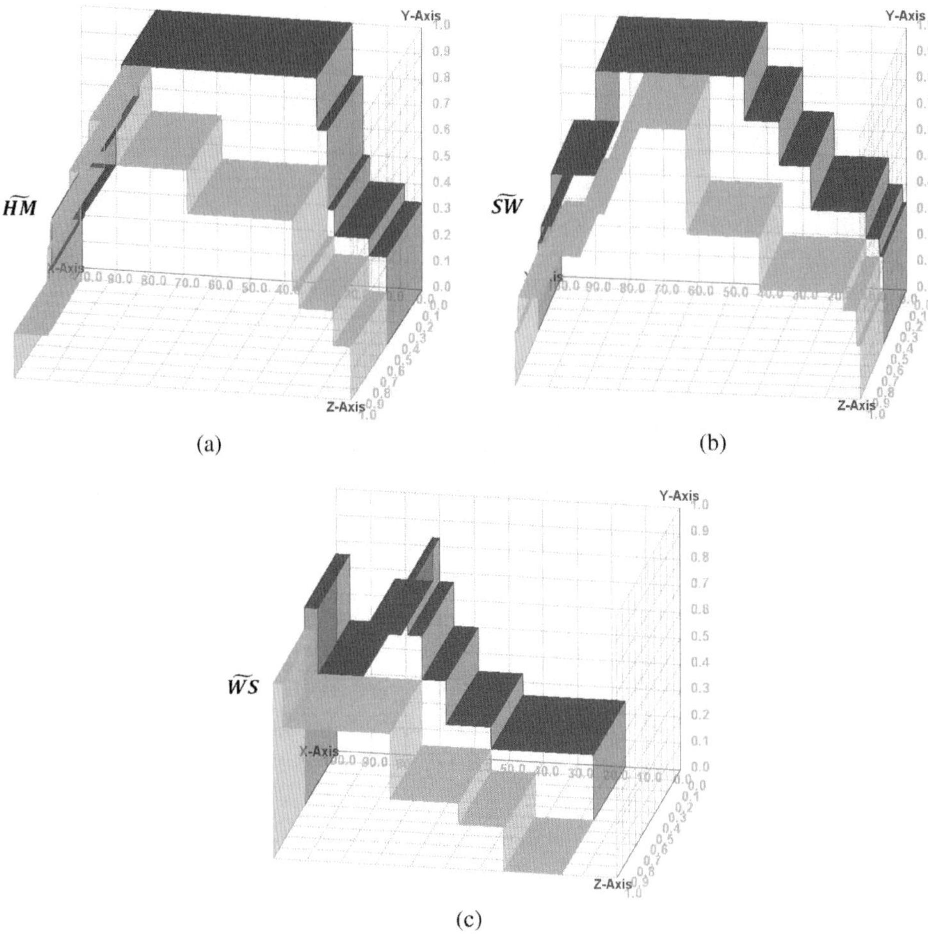

Figure 23.7: general type-2 fuzzy sets for (a) the concept of *overall quality* of (a) *Homemade* ($\tilde{HM}$) (b) *Saltwater* ($\tilde{SW}$) and (c) *World Service* ($\tilde{WS}$). Note that the zSlice $\tilde{Z}_2$ (front (light gray)) protrudes from $z = 0$ to $z = 1$ but is shown to protrude from $z = 0.5$ to $z = 1$ to improve visibility.

i.e., all ratings that were present in the models of the first *and* second iteration are included in the zSlice protruding to the zLevel $z = 1$ (front (light gray) in Figure 23.7), while other ratings that were present in only one of the surveys are only captured in the zSlice protruding to the zLevel $z = 0.5$ (rear (dark gray) in Figure 23.7).

The sets of the restaurants *Homemade* (HM) and *Saltwater* (SW) show that there is some uncertainty in individual participants' perceptions over the two surveys and between participants. Both sets cover a large amount of the domain, and have zSlices that are significantly different from one another. This shows that some participants expressed a (relatively) high level of uncertainty in their answers, that there was a (relatively) low level of agreement (across all participants), and that their perceptions altered between the first and second surveys. Overall both sets are weighted towards the middle/high end of the quality scale. The set produced for *World Service* is different. In this set the area covered by higher membership degrees is much smaller, opinion is more consistently focused on the high end of the quality scale, and the zSlices are more alike. This indicates that participants were more certain of their answers, exhibited higher agreement with one another, and gave more consistent responses over the two surveys.

Similarity is computed using the extended Jaccard similarity measure shown in Equation (5). The resulting similarities between the restaurants are shown in Table 23.12. Looking at the fuzzy sets in Figure 23.7 it can be seen that the results of applying a similarity measure reinforce the impression that HM and SW are most alike, and that *World Service* is different in terms of the model of overall quality.

There are a number of extensions that could be made to our example application to make it more useful. Initially we stated that our aim was to allow the comparison of restaurants through questions like "*My favorite restaurant is x, which other restaurants are like x?*". In the example we gave questions asking participants to rate restaurants on a scale from negative to positive, clearly most people would want to go to the restaurant that has the most positive response. For example, we can reasonable expect that nobody would say "*I'd like visit a restaurant where the food is rancid, which restaurants have food that is most similar to rancid?*". They may however ask "*I like restaurant x, which restaurants are* at least *as good as x?*". To compute this we would need to use a similarity measure that not only takes into account the proximity of the fuzzy representations of concepts, but also maintained information about in which direction (negative or positive) restaurant x is from restaurant y.

We could also create a different set of questions that relate to characteristics of an establishment rather than its quality, that do not rely on a positive/negative scale. For example, we could ask questions like "*Do you consider pub x to be traditional, or modern?*", or "*Do you consider restaurant y to have a clientèle that is young or mature?*". This kind of questioning will result in answers across the domain which describe a type of venue, rather than the perceived quality of a venue. Models of concepts like these are much more fitting for the purpose of recommending venues. For example, if a person likes a pub that is modern with a young clientèle, we can

Table 23.12: Comparison results.

Restaurants		Similarity
HM	SW	0.8202
WS	SW	0.3998
HM	WS	0.3561

use similarity measures to find other pubs that are similar to the concept models associated with this pub, i.e., they are modern with a young clientèle. In addition to this we can also create profiles for individuals with questions such as "*Do you prefer pubs that are traditional or modern?*" and use a personal profile to match an individual with establishments that they may be interested in visiting. Part of this type of survey could be to use word models like *Modern* created using the approach seen in the first example, and then allow participants to use words to describe their preferences. These can then be used to identify venues whose concept models have a high degree of similarity with the relevant word models. Initial aspects of this work can be found in McCulloch *et al.* (2015).

23.3.12. *Summary*

In this case study we have seen how both word and concept T1FS models can be created using interval valued survey data and the IAA, and how similarity measures enable us to measure the association between adjectives describing concepts specific to pubs and the perception of those concepts in the context of a particular pub. In other words, the approach enables the generation of user (group) specific ratings of venues or other things (cars, employers, etc.). While the final outputs can be used directly, for example, to generate a linguistic summary for a venue, the process itself generates a wealth of information. This includes detailed T1FS-based models which illustrate the interpretation of a given word/concept in a given context as perceived by a given group of users at the time of the data capture (here, at the time of the survey).

Following this, we saw how multi-iteration survey data can be employed to generate GT2FSs that allow us to compare restaurants. Again, the process itself generates interesting models which highlight the variation in the responses both on the intra-user as well as the inter-user level. We have shown how GT2FSs uniquely allow the capturing and modeling of the stability of perceptions (over repeated surveys) and how an extended Jaccard similarity measure (McCulloch *et al.*, 2013) can be employed to compare the resulting models.

We stress that *none* of the data used in this article are representative of the actual perception of any of the venues by the Nottingham city community (or any other community). The surveys conducted included only a relatively small, demographically non-balanced set of participants. The example's sole aim is the demonstration of how the selected methods can be applied.

23.4. Conclusions

In this chapter, we have demonstrated two approaches that employ CI techniques in human decision-making problems. We have seen how parts of expert decision-making processes can be modeled using a combination of EAs and OWAs, and how the resulting OWAs can be used to inform about the importance of specific sub-components of an overall decision. It has also been shown that the perceptions of survey participants can be modelled using T1 and GT2FSs through the IAA, and a similarity measure can be used with the resulting models can be used to create profiles of objects of interest (e.g., pubs) and make recommendations based upon a user's preferences.

Clearly, the scope for using CI techniques in decision-making problems is vast, here we have given just two specific (and related) examples. In reality, Fuzzy Logic, Evolutionary Computing, Artificial Neural Networks, and combinations of them are used in a multitude of projects that aim to aid the process of decision making.

References

Bustince, H. (2000). Indicator of inclusion grade for interval-valued fuzzy sets. Application to approximate reasoning based on interval-valued fuzzy sets. *Int. J. of Approx. Reason.* 23(3), pp. 137–209.

Coupland, S., Mendel, J. and Wu, D. (2010). Enhanced interval approach for encoding words into interval type-2 fuzzy sets and convergence of the word FOUs. In *2010 IEEE Int. Conf. on Fuzzy Systems (FUZZ)*, pp. 1–8.

Gorzalczany, M. (1987). A method of inference in approximate reasoning based on interval-valued fuzzy sets. *Fuzzy Sets and Systems*, 21(1), pp. 1–17.

Jaccard, P. (1908). Nouvelles recherches sur la distribution florale, *Bulletin de la Societe de Vaud de Sciences Naturelles*, 44, p. 223.

Liu, F. and Mendel, J. (2007). An interval approach to fuzzistics for interval type-2 fuzzy sets. In *Fuzzy Systems Conference. FUZZ-IEEE 2007. IEEE International*, pp. 1–6.

McCulloch, J. Wagner, C., Bachour, K. and Rodden, T. (2015) Give me what I want" — Enabling Complex Queries on Rich Multi-Attribute Data, to appear in Fuzzy Systems (FUZZ-IEEE), *IEEE Int. Conf.*, pp. 1–8.

McCulloch, J., Wagner, C. and Aickelin, U. (2013). Extending similarity measures of interval type-2 fuzzy sets to general type-2 fuzzy sets. In *Submitted to the 2013 IEEE Int. Conf. Fuzzy Syst.* (Hyderabad, India.).

Mendel, J. and Wu, D. (2010). *Perceptual Computing: Aiding people in making subjective judgments,* IEEE Press Series on Computational Intelligence (Wiley).

Miller, S., Wagner, C. and Garibaldi, J. (2012). Constructing general type-2 fuzzy sets from interval-valued data. In *IEEE Int. Conf. Fuzzy* (Brisbane, Australia).

Mitchell, H. (2005). Pattern recognition using type-ii fuzzy sets. *Inform. Sci.*, 170(2), pp. 409–418.

Nguyen, H. and Kreinovich, V. (2008). Computing degrees of subsethood and similarity for interval-valued fuzzy sets: Fast algorithms. In *Proceedings of the 9th International Conference on Intelligent Technologies (InTech'08)*. Samui, Thailand, pp. 47–55.

Wagner, C. and Hagras, H. (2010). Toward General Type-2 Fuzzy Logic Systems Based on zSlices. *Fuzzy Systems, IEEE Transactions*, 18(4), pp. 637–660.

Wagner, C., Miller, S., Garibaldi, J. M., Anderson, D. T. and Havens, T. C. (2015). From interval-valued data to general type-2 Fuzzy Sets. *Fuzzy Systems, IEEE Transactions*, 23(2), pp. 248–269.

Wu, D. and Mendel, J. (2008). A vector similarity measure for linguistic approximation: Interval type-2 and type-1 fuzzy sets. *Inform. Sci.*, 178(2), pp. 381–402.

Wu, D. and Mendel, J. (2009). A comparative study of ranking methods, similarity measures and uncertainty measures for interval type-2 fuzzy sets. *Inform. Sci.*, 179(8), pp. 1169–1192.

Yager, R. (1988). On ordered weighted averaging aggregation operators in multicriteria decisionmaking. *T. Syst. Man Cyb., IEEE*, 18(1), pp. 183–190.

Yang, M. and Lin, D. (2009). On similarity and inclusion measures between type-2 fuzzy sets with an application to clustering. *Comput. Math. Appl.*, 57(6), pp. 896–907.

Zeng, W. and Li, H. (2006). Relationship between similarity measure and entropy of interval valued fuzzy sets. *Fuzzy. Set. and Syst.*, 157(11), pp. 1477–1484.

Chapter 24

Applications of Computational Intelligence to Process Industry

Jose Macias Hernández

The process industry and, more specifically, chemical engineering processes have great opportunities to develop, test, and extensively implement tools with smart computing features. The complexity of the processes, the variety of interaction mechanisms that occur in these processes, and the infinite possibilities of design, in addition to failure testing, optimization, production planning, etc., can cause a myriad of computational intelligence (CI) applications to be possible. In this paper, we aim to review all these possibilities by listing some of the opportunities and developments, also to give some examples of problem solving. Potential opportunities for the use of CI can be identified throughout the design sequence of an industrial plant, from the conceptual design process to startup and troubleshooting. Similarly within an operating plant an identification of CI applications can be made if we analyze the structure of a facility by job function and from there select those areas or issues which also require a contribution to solving problems.

24.1. Introduction

Computational intelligence (CI) should first be defined. Terms such as "artificial intelligence", "computer intelligence" and "soft computing" are often confused. Although it is a difficult problem and is subject to a great deal of debate, one of the best ways we can define this particular family of intelligent systems is by using a definition from Krishnakumar (2003) that clearly defines the term.

> *"From the perspective of computation, the intelligence of a system can be characterized by its flexibility, adaptability, memory, learning, temporal dynamics, reasoning, and the ability to manage uncertain and imprecise information".*

Some examples of tools that comply with this definition are neural nets, genetic algorithms, fuzzy systems, evolutionary programming, genetic algorithms, and evolutionary programming.

Early definition of process industrial intelligent applications is shown in Mc Avoy (2002) where partial least squares (PLS) and Expert Systems are used.

Same approach can be seen in Macias (2001) and Macias *et al.* (2001). In this paper, we will focus on the evolving and fuzzy capabilities of CI.

Once the tool has been defined it is necessary to show the application. One such application is within the Process Industry. Here, we find very complex activities that rely strongly upon personal knowledge, processes, and technology. There is plenty of room to use these tools in the Process Industry.

The success of a process in the industry starts from the initial stage of development of the conceptual design and continues throughout the life of the plant until its retirement. It is therefore necessary to develop new products from raw materials that allow different processes to adapt to the needs of increasingly competitive markets, more stringent environmental restrictions, and tighter costs. This makes the use of process tools and simulation data in turn increasingly complex. Information processing must take into account the multiple interactions between data, and also the imprecise and variable behavior that the data has over time. That is why possibly intelligent tools such as fuzzy data processing are a possible solution to these increasingly complex problems.

An example is the Oil and Gas (O&G) sector which is one of the most complex process industries. In these processes, Intelligent Systems can play an important role to maintain profitability in this very economically competitive world. Process industries in general and O&G in particular require:

- Constant product supervision (high number of process variables).
- Cost reduction (optimization).
- Continuous Innovation for new products, processes (conceptual design tools).

To cope with these requirements the application of Intelligent Computing needs a huge amount of data. Nowadays, in process industries there is a large amount of data available.

There are several reviews in the literature that describe the uses of intelligent technologies in process industries. One of them, Kahraman (ed.) (2012) makes this analysis from the technological point of view. This is by grouping applications by computing intelligent tools.

In this approach, we are considering the problem itself and seeing which technology could be more suitable to solve it.

24.2. Information Systems

Every Process Plant has a supervisory system in place. Even the smallest plant has a "PLC" (Programmable Logic Controller) and a "SCADA" (Supervisory Control and Data Acquisition). These systems generate huge volumes of data that are processed and stored in sophisticated Information Systems.

The operator of a typical Distributed Control System ("DCS"), in a process industry, controls and monitors several process units and is responsible for more than 400 valves. The instrumentation database can have as many as 10,000–12,000 continuous data points. Laboratory samples are routinely analyzed and more than 200–2,000 characteristics could be reported every day. The process operators continuously make decisions based on previous experience to drive the process towards targets. However, with "soft" sensors this process could be automated.

Data generated by "DCS" are normally of high-resolution (snap values) with a limited time frame. In the majority of cases there is low-resolution (average data values) with probably several years of data history.

This data feeds several corporate applications for data reconciliation (mass balance), logistics, and product movements, etc. As a result, it is possible to monitor the complete process flow and to analyze the plant performance and give full support to departments such as planning, process accounting, and operations.

There are, although, several problems associated with this kind of data, the most important are the high correlation and noise.

Because of high data correlation, the amount of useful information that is contained is much lower. In addition to that the problems and events associated with a running process plant make it very difficult to diagnose a problem in the operation or in the performance of the plant. Therefore, deep understanding of the process unit is challenging.

As a result, troubleshooting of a process unit when the problem has fully developed is more frequent than early diagnosis.

Also, the operation of the plant is normally set around process values and because of this short operational window the magnitude of the noise is almost as high as the magnitude of the process variations. Care should be taken to design models with high information content and robustness.

Definitely, it is necessary to have more tools to manipulate the data and convert it to information, so it can be used to help in diagnostics and process follow-ups.

If information can be successfully extracted from data, it can be made available to Operators, Process Engineers, Control Engineers, and Managers so they can better understand their respective plant processes and therefore make the necessary actions to optimize and lower cost. The "eTS+" (Angelov and Zhao, 2006) approach can probably be used among others to effectively extract this valuable information.

To illustrate this concept the classical control pyramid with the relation between decision level and data volume can be used (see Figure 24.1). The greater the time frame, the greater the economic impact is or the more important a decision, the greater the application scope. Also, the volume of data gets reduced where it is converted to information.

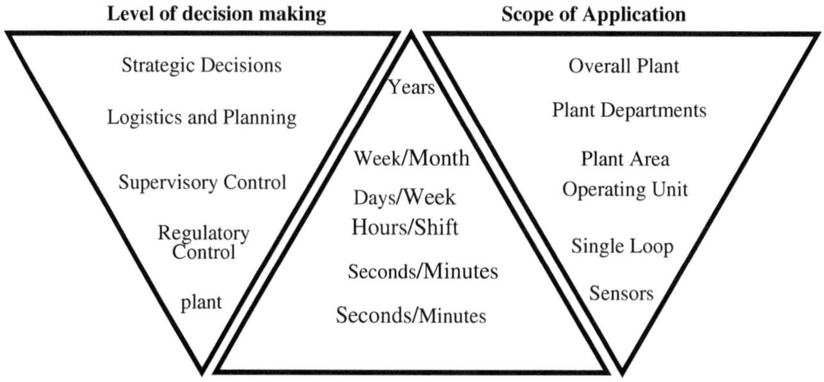

Figure 24.1: Time frame and its relation to the decision level and application scope.

24.2.1. *Data Reconciliation*

A very important characteristic of process data, for subsequent analysis, is that it should be balanced; i.e., the material balances (mass components) and energy balances are met. The reconciliation data is commonly done using optimization software to reduce measurement error. The cumulative error (observed value and reconciled value) of all instrumentation is used as an objective function, along with some appropriate criteria. Recently, by using fuzzy logic, this process can be simplified significantly as Dr. Tan discusses in (Tan *et al.*, 2009). In Dr. Tan's paper, he writes how it is possible to obtain the value reconciled with a simple approximation of the observed value with the triangular or trapezoidal function and subsequent arithmetic fuzzy logic.

24.3. Raw Materials

Profitability starts when purchasing raw materials. This is most of the time true, because the price of raw materials is one of the most contributing factors to final product price. In the O&G industry, for instance, the price of raw material (crude oil) is around 90–95% of the final retail price. Therefore, a bad price of crude oil or purchasing by mistake could damage a Refinery's bottom line. Whereas, purchasing well-balanced crude oil at a good price can make more money than the refining activity itself. There is a vast variety of crude oil with different properties that will give different cuts and yields when processing. The price of crude oil depends on several factors, ranging from its intrinsic chemical properties to political stability in the country of supply, and short- and long-term market behavior. Supply chain, trading departments have to balance "spot market" contracts and "long term" contracts to maintain a stable crude oil supply to their refineries.

How do you go about selecting the right crude oil and how do you fix the break-even price on crude purchasing? The crude oil cuts should be balanced to account for the market share of the refinery's products, therefore only producing what you are able to sell. Any unbalance is normally undesirable. There are tools designed to help do this, but problems arise if their predictions are not correct. The real problem is to evaluate crude oil selection with actual plant performance. Again, there is a huge amount of data which is highly collinear.

24.4. Application Opportunities

A process plant is a very complex installation because of the number of interconnected process operations (pumping, distillation, reaction, heating, etc.). Also, it is because of work organization. If we make the effort to analyze the work flow in a typical installation we can identify different possible implementations of intelligent technologies and those will not be limited to instrument data mining.

The majority of these areas can be found in any complex industrial installation.

24.5. The Process of Designing a Design Process

The design process starts whenever a product demand or service is created.

24.5.1. *Process Integration*

Once you have created the need to produce a particular product from certain raw materials, the first step of the design is the conceptual design. This methodology consists of a series of decisions that are based on rules that define the design of the plant as defined by Douglas (1988) and Smith (2005). These rules are rigid and do not have any fuzzy treatment. These rules, on the whole, are the result of the combination of past experiences in processes, raw materials, and product properties. In some stages of conceptual design, such as the energy integration level, some interesting contributions have been made by the application of intelligent tools. But, in general, there are many opportunities to develop applications in this field. The last part of the design (energy integration) is when the number of design alternatives is complicated and it is necessary to use optimization rules and more complex evaluation. Recently there has been an initiative to incorporate fuzzy arithmetic to the analysis of heat exchange networks (Hussein *et al.*, 2013).

Similarly, the impact assessment of the life cycle (LCA) has references on the use of fuzzy tools for evaluation of alternatives (Tan, 2005). In this paper a model of decision support tools based on fuzzy is proposed. The subject is the selection of motor fuels.

24.5.2. *Process Engineering*

For the design, process engineers use simulation tools that use rigorous mathematical formulation of the basic operations of chemical engineering and thermodynamics.

Besides the steady state, engineers use dynamic models that provide insight into the best control strategies and design virtual plants that allow the training of plant operators even before they have been built. Neural networks and neuro-fuzzy models have been used to speed up the computing capacity and more simple and robust models as seen in Macias *et al.* (2001).

24.6. Planning and Scheduling

The complexity and the opportunities of CI come from the very beginning with the purchase of raw materials. As shown before, for instance, in an Oil Refinery there is a tradeoff between quality, yields, spot and long-term deals, and international polices.

These problems are complex, nonlinear, and non-stationary and a model to develop should take into account all this information which is highly uncertain (ERTC, 2004; Goel and Prashant, 1999). Some companies reported commercial products that address these problems e.g., Aspentech, GenSym, but clearly there is an opportunity for more advanced solutions in this area.

Also, backcasting planning operations are necessary to correlate better prediction models. None of the commercial softwares available today can do this using an intelligent application that automatically identifies opportunities and evolves itself.

24.7. Operations

Most industrial plants are very complex in nature. From the processing of raw materials to finished products there are not only several, but hundreds of process operations. For every process operation, it is also necessary to consider raw material properties. Both, operations and process engineering departments have to cope with these problems. Clearly, the problems associated with it are difficult to analyze in real time. They have to deal with short-term process troubleshooting, security, and quality management. Process operators have to deal with problems associated with process security, stability, quality, and optimization targets of the plant. If we think of automatic data processing and diagnosis, there definitely are quite a few application opportunities of Evolving Intelligent System technologies in the field of process operation, like:

24.7.1. *Operator Advisory Applications*

Advisory Systems are required to help operators with real-time decision-making processes to maintain security, stability and, process optimization (Macías, 2001). Intelligent Systems can be very useful for tackling these problems.

24.7.2. *Alarm Monitoring and Rationalization*

The main goal here is to identify scenarios and analyze the sequence of events to determine the initial detection agent. Once the agent is identified, rationalization means to suppress any superfluous alarm that does not add new information but reduces the capability of the operator to react safely. Tools that can be useful and efficient are eClustering+ and eTS+. For instance, (Geng *et al.*, 2005) proposes a new system alarm optimization technique, based on a fuzzy clustering–ranking ("FCR") algorithm, according to the correlativity among process-measured variables.

24.7.3. *Emergency Manager*

Emergency Manager is related to alarm monitoring and rationalization, but here, the goal is to help the operator to manage emergency situations. In Foong *et al.* (2010), the author proposes a Decision Support System for Alarm Rationalization using Risk Assessment Matrix ("ARRAM"). This method uses crisp rules although the author intends future work to be done on fuzzy data processing.

24.8. Maintenance

The cost of a mechanical failure or breakage should include the interruption of production, material outside of specifications, safety issues, etc. Therefore, early detection of potential failure or failure is a very important predictive maintenance program task. It is not always possible in a direct way to determine if a fault is occurring or can occur. On many occasions this detection can be inferred from the interpretation of the data (vibration analysis, mean time between failures ("MTBF'), process variables, indicators of corrosion, etc.). Therefore, detecting what, how and when it will happen is a very good opportunity to use smart computing tools. An early detection failure sensor is, in general, an open problem. There are successful applications where this is the case, like vibration analysis, but cross correlation between process operating data and equipment failure is not done in an automatic fashion. eClustering+ and eTS+ are very promising tools for this problem (Filev and Tseng, 2006).

24.9. Process Control

There are lots of references of using CI for Process Control. A review can be found in Precup and Hellendoorn (2010). Control Engineering has several general open issues:

24.9.1. *Software Sensors*

This is an area of very successful soft sensor applications (Barsamian and Macías, 1998; Fortuna *et al.*, 2007; Baht *et al.*, 2003, etc.). Most of them, however, are based on offline black-box type models. They are not able to re-calibrate, neither to provide an insight for the process (are not transparent), do not take into account environmental dynamics and internal changes in the plant (different operating modes, ageing, contamination), etc. As a result, the life cycle costs of conventional soft sensors are high.

A review of Bayesian methods can be found in Khatibisepehr *et al.* (2013) for use both in "steady state" and in "dynamic" mode.

24.9.2. *Dynamic Model Identification*

The classical control theory provides a solid theoretical basis for the linear algebra systems and a limited number of nonlinear systems. Data mining is suitable for off-line cases, while dynamic model identification is a very promising area, but for the general nonlinear case there are practically no ready solutions apart from computing intelligence.

24.9.3. *Detecting Drift and Shift in the Data Pattern in Streaming Data*

An interesting article can be found in Angelov and Zhou (2008).

24.9.4. *Controller Tuning*

There are references using fuzzy logic to tune the controllers (Gaddam and Rajani, 2006). The main benefits of using Fuzzy Logic appear when process nonlinearities such as variable saturation are significant. A balance is obtained between both rise time and overshoot in response with this implementation. In this implementation a two degree parameter is sufficient to tune the controller. (Kratmüller, 2009), remarks that Fuzzy logic controllers are in general considered being applicable to plants that are mathematically poorly understood and where the experienced human operators are available. In indirect adaptive fuzzy control, the fuzzy logic systems are used to model the plant assuming that the fuzzy logic system represents the true plant.

The problem of detecting internal loop problems versus external influences can be addressed by eClustering+ and eClass.

24.9.5. *Hybrid controllers (Multivariable Predictive Control, MPC + Fuzzy techniques)*

MPC tools are mature; however, their utilization depends on a properly designed controller and the selection of variables. The first part is usually done in practice using Lyapunov theory, LMI, etc., by the design engineer. The variable selection is an important task which can be done automatically. However, a non-stationary system requires continuous model update. Fuzzy logic also arrived in these very popular

Table 24.1: Potential application areas for the use of Intelligent Systems in process industry.

Departments/Areas	Application Type
Operations	Alarm monitoring, operator advisory, emergency management
Price prediction	Regression and time-series prediction models, e.g., eTS+
Process Engineering	Process diagnostics, e.g., eClustering+
Information Systems	Mining data streams, e.g., eTS+
Predictive Maintenance	Machine health monitoring and prognostics, e.g., eClustering+ and eTS+ (Filev and Tseng, 2006)
Control Engineering	eControl, Guided rule-base adaptation (Filev *et al.*, 2000)
Soft Sensors	eSensor

industrial control systems. This paper (Sarimveis, 2003) introduces a new fuzzy control technique that modifies the general idea of linear MPC. The method is based on a dynamic fuzzy model of the process to be controlled, which is used for predicting the future behavior of the output variables. The method can be used with any type of fuzzy model and is particularly useful when a direct fuzzy controller cannot be designed due to the complexity of the process and the difficulty in developing fuzzy control rules. The method is illustrated via the application of a nonlinear single-input single-output reactor, where a Takagi–Sugeno model serves as a predictor of the processes future behavior.

In the Table 24.1, a summary of the application areas of Intelligent Systems is shown in relation to the Department or Areas that normally are of interest in an industry.

24.10. Process Industry, Oil Refinery Case

Once we have analyzed the different functions in a process facility (maintenance, engineering, process control, purchasing, etc.), it is also important to review a typical installation to identify opportunities for using CI in each process plant. An Oil Refinery can serve as an illustrative example of the use of smart technologies in process industries. A refinery is an industrial facility where crude oil is separated into its fraction and then, these fractions are treated to produce other intermediate products with a higher end value. Intermediate products will be blended to produce final products. These blends should be combined in the right proportions to comply with commercial specifications, producing as much final product with the lowest production cost possible (see Figure 24.2).

The sale of final products has to pay for the raw material and all the associated costs. Because of the high raw material cost, the petroleum refining process does not have a high economic return in terms of the percentage of the capital employed, but receives profit from the huge volume of crude oil processed.

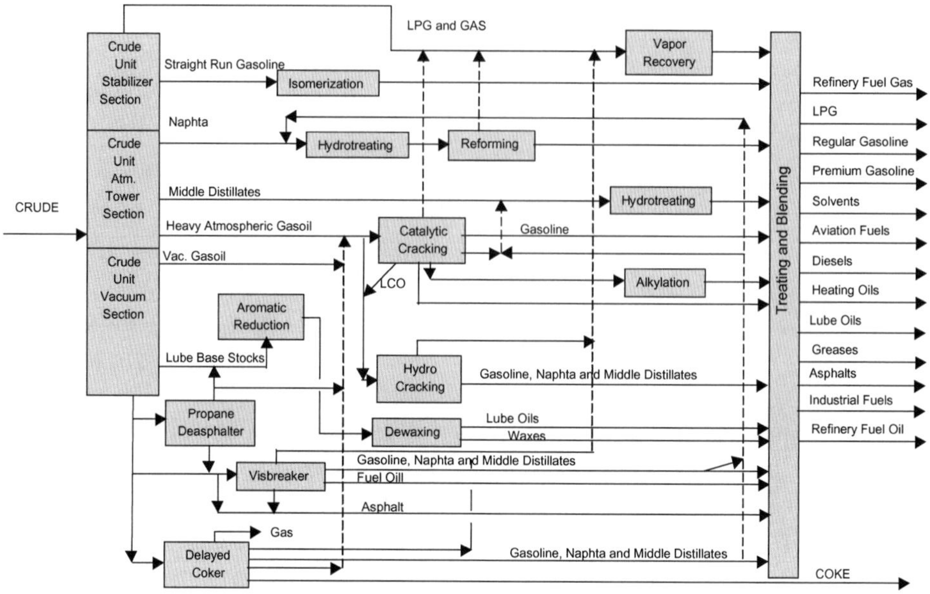

Figure 24.2: Typical oil refinery flow sheet.

Today, there is very little room to improve economic performance apart from reducing costs and improving the transformation processes.

To support these arguments, we should describe the refining process. Those areas in which the uses of smart technologies provide value will also be discussed.

24.11. Raw Material

The most interesting qualities of oil (other than product yield), which are present and which have the greatest impact on refinery economics are the sulfur content, density, parafinicity, and the residue carbon, salts, nitrogen and metals content. In analysis, crude oil qualities and their impact on production cost can explain part of the process of crude oil price construction.

The sulfur content impacts the economy of a refinery because the use of desulfurization units for most oil fractions is required. Acids or high-sulfur crude oil, where more sulfur has to be removed are cheaper than sweet or low-sulfur crude oil.

Low density crude oil correlate with lighter crude oil which produces much smaller amounts of residue, which is one of the fractions with the smallest value. Crude Oil is more expensive than the residue; therefore, this amount must be reduced to a minimum in any refinery.

The transformation of the naphtha into gasoline requires increasing the aromaticity of the oil fraction which uses energy and other manufacturing processes.

Naphthenic naphtha converts to aromatics much more easily than its brother paraffinic naphtha, reducing the energy and other manufacturing processes needed. Consequently, the market cost of oil with a higher paraffinic content is cheaper.

The Carbon Residue is related to asphalt content, which is the cheapest fraction.

Salt produces corrosion in the process units. Therefore, the higher the salt content, the cheaper the crude oil.

Nitrogen and sulfur cause catalyst poisoning and must be removed and metals also produce catalyst poisoning and severe deactivation. Because of the high price of the catalyst employed in refinery process units, catalyst deactivation impacts very heavily on the economic performance of the refinery.

24.12. Process Units

The opportunities for the use of CI technology in process units can be analyzed mainly from the point of view of quality monitoring and control. Because there are a high number of processes, we select only the most typical ones. The same ideas can be extrapolated to others.

The principal operations required in a typical refinery are:

- Crude oil distillation.
- Reforming.
- Hydrotreating.
- FCC.
- Visbreaking.

24.13. Crude Oil Distillation

24.13.1. *Process Description*

It is the first unit in the refinery flow sheet (see Figure 24.3); its mission is to separate by distillation the different crude oil fractions by means of boiling the crude oil and then condensing it. Steam is added to improve the separation. The fractions extracted by side streams in the tower are:

- Naphtha.
- Kerosene.
- Gas oil.
- Fuel Oil.

Fuel Oil can be fed from the main distillation tower into a secondary "vacuum distillation tower", if available, where asphalt or vacuum fuel oil is produced.

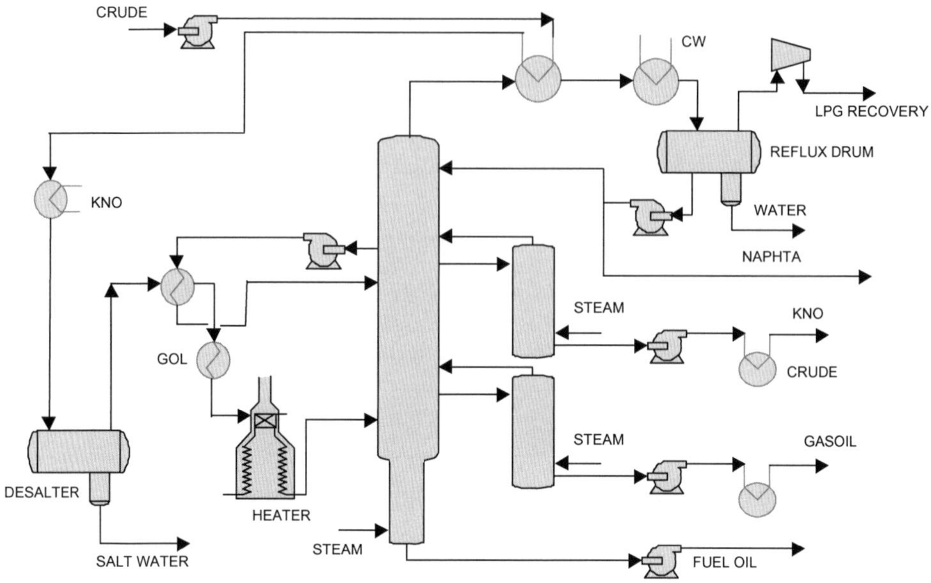

Figure 24.3: A reduced schematic of a crude oil distillation unit.

24.13.2. *Process Key Variables*

The most important key operating variables are:

- Furnace temperature.
- Top reflux, temperature, and pressure.
- Side tower heat removal (cooling).
- Side stream flows.

These variables produce different ranges of side stream qualities. These qualities are important and have to be correct and stable because there are no more opportunities to correct them. If any product is left above or below the side stream it will be redirected to a different final product and this effect will impact the refinery economics.

24.13.3. *Opportunities for CI*

The opportunities of CI in quality monitoring are mainly through the use of **"soft" sensors**. For example, "soft" analyzers for side stream cut point calculations instead of real distillation analyzers that are expensive and highly maintenance-dependent. The currently used technologies are offline NN (neural networks), but there are successful applications using PLS and bias updates (Macías, 1998). This latter is especially important for close loop "soft" control due to its robustness.

Process units are pushed to their maximum capacity and in that region problems of **"flooding"** in the tower can arise. Therefore, there is a need to diagnose and maintain the distillation tower to its limits and "soft" fuzzy sensors will help for that tower loading calculations.

Another interesting application is the development of a fuzzy rule-based model for unit optimization to solve problems like:

(1) **Crude switch**: Any time there is a change in the crude oil supply to a distillation unit, the unit should be adjusted to maintain side stream qualities. The transient response of the unit is different to the one that happens in normal operation. Therefore, the transient should be detected and corrected in advance so the time that a product is off specification is reduced to a minimum. Detecting, evaluating and coping with this situation, represents an unsolved problem for refineries.

(2) **Feed properties and operation conditions**: The crude oil tower behaves differently from one crude oil type to another. The unit should be adjusted to the new optimum settings. This is typically accomplished by analyzing the process database to find the best operating conditions of the unit or using case-based reasoning. An alternative is to use CI for online updates in new conditions. A good example of a CI is the guided rule-based initialization applied to advanced manufacturing (Filev *et al.*, 2000).

24.14. Hydro Treating

24.14.1. *Process Description*

Hydro-treaters treat a feed (naphtha, kerosene, or gas oil) where hydrogen is added to convert the sulfur combined with the hydrocarbons into SH_2 (see Figure 24.4).

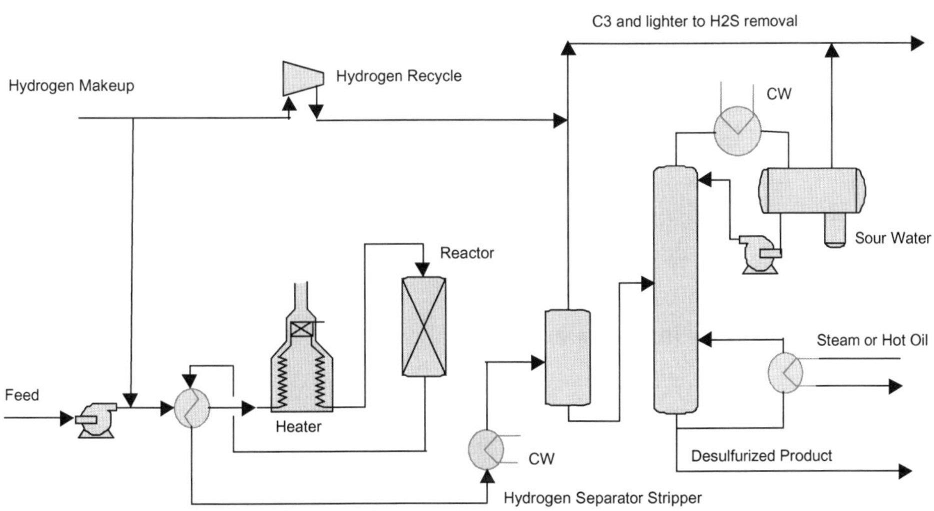

Figure 24.4: Hydro-treating unit.

The SH_2 gets partially dissolved in the liquid and will have to be removed in a stripper tower. This unit is used for treatment of naphtha, kerosene, and gas oil. The reaction takes place in presence of a catalyst at high temperature and pressure. The reactor pressure will depend on the hydrocarbon type and hydrogen purity, the higher the hydrocarbon boiling point, the higher the operating pressure. Metals must be removed before hand because they poison the catalyst. During the process, coke is formed due to cracking. Hydrogen is also used to minimize cracking in the reactor.

24.14.2. *Process Key Variables*

The key variables that control the severity of the reaction are:

- Reactor temperature.
- Hydrogen partial pressure.
- Spatial velocity.

The partial pressure in the reactor is maintained with the separator pressure and the hydrogen recycling. Hydrogen benefits the RUN length or the time that the unit can be in service between having to regenerate the catalyst. The temperature or steam flow in stripper bottoms is controlled to remove the SH_2 dissolved in the reactor effluent.

24.14.3. *Opportunities*

Reactor models are only a mathematical approximation of the process and should be adjusted to process variables. Also, the **activity of the catalyst changes** and therefore a long-term adjustment should be made. Modeling reactors have a calibration problem subject to **time variations**. This important adjustment problem calls for self-calibration models (evolving). The difficulty arises due to the fact that the feed is not perfectly characterized. This requires the use of fuzzy sets. eTS+ are thus, perfectly placed to be used as a backbone technology for the development of advanced evolving "soft" sensors (eSensors) to address this problem.

These evolving models can be of utility for integrated simulation models for monitoring and reaction control.

24.15. Catalytic Reforming Unit

24.15.1. *Process Description*

Reforming is a catalytic process designed to increase the aromatic and isoparafinic content of naphtha and therefore produces high-octane gasoline. The product is called reformate and because of its high aromatic content, it is also used to produce aromatics as a raw material for petrochemical facilities.

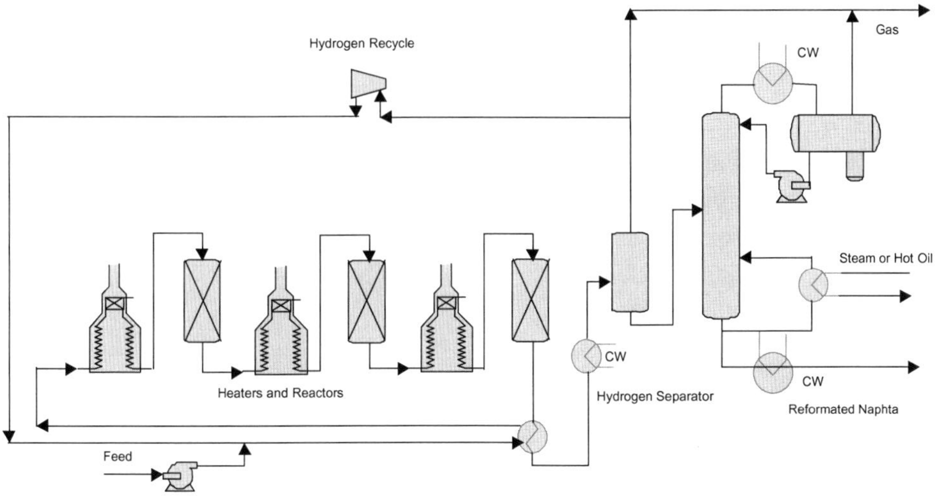

Figure 24.5: Catalytic reforming unit.

This chemical process takes place in several reactors in series using hydrogen to protect the catalyst preventing the poisoning from coke laydown. Hydrogen is produced also in the process unit due to dehydrogenation reactions. Some cracking reactions also take place producing liquefied petroleum gas (LPG) and refinery gas, (see Figure 24.5).

24.15.2. *Process Key Variables*

The key variables that control the severity of the reaction are, among others:

- Reactor temperature.
- Hydrogen partial pressure.
- Spatial velocity.
- Water/chlorine balance in the catalyst.

The temperature and spatial velocity are the most important short term key variables, while water/chlorine balance has long-term contribution. A post-fractionation unit separates the LPG and gas from reformatted naphtha. The operation variables in that tower are the **reflux ratio** and the **bottoms temperature**. Quality control variables are the octane number and the Reid vapor pressure of the reformatted naphtha. The higher the octane number, the higher aromatic content of reformate.

24.15.3. *Opportunities*

Like any process unit with catalysts, the activity of the unit will depend on the type of catalysts and also on the time that the unit works continuously. Therefore,

CI models should cope with variations in catalyst activity to predict qualities like octane number and product yields. Such a model is much more complicated than the hydro-treating one due to the fact that the number of reactions is much higher.

Ideally, it should be able to re-calibrate and re-train automatically. It is not frequent to have octane analyzers in the bottom of the fractionation tower, so a CI-based soft sensor can be designed based upon operating conditions and type of feed. This latter characteristic should be derived upstream in the crude oil unit and naphtha hydro-treating units.

24.16. Catalytic Cracking

24.16.1. *Process Description*

Fluid catalytic cracking is a technology to break the vacuum gas oil into gasoline and lighter fractions. Due to the very high speed of catalyst deactivation and as the consequence of the severe operating conditions, the regeneration process takes place simultaneously in a second regenerator reactor. The catalyst moves from the reactor to the regenerator. The catalyst coke formed is burned in the regenerator using air (see Figure 24.6).

24.16.2. *Process Key Variables*

With a fixed type of feedstock, the major operating variables that affect the conversion and product distribution are;

- Cracking temperature.
- Catalyst to feed ratio.

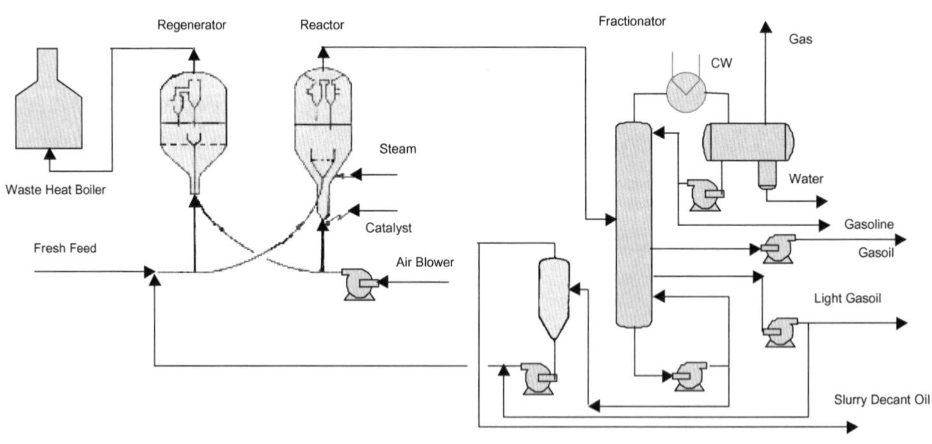

Figure 24.6: Fluid catalytic cracking unit.

- Space velocity.
- Type of catalyst.
- Recycle ratio, air.

To increase the conversion, we must increase reaction temperature, catalyst to feed ratio, catalyst activity, and reaction time. The limitations come from the limit on burning activity, limit in the air compressor, and temperature limitation in the regenerator. Sometimes, oxygen is added to increase the burning capability of the regenerator reactor.

24.16.3. *Opportunities*

Because of the high added-value of this process unit to a Refinery, it is very frequent to see models to optimize the unit performance. This is an important opportunity to use CI-based **"soft" analyzers** to calculate the octane number of the gasoline and product distribution. There is also a case for **hybrid models** to simulate the reaction and regeneration sections in a mixed approach using rigorous simulation in the main fractionation and to balance catalyst activity with time and severity using e.g., eTS+.

A difficult and challenging task is to early detect and identify different types of feed that facilitates a faster move to unit limits. There is a large scope to address these using techniques such as eClustering+, for example. In recent articles, it is hard to see real examples of the use of CI. An example of the combination of process control (MPC approach) and process simulation can be found in Mihaela and Agachi (2010). Another paper, also using MPC and soft sensor can be seen in Yang *et al.* (1998). In none of these papers is there a fuzzy approximation for soft sensors either in steady state or in dynamic mode. This is definitely an open issue.

24.17. Thermal Cracking

Visbreaking of soaker type

24.17.1. *Process Description*

Visbreaking is a type of thermal cracking that reduces the viscosity of a heavier feed to a lower viscosity fuel by means of breaking higher molecular weight molecules into gasoline, kerosene, gas oil, and lower viscosity fuel. The reaction takes place by temperature and space velocity in the furnace (coil visbreakers) or a soaker drum (soaker visbreaker). The former achieves conversion by temperature, the latter by space velocity. As a result, soaker drum visbreakers get longer run times that coil visbreakers. The reactor effluent is separated in fractions in a fractionation and

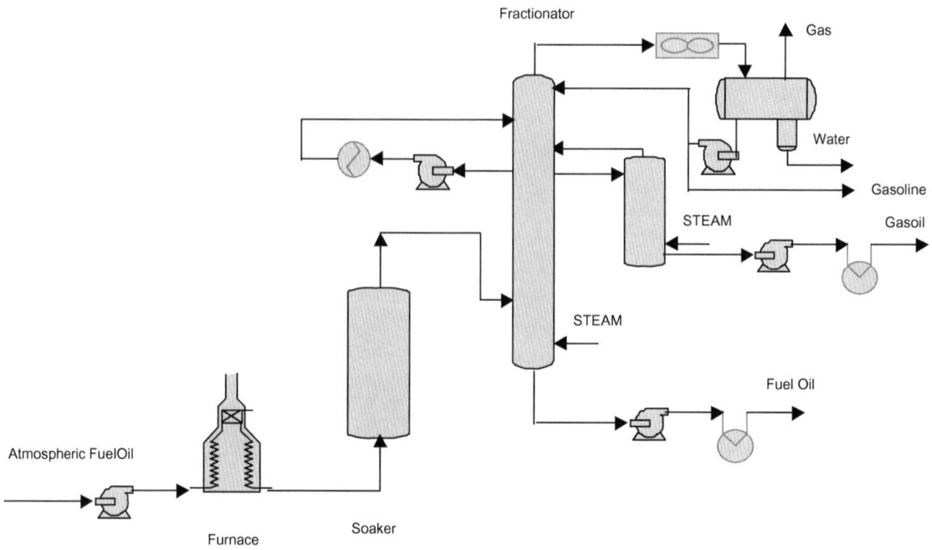

Figure 24.7: Visbreaking unit, soaker type.

stabilizer towers. Run length is controlled by coke deposition in the furnace that limits skin temperature.

24.17.2. *Process Key Variables*

The key process variables are the temperature and the spatial velocity. There are other operating variables in the fractionation tower like steam, reflux ratio, and heat distribution. The key variable is the stability of the fuel oil, which is drawn from the fractionation bottoms.

A big practical obstacle is the lack of analyzers for stability. Manipulating extraction side streams and stripping steam should control side streams cut point. Some types of feed are more sensitive to coke lay down than others. Prediction of coke lay down is important to optimize the run length.

24.17.3. *CI Opportunities*

There are great opportunities for CI-based “soft” analyzers:

- Predicting the stability of the fuel oil, profit key variable in this process unit.
- Soft Analyzers for cut point side stream control.
- Hybrid integrated models (vis-breaking reaction model and rigorous steady state tower simulation).
- There is a need for feed characterization for its crack ability and stability to predict coke laydown, run length, and maximum severity.
- Use this information to manipulate operating variables between feed switch.

24.18. Conclusion

Process Industry is normally very complex. There are a high number of process variables and lab samples and therefore a huge database. As a result there are a high number of opportunities for the implementation of Intelligent Systems.

CI can be applied to several fields ranging from operations or process engineering to maintenance, accounting, and supply chain. This increases the complexity of any application due to the fact that it has to account for the implication of different Departments of a process industry.

The information available in the oil refinery has several inherent characteristics: a high number of variables in a small range of variations, highly collinear and noisy data. Most of the time there is no clear relation between the data and type of feed. These factors increase uncertainty and noise.

The tools that are most commonly used include "soft" analyzer, model building, and time series predictors. The use of fuzzy rule-based systems is suitable for operator advisory systems in normal and emergency situations. Alarm management tools can be a special case of this application.

Control engineering is one of the activities with the highest number of opportunities for implementation of CI. It is very well suited for hybrid control, mixing between conventional control theory and fuzzy systems.

Even though there are a lot of tools already available in the market there are still so many unsolved problems that will make eTS+ and other CI interesting for the petrochemical and other process industries in the future.

References

Angelov, P. and Zhou, X. (2006). Evolving fuzzy systems from data streams in real-time. In *Proc. 2006 International Symposium on Evolving Fuzzy Syst.* Ambleside, UK, pp. 29–35.

Angelov, P. and Zhou, X. (2008). On line learning fuzzy rule-based system structure from data streams. In *Proc. World Congress on Computational Intelligence*. Hong Kong.

Baht, S., Chatterjee, D. and Saraf, N. (2003). On line data processing and product properties prediction for crude distillation units. *AIChe 2003 Spring National Meeting*. New Orleans, Luisiana, USA.

Barsamian, A. and Macías, J. (1998). Neural Network-based inferential property predictors. *Hydrocarb. Process.*, 77(10).

Douglas, J. (1988), *Conceptual Design of Chemical Processes*. New York: McGraw-Hill.

Filev D. and Tseng, T. (2006). Novelty detection-based machine health prognostics, In *Proc. 2006 International Symposium on Evolving Fuzzy Systems*, IEEE Press, pp. 193–199.

Foong *et al.* (2010). Decision support system for alarm rationalization using risk assessment matrix. *Int. J. Comput. Appl.*, (0975–8887), 4(9).

Fortuna L., Graziani, S., Rizzo, A, and Xibilia, M. G. (2007). Soft sensor for monitoring and control of industrial processes. In Grimble, M. J. and Johnson, M. A. (eds.), *Advances in Industrial Control Series.* Berlin, Germany: Springer-Verlag.

Gaddam, M. and Rajani, A. (2006). Automatic tuning of pid controller using fuzzy logic, *International Conference on development and application system. Suceava, Romania.*

Geng, Z. *et al.* (2005). A fuzzy clustering–ranking algorithm and its application for alarm operating optimization in chemical processing. *Process Saf. Prog.*, 24(1), pp. 66–75.

Hussein, M. H. *et al.* (2013). Fuzzy analogical gates approach for heat exchangers networks. *Int. J. Comput. Appl.*, (0975–8887). 73(21).

Kahraman, C. (ed.) (2012). *Computational Intelligence Systems in Industrial Engineering*, Atlantis Computational Intelligence Systems 6, Atlantis Press. doi: 10.2991/978-94-91216-77-0_1.

Khatibisepehr, S. *et al.* (2013). Design of inferential sensors in the process industry: A review of Bayesian methods. *J. Process Contr.*, 23, pp. 1757–1596.

Kratmüller, M. (2009). Adaptive fuzzy control design. *Acta Polytech. Hung.*, 6(4), pp. 29–49.

Krishnakumar (2003). Intelligent systems for aerospace engineering — an overview, *NASA Technical Report.* Document ID: 30020105746.

Macías H. J. (2001). Design of a production expert system to improve refinery process operations. *EUNITE Symp.*, Tenerife, Spain.

Macías, H. and Feliu J. A. (2001). Dynamic study of inferential sensor (NN) in quality prediction of crude oil distillation tower side streams. 11th *Euro Symp. Comp. Aided Proc. Eng., ESCAPE 11*, Kolding, Denmark.

Macias, J., Feliu, J. and Bosch, A. Simulation workbench between HYSYS rigorous model and its NN extension: Case study of a complex simulation with re-circulation, 4th *European Congress on Chemical Engineering, ECCE 4.* McAvoy, T. (2002). Intellingent control applications in the process industries, *Annu. Rev. Control.* 26, pp. 75–86.

Mihaela, I. and Agachi, P. S. (2010). Optimal process control and operation of an industrial integrated fluid catalytic cracking plant using model predictive control. 20th *European Symposium on computer Aided Process Engineering — ESCAPE20*, Elsevier B.V.

Precup, R. and Hellendoorn, H. (2011). A survey of industrial applications of fuzzy control, *Computers in Industry.* 62, pp. 213–226.

Sarimveis, H. *et al.* (2003). Fuzzy model predictive control of nonlinear processes using genetic algorithms. *Fuzzy Set. Syst.*, 139, pp. 59–80.

Smith, R. (2005). *Chemical Process: Design and Integration.* Wiley. Takagi, T. and Sugeno, M (1985). Fuzzy identification of systems and its applications to modeling and control. *IEEE T. Syst, Man Cyb.*, 15(1), pp. 116–132.

Tan *et al.* (2005). A fuzzy decision support model for the selection of environment-friendly fuels for road vehicles. *Journal of the Eastern Asia Society for Transportation Studies.* 6, pp. 3264–3275.

Tan *et al.* (2009). Fuzzy data reconciliation in life cycle inventory analysis. De la Salle University Library.

Yang, S. H. *et al.* (1998). Soft sensor based predictive control of industrial fluid catalytic cracking processes, *Trans IChemE.*, 76, Part A, Institution of chemical Engineers.

Chapter 25

Applications of Computational Intelligence to Robotics and Autonomous Systems

Adham Atyabi and Samia Nefti-Meziani

This chapter discusses the application of computational intelligence (CI) in the field of autonomous mobile robotics. The chapter is focused on basic concepts of computational intelligence in robotic domain with an emphasis on essential aspects of navigation such as localization, path planing, and obstacle avoidance both on single and swarm robots. The chapter reviews recently published studies on these aspects aiming to highlight the recent trends on the field. In addition, the applications of navigation and motion planning on robotic arms, haptic devices, humanoid robots, and robotic hands are discussed.

25.1. Introduction

25.1.1. *What is Computational Intelligence (CI)*

CI is defined as a set of nature-inspired computational approaches designed to handle complex problems to which classical and traditional approaches are ineffective (Wlodzislaw, 2007). This ineffectiveness is either due to not being possible to formulate the problem or the problem being NP-hard. Bezdek (1994) offered one of the early definitions for CI as: "*A system is called computationally intelligent if it deals only with numerical (low-level) data, has a pattern recognition component, and does not use knowledge in the AI sense; and additionally, when it (begins to) exhibit* (i) *computational adaptivity*; (ii) *computational fault tolerance*; (iii) *speed approaching human-like turnaround; and* (iv) *error rates that approximate human performance*".

Wlodzislaw (2007) considered two different sets of cognitive functions namely low-level ("perception, object recognition, signal analysis, discovery of structures in data, simple association, and control") and high-level ("systematic thinking, reasoning, complex representation of knowledge, episodic memory, planning, understanding of symbolic knowledge"). The low-level cognitive functions handle the problem via combinations of either supervised or unsupervised learning methods and adaptive systems. Examples of these methods are neural, fuzzy, evolutionary, probabilistic, and statistical (Bayesian networks or kernel) methods. The high level cognitive functions are commonly considered for addressing "non-algorithmizable" problems through the use of Artificial Intelligence (AI)-based approaches (Wlodzislaw, 2007). Wlodzislaw considered Sequence learning, reinforcement learning, machine learning, and distributed multi-agent systems as areas in which the low and high level cognitive functions overlap with each other (Wlodzislaw, 2007). Poole *et al.* (1998) considered CI as the study of intelligent, agents (an agent is defined as an entity that acts in an environment and does something). An intelligent agent is considered as a system that acts intelligently, and it is flexible to environmental and goal changes, and capable of learning from experience. The authors considered the overall goal of CI as understanding the principles that results in intelligent behaviors (in either natural or artificial systems). However, Wlodzislaw (2007) disagreed with this view: "*Computational intelligence is certainly more than just the study of the design of intelligent agents, it includes also study of all non-algoritmizahle processes that humans (and sometimes animals) can solve with various degree of competence*". Fukuda and Kubota (1997) explained the difference between CI and AI as: "*CI aims to construct intelligence from the viewpoints of biology, evolution and self-organization. CI tries to construct intelligence by internal description, while classical AI tries to construct intelligence by external (explicit) description. Therefore, information and knowledge of a system in CI should be learned or acquired by itself*". There are several opinions regarding to the relationship between CI and AI and in here three of these opinions raised by some of the pioneers in the field are presented in order to better reflect the existing viewpoints.

- Marks (1993) considered CI as an alternative to AI: "*Although seeking similar goals, CI has emerged as a sovereign field whose research community is virtually distinct from AI*".
- Bezdek (1994) concluded that CI is a sub-set of AI after analyzing three levels of system complexity.
- Fogel (1995) emphasized on adaptation as an important feature of intelligence and declared that traditional symbolic AI systems are focused on artificial rather than intelligence since they do not adapt to the new problems in new ways. As a result, Fogel implied that only CI systems are intelligent.

25.1.2. *Robotics Community and CI*

The advanced robotic systems are often considered to replace human being in critical and dangerous tasks. Such systems collect information from the surrounding environment and react to the situations. CI (i.e., Neural Network, fuzzy systems, evolutionary approaches) and behavior-based AI methods are commonly used in order to realize intelligence in such robotic systems (Fukuda and Kubota, 1997). A review of application of CI in autonomous mobile robotics can be found in Wang (2002). Robot Motion Planning attracted the attention of academics in robotics community due to its complexity (being NP-complete) and its importance when dealing with various robotic applications. Bullinaria and Li (2007) considered the CI-based techniques such as neural competition, evolutionary computation, and fuzzy logic abilities in terms of providing powerful tools for realization of efficient control framework with adaptable parameters as one of the main reasons for their common use in robotic problems.

This chapter discusses the application of CI in the field of autonomous mobile robotics. The paper is focused on basic concepts of CI in robotic domain with an emphasis on essential aspects of navigation such as localization, path planning, and obstacle avoidance both on singular and swarm robots. The paper reviews recently published studies on these aspects aiming to highlight the recent trends on the field. In addition, the applications of navigation and motion planning on robotic arms, haptic devices, humanoid robots, human robot interactions, and robotic hands are presented.

The outline of this chapter is as follows: Section 2 introduces Navigation, localization, and Path Planning, discusses various classical and heuristic-based approaches proposed over the years to handle the motion-planning problem and also presents some of their recent applications. Section 3 presents Swarm Intelligence and its application on Swarm Robotics and Section 4 focuses on other application of motion planning and obstacle avoidance approaches including haptics, surgical devices, robotic hands and arms, and wearable robots. Conclusion is presented in Section 5.

25.2. Navigation and Motion Planning

Definition 1: **Navigation:** *The process or activity of accurately ascertaining one's position and planning and following a route.*[1]

Navigation is the art of steering a course through a medium and consists of two essential components known as Localization and Path Planning. In mobile robots, localization is the ability of projecting one's real world position to a location inside a map. In other words, the term localization in robots refers to the ability of determining accurate positions in the search space according to the sensory information of the environment (Roy *et al.*, 1999). Planning in mobile robots is the ability to find a short, collision-free path from the starting position towards the predefined ending location.

[1] Oxford Dictionaries: http://www.oxforddictionaries.com/definition/english/navigation.

25.2.1. *Localization*

Definition 2: **Localization:** *a determination of the place where something* is.[2]

As suggested by Pugh and Martinoli (2006, 2007); Pugh and Zhang (2005); Roy *et al.* (1999), some standard simulation-based localization methods have failed in real-world applications due to their inability to overcome the environmental conditions. These conditions and constraints can be categorized as follows:

- The results of small differences between training and testing phases in terms of initial locations (i.e., in real robots, a small change in the location of maps components or small differences between the training and testing phases can affect the overall performance of the entire process (Pugh and Martinoli, 2007)).
- Robots heterogeneity (i.e., in physical robots, even identical robots tend to have small differences which result in different environmental perceptions in the same states. Such an issue contributes to problems for homogeneous robots during knowledge sharing process. Consequently, the real-world robotic applications consists of robots with different types of abilities (Pugh and Martinoli, 2007; Pugh and Zhang, 2005)).
- As the literature suggested by Roy *et al.* (1999), in real-world applications, robots' environmental perceptions are unreliable due to the uncertain nature of the world.
- Due to the dynamic nature of real-world domains, the accuracy of the map and objects' locations would be uncertain (Roy *et al.*, 1999).

Localization is a challenging problem that can be found in various robotic scenarios such as multi-robot mapping, search and rescue, chemical leak detection and chemical source localization (Lu, 2013), underwater acoustic-based navigation (Webster *et al.*, 2014), or rendezvous search where two robots are meant to localize themselves in an unknown environment and then search for each other (Ozsoyeller *et al.*, 2014). Simultaneous localization and mapping (SLAM) is an approach utilized by robots in order to generate maps for unknown environments for which *no priori* knowledge exists or for updating maps of the environments for which *priori* information are provided, while simultaneously tracking their current location in the map. Variations of SLAMs can be categorized based on their sensory system to laser-based, sonar-based, and vision-based systems. Other variations of sensorial sources includes compasses, infrared, and global positioning system (GPS). The used sensorial systems are often subject to measurement noise and range limitations. Probabilistic approaches such as Kalman Filter (KF), Extended Kalman Filter (EKF), Particle Filter, and Expectation Maximization (EM) are filtering approaches that are commonly used in SLAM studies to address the sensory unit limitations and its associated problems (Aulinas *et al.*, 2008). These filtering methods and their

[2]Vocabulary Dictionary: http://www.vocabulary.com/dictionary/localization.

Table 25.1: Commonly utilized Filtering approaches in SLAM studies and their advantages and shortcomings (Aulinas *et al.*, 2008).

Filtering approach	Pros and cons	References
Variations of KF	**pros:** Have high convergence and capable hof handling uncertainty **cons:** Uses Gaussian assumption and it is slow in high dimensional maps	Davison and Murray (2002); Guivant and Nebot (2001); Jensfelt *et al.* (2006); Newman and Leonard (2003); Se and Lowe (2002)
Particle Filter	**pros:** Capable of addressing nonlinearities and non-Gaussian noise **cons:** Growth in complexity	Montemerlo *et al.* (2002, 2003)
EM	**pros:** Handles data association problem and is optimal for map building **cons:** Inefficient in high dimensional environments and inefficient cost growth	Burgard *et al.* (1999); Montemerlo and Thrun (2007)

associated advantages and shortcomings are presented in Table 25.1. In addition to sensor-based categorization, the SLAM methods can be categorized based on the working environment to ground-based (indoor and/or outdoor) (Davison and Murray, 2002; Estrada *et al.*, 2005; Kim and Sukkarieh, 2003; Newman and Leonard, 2003; Newman, 1999) air-borne (Kim and Sukkarieh, 2003, 2004), and underwater (Eustice, 2005; Eustice *et al.*, 2006; Pizarro *et al.*, 2004; Sez *et al.*, 2006; Williams *et al.*, 2000).

Kim and Eustice (2013) used a visual SLAM algorithm for underwater vehicle scenarios. The algorithm considered two types of visual saliency measures called local and global saliences in order to tackle common challenges in underwater visual SLAMs such as limited field of view imagery and regions that are feature-poor. In Local Saliency normalized measure of intraimage feature diversity is considered, while the global saliency uses a normalized measure of interimage rarity. The proposed visual SLAM navigation approach is novel in the sense that it considers the imageries that are more informative and better contribute in construction of the map.

Mirkhani *et al.* (2013) provided comparison results among three approaches for mobile robot localization. The considered algorithms included GA-based localization (GLASM), Harmony-Search-based Localization (HSL), and hybrid Harmony and Deferential Evaluation-based localization (HIDE). The authors claimed that HSL is capable of addressing global localization problems due to its ability to deal with the existing arbitrary noise distribution in robotic environments. Various advantages for HSL can be considered over other optimization based localization approaches such as (1) having fewer mathematical requirements, (2) not being dependent to derivative information, and (3) involving all vectors when a new solution is being generated. The HSL method compensate for the noise through representing the robot's pose uncertainty using a set of estimates that are weighted by a fitness function. The proposed hybrid HS and DE approach has advantages such as faster convergence and exploring the potential solution space. The results indicated superiority of HSL over GLASM approach with ability to guarantee safe navigation in unknown environments with the drawback of having slow convergence. The hybrid HIDE approach showed promising results due to utilizing the fast convergence speed on DE with search quality of HS approaches.

Webster *et al.* (2014) provided a comparison study among various acoustic-based navigation approaches for underwater vehicles. The study considered a single-beacon cooperative acoustic navigation problem in which the ranges and state information gathered from a single reference source with an unknown location is employed to improve the localization and navigation in a UV. In this scenario, the acoustic broadcasts between a server and a client is used to assist localization and navigation of the UV. Decentralized extended information filter (DEIF) used in this study plays the role of a filter that is applied to acoustic broadcasts on both server and client sides in order to facilitate the low-bandwidth requirements in addition to allowing the client side to reconstruct the time of launch information from the server's acoustic broadcasts. The results indicate suitability of the DEIF approach in comparison to other decentralized acoustic cooperative localization methodologies suggested by literature for underwater vehicle navigation.

Drevelle and Bonnifait (2014) discussed an estimation approach capable of quantifying the localization confidence based on constraint propagation and interval analysis. The approach is capable of providing continuous estimates of vehicle position through fusion of GPS and 3D map data. The constraint propagation of a precise 3D map and the GPS measurements are used to generate tightly coupled position domains and the GPS wrong measurements are compensated using proprioceptive history data. The 3D map and the data history contains information regarding to the drivable roads. The use of road data in constraint propagation process allows elimination of dead-reckoning drifts and reduction of positioning ambiguities. The experimental results gathered from a navigation scenario in urban environment using up to 2 satellites indicated suitability of the proposed approach for real-time positioning.

Murillo *et al.* (2013) studied image-based localization and proposed an approach that takes advantage of a global gist descriptor for panoramas images. The proposed approach provides adequate similarity measurement that results in a balance between discriminability and computational complexity in urban environments. The similarity measurement is facilitated through an algorithm that detects the loop-closure. In addition, a tree based approach is utilized that takes advantage of principle component analysis (PCA) for decomposing the panoramic gist descriptor.

The results achieved from evaluating the approach against state-of-the-art loop-closure detectors based on local features indicated the potential of the technique with ability to provide favorable or comparable performance to other algorithms commonly used in the field of image-based localization.

Colle and Galerne (2013) presented a global localization method that is capable of fusing data from heterogeneous set of sensors (on-board sensors, environmental sensors, and sensory units of other robots). The proposed approach takes into account constraints such as (1) number of measurements, (2) generic goniometric measurements, (3) information regarding to the degree of inaccuracy presented as an interval deduced from sensor tolerances, and (4) associated complexities to the incorporation of sensory data originated from heterogeneous sources.

25.2.2. *Path Planning*

Definition 3: **Motion planning:** *is a term used in robotics for the process of breaking down a desired movement task into discrete motions that satisfy movement constraints and possibly optimize some aspect of the movement.*[3]

Path planning is one of the essential components in navigation of mobile robots and is known as the art of finding an optimized collision-free path from the starting location toward the predefined destination (Qin *et al.*, 2004). Qin *et al.* (2004) suggested two types of path planning in the robotic domain known as (1) global path planning and (2) local path planning. In global path planning, robots have complete information about the environment (i.e., they have access to a map which provides knowledge about the positions of located obstacles and goals in the environment), while in local path planning, robots have no information about the environment or the information is not complete (partial information) (Qin *et al.*, 2004). Although simplicity and computational efficiency are known as two major advantages of path planning techniques (in static, certain, and predictable environments), the overall performance in these techniques are highly dependent on the reliability of the information, especially the map. As Gu *et al.* (2003) has discussed, due to the dynamic, noisy and unpredictable nature of real-world robotic applications, it is quite difficult to implement a path planning technique based on a well-known predefined map. Although it is possible to use path planning techniques in such a scenario, it would be costly due to the huge amount of computations (i.e., in such a case, it would be necessary to compute huge amount of possibilities). In addition, it is almost impossible to predict all possible situations and potential actions that mobile robots might encounter in the real-world

---

[3]Cyclopaedia: http://en.cyclopaedia.net/wiki/Navigation-problem.

applications. As such, strategies based on specifying all possible behaviors would be brittle.

The approaches used in motion and path planning can be categorized to two groups of classical and heuristic based methods (Masehian and Sedighizadeh, 2007). The common classical methods are cell decomposition (CD), potential field (PF), road map and subgoal network (SN), and CI-based methods such as neural network (NN), Evolutionary Algorithms (e.g., genetic algorithm (GA), particle swarm optimization (PSO) and ant colony optimization (ACO)), and Fuzzy Logic. Due to the heuristically nature of the CI-based methods, in this study, they are categorized as heuristic-based. Elshamli *et al.* (2004) argued that the classical methods are capable of finding the optimal solution (if one exists) while sacrificing computation- time but heuristic-based methods generate solutions with good quality with the advantage of being computation-time efficient. More detailed description of these algorithms are presented in following section.

25.2.2.1. *Classical methods*

Classical methods guarantee to find a solution if such a solution exists and their main disadvantage is being computationally expensive and being incapable of coping with uncertainty. These disadvantages make the usage of classical approaches challenging in real world applications since such applications are unpredictable and uncertain. Methods such as *CD*, *PF*, Road Map, and Subgoal Network are employed in path planning and are categorized as classical methods.

CD, given the challenging nature of dealing with large environments and the challenging exploration problems associated with it in robot navigation scenarios, several studies suggested segmentation/re-scaling of the larger search spaces to several reduced spaces that are more manageable (Fujii *et al.*, 1998; Park *et al.*, 2001; Yang and Gu, 2004).

In *CD* a cell representation of the search space is utilized aiming to generate a sequence of collision-free cells that drives the robot from starting point to the destination. In this method, cells that contain obstacles are divided to new cells and only obstacle-free cells would be added to the sequence of collision-free path. Consequently, sequences of cells that start from the start position and end in the destination represent the path between these two positions (Faverjon and Tournassoud, 1987; Herman, 1986; Kondo, 1991; Lingelbach, 2004; Lozano-Perez *et al.*, 1987; Lozano-Perez and Wesley, 1979; Seda, 2007). Seda (2007) suggested following steps for using *CD* as motion planner for a robot.

(1) Divide the search space to connected cells.
(2) Construct a graph through adjacent cells (i.e., vertices denoting cells and edges connect cells with common boundary).

(3) Determine destination and start cells and generate a sequence from the start to the destination cells that is obstacle-free cells.
(4) Generate a path from obtained cell sequence.

CD can be divided to sub categories such as Exact CD (Barbehenn and Hutchinson, 1995a; Schwartz and Sharir, 1983; Sleumer and Gurman, 1991) Approximate Cell Decomposition (Barbehenn and Hutchinson, 1995b; Conte and Zullil, 1995; Zhu and Latombe, 1991), and Probabilistic Cell Decomposition (Lingelbach, 2004; Rosell and Iniguez, 2005).

Exact *CD* decomposes the C-space to convex polygons resulting in centering points of cell boundaries connected together with lines in order to generate a path. The generated paths have the disadvantage of containing unnecessary turning points which makes the motion unnatural (Nakju *et al.*, 2007). Approximate *CD* divides the search space to a grid with higher resolution with each cell in the grid representing a segment of the environment and containing a flag to indicate if they are collision free. Although the method is easy to implement, the inability to offer natural presentation of the environment makes the approach inefficient for path planning (Sleumer and Gurman, 1991). Probabilistic *CD* (*PCD*) is similar to approximate *CD* with the exception of cells having predefined shapes and cells' boundaries not representing any physical meaning. Although approximate and probabilistic *CD* are faster in implementation, they are not reliable when the fraction of the free-space in the environment is small (Lingelbach, 2004).

Lingelbach (2004) used a *PCD*-based path planning in a scenario in which the robot is tasked to fetch milk from the refrigerator and place it on the kitchen's table. The *PCD* algorithm is decomposed to components of graph search, local planning, cell splitting, and probabilistic sampling. The algorithm identifies a collision-free path by iteratively refining the *CD* and in each step the probabilistic sampling is led to regions of interest by *CD*. The study provided comparison between *PCD* and Rapidly-exploring Random Trees method (RRD).

Pinder *et al.* (2013) studied the potential of a fuzzy controlled Air Vehicle (AV) that is coupled with an approximate CD method acting as the path planner in a scenario based on landing an autonomous AV on a helipad. The choice of CD as the path planner is made due to offering less complexity with respect to the landing helipad and the surrounding areas.

Some general drawbacks are considered for *CD* including combinatorial explosion, limited granularity and generating infeasible solutions (Seda, 2007). Road-map and PF can be considered as alternatives to this approach.

PF: In principle, PF can be imagined as the differential of two opposite forces of attraction and repulsion in a way that locations that direct the robot towards the destination introduce attraction force while other locations (including obstacles and other objects) in the environment introduce repulsive forces. The robot take the directions based on the combination of these forces in order to travel from the starting point toward the ending location (Cheng and Zelinsky, 1995; Dunias, 1996; Latombe, 1991; Randal and McLain, 2003; Song, 2002).

Song (2002) utilized a decentralized PF-based controller for directing teams of robots in a scenario based on approaching, trapping, and transporting objects towards a destination location. Cheng and Zelinsky (1995) employed *PF* for obstacle avoidance in a simulation study. The author suggested the use of high temporary attraction forces toward random locations whenever the robot is stagnated between obstacles aiming to force the robot to get away from the locations in which it can get stuck. The suggested modification is useful for addressing weakness of PF in situations in which high concentration of close-by obstacles with high repulsive forces exist. Such circumstances can result in local minima convergence in PF (Rimon and Koditschek, 1992; Seda, 2007; Wang and Chirikjian, 2000).

Road-Map: Road-map (Retraction, Skeleton, or Highway) approach is designed as a set of paths containing areas that are collision-free. In this context, path planning can be seen as finding the shortest path from all possible collision-free paths (gathered in a graph) presented by the road-map from the starting position to the destination location (Siegwart and Nourbakhsh, 2004). Voronoi and visibility graphs are two of the most commonly used approaches for generating road-map graphs. In Visibility approach, the vertices of the graph represent either the locations of the start and the end points or they represent the vertices of polygonal obstacles. In this approach the edges represent the connection between nearby vertices in addition to the edges of the obstacles. Although the mentioned representation of the existing paths is advantageous for identifying minimum-length path, it also allows robots to get too close to the edges of the obstacles which can cause safety problems specially when obstacles with sharp edges exist in the environment. This issue can be resolved by Voronoi diagram approach in which the generated road-map graph tends to maximize the distance of the road from the obstacles. The main drawback of Voronoi diagram is its dependency to the length of localization sensory unit and their accuracy. That is due to the focus of the approach on generating road-maps in which the distances between the obstacles and the road are maximized and as a result it is not suitable for robots with short-range sensors. The execute-ability (i.e., the ability to easily be adopted and executed by physical robots) of the Voronoi diagram method makes it more favorable in real-world robotic applications (Siegwart and Nourbakhsh, 2004).

SN: The approach is commonly used to address motion planning problem and uses a list of reachable configurations from the starting location (Chen and Hwang, 1992; Faverjon and Tournassoud, 1987; Hwang and Ahuja, 1992; Randal and McLain, 2003). Chen and Hwang (1992) suggested a variation of SN-based on hierarchical path search in which the *SN* is utilized as the global planner and a local planner is used to assess the reach-ability of subgoals. The global and local planners are switched repeatedly until either a path is found or subgoal sequence is emptied. Glavina (1990) presented a randomized motion planning based on *SN* in which the planner generates random subgoals configurations and a local planner connects the subgoals in order to construct a graph of free spaces connectivity. The main contribution of the proposed approach is its ability on search in the discrete free space rather than computational geometry. In a series of studies, Chen and Hwang (1992) introduced a search strategy called SANDROS (Chen and Hwang, 1992, 1998; Hwang and Chen, 1995) that is usable in motion planning. The SANDROS employs a local planner for connecting sequences of subgoals with the drawback of being inefficient for finding paths through winding tunnel. Bessire *et al.* (1993) employed hybrid of *SN* and *GA* in motion planning study. The suggested hybrid method utilized *GA* for evenly placed point-subgoals (landmarks) in the free space and used an additional procedure for connecting the landmarks to the goal.

The main drawbacks of the classical methods are their lack of adaptability and the lack of robustness to environmental changes (Elshamli *et al.*, 2004). This is the result of using sequential based searching algorithms (Elshamli *et al.*, 2004). To overcome the weakness of these approaches Heuristic based approaches are suggested.

25.2.2.2. *Heuristic-based methods*

As mentioned earlier, the reliability of the map and the ability of a robot to localize itself in the map play major roles in navigation problems. However, dynamism and unpredictability of real world applications which result in generation of unreliable maps often make the navigation task challenging. Probabilistic algorithms such as probabilistic roadmaps PRM and RRT are commonly considered to address general drawbacks of classical path planning methods such as high time complexity in environments with high dimensions and trapping in local minima. The main advantage of the probabilistic algorithms over classical methods is their high-speed implementation (Masehian and Sedighizadeh, 2007). An alternative to classical approaches is behavior-based methods (Cheng and Zelinsky, 1995). These methods use a set of simple and predefined behaviors that are designed to handle complex scenarios. The dependency of these methods to their current state which get influenced by environmental conditions and their ability to switch their behavior in a way to handle their current state makes them suitable for addressing scenarios based on dynamically changing environments. However, uncertainty in environmental readings can result in erroneous setting of their current state and consequently erroneous setting of their associated behaviors which results in dead-lock in robot's state (Cheng and Zelinsky, 1995).

Other studies also referred to the heuristic-based methods as population-based and behavior-based methods too. That is due to dealing with sub-set of solutions in an iterative manner in these methods. In these methods, the population is evolved in each of the iterations. Although these approaches do not guarantee to find a solution (in contrast to classical methods) but if such a solution is found, the required time would be shorter compared with classical methods. Below, some of these methods are presented and their applications in robot motion planning are discussed.

Artificial Neural network (ANN) is a mathematical model inspired from biological neural networks designed to replicate brain computational capability in terms of processing information, adapting to data, tolerating noise, and identifying patterns. The ANN is a common method for controlling robot motions. The ANN capability in terms of solving problems can be tuned by its architectural design and learning paradigm. ANN consists of interconnected artificial neurons that are each capable of performing simple tasks. The neurons/nodes in ANN map input data to an output using weights and bias factors. The learning in the network is implemented by adjusting the weights and bias of nodes in an iterative manner in a way that nodes that best augment the performance get to increase their weights while others decrease them in order to increase the overall classification performance of the network. The process of modifying and adjusting the weights in ANNs is referred to as the *training algorithm. Feedforward* and *Feedback* are two commonly used topologies in the learning phase of ANNs. In *Feedforward* no back/return connection between different units (layers) is allowed and information flows forward in one direction, from input layer toward output layer. This is in contrast to *Feedback* ANNs where the cycles of connections between different layers is allowed. Feedforward ANNs are more time efficient in their learning phase in comparison with Feedback ANNs. The use of *NN* in robotic problems can be pictured in categories such as Interpreting the sensory data, Obstacle avoidance, and Path planning (Zou *et al.*, 2006). Zou *et al.* (2006) argued that hybrid of *NN* and other AI-based methods including fuzzy logic, knowledge-based systems, and evolutionary approaches better address the robot navigation problem in real world applications (Zou *et al.*, 2006). Yangmin and Xin (2005) employed the combination of particle swarm optimization (PSO) and Adaptive *NN* for navigation of a mobile robot. In the suggested approach *PSO* is used as the path planner in order to generate a smooth trajectory for the adaptive *NN* controller. The Adaptive *NN* is employed to drive the robot towards the goal location while avoiding the collision with obstacles. Pugh and Martinoli used single-layer discrete-time *ANN* in order to control a heterogeneous swarm of physical robots in an obstacle avoidance scenario (Pugh and Martinoli, 2007).

GA: Introduced by John Holland in 1975 is a population based approach that utilizes operators such as natural selection, crossover, and mutation (Han, 2007). *GA* is widely used in variety of optimization problems including classical traveling salesman, flow-shop optimization, and job shop scheduling. In these problems the aim is to optimize or find the best solution (in *GA* each solution (member of the population) is presented as a chromosome or genotype) out of a population of possibilities (Konar, 2005). *GA*'s inherently parallel search characteristic is the source of its attractiveness for developing near-optimal solutions (Elshamli *et al.*, 2004). *GA*'s steps such as Selection, Crossover, and Mutation are used in path planning problems. The operation of chromosome ranking and selecting a subset of chromosomes with high ranks for generating new population is called Selection. The ranking of chromosomes is based on their fitness. The new population is generated by Crossover by exchanging portions of the chromosomes nominated by the Selection operator with each other. Mutation is the operation of randomizing one or a sub-set of chromosomes that are not achieving better fitness results over certain number of iterations in full or partially. Elitism is considered as maintaining the best performing chromosome of each generation in the new population.

Various studies have been done based on applying *GA* to different aspects of path planning and navigation problems ranging from dynamic multicast routing scenario (Brits *et al.*, 2003), multi path planning scenarios (Brits *et al.*, 2003; Hwang and Chen, 1995; Pugh and Zhang, 2005) path planning and finding the shortest path (Deneb, 1994), and navigation (Sadati and Taheri, 2002). The main shortcoming of the *GA* in path planning problems is its infeasibility in dynamic environments due to operating in a grid map or utilizing a fixed resolution in the search space. This results in inability to control the population diversity causing premature convergence.

PSO: Is an evolutionary approach that iteratively evolve a population of possible answers toward an optimum and it is inspired from animals' social behaviors (Masehian and Sedighizadeh, 2010). PSO favors convergence toward global optimum due to the identified social and cognitive behaviors in its swarm's implementation which influence the evolvement procedure of the particles. In PSO each member of the swarm population is referred to as particle. Each particle represents a possible solution for the problem at hand and it is modeled based on a position in the search space (a solution) and a velocity that derived the particle from its previous position to the new one in the search space. Cognitive and social components of the swarm formulation mimics attraction towards positions in the search space that either represent the best personal finding of the particle or the swarm's best finding. These locations in the search space are referred to as local and global-best positions respectively (Stacey *et al.*, 2003). The impact of this attraction force is controlled in the PSO's formulation by *Acceleration Coefficients*. In addition, another coefficient referred to as *Inertia Weight* is used in order to control the influence of the adjusted velocity in previous iteration on the new one. The particles in the swarm update their positions in the search space by adding their updated velocity to their last location in the search space. Various neighborhood topologies are suggested to address knowledge sharing among particles. The neighborhood topology can play an important role on how the swarm evolve over iterations since it affects the global best position of the swarm by dictating which particles can share their personal best findings with each other. PSO's overall performance depends on aspects such as how to adjust/control its parameters, how to address premature convergence (Pasupuleti and Battiti, 2006; Ratnaweera *et al.*, 2004; Vesterstrom and Riget, 2002). Several parameter adjustment and controlling mechanisms are suggested to address the PSO's problems including (1) linearly decreasing inertia weight (LDIW), (2) time varying inertia weight (TVIW), (3) random inertia weight (RANDIW), (4) fixed inertia weight (FIW), (5) time varying acceleration coefficient (TVAC), (6) random acceleration coefficients (RANDAC), and (7) fix acceleration coefficients (FAC). It is also observed that in some problems the overall performance of the swarm improves if the velocity equation is modified by either ignoring one or more than one component or adding new components to the equation (Chang *et al.*, 2004; Pasupuleti and Battiti, 2006; Peer *et al.*, 2003; Peram *et al.*, 2003; Ratnaweera *et al.*, 2004; Yang and Simon, 2005). More detailed discussion on PSO can be found in Atyabi *et al.* (2007); Atyabi and Powers (2013a); Atyabi and Samadzadegan (2011).

PSO's potential in solving complex problems makes it favorable in various scenarios and domains. Modified versions of *PSO* are used in several path planning, searching scenarios, and robots navigation studies. Two variations of mutation-based PSO are employed for path planning in a study by Yuan-Qing *et al.* (2004) and to handle the conveying tasks in Guillaume, Frddrique and Beat study (1998), Pugh and Martinoli (2006); Pugh and Zhang (2005) used PSO with local neighborhood topology in multi-robot search optimization problem and showed that *PSO* is capable of outperforming *GA* in such problems. A modified version of *PSO* called *DEADALUS* is suggested by Suranga (2006) to handle cul de sac problem (robots' stagnations problem) in a simulated obstacle avoidance scenario. A variation of PSO that utilized a stream function called Potential Flow for obstacle avoidance proved to be feasible for robot navigation scenarios with static and dynamic obstacles (Chengyu *et al.*, 2007). Masehian and Sedighizadeh (2010) employed two variations of PSO namely Multi-Objective PSO (MOPSO) and negative PSO (NPSO) in hybrid with probabilistic roadmap (PRM) method for robot path planning. The study provided comparison between MOPSO-PRM, NPSO-PRM, and pure PRM methods and indicated that NPSO showed slight advantage over PSO and generated shorter and smoother paths in comparison to pure PRM while being more time efficient.

ACO: The first *ACO* algorithm referred to as the ANT System is introduced by Marco Dorigo and his colleagues (Latombe, 1991). *ACO* is inspired by the social behavior of the ants when foraging for a food source and the ability to guide other ants toward regions of interest using their deposited pheromones (Han, 2007). In *ACO*, the paths' qualities are evaluated based on the quantity of the pheromones deposited by ants that traveled that path considering Concentration and Proportion factors that indicate the length of the path and the number of ants that traveled the path respectively (Hao *et al.*, 2006). The rapid algorithm execution of *ACO* is one of its main advantages over *GA* (Han, 2007).

Several studies employed *ACO* in robotic path planning scenarios (Hasiao *et al.*, 2004; Shirong *et al.*, 2006; Taylor *et al.*, 2006). Hao *et al.* (2006) used the hybrid of *ACO* and Artificial Potential Field (APF) approach aiming to use *ACO* as a global path planning and APF as local path planning approach. In the algorithm, *ACO* and APF cooperated with each other through using pheromone trajectory of *ACO* in APF to prevent trapping in local minima. McLurkin and Yamins (2005) suggested 4 algorithms for role switching between a team of robots in a dynamic path planning study. Shi *et al.* (2008) used the combination of *ACO* and *PSO* in a robot path planning study in which *ACO* is utilized to plan paths in robots transitable territory and *PSO* is utilized in order to optimize the parameters of *ACO*.

Riadi *et al.* (2013) reported comparison results of various benchmark functions on a variation of ACO method called ACO-PT that utilizes Prospect Theory (a widely used algorithm in economics). The results indicated considerable improvement in state transition strategy when PT algorithm is used causing overall improvement of the ACO performance. The study is inspired from earlier investigations carried in Autonomous Systems and Robotics Research Center in Salford University under Prof Nefti-Meziani's supervision with a focus on utilization of PT algorithm for modifying the decision-making process in Evolutionary-based methods such as PSO and ACO (Bunny, 2012; Riadi, 2014).

Several advantages and short comings can be named for *ACO*. The advantages includes inherent parallelism, positive feedback which contributes in rapidly discovering good solutions, feasibility to be used in problems similar to Traveling Salesman, and its adaptability to dynamically changing environments. The disadvantages include complexity of the theoretical analysis, possibility of generating sequences of random decisions, iteratively changing probability distribution, and uncertainty in the time to convergence.

Other heuristic-based path planning methods: this subcategory includes several other approaches that are utilized by robotic community to handle path planning problems including simulated annealing (SA), Stigmergy, Wavelets, tabu search (TS).

25.2.2.3. *Applications of classical and heuristic-based methods in global path planning*

Otte and Correll (2013) suggested a multiple parallelized tree structure called C-FOREST for generating the shortest path. The parallelization is designed in a way to allow the knowledge sharing (i.e., the shortest path found so far) between trees at each step of the algorithm. The overall performance of the C-FOREST approach is assessed against three different experimental setups including a manipulator arm, robotic team, and alpha benchmark and the results illustrated the feasibility of the proposed approach in terms of superlinear speedup with both manipulator arm and robotic team and its in-feasibility with alpha benchmark within path planning problems.

Murphy and Newman (2013) proposed a risky planning approach for path planning problem. The proposed approach utilizes probabilistic costmaps in combination with fast heuristic searches. The authors argued that often in robotic problems it is more desirable to find "good" paths quickly rather than finding the shortest path in a time consuming manner. Based on this principle the proposed approach generates pseudo-optimal paths that exceed the length of the optimal path by 30%, 20% reduction in the required search time can be achieved. The experimental results also indicate that if only on 50% of the executions finding the shortest path is targeted, 60% reduction on the required search time can be achieved.

Jaillet and Porta (2013) introduced a sampling-based path planner approach called AtlasRRT that is especially tailored to address problems with kinematics constraints. AtlasRRT utilizes a coordinated construction of an atlas and a RRT. The atlas is employed for generating branches in the C-space manifold and in order to retain the efficiency of the RRT exploration and the RRT algorithm is utilized as a tool for specifying the expansion directions for the atlas. Jaillet and Porta (2013) adapted various approaches for accelerating the convergence of asymptotically-optimal planners resulting in developing two variations of the AtlasRRT method called AtlasRRT* and AtlasBiRRT* that utilizes bidirectional search strategy, propagation of the improvements found in new samples, and tools for generating atlas that parameterizes the configuration space of manifold with high-dimensional continuation.

Roadmap is considered as one of the classical approaches used in path planning. Probabilistic roadmap approach generates a graph that represents the layout of the C-space. The created roadmap graph in offline mode is utilized during the online mode inorder to rapidly generate feasible solutions. Smoothing and hybridization of multiple graphs are considered as two of the standard approaches for improving the quality of the paths generated by roadmap. An alternative approach for improving the paths quality is to use larger and denser roadmaps. Such approaches tend to generate solutions with optimal costs (asymptotic optimality) with the drawback of being cost demanding in the sense that their required struction time, storage, and transmission are inefficient.

Marble and Bekris (2013) proposed two approaches that construct roadmaps that gaurantees asymptotic near-optimality through interleaving asymptotically optimal RPM* approach with graph spanners. The first method sequentially applies the graph spanner to the outputs of the PRM* and the second method eliminates some edges during the roadmap construction phase following an incremental approach. The experimental results indicated the feasibility of both approaches for generating asymptotically near-optimal paths with the advantage of reducing construction time, roadmap density.

Masoud (2013) employed harmonic potential field (HPF) approach in a simulation study. The proposed method synchronizes the control signal in order to align the gradient of the HPF and the velocity of the robot. The simulation results indicated suitability of the approach for situations with the presence of actuator noise, saturation, and uncertainty. In addition, the approach is favorable due to its simplicity and its ability to migrate the kinematic path characteristics from an HPF to the dynamic trajectory of UGV.

Workspaces containing serial manipulators with large degree of freedom are another domain that benefit from path planning approaches. Shukla *et al.* (2013), used the concept of monotonic optimality for optimizing the manipulators' paths in addition to utilizing proximity based penalizing schemes for obstacle avoidance to address path planning problem in such workspaces. The use of B-spline function model for path representation resulted in local control of the trajectory and smoother joint movement. The experimental results indicated decrease in path length and monotic optimality of the paths.

Martinez *et al.* (2013) explained a real-time vision based motion and tracking approach that is capable of robustly track large, rapid drogue motions within 30 frames per second. The used vision strategy approach consisted of 3 steps: (1) Hierarchical Multi-Parametric Multi-Resolution Inverse Compositional Image Alignment approach that utilizes robust tracking, (2) segmentation and template matching approach that utilizes detection, and (3) 3D position estimation. The proposed approach showed potential during the experiments based on autonomous aerial refueling problem with only loosing the drogue's position when it is located out of the site of view.

Kala (2012) employed co-evolutionary Genetic Programming method for multi-robot motion planning problem in which various sources and goals are considered for each member of the robot team. The study used genetic programming for generating path in a simulated maze-like map (individual robot level) and utilized a master evolutionary method in order to facilitate overall path optimality requirements (swarm level). The feasibility of the proposed approach is assessed within several simulation studies with variety of swarm sizes.

25.2.2.4. *Applications of classical and heuristic-based methods in local path planning*

In real-world hazardous scenarios, it will often happen that the navigation is impossible. In such scenarios, the map is not reliable. Unreliability in these scenarios is due to the dynamic and unpredictable nature of real world applications. The problem of path planning in scenarios in which the prior generated maps and environmental informations are unreliable or incomplete is referred to as Local Path Planning. To solve such problems, behavioral-based approaches are suggested (Cheng and Zelinsky, 1995). In behavioral-based approaches, a set of simple, predefined behaviors would be designed in a way to solve complex scenarios. The advantage of these approaches is their reliability in dynamic environments due to their dependency on their current situation (state) and the set of behaviors designed for that state instead of localization and planning. Although behavior-based approaches are reliable in dynamic environments, they still have difficulties with uncertainty. Cheng and Zelinsky (1995) argued that in behavior-based approaches uncertainty causes faults in terms of chosen states. This problem is known as irresolvable state. Irresolvable states would often cause dead-lock in agents' states.

Faigl *et al.* (2013) investigated a multi-goal path planning problem in which a closed shortest path in a polygonal map is desired in a way that all goals be visited by the robot. The study takes advantage of self-organizing map (SOM) for addressing the traveling salesman problem. The authors considered three variations of SOM referred to as alternate goal, attraction, and goal interior in order to address polygonal goals. The goal interior approach is a simple adaptation of the centroids of the polygonal goals in which nodes that are not inside the polygonal goal are moved toward the centroid. The attraction point approach aims to generate shorter paths by introducing new attraction points at the border of polygonal goals. In the alternate goal approach, the closest point to a node that is located on the border of the polygonal goal is used instead of the centroid point.

Faigl *et al.* (2013) studied the problem of active visual search (AVS) in unknown or partially known large environments using uncertain semantics of the environments. The proposed approach takes advantage of existing knowledge from possible worlds with spatially similar models in order to generate a model for the unknown environment. The proposed methodology is validated through comparison with human performance and a greedy coverage-based search strategy and showed potential in addressing the AVS problem.

Gerstmayer-Hillen *et al.* (2013) proposed a vision-based controlling system for mapping the environment in a cleaning robot application. The proposed approach is novel in the sense that instead of acquiring robot's exact position in the environment it relies on partial position estimation. That is the robot estimates its distance from the previously visited lanes and uses its orientation in the world in order to generate an estimation of its partial position. The experimental results indicated feasibility of the proposed approach with minimal overlaps or gaps between the lanes.

25.2.2.5. *Obstacle avoidance*

One of the classical problems in robotics is Obstacle Avoidance in which the task is to satisfy some control objectives while maintaining non-collision constraints. It is customary to consider obstacle avoidance as a sub-routine or extra constraint/condition in path planning and therefore categorize the methods to two categories of local and global approaches (Khansari-Zadeh and Billard, 2012). It is shown that local obstacle avoidance approaches such as the Bug's algorithm (Lumelsky and Skewis, 1990), the Vector Field Histogram (Borenstein and Koren, 1991) and the Curvature-Velocity (Simmons, 1996) are capable of providing fast responses when perturbations occur with the drawback of resulting in paths that in most cases are only locally optimal. In contrast, the global methods such as those introduced in global path planning guarantee to find a feasible path (if it exists) with the drawback of being computationally intensive which makes them unsuitable for dynamically changing environments in which the obstacles appear suddenly (Khansari-Zadeh and Billard, 2012).

This section presents a short review on some of the recently developed obstacle avoidance approaches that are less generic compared with the classical and the heuristic-based approaches discussed previously and are more problem specific.

Rufli *et al.* (2013) investigated the potential of decentralized motion planning agents using continuous control obstacle ($C^n - CO$). The presented method can be considered as an extension to reciprocal velocity obstacle (RVO) approach in such a way that the trajectory segments consider C^n continuity instead of piecewise linearity. The approach constructs a collision free motion for a team of homogeneous agents through choosing a potential trajectory from ($C^n - CO$) complement. In the study, ($C^n - CO$) is a set of feedback controlled trajectories that result in collision between agents and the complement of this set is expected to provide a collision free motion. The proposed approach is infeasible for heterogeneous teams of robots that have non-circular shapes or follow different collision-avoidance strategies.

Gomez *et al.* (2013) suggested the use of fast marching square (FM^2) approach for path planning of the robot formation problem. The proposed algorithm is capable of providing safe and collision free paths under various environmental constrains including uncertainty (on both robots' and obstacles' locations) and existent of static or dynamic obstacles. FM^2 approach is considered as a path planning approach with no local minimum capable of generating smooth trajectories in addition to significantly reducing the computational load when employed under uncertain environments. In path planning based on FM^2 approach, the original Fast Marching (FM) algorithm is applied in two different phases in which, in the first phase, FM is applied to the map in order to generate a new map in which each pixel is associated with a value between 0 and 1 in which lower values represent improbable regions with value of 0 representing obstacles and walls (depicted as black regions in the map) and 1 representing highly probable regions (depicted as lighter regions in the map). In the second phase, FM is applied to the resulting map of the first phase with inclusion of time of arrival as a new axis to the 2D map. In this phase a new potential is generated that represents the propagation of an electromagnetic wave and considering the goal as the origin of the wave, the propagation is continued until the current position of the robot is reached.

Madani *et al.* (2013) conducted experiments based on moving obstacles scenarios. The proposed approach models the robot manipulators using *a priori* knowledge. The mechanism takes advantage of one step direct calculation and it does not specify any inversion model. The experimental results with a robot with 3 DOF manipulators indicated the effectiveness of the proposed approach in comparison with some other variable structure controllers.

Hardy and Campbell (2013) presented a contingency path planning approach that utilizes a path optimization algorithm that simultaneously optimizes several contingency paths. The resulting framework allows the robot to maintain a deterministic path while it is capable of predicting multiple mutually exclusive obstacles. In order to achieve fast optimization within multiple contingency paths, a spline-based representation of the contingency path is employed in the path optimization algorithm. In order to avoid the obstacles a collision probability bound is proposed that allows avoidance with uncertain relative orientation and location. The simulation results indicated the potential of the proposed approach within aspects such as safety in terms of resulting in less collision and aggressiveness in terms of obstacle spacing.

Purcaru *et al.* (2013) a gravitational search algorithm (GSA)-based method in a motion planning study comprising partially unknown environment with the presence of static and dynamic obstacles. The feasibility of the GSA approach is assessed by providing comparison results with basic PSO.

Rakshit *et al.* (2013) presented an adaptive memetic algorithm based on hybridization of Q-learning and artificial bee colony (ABC). The choice of such hybridization is made considering global and local search abilities of ABC and Q-learning methods respectively. In addition to providing comparison results on multi-robot path planning scenarios, the study offers performance evaluation and assessment on 25 well-known benchmark functions. The results indicate feasibility of the proposed approach compared to four variations of differential evaluation (DE) method.

Hinojosa *et al.* (2011) assessed the potential of a hybrid fuzzy and reinforcement learning method called generalized probabilistic fuzzy RL (GPFRL) in three robot control problems with stochastic and uncertain nature under both deterministic and continuous environments. The proposed RL approach combines the universal-function-approximation capability of fuzzy systems, while considering probability distributions over possible consequences of an action. The GPFRL modified actor-critic (AC) learning architecture while enhancing the learning structure through the use of probability measure. The proposed approach facilitates convergence through utilizing gradient-decent-weight-updating algorithm. The approach is assessed in three problems namely cart-pole balancing problem, DC-motor control problem, and mobile robot navigation against conventional methods. The results indicated the GPFRL is robust under probabilistic uncertainty in addition to offering enhanced learning speed.

Theodoridis and Hu (2006) tackled the strategic route learning problem in mobile robots using a novel algorithm called Fuzzy Sarsa (λ) Learning (FSλL). The approach hybridizes Reinforcement Learning (RL) and Fuzzy Logic (FL) in addition to utilizing a learning algorithm called Sarsa (λ) in order to tune FL controller. The experimental design is based on route learning task in which experience is developed in exploring robot, while interacting with the environment using a discretized FL controller and later on optimal policies necessary for achieving goals and minimizing training error are learned. The results achieved from experiments indicated that FSλL performs considerably better than conventional Sarsa (λ) method and provided higher learning rate.

25.3. Swarm Robotics and the Navigation Problem

Since developing robots with high abilities, skills, and intelligence is very expensive and complicated, using a group of simpler robots with simpler skill-sets that are expendable and are capable of cooperating with each other in order to solve complicated tasks is more reasonable. Such advantages attracted scientists and resulted in application of swarm-based approaches for solving a variety of robotic problems (Jiang and Kumar, 2013; Trueba *et al.*, 2013; Williams and Sukhatme, 2013). Coordination and Cooperation are two main components of swarm-based multi-robot approaches.

Swarm Robotics is one of the approaches utilized for coordinating multi-robot systems. In such systems a desired collective behavior emerges from interaction of robots with each other and the environment. Within a swarm of homogeneous robots this can be seen as constant sharing of information among the swarm members in order to make a decision either in the swarm or individual robot level. Within a swarm of heterogeneous robots this can be imagined as having a central controller robot that receives information from swarm members and makes the swarm level decisions and issues commands to all or individual members. This section presents recent developments on coordination and cooperation aspects of multi-robot systems.

Jiang and Kumar (2013) presented an approach for multi-robot coordination in congested systems. The authors suggested a modified behavior regulation for amplifying the robot's velocity and a direct control of robot velocity in the behavioral dynamics. The amplification of robot's velocity is achieved through utilization of interaction force among robots and helps the robot to slow down in certain places. The results achieved from simulation study indicated effectiveness of the proposed methodology for multi-robot coordination in congested systems with bottlenecks.

Kudelski *et al.* (2013) reported development of a simulated environment called RoboNetSim that models network complications and constrains in multi-robot scenarios. The developed simulator is advantageous in the sense that it provides more realistic measurements on efficiency of the networking and multi-robot communication aspects of the generated scenarios which results in better compatibility of the generated approaches for real-world environments.

Yamamoto and Okada (2013) introduced an approach for controlling the swarm that is inspired from the appearance of congestion in crossing pedestrian flows in high density urban areas. In crossing pedestrian flow problem, the pedestrians use a self-organized phenomena based on avoidance of collision with other pedestrians. The authors proposed continuum model of the crossing pedestrians flow that generates a density factor from dynamic changes of the congestion and utilized a control method in order to improve the average velocity. The principle idea in the approach is to take advantage of dynamic interactions among diagonal stripe patterns that are shaped by the crossing pedestrians to guide the person/object that is aiming to move in to the flow. The approach is validated through simulation study.

de Lope *et al.* (2013) studied coordination of multiple robots in the sense of heterogeneous task selection. The study considered generation of decentralized solutions in the sense that robots autonomously and individually select tasks in a way that it maintains optimal task distribution. This is facilitated through utilizing Response Threshold Model and Learning Automata-based probabilistic algorithms. The authors employed random and maximum principle approaches for task selection and based on the results achieved from simulation studies concluded that the latter is a better fit for the task. In addition the results indicated noise robustness of the response threshold method and also higher time demand from the learning automata-based probabilistic approach in some cases. The additive noise influences the system in the sense of simulation of robots' erroneous estimation of the real number of pending tasks. The results also indicated feasibility of the proposed approaches for task selection/allocation in autonomous and individual manner for a team of multiple robots without the need for any central task scheduler unit.

Zhu *et al.* (2013) proposed a combination of bottom up and high level layer structure for navigation of a swarm of robots in which individual robots are independent and capable of providing some degree of autonomy and intelligence thanks to the bottom-up (low-level) layer, while a higher level layer deals with contingency and guarantees convergence in complex circumstances. The unique capability of the proposed bottom-up approach in terms of allowing the advantage of various algorithms to address different situations makes it more favorable compared with the top-down hybrid architectures.

In contrast to the multilayer level of intelligent presented in Zhu *et al.* (2013), Pimenta *et al.* (2013) presented an approach in which the principle idea is based on the utilization of a single software/algorithm for controlling a swarm of robots rather than allowing independent decision-making and behavior among the swarm members. The proposed approach aims to direct the swarm of robots (as whole) towards region of interest and is advantageous in terms of not being dependent on individual swarm members and robust to dynamic addition and deletion of swarm members. This proposed approach uses smoothed-particle hydrodynamics (SPH) simulation technique for generating an abstract representation of the swarm in the sense of incompressible fluid that is subject to external forces which provides a loose way for controlling the swarm. The results achieved from simulation and actual studies indicated efficiency of the approach with ability to deal with high number of agents (>1000 in simulation) and also smaller swarm sizes (in experiments with actual robots).

Hemakumara and Sukkarieh (2013) suggested a system identification method that is based on the dependent Gaussian process for addressing modeling constraints of stability and control derivations of UAVs. The considered modeling constraints include inability to represent a wide flight envelope and being dependent on prior knowledge of the model structure. The proposed method addresses the control derivatives and system stability through capturing cross coupling of input parameters and it is evaluated through simulation study using a highly coupled oblique wing vehicle in addition to being utilized on a delta-wing UAV platform. The results highlighted advantages such as better identification of coupling flight modes, being more robust to uncertain estimations, and being applicable to wider flight envelopes for the proposed approach in comparison to traditional methods.

Atyabi (2009); Atyabi *et al.* (2010a, 2010b) Atyabi and Powers (2010, 2013b), investigated the potential of two modified PSO approaches called area extended PSO (AEPSO) and cooperative AEPSO (CAEPSO) for controlling a small swarm of simple robots in various scenarios. The study showed AEPSOs capability to perform better local search compared to basic PSO, random search and linear search in time dependent and dynamic domains. Moreover, due to the existence of higher level of cooperation between agents controlled by AEPSO and CAEPSO, they were robust to noise and tasks' time-dependency. The robustness is achieved through heuristics that provided knowledge sharing and a better balancing system between essential behaviors of the swarm (exploration and exploitation). Furthermore, CAEPSO showed its reliability with homogeneous agents by providing higher level of cooperation and experience/knowledge sharing resulting in reduction of illusion effect (a rare case of combinatorial uncertainty) from the environment. The cooperation between agents also allowed CAEPSO to improve the overall search performance.

Formation control is one of the popular problems in robot swarm cooperation that refers to the task of controlling a set of robots that follow a predefined path and maintains a specific formation pattern. Lin *et al.* (2013) categorized existing swarm based approaches for formation control problem to three basic categories of behavioral, virtual structure, and leader-follower. In virtual structure category the swarm is considered as a single rigid robot and therefore the path planning problem for a swarm of robots is simplified to path planning for a rigid robot which is advantageous due to the ease of implementation with the drawback of having low path planning flexibility. In behavior-based category a set of desired behaviors (movement towards destination, obstacle avoidance, maintaining the formation) are defined for each robot in order to create its trajectory. In the leader-follower category, the robot's ability depends on its role in the swarm. In such approaches one or more robots act as leaders with responsibility for moving along a predetermined trajectory, while the remaining swarm members are responsible for following the leaders, while maintaining the desired relative position from each other and the leader (Lin *et al.*, 2013).

Fukushima *et al.* (2014) reported on development of a formation control law that is capable of converting the optimal control problem to a mixed-integer quadratic programming problem through utilizing feedback linearization with a model predictive control (MPC). In addition, a branch-and-bound (B&B) approach is used in order to address obstacle avoidance problem. The numerical experiments indicated significant computation time reduction.

Peng *et al.* (2013) extended the trajectory tracking control of a single robot to a simulation-based formation control study based on multiple non-holonomic mobile robots. The proposed methodology consists of a back-stepping technique that utilizes leader's proposed kinematic controller for real-time tracking, an angular velocity control law for addressing asymptotic stability (i.e., global stability for follower and local stability for the team formation), and a bioinspired neurodynamic approach for addressing the velocity jumps (The impractical velocity jump is considered as a traditional drawback of the back-stepping techniques). The simulation results indicated the effectiveness of the proposed approach with understanding that the utilized scenario is noiseless and no delay is considered in the operation of the mobile robots which caused occasional unexpected stability in the results.

Chand and Carnegie (2013) investigated feasibility of a hierarchy of task allocation and sensory capabilities within a heterogeneous swarm of robots for mapping and exploration problems. The proposed hierarchical system consists of various robots with different computational and sensing capabilities in which the most capable robots (in terms of computational power) are declared as the managers and other robots in the swarm with lower sensing and computation power are allocated with less demanding tasks and are coordinated with manager robots. The manager robots maintain a global information gathered from lower rank robots in the hierarchy and generates a map. Within the second and third level of the proposed hierarchy, planner and explorer robots are considered and take advantage of global maps constructed on manager robots in order to execute their path planning and map building tasks.

Martin-Ortiz *et al.* (2013) proposed an approach called selective inspection method based on auctions (SIMBA) in a swarm robotic study. The SIMBA method is inspired from competitive spirit of animal and insect communities in a sense to compensate for the lack of communications between the swarm members by introducing a competitive bidding mechanism that allows robots to make their own decisions in a competitive environment in a way to benefit the overall team gain. The proposed bidding mechanism is designed as a loop that continuously evaluate robots bids (solutions for routing problem) until all the bids become winners. The experimental results in both simulation and real-world scenarios indicated the feasibility of the proposed approach even when communication is lacking or restricted between the swarm members.

A summary of advantages and shortcomings of various classical and heuristic based path planning methods are presented in Table 25.2.

25.4. Other Applications of Motion Planning in Robotic Domain

The application of navigation and motion planning often exceeds from controlling the maneuvers of simplistic wheeled robots between an start and an end location to controlling robots with complex designs and functionalities, while they are performing complicated tasks in more complex environments and under more sophisticated constraints. Other sectors that benefit from applications of the robot motion planning includes Automative, Food industry, pharmaceutical, medical, health care, and rehabilitation, and so on (i.e., Haptics, Surgical

Table 25.2: Summary of pros and cons of classical and heuristic-based approaches utilized in robot motion planning problem.

Approach	Pros and cons
	Classical
CD	**cons**: Combinatorial explosion, limited granularity, generating infeasible solutions
PF	**pros**: Simple implementation **cons**: Computationally expensive, traps in local minima
Visibility Graph	**pros**: Advantageous for identifying minimum-length path **cons**: Not suitable in the presence of obstacles with sharp edges
Voroni Diagram	**pros**: Execute-ability, suitable in the presence of obstacles with sharp edges **cons**: Not suitable for robots with short range sensors
SN	**pros**: Requires small amount of memory **cons**: Its computationally intensiveness depends on the local operator used PF is suggested as the best local-operator for SN
	Heuristic-based
ANN	**pros**: Easy to implement, capable of approximating any input/output mapping **cons**: Requires extensive amount of training data, the training phase is computationally intensive
GA	**pros**: Easy to implement, no parameter to adjust **cons**: Premature convergence due to inability to control the population diversity
PSO	**pros**: Easy to implement, few parameters to adjust fast searching ability **cons**: Premature convergence, lack of justifiable rules for parameter settings
ACO	**pros**: Rapid algorithm execution, inherent parallelism adaptability to dynamic environments, suitable for traveling sales man type problems **cons**: Complexity of theoretical analysis, generating sequence of pseudo-random solutions, iteratively changing probability distribution, unpredictable convergence time

Devices, Robotic Arms, Grasping Hands, Humanoid, and Wearable Robots). This section discusses the application of motion planning and navigation in such other robotic areas.

25.4.1. *Haptics and Surgical Devices*

Several advantages can be counted for the use of haptic devices for training the novice and intermediate personals in hospitals. The general approach for the novice trainees to be trained on surgical devices and procedures is to first take theoretical study (books, lectures, video files), then under mentor-ship, and finally under real situations with required supervision. The use of multi-modal virtual reality platforms have advantages such as safety, availability, repeatability, and flexibility of the training in terms of being able to tailor the training session to more on reflect sub-skills in the procedure in which the trainee has less experience (Gosselin *et al.*, 2013).

Pose SLAM is a variation of SLAM in which only the robot path gets estimated and the landmarks are utilized only for generating relative constraints between positions. Valenci *et al.* (2013) utilized Pose-SLAM graph of constraints in order to identify a path to the goal that contains lowest accumulated pose uncertainty. The proposed approach uses pose of the Pose-SLAM map as nodes of a belief roadmap (BMR) for generating reliable routs. The authors considered the BMR since it is considered as a variation of SLAM that best address the stochastic nature of the SLAM. In BMR, the edges of the roadmap contains information regarding to the changes in the uncertainty when it is traversed. The original BMR approach has the drawback of being dependent to having known model of the environment, while this is not always possible in real world applications. In their study, Valenci *et al.* (2013) utilized the maps generated by Pose SLAM as a BMR. The authors assessed the potential of the proposed approach against standard path planning approaches and illustrated its feasibility in addition to counting advantages such as being defined in the belief space, only utilizing the uncertainty raised by moving between positions, and being scalable to large environments due to using approximated marginal covariances.

Valenci *et al.* (2013) discussed the use of CardioArm robot for diagnosing and treating ventricular tachycardia (VT) of epicardial origin. CardioArm is a snake-like medical robotic system that is highly flexible and is designed to allow physicians to view, access and perform procedures on the heart with the advantage of only requiring one access point. The potential of the CardioArm in the context of epicardial mapping is assessed through utilizing it for small surgeries on Nine animals and three human patients (the patients experienced multiple failed attempts with endocardial technique prior to the study) and the results indicated technical success for navigating, mapping, and ablation tasks on all subjects except for one of the human patients in whom the blood obscured visualization.

Arcese *et al.* (2013) presented the controller design of a microrobotic system that is magnetically guided in blood vessels with application for performing minimal invasive medical procedures. The authors presented a nonlinear model that takes into account contact and electrostatic forces in addition to non-Newtonian behavior of the blood and generates a trajectory that minimizes the control efforts. In addition, an adaptive back-stepping control method is utilized in order to synthesize the Lya-punov stabilizing control law. The simulation results indicated the robustness of the proposed model to noise and uncertainty arising from physiological parameters.

Pisla *et al.* (2013) discussed dynamic behavior and the kinematics of a parallel hybrid surgical robot called PARASURG-9M that contains a robotic arm, a PARASURG-5M unit with five motors, and a PARASIM (a robotized surgical instrument with four motors). In comparison to serial robots, the presented parallel robot has advantages in terms of providing higher stiffness, smaller mass, and more precise manipulation. In terms of its application in an operating room, the robot is a compact solution and more affordable and uses analytical methods to address the inverse kinematics problem.

Becker *et al.* (2013) employed a virtual fixture framework combined with motion scaling behaviors in Micron platform for vein tracing and conducting surgery on retina membrane peeled with tissue contact. The authors utilized hard virtual fixtures in order to constrain the tip and ensuring that some constraints were never violated in addition to using tremor suppression filters to compensate for unwanted motions with high frequency. The proposed framework uses stero cameras mounted on the microscope in order to generate real time virtual fixtures and task-independent behaviors to the operator.

Gosselin *et al.* (2013) discussed the importance of properly specifying and designing haptics for training sensorimotore skills. The authors developed a haptic interface with capabilities and advantages such as workspace, force, stiffness, transparency, and bandwidth. The developed platform is utilized for training sensorimotor drilling skills. The system is judged by expert surgeons and it is considered as very realistic with the ability to reproduce similar force and position behaviors as it is felt and observed in real surgeries. In addition, the results achieved from using the platform for training novice and intermediate residents indicated their ability to progress after three weeks of training.

25.4.2. *Robotic Arms and Grasping Hands*

In addition to localization, mapping, path planning, and obstacle avoidance other capabilities such as object detection, recognition, and manipulation are required in order for mobile robots to carry out manipulation tasks in domestic environments (Stuckler *et al.*, 2013). The application of robotic manipulators in manufacturing varies from sheet forming (Belchior *et al.*, 2013) to welding (Chen *et al.*, 2013). Stuckler *et al.* (2013) proposed an approach for grasping objects from planar surface. The proposed approach uses scene segmentation to process depth images in real time and generates feasible and collision free paths for grasping objects in segmented images. Authors suggested two variations of grasping called side-grasp (approaching the object along vertical axis and keeping the grippers horizontally aligned) and top-grasp (approaching the object from top grasping the object with finger tips). In addition, collision free grasping method is used to sample grasping candidates (e.g., based on pose and shape) and omit infeasible grasps and solutions that include collisions and rank the remaining candidates in order to identify the most promising one. The omission occurs through a filtering mechanism that considers factors such as grasp width, object hight, reachability, and collisions and the ranking of the remaining solutions is achieved through considering factors such as distance to object center, grasp width, grasp orientation, and distance from robot. The results indicate that the proposed approach is feasible with situations in which the object is spatially distinguishable (Stuckler *et al.*, 2013). A detailed review of various grasping application can be found in Sahbania *et al.* (2012).

Grasp control which is focused on the evaluation and identification of the required grasping force in order to provide stable and feasible grasping is another challenging area in this field specially in the presence of external disturbances (Lippiello *et al.*, 2013). Lippiello *et al.* (2013), investigated grasping force optimization problem for bimanual dextrous- hand and proposed an iterative formulation based approach with low computational load that takes advantage of a sub-optima single hand optimization algorithm joined with an initial-point evaluation method (Lippiello *et al.*, 2013). The utilized iterative formulation approach reduces the computational load by avoiding evaluation of the initial point at the beginning of each iteration. The results achieved from simulations indicated the feasibility of the proposed approach.

Many degrees of freedom on robotic hands that are needed in order to imitate human hand movement causes complications in the design and controller of such devices due to the high number of motors required. Gioioso *et al.* (2013) tackled this problem through designing a synergy-based mapping approach that uses a virtual object in order to specify the mapping in the task space in addition to avoid dissimilarities between kinematics of human and robotic hands. The use of synergy-based mapping is also beneficial under uncertain conditions. The results of the simulation study with two different robotic hands with dissimilar kinematics highlighted the potential of the proposed approach specifically in terms of being more efficient in internal force mapping and direction of motion (Gioioso *et al.*, 2013).

Chen *et al.* (2013) described a J-groove joint robot used for generating welding paths. The proposed solution incorporates interpolation and local modification modules in order to address complex welding paths such as cubic B-spline curves in addition to utilizing PSO for partitioning of the path in its point inversion module. The experimental results indicated the efficiency of the approach in terms of generating high quality welding solutions in addition to the feasibility of the methodology and the resulting robotic arm for welding applications.

Zacharia *et al.* (2013) studied the implication of task scheduling and motion planning for industrial manipulators. Within the industrial systems, it is crucial to navigate the manipulators around multiple obstacles in order to reach to some task points and perform some predefined tasks. The solutions are required to be generated within time optimum sequence in the sense that the manipulators are needed to visit the task points in a collision free manner. The authors formulated an objective function through projecting the workspace on the B-Surface. The formulated function is utilized in order to minimize the required visiting time for multiple task points. The proposed approach consists of a GA for encountering the robot inverse kinematics. The simulation results indicated the capability of the proposed approach for generating near optimal touring solutions for multi-goal path planning for environments constrained by obstacles.

Baranes and Oudeyer (2013) introduced a self adaptive goal generation architecture called SAGG–RIAC for high dimensional redundant robots that allow active learning of inverse models. The architecture is novel in the sense that based on competence progress it samples task parameterizations. This novel task parameterization sampling process allows the robot to solve the task through triggering learning of low-level motor parameters. The proposed architecture is examined over three robotic setups of robotic arm (for learning the inverse kinematics), quadruped robot (for learning omnidirectional locomotion), robotic arm (learning to control a fishing rod), and the results indicated that the exploration in task space is much faster than actuator space when working with redundant robots. In addition, the results showed that the efficiency can be improved significantly if the tasks are selected based on the proposed competence progress rather than random task selection.

Popescu *et al.* (2013) studied the control problem in a hyper redundant robot arm. The utilized model consists of a chain of periodically spaced vertebrae with passive joints that provide rotation, controllable friction force, and elastic contact. The utilized controller consists of two components of "boundary torque variable structure" and "damping force control" which facilitates simple solutions for both arm and task control with guaranteed convergence in spite of existing errors caused by the model parameter's uncertainty. The experimental results indicated the feasibility of the proposed approach for controlling hyper redundant robot arms.

Crespi *et al.* (2013) introduced a robotic system called Salamander that takes advantage of four legs and an actuated spine and is capable of walking and swimming. The authors justified the need for generating robots with actuators that allow robot's movement similar to animals by expressing the necessity of generating robots with realistic embodiments and environmental interactions that can be used for studies in which the complex movements cannot be simulated as in sensorimotor loop and motor activity investigation in neuroscience in which such embodiment is crucial. The authors provided comparison results with real salamanders in terms of body and limb movement and illustrated similarities between the Salamander robots movement and the real salamander.

Keating and Oxman (2013) considered the existing application of robotic arm in industry as inflexible and underutilized since they are mostly used for cyclic tasks rather than as a multi-process, multi-parametric system. That is, the current utilization of the robotic arm systems in the industrial application is within the computational modeling of the environment that does not support generative design platforms due to the existing restrictions in design process and protocols. However, taking advantage of a multi-process, multi-parametric system as suggested by authors has advantages such as reduction in cost, minimization in physical footprint, and integrated performance capabilities. The study utilized the proposed approach for robotic fabrication by combining additive, formative, and subtractive fabrication technologies using a six-axis robotic arm.

Tansel *et al.* (2013) presented a two phase robot selection decision support system (ROBSEL) to assist the decision makers with the question of which robot is the best choice for the problem at hand. The aim of the system is to minimize dependency of the industrial people on expert personell for selection of suitable robots for their business. The ROBSEL takes advantage of a fuzzy analytical hierarchy process (FAHP) system to rank the feasible robots that are survived in the elimination phase in which the decision support system eliminates unsuitable choices based on the received parametrization from the users. The required parametrization is shaped based on the answers that are received from the customers on various criteria in the first phase. The proposed model is advantageous in comparison to existing systems due to the use of correlation test which minimizes the number of criteria and shapes an independent set of criteria. The resulting minimal criteria set contributes to the ROBSEL system by making the system more sensitive to changes in the criteria weights and also adding the capability of differentiating between robots with similar technical specifications.

Ignjatovic *et al.* (2013) tackled the problem of optimization of complex robotic cell in terms of energy efficiency and air compression. Various approaches are considered in the study for defining the parameters of influence that optimizes the working cycle, maximizes the productivity, and energy efficiency and their feasibility is evaluated experimentally considering factors such as manipulators' velocity, robots position in the working space, trajectory of the robot, the pressure of the compressed air, and the length of the tube. The authors described the optimal method for such a problem as a method that considers steps such as (1) establishing and identifying the primary criterion (minimum manufacturing costs, maximum productivity, ...), (2) optimizes the critical parameters that influences the electricity consumption first, and (3) adjusts the related parameters to the air compressor based on the robot and applied criterion constraints.

25.4.3. *Humanoid and Wearable Robots*

Kajita and Yokoi (2013) studied the foot slippage impact on humanoid platform. The authors hypothesized that the the minimization of the power caused by floor friction is the cause of the turning motion and described a model based on this friction which focuses on determining the amount of rotation from a slip by only considering the trajectory and shape of the feet. The authors suggested that the feet velocity and the friction coefficient between the soles of the robot and the floor does not affect the turning angle. The hypothesis is examined and confirmed using a HRP-2 humanoid robot.

Escande *et al.* (2013) discussed a planner method for humanoid robots for multipurpose, multi-contact motions through loosening up the possible contacts that may occur between parts of the robot and the environment. The proposed approach employs a tree representation of possible contact configurations using inverse kinematics that is formulated as an optimization problem. The proposed contact planner is a modified version of potential field planner called best first planning (BFP). The BFP approach generates a tree configuration of contact space that in each iteration only the best performing leafs expands. The best leaf is considered as the leaf with highest potential over configuration space. The planner method is examined on three scenarios of ladder climbing, passing through narrowed passages (tunnel), and siting on the table using HRP-2 humanoid robot. The results indicate feasibility of the proposed approach in all scenarios considered in experiments.

Rouanet *et al.* (2013) studied the impact of various human-robot interfaces in training humanoid robots to recognize some objects. The study employed four interfaces that vary in terms of the type of feedback that they provide and they include media-based artifacts such as smart phone, Wiimote, and Wiimote with laser, and natural human gesture based interfaces such as Wizard-of-Oz recognition system. The study compared these interfaces with each other and evaluated their efficiency in terms of usability, learning, and user's experience. The designed experiments is based on teaching the difference between 12 visual objects and the results indicated that smart-phone interface is more suitable for non-expert users and allows them to provide training examples in a level as efficient as expert users. The study also showed that artifact-mediated teaching interfaces are more efficient for teaching the robot and offer better user's experience and usability due to the associated gesture-based interaction component.

Stegall *et al.* (2013) explored the the importance of the anterior lunge DOF in robotic exoskeleton. The study employed an active leg exoskeleton (ALEX) II in the experiments and proposed two configuration to address the issue. These configurations varied in terms of their locking mechanism. In the first configuration, the anterior/posterior translation of the exoskeleton is locked while the rest of the system is left unlocked, while in the second configuration the anterior/posterior DOF is left unlocked. The experimental design is based on inviting subjects to walk for a period of time at their own pace on a treadmill and meanwhile be trained to learn the required gain template. The results indicated that the unlocked configuration approach provides better overall performance in terms of retention and adaptation.

Vitiello *et al.* (2013) reported the development of an assistive wearable robot (elbow exoskeleton) for rehabilitation purposes. The developed device is called neuro-robotics elbow exoskeleton (NEUROExos) and it is designed to assist patients with post-stroke rehabilitation. The authors counted three main features required in a rehabilitation device such as (1) comfortable human-robot interface (in order to transmit the interaction torque), (2) kinematic compatibility between the human and the device (in order to avoid the risk of human articulations overloading caused by improper torque transmission to the patient's joints), and (3) effective actuation system (in order to address both condition of human-in-charge and device-in-charge). The developed NEUROExos device addresses these required features through utilizing features such as 4 DOF passive mechanism, double-shade links, and an actuation system with compliant antagonistic.

The physical human–robot interface design in wearable devices plays an important role in their efficiency given that it determines the compatibility of the device's kinematics with the patient's skeleton, robot efficiency, and adaptation to various anthropometrics. Cempini *et al.* (2013) argued that failure to address these issues results in misalignment of the robot's and patient's joints which causes ineffective torque control and consequently inappropriate articulations' loading forces and soft tissues' loading forces. Cempini *et al.* (2013) investigated this issue and proposed a self-alignment mechanism in the context of a general analytical approach based on a kinematic analysis of human-robot skeleton for the design of exoskeletons that do not suffer from such misalignment effects.

25.5. Conclusion

This chapter presented the application of CI in the field of autonomous mobile robotics. The chapter started by explaining the relationship between CI and AI and discussed basic concepts of CI in robotic domain emphasizing on essential components of navigation such as localization and path planing. A set of classical- and behavior-based path planning methods are explained and their application on both local and global path planning problems are presented. In addition, the application of motion planning on swarm robotics is explained and two aspects of swarming such as coordination and cooperation and their applications are discussed. The chapter is concluded by presenting recent developments in robot motion planning in robotic systems with complex designs and functionalities such as those used in Automotive, Food industry, pharmaceutical, health care and rehabilitation, and so on.

Acknowledgments

This Research/research paper was supported by the GAMMA Programme which is funded through the Regional Growth Fund. The Regional Growth Fund (RGF) is a £3.2 billion fund supporting projects and programs which are using private sector investment to generate economic growth as well as creating sustainable jobs between now and the mid-2020s. For more information, please go to www.bis.gov.uk/rgf.

References

Arcese, L., Fruchard, M. and Ferreira, A. (2013). Adaptive controller and observer for a magnetic microrobot. *IEEE T. Robot.*, 29, pp. 1060–1057.

Atyabi, A., PhonAmnuaisuk, S., Chin, K. H. and Samadzadegan, S. (2007). Particle swarm optimizations: A critical review. In *Proceeding of Conf IKT07, Third Conference of Information and Knowledge Technology*, Ferdowsi University, Iran, pp. 1–7.

Atyabi, A., Amnuaisuk, S. P. and Ho, C. K. (2010a). Applying area extension pso in robotic swarm. *J. Intell. Robot. Syst., Springer*, 58, pp. 253–285.

Atyabi, A., Amnuaisuk, S. P. and Ho, C. K. (2010b). Navigating a robotic swarm in an uncharted 2d landscape. *Appl. Soft Comput.*, Elsevier, 10, pp. 149–169.

Atyabi, A. and Powers, D. M. W. (2010). The use of area extended particle swarm optimization (aepso) in swarm robotics. In *11th International conference on Control Automation Robotics & Vision, ICARCV*, pp. 591–596.

Atyabi, A. and Powers, D. M. W. (2013a). Review of classical and heuristic-based navigation and path planning approaches. *International Journal of Advancements in Computing Technology, IJACT*, 5, pp. 1–14.

Atyabi, A. and Powers, D. M. W. (2013b). Cooperative area extension of pso-transfer learning vs. uncertainty in a simulated swarm robotics. In *11th International Conference on Informatics in Control, Automation and Robotics, ICINCO*, pp. 177–184.

Atyabi, A. and Samadzadegan, S. (2011). Particle swarm optimization: A survey. In Walters, L. P. (ed.), *Applications of Swarm Intelligence*. Hauppauge, USA: Nova Publishers, pp. 167–178.

Atyabi, A. (2009). Navigating agents in uncertain environments using particle swarm optimization. MSc Thesis. Multimedia University of Malaysia.

Aulinas, J., Petillot, Y., Salvi, J. and Llado, X. (2008). The slam problem: A survey. In *Proceedings of the 2008 Conference on Artificial Intelligence Research and Development: Proceedings of the 11th International Conference of the Catalan Association for Artificial Intelligence*, pp. 363–371.

Baranes, A. and Oudeyer, P.-Y. (2013). Active learning of inverse models with intrinsically motivated goal exploration in robots. *IEEE T. Robot.*, 29, pp. 308–320.

Barbehenn, M. and Hutchinson, S. (1995a). Toward an exact incremental geometric robot motion planner. In *IEEE/RSJ Int. C. Int. Robot.*, pp. 39–44.

Barbehenn, M. and Hutchinson, S. (1995b). Efficient search and hierarchical motion planning by dynamically maintaining single-source shortest paths trees. In *IEEE T. Robotics Autom.*, 11(2), pp. 198–214.

Becker, B., MacLachlan, R., Lobes, L. and Hager, G. (2013). Vision-based control of a handheld surgical micromanipulator with virtual fixtures. *IEEE T. Robot.*, 29, pp. 674–683.

Belchior, J., Guillo, M., Courteille, E., Maurine, P., Leotoing, L. and Guines, D. (2013). Offline compensation of the tool path deviations on robotic machining: Application to incremental sheet forming. *Robot. Cim-Int. Manuf.*, 29, pp. 58–69.

Bessire, P., Ahuactzin, J., Talbi, E. and Mazer, E. (1993). The adriane's clew. algorithm: Global planning with local methods. In *Proc. 1993 IEEE/RSJ Int. C. Int. Robot., IEEE*, pp. 1373–1380.

Bezdek, J. (1994). What is computational intelligence?. In Zurada, J. M., Marks II, R. J. and Robinson, C. J. (eds.), *Computational Intelligence, Imitating Life*. IEEE Computer Society Press, pp. 1–12.

Borenstein, J. and Koren, Y. (1991). The vector field histogram fast obstacle avoidance for mobile robots. *IEEE T. Robot. Autom.*, 7, pp. 278–288.

Brits, R., Engelbrecht, A. and Bergh, F. (2003). Scalability of niche pso. In *Proceedings of the 2003 IEEE Swarm Intelligence Symposium, SIS '03.*, pp. 228–234.

Bullinaria, J. and Li, X. (2007). An introduction to computational intelligence techniques for robot control. *Ind. Robot.*, 34(4), pp. 295–302.

Bunny, M. N. (2012). The use of prospect theory framework in constrained multi-objective particle swarm optimisation. Ph.D. Thesis. School of Computing, Science and Engineering College of Science and Technology University of Salford, Salford, UK.

Burgard, W., Fox, D., Jans, H., Matenar, C. and Thrun, S. (1999). Sonar-based mapping with mobile robots using em. In *Proceedings — 16th International Conference on Machine Learning.*

Cempini, M., Rossi, S. D., Lenzi, T., Vitiello, N. and Carrozza, M. (2013). Self-alignment mechanism for assistive wearable robots: A kinetostatic compatibility method. *IEEE T. Robot.*, 29, pp. 236–250.

Chand, P. and Carnegie, D. A. (2013). Mapping and exploration in a hierarchical heterogeneous multi-robot system using limited capability robots. *J. Robot. Auton. Syst.*, 61, pp. 565–579.

Chang, B., Ratnaweera, A., Halgamuge, S. and Watson, H. (2004). Particle swarm optimization for protein motif discovery. In *Genet. Program. Evol. M.*, pp. 203–214.

Chen, C., Hu, S. and Shen, J. (2013). An approach to the path planning of tube-sphere intersection welds with the robot dedicated to j-groove joints. *Robot. Cim.-Int. Manuf.*, 29, pp. 41–48.

Chen, P. and Hwang, Y. (1992). Sandros: A motion planner with performance proportional to task difficulty. *Proc. IEEE Int. Conf. Robot.*, 3, pp. 2346–2353.

Chen, P. and Hwang, Y. (1998). Sandros: A dynamic graph search algorithm for motion planning. *IEEE T. Robotic. Autom.*, 14(3), pp. 390–403.

Cheng, G. and Zelinsky, A. (1995). A physically grounded search in a behavior based robot. In *Proc. Eighth Australian Joint Conference on Artificial Intelligence*, pp. 547–554.

Chengyu, H., Xiangning, W., Qingzhong, L. and Yongji, W. (2007). Autonomous robot path planning based on swarm intlligence and stream functions. In *Springer, ICES2007, LNCS 4684*, pp. 277–284.

Colle, E. and Galerne, S. (2013). Mobile robot localization by multiangulation using set inversion. *Robot. Auton. Syst.*, 61, pp. 39–48.

Conte, G. and Zullil, R. (1995). Hierarchical path planning in a multi-robot environment with a simple navigation function. *IEEE T. Syst., Man, Cyb.*, 25(4), pp. 651–654.

Crespi, A., Karakasiliotis, K., Guignard, A. and Ijspeert, A. (2013). Salamandra robotic ii: An amphibious robot to study salamander-like swimming and walking gaits. *Robot. Auton. Syst.*, 61, pp. 49–73.

Davison, A. and Murray, D. (2002). Simultaneous localization and map-building using active vision. *IEEE T. Pattern Anal.*, 24(7), pp. 865–880.

de Lope, J., Maravall, D. and Quinonez, Y. (2013). Response threshold models and stochastic learning automata for self-coordination of heterogeneous multi-task distribution in multi-robot systems. *Robot. Auton. Syst.*, 61, pp. 714–720.

Deneb, (1994). Telegrip user manual. *Deneb Robotics Inc.*

Drevelle, V. and Bonnifait. P. (2014). Localization confidence domains via set inversion on short-term trajectory. In *IEEE T. Robot.*, pp. 1–13.

Dunias, P. (1996). Autonomous robots using artificial potential field. In *CIP-Data library Technische universiteit Eindhoven.*

Elshamli, A., Abdullah, H. and Areibi, S. (2004). Genetic algorithm for dynamic path planning. In *Proc. IEEE CCECE 2004*, pp. 677–680.

Escande, A., Kheddar, A. and Miossec, S. (2013). Planning contact points for humanoid robots. *Robot. Auton. Syst.*, 61, pp. 428–442.

Estrada, C., Neira, J. and Tardos. J. (2005). Hierarchical slam: Real-time accurate mapping of large environments. *IEEE T. Robot.*, 21(4), pp. 588–596.

Eustice, R. (2005). Large-area visually augmented navigation for autonomous underwater vehicles. PhD Thesis.

Eustice, R., Singh, H., Leonard, J. and Walter, M. (2006). Visually mapping the rms titanic: Conservative covariance estimates for slam information filters. *IEEE T. Robot.*, 22(6), pp. 1100–1114.

Faigl, J., Vonasek, V. and Preucil, L. (2013). Visiting convex regions in a polygonal map. *J. Robot. Auton. Syst.*, 61, pp. 1070–1083.

Faverjon, B. and Tournassoud, P. (1987). A local-based approach for path planning of manipulators with a high number of degrees of freedom. In *Proc. 1987 IEEE Int. Conf. Robot., IEEE*, pp. 1152–1159.

Fogel, D. (1995). Review of computational intelligence imitating life. *IEEE T. on Neural. Networ.*, 6, pp. 1562–1565.

Fujii, T., Arai, Y., Asama, H. and Endo, I. (1998). Multilayered reinforcement learning for complicated collision avoidance problems. *Proc. IEEE Int. Conf. Robot.*, 3, pp. 2186–2191.

Fukuda, T. and Kubota, N. (1997). Computational intelligence in robotics and mechatoronics. In *23rd International Conference on Industrial Electronics, Control and Instrumentation, IECON'97*, pp. 1517–1528.

Fukushima, H., Kon, K. and Matsuno, F. (2014). Model predictive formation control using branch-and-bound compatible with collision avoidance problems. *IEEE T. Robot.*, pp. 1–10.

Gerstmayer-Hillen, L., Roben, M. K. F., Kreft, S., Venjakob, D. and Moller, R. (2013). Dense topological maps and partial pose estimation for visual control of an autonomous cleaning robot. *J. Robot. Auton. Syst.*, 61, pp. 497–516.

Gioioso, G., Salvietti, G., Malvezzi, M. and Prattichizzo, D. (2013). Mapping synergies from human robotic hands with dissimilar kinematics: An approach in object domain. *IEEE T. Robot.*, 29, pp. 825–837.

Glavina, B. (1990). Solving findpath by combination of goal-directed and randomized search. In *Proc. 1990 IEEE Int. Conf. Robot., IEEE*, pp. 1176–1181.

Gomez, J. V., Lumbier, A., Garrido, S. and Moreno, L. (2013). Planning robot formations with fast marching square including uncertainty. *J. Robot. Auton. Syst.*, 61, pp. 137–152.

Gosselin, F. Bouchigny, S. Megard, C. Taha, F. and Delcampe, P. (2013). Haptic systems for training sensorimotor skills: A use case in surgery. *Robot. Auton. Syst.*, 61, pp. 380–389.

Gu, D., Hu, H., Reynolds, J. and Tsang, E. (2003). Ga-based learning in behaviour based robotics. In *Proc. IEEE International Symposiom on Computational Intelligence in Robotic and Autonomous*, pp. 101–106.

Guillaume, B., Frddrique, B. and Beat, H. (1998). Multi-robot path-planning based on implicit cooperation in a robotic swarm. In *Proc. of the Second Int. Conf. Auton. Agents*. Minneapolis, United States, pp. 39–46.

Guivant, J. and Nebot, E. (2001). Optimization of the simultaneous localization and map-building algorithm for real-time implementation. *IEEE T. Robot. Autom.*, 17(3).

Han, K. (2007). Collision free path planning algorithms for robot navigation problem. In M.Sc Thesis. Department of Electrical and Computer Engineering, Missouri-Columbia University, Columbia.

Hao, M., Yantao, T. and Linan, Z. (2006). A hybrid ant colony optimization algorithm for path planning of robot in dynamic environment. In *Int. J. Inf. Tech.*, 12(3), pp. 78–88.

Hardy, J. and Campbell, M. (2013). Contingency planning over probabilistic obstacle avoidance for autonomous road vehicles. *IEEE T. Robot.*, 29, pp. 913–929.

Hasiao, Y., Chnang, C. and Chien, C. (2004). Ant colony optimization for best path planning. In *Proc. IEEE/ISCIT'04*, pp. 109–113.

Hemakumara, P. and Sukkarieh, S. (2013). Localization in urban environments using a panoramic gist descriptor. *IEEE T. Robot.*, 29, pp. 813–824.

Herman, M. (1986). Fast, three-dimensional, collision-free motion planning. In *Proc. IEEE Int. Conf. Robot.*, New York, pp. 1056–1063.

Hinojosa, W. M., Nefti-Meziani, S. and Kaymak, U. (2011). Systems control with generalized probabilistic fuzzy-reinforcement learning. *IEEE T. Fuzzy Syst.*, 19(1), pp. 51–64.

Holland, J. (1975). Adaptation in natural and artificial systems. In *University of Michigan Press, Ann Arbor*.

Hoshino, S. and Seki, H. (2013). Multi-robot coordination for jams in congested systems. *Robot. Auton. Syst.*, 61, pp. 808–820.

Hwang, Y. and Ahuja, N. (1992). Gross motion planning — a survey. In *ACM Comput. Surv.*, 24, pp. 219–291.

Hwang, Y. and Chen, P. (1995). A heuristic and complete planner for the classical mover's problem. In *Proc. 1995 IEEE Int. Conf. Robot. IEEE*, pp. 729–736.

Ignjatovic, I., Komendal, T., Seslija, D. and Malisa, V. (2013). Optimization of compressed air and electricity consumption in a complex robotic cell. *Robot. Cim-Int. Manuf.*, 29, pp. 70–76.

Jaillet, L. and Porta, J. (2013). Path planning under kinematic constraints by rapidly exploring manifolds. *IEEE T. Robot.*, 29, pp. 105–117.

Jensfelt, P., Kragic, D. Folkesson, J. and Bjrkman, M. (2006). A framework for vision based bearing only 3D slam. In *Proc. — IEEE Int. Conf. Robot., and Automation*, ICRA, pp. 1944–1950.

Jiang, Q. and Kumar, V. (2013). The inverse kinematics of cooperative transport with multiple aerial robots. *IEEE T. Robot.*, 29, pp. 136–145.

Kala, R. (2012). Multi-robot path planning using co-evolutionary genetic programming. *Expert Syst. Appl.*, 39(3), pp. 3817–3831.

Keating, S. and Oxman, N. (2013). Compound fabrication: A multi-functional robotic platform for digital design and fabrication. *Robot. Cim-Int. Manuf.*, 29, pp. 439–448.

Khansari-Zadeh, S. and Billard, A. (2012). A dynamical system approach to realtime obstacle avoidance. *Springer Verlag Auton. Robot.*, 32(4), pp. 433–454.

Kim, A. and Eustice, R. (2013). Real-time visual slam for autonomous underwater hull inspection using visual saliency. *IEEE T. Robot.*, 29, pp. 719–733.

Kim, J. and Sukkarieh, S. (2003). Airborne simultaneous localisation and map building. *Proc. — IEEE Int. Conf. Robot.*, 1, pp. 406–411.

Kim, J. and Sukkarieh, S. (2004). Autonomous airborne navigation in unknown terrain environments. *IEEE T. Aero. Elec. Sys.*, 40(3), pp. 1031–1045.

Konar, A. (2005). Computational intelligence principles, techniques and applications. Springer Verlag.

Kondo, K. (1991). Motion planning with six degrees of freedom by multi-strategic, bidirectional heuristic free space enumeration. *IEEE T. Robotic. Autom.*, 7(3), pp. 267–277.

Kudelski, M., Gambardella, L. and Caro, G. D. (2013). Robonetsim: An integrated framework for multi-robot and network simulation. *Robot. Auton. Syst.*, 61, pp. 483–496.

Latombe, J. (1991). Robot motion planning. *Kluwer Int. Ser. Eng. C.*, London.

Lin, C., Chen, K., Hsiao, P. and Chuang, W. (2013). Motion planning of swarm robots using potential-based genetic algorithm. *Int. J. Innov. Comput., I. ICIC*, 9, pp. 305–318.

Lingelbach, F. (2004). Path planning using probabilistic cell decomposition. *Int. Conf. Robot.*, pp. 467–472.

Lippiello, V., Siciliano, B. and Villani, L. (2013). A grasping force optimization algorithm for multiarm robots with multifingered hands. *IEEE T. Robot.*, 29, pp. 55–67.

Lozano-Perez, T., Jones, J., Mazer, E., O'donnell, P., Grimson, E., Tournassoud, P. and Lanusse, A. (1987). Handey a robot system that recognizes, plans, and manipulates. In *Proc. IEEE Int. Conf. Robot.*, New York, pp. 843–849.

Lozano-Perez, T. and Wesley, M. (1979). An algorithm for planning collision-free paths among polyhedral obstacles. In *Commun. ACM*, 22, pp. 560–570.

Lu, T. (2013). Indoor odour source localisation using robot: Initial location and surge distance matter. *Robot. Auton. Syst.*, 61, pp. 637–647.

Lumelsky, V. and Skewis, T. (1990). Incorporating range sensing in the robot navigation function. *IEEE T. Syst. Man Cyb.*, 20, pp. 1058–1069.

Madani, T., Daachi, B. and Benallegue, A. (2013). Adaptive variable structure controller of redundant robots with mobile/fixed obstacles avoidance. *J. Robot. Auton. Syst.*, 61, pp. 555–564.

Marble, J. and Bekris, K. E. (2013). Asymptotically near-optimal planning with probabilistic roadmap spanners. *IEEE T. Robot.*, 29, pp. 432–444.

Marks, R. (1993). Computational versus artificial. *IEEE T. Neural. Networ.*, 4, pp. 737–739.

Martinez, C., Richardson, T., Thomas, P., du Bois, J. and Campoy, P. (2013). A vision-based strategy for autonomous aerial refuling tasks. *J. Robot. Auton. Syst.*, 61, pp. 876–895.

Martin-Ortiz, M., de Lope, J. and de la Paz, F. (2013). Action based method for graphiclike maps inspection by multi-robot system in simulated and real environments. *J. Robot. Auton. Syst.*, 61, pp. 676–681.

Masehian, E. and Sedighizadeh, D. (2007). Classic and heuristic approaches in robot motion planning — a chronological review. *Proc. Wrld. Acad. Sci., E.*, 23, pp. 101–106.

Masehian, E. and Sedighizadeh, D. (2010). Multi-objective pso-and npso-based algorithms for robot path planning. *Adv. Electr. Comput. Eng.*, 10(4), pp. 69–76.

Masoud, A. A. (2013). A harmonic potential field approach for joint planning and control of a rigid, seperable nonholonomic, mobile robot. *J. Robot. Auton. Syst*, 61, pp. 593–615.

McLurkin, J. and Yamins, D. (2005). Dynamic task assignment in robot swarms. In *Proc. of Robotics: Science and Systems*, Cambridge, USA.

Mirkhani, M., Forsati, R., Shahri, A. and Moayedikia, A. (2013). A novel efficient algorithm for mobile robot localization. *Robot. Auton. Syst.*, 61, pp. 920–931.

Miura, K., Kanehiro, F., Kajita, S. and Yokoi, K. (2013). Slip-turn for biped robots. *IEEE T. Robot.*, 29, pp. 875–887.

Montemerlo, M., Thrun, S., Koller, D. and Wegbreit, B. (2002). Fastslam: A factored solution to the simultaneous localization and mapping problem. In *Proceedings of the National Conference on Artificial Intelligence*, pp. 593–598.

Montemerlo, M., Thrun, S., Koller, D. and Wegbreit, B. (2003). Fastslam 2.0: An improved particle filtering algorithm for simultaneous localization and mapping that provably converges. In *18th Int. Joint Conf. Artif., IJCAI.*, Acapulco, Mexico, pp. 1151–1156.

Montemerlo, M. and FastSLAM, S. T. (2007). A scalabale method for the simultaneous localizaton and mapping problem in robotics. *Spr. Tra. Adv. Robot.*, 27.

Murillo, A., Singh, G., Kosecka, J. and Guerrero, J. (2013). Localization in urban environments using a panoramic gist descriptor. *IEEE T. Robot.*, 29, pp. 146–160.

Murphy, L. and Newman, P. (2013). Risky planning on probabilistic costmaps for path planning in outdoor environments. *IEEE T. Robot.*, 29, pp. 445–457.

Nakju, L., Chanki, K. and Chung, W. (2007). A practical path planner for the robotic vacuum cleaner in rectilinear environments. *IEEE T. Consum. Electr.*, 53, pp. 519–527.

Neuzil, P., Cerny, S., Svanidze, O., Bohuslavek, J., Plasil, P., Jehlicka, P., Holy, F., Petru, J., Kuenzler, R. and Sediva, L. (2013). Single-site access robot-assisted epicardial mapping with a snake robot: prepration and first clinical experience. *J. Robot. Surg.*, 7, pp. 103–111.

Newman, P. and Leonard, J. (2003). Consistent, convergent and constant-time slam. In *Int. Joint Conf. Artif. IJCAI*, pp. 1143–1150.

Newman, P. (1999). On the structure and solution of the simultaneous localization and mapping problem. PhD Thesis, University of Sydney.

Otte, M. and Correll, N. (2013). C-forest: Parallel shortest path planning with superlinear speedup. *IEEE T. Robot.*, 29, pp. 798–806.

Ozsoyeller, D., Beveridge, A. and Isler, V. (2014). Symmetric rendezvous search on the line with an unknown initial distance. *IEEE T. Robot.*, pp. 1–14.

Park, K., Kim, Y. and Kim, J. (2001). Modular q-learning based multi-agent cooperation for robot soccer. *Robot. Auton. Syst.*, 35, pp. 109–122.

Pasupuleti, S. and Battiti, R. (2006). The gregarious particle swarm optimizer (g-pso). In *Proceedings of the 8th Annual Conference on Genetic and Evolutionary Computation*, Seattle, Washington, USA, pp. 67–74.

Peer, E., Bergh, F. and Engelbrecht, A. (2003). Using neighbourhood with the guaranteed convergence pso. In *Proceedings of the 2003 IEEE Swarm Intelligence Symposium SIS'03*, pp. 235–242.

Peng, Z., Wen, G., Rahmani, A. and Yu, Y. (2013). Leader-follower formation control of non-holomonic mobile robots based on bioinspired neurodynamic based approach. *J. Robot. Auton. Syst.*, 61, pp. 988–996.

Peram, T., Veeramachaneni, K. and Mohan, C. (2003). Fitness distance ratio based particle swarm optimization (fdr-pso). In *Swarm Intelligence Symposium, SIS'03*, pp. 174–181.

Pimenta, L., Pereira, G., Michael, N., Mesquita, R., Bosque, M., Chaimowicz, L. and Kumar, V. (2013). Swarm coordination based on smoothed particle hydrodynamics technique. *IEEE T. Robot.*, 29, pp. 383–399.

Pinder, J. M., Theodoridis, T. and Nefti-Meziani, S. (2013). Autonomous aerial vehicle using a single camera for flight stabilisation. In *International Workshop on Human-Machine Systems, Cyborgs and Enhancing Devices, IEEE Robotics & Automation Society*, pp. 1–2.

Pisla, D., Gherman, B., Vaida, C., Suciu, M. and Plitea, N. (2013). An active hybrid parallel robot for minimally invasive surgery. *Robot. Cim-Int. Manuf.*, 29, pp. 203–221.

Pizarro, O., Eustice, R. and Singh, H. (2004). Large area 3D reconstructions from underwater surveys. *Ocean'04 — MTS/IEEE Techno-Ocean: Bridges across the Oceans — Conference Proceedings*. 2, pp. 678–687.

Poole, D., Mackworth, A. and Goebel, R. (1998). Computational intelligence: A logical approach. *Oxford University Press*.

Popescu, N., Popescu, D. and Ivanescu, M. (2013). A spatial weight error control for class of hyper-redundent robots. *IEEE T. Robot.*, 29, pp. 1043–1050.

Pugh, J. and Martinoli, A. (2006). Multi-robot learning with particle swarm optimization. In *International Conference on Autonomous Agents and Multi Agent Systems AAMAS'06. Hakodate, Japan*, pp. 441–448.

Pugh, J. and Martinoli, A. (2007). Parallel learning in heterogeneous multi-robot swarms. In *IEEE C. Evol. Computat. CEC'07. Singapore*, pp. 3839–3846.

Pugh, J. and Zhang, Y. (2005). Particle swarm optimization for unsupervised robotic learning. In *Proceedings of 2005 IEEE in Swarm Intelligence Symposium, SIS05*, pp. 92–99.

Purcaru, C., Precup, R.-E., Iercan, D., Fedorovici, L.-O., David, R.-C. and Dragan, F. (2013). Optimal robot path planning using gravitational search algorithm. *Int. J. Artif. Intell.*, 10(S13), pp. 1–20.

Qin, Y.-Q., Sun, D.-B., Li, N. and Cen, Y.-G. (2004). Path planing for mobile robot using the particle swarm optimization with mutation operator. In *Proc. International Conference on Machine Learning and Cybernetics*. Shanghai, pp. 2473–2478.

Rakshit, P., Konar, A., Das, S. and Nagar, A. K. (2013). Abc-tdql: An adaptive memetic algorithm. In *Proc. 2013 IEEE Workshop on Hybrid Intelligent Models and Applications*. Singapore, pp. 35–42.

Randal, W. and McLain, T. (2003). Motion planning using potential fields. In Brigham Young University, Provo, Utah.

Ratnaweera, A., Halgamuge, S. and Watson, H. (2004). Self-organizing hierarchical particle swarm optimizer with time-varying acceleration coefficients. *IEEE T. Evolut. Comput.*, 8(3): pp. 240–255.

Riadi, I., Nefti-Meziani, S., Theodoridis, T. and Wahab, M. N. A. (2013). Ant colony optimization with prospect theory for continuous optimization problems. In *International Workshop on Human-Machine Systems, Cyborgs and Enhancing Devices, IEEE Robotics & Automation Society*, pp. 1–2.

Riadi, I. (2014). Cognitive ant colony optimization: A new framework in swarm intelligence. PhD Thesis. School of Computing, Science and Engineering College of Science and Technology University of Salford, Salford, UK.

Rimon, E. and Koditschek, D. (1992). Exact robot navigation using artificial potential functions. *IEEE T. Robotic. Autom.*, 8(5), pp. 501–518.

Rosell, J. and Iniguez, P. (2005). Path planning using harmonic functions and probabilistic cell decomposition. *Int. Conf. Robot.*, pp. 1803–1808.

Rouanet, P., Oudeyer, P., Danieau, F. and Filliat, D. (2013). The impact of human-robot interfaces on the learning of visual objects. *IEEE T. Robot.*, 29, pp. 525–541.

Roy, N., Burgard, W., Fox, D. and Thrun, S. (1999). Coastal navigation-robot motion with uncertainty. In *IEEE/RSJ Int. Conf. Robot.*

Rufli, M., Alson-Mora, J. and Siegwart, R. (2013). Reciprocal collision avoidance with motion continuity constraints. *IEEE T. Robot.* 29.

Sadati, N. and Taheri, J. (2002). Genetic algorithm in robot path planning problem in crisp and fuzzified environments. In *Proc. IEEE ICIT'02*, Bangkok, Thailand.

Sahbania, A., El-Khoury, S. and Bidaud, P. (2012). An overview of 3d object grasp synthesis algorithms. *Robot. Auton. Syst.*, 60, pp. 326–336.

Schwartz, J. and Sharir, M. (1983). On the piano movers problem I: The case of a two-dimensional rigid polygonal body moving amidst polygonal barriers. *Commun. Pure and Appl. Math.* 36, pp. 345–398.

Se, S. Lowe, D. and Little, J. (2002). Mobile robot localization and mapping with uncertainty using scale invariant visual landmarks. *Int. J. Robot. Res.*, 21(8), pp. 735–758.

Seda, M. (2007). Roadmap method *vs.* cell decomposition in robot motion planning. In *Proceedings of 6th WSEAS International Conf. on Signal Processing, Robotics and Automation*, Grees, pp. 127–132.

Sez, J., Hogue, A., Escolano, F. and Jenkin, M. (2006). Underwater 3D slam through entropy minimization. In *Proc. — IEEE Int. Conf. Robot. 2006*, pp. 3562–3567.

Shi, C., Bu, Y. and Liu, J. (2008). Mobile robot path planning in three-dimensional environment based on aco-pso hybrid algorithm. In *Proceedings of the 2008 IEEE/ASME International Conference on Advanced Intelligent Mechatronics*. Xi'an, China, pp. 252–256.

Shirong, L., Linbo, M. and Jinshou, Y. (2006). Path planning based on ant colony algorithm and distributed local navigation for multi-robot systems. In *Proc. IEEE Int. Conf. on Mechatronics and Automation*, pp. 1733–1738.

Shukla, A., Singla, E., Wahi, P. and Dasgupta, B. (2013). A direct variational method for planning monotonically optimal paths for redundent manipulators in constrained workspaces. *J. Robot. Auton. Syst.*, 61, pp. 209–220.

Siegwart, R. and Nourbakhsh, I. (2004). Introduction to autonomouse mobile robots. In MIT Press.

Simmons, R. (1996). The curvature-velocity method for local obstacle avoidance. *Proc. of the IEEE Int. Conf. Robot.*, 4, pp. 3375–3382.

Sleumer, N. and Gurman, N. (1991). Exact cell decomposition of arrangements used for path planning in robotics. *Swiss Federal Institute of Technology.*

Song, P. (2002). A potential field based approach to multi-robot manipulation general robotics. In *IEEE Int. Conf. Robot., ICRA'02.*

Stacey, A., Jancic, M. and Grundy, I. (2003). Particle swarm optimization with mutation. In *IEEE Evol. Computat., CEC'03*, pp. 1425–1430.

Stegall, P., Winfree, K., Zanotto, D. and Agrawal, S. (2013). Rehabilitation exoskeleton design: Exploring effect of the anterior lunge degree of freedom. *IEEE T. Robot.*, 29, pp. 838–846.

Stuckler, J., Steffens, R., Holz, D. and Behnke, S. (2013). Efficient 3d object perception and grasp planning for mobile manipulation in domestic environments. *J. Robot. Auton. Syst.*, 61, pp. 1106–1115.

Suranga, H. (2006). Distributed online evolution for swarm robotics. In *Auton. Agent. and Multi-Ag.*

Tansel, Y., Yurdakul, M. and Dengiz, B. (2013). Development of a decision support system for robot selection. *Robot. Cim-Int. Manuf.*, 29, pp. 142–157.

Taylor, N., Mohamad, M. and Dunnigan, M. (2006). Articulated robot motion planning using ant colony. In *Proc. IEEE Int. Conf. Optimization. Intel. Sys.*, pp. 690–695.

Theodoridis, T. and Hu, H. (2006). The fuzzy sarsa (?) learning approach applied to a strategic route learning robot behaviour. In *IEEE/RSJ Int. Conf. Intell. Robots Sys. (IROS'06)*, pp. 1767–1772.

Trueba, P., Prieto, A., Bellas, F., Caamano, P. and Duro, R. (2013). Specialization analysis of embodied evolution for robotic collective tasks. *Robot. Auton. Syst.*, 61, pp. 682–693.

Valenci, R., Morta, M. and Andrade-Cetto, J. (2013). Planning reliable paths with pose slam. *IEEE T. Robot.*, 29, pp. 1050–1059.

Vesterstrom, J. and Riget, J. (2002). Particle swarms extensions for improved local, multimodal and dynamic search in numerical optimization. Master's thesis. Department of Computer Science, University of Aarhus, Aarhus C, Denmark.

Vitiello, N., Lenzi, T., Roccella, S., Rossi, S. D., Cattin, E., Giovacchini, F., Vecchi, F. and Carrozza, M. (2013). Neuroexos: A powered elbow exoskeleton for physical rehabilitation. *IEEE T. Robot.*, 29, pp. 220–235.

Wang, Y. and Chirikjian, G. (2000). A new potential field method for robot path planning. In *Proc. 2000 IEEE Int. Conf. Robot.*, pp. 977–982.

Wang, L. (2002). Computational intelligence in autonomous mobile robotics — a review. In *Proceedings of 2002 International Symposium on Micromechatronics and Human Science, 2002. MHS 2002*, pp. 227–235. doi: 10.1109/MHS.2002.1058040.

Webster, S., Walls, J., Whitcomb, L. and Eustice, R. (2014). Decentralized extended information filter for single-beacon cooperative acoustic navigation: Theory and experiments. *IEEE T. Robot.*, 29, pp. 957–974.

Williams, R. and Sukhatme, S. (2013). Constrained interaction and coordination in proximity-limited multiagent systems. *IEEE T. Robot.*, 29, pp. 930–944.

Williams, S. B., Newman, P., Dissanayake, M. and Durrant-Whyte, H. (2000). Autonomous underwater simultaneous localisation and map building. In *Proc. IEEE Int. Conf. Robot.*, San Francisco, USA, pp. 1143–1150.

Wlodzislaw, D. (2007). What is computational intelligence and what could it become? *Challenges for Computational Intelligence*, pp. 1–11.

Yamamoto, K. and Okada, M. (2013). Control of swarm behaviour in crossing pedestrians based on temporal/spatial frequencies. *Robot. Auton. Syst.*, 61, pp. 1036–1048.

Yang, E. and Gu, D. (2004). Multi-agent reinforcement learning for multi-robot systems: A survey. In Technical report, Department of Computer Science, University of Essex Technical Report CSM-404, UK.

Yang, C. and Simon, D. (2005). A new particle swarm optimization technique. In *18th International Conference on Systems Engineering, ICSEng 2005*, pp. 164–169.

Yangmin, L. and Xin, C. (2005). Mobile robot navigation using particle swarm optimization and adaptive nn. In *Springer, ICNC 2005*, pp. 628–631.

Yuan-Qing, Q., De-Bao, S., Ning, L. and Yi-Gang, C. (2004). Path planning for mobile robot using the particle swarm optimization with mutation operator. In *Proceedings of the Third International Conference on Machine Laming and Cybemetics*.

Zacharia, P., Xidias, E. and Aspragathos, N. (2013). Task scheduling and motion planning for an industrial manipulator. *Robot. Cim-Int. Manuf.*, 29, pp. 449–462.

Zhu, Y., Zhang, T., Song, J. and Li, X. (2013). A hybrid navigation strategy for multiple mobile robots. *Robot. Cim-Int. Manuf.*, 29, pp. 129–141.

Zhu, D. and Latombe, J. (1991). New heuristic algorithms for efficient hierarchical path planning. *IEEE T. Robot. Autom.*, 7(1), pp. 9–20.

Zou, A., Hou, Z., Fu, S. and Tan, M. (2006). Neural networks for mobile robot navigation: A survey. In Berlin, Heidelberg, Springer-Verlag, pp. 1218–1226.

Chapter 26

Selected Automotive Applications of Computational Intelligence

Mahmoud Abou-Nasr, Fazal Syed and Dimitar Filev

With the increasing demand on the energy resources and the drive towards environmentally friendly vehicles, embedded computers have been long employed within the complex automotive architecture for various tasks like engine control, anti-lock braking, fault detection, and diagnostics. Our automobiles have evolved over the years to be more powerful, easier to drive and control, safer and more connected than ever. Recently, computational intelligence (CI) paradigms have found their way in our automobiles, helping us navigate, park, and intelligently control the cruising speeds of our cars. Intelligent drive assist features and autonomous vehicles are becoming a part of our current vocabulary. In this chapter, we introduce the CI paradigm within the framework of the other traditional computational paradigms. We then present applications of CI in automotive. The first application discusses a NN that learns, from sample data, how to detect intruders who may be hiding in the vehicle based on their heartbeat. The second is about NNs that learn to optimize fuel consumption while maintaining an ultra-capacitor state of charge at an average target level. The third application is about a fuzzy rule-based system for minimizing high voltage batteries power limits. In the last application, we present hybrid learning models for learning the preferences of the drivers, in the context of the driver aware vehicle concept.

26.1. Introduction

As much as computers and computational devices are part of our everyday life, we still aspire for a future in which we do not have to program them. One answer to this was the logic programming paradigms in which we tell our computers our goals and let them figure out ways to achieve these goals. Even with some successes in early expert systems, there is still a lot to be desired. Despite of the advances in computational speed and algorithms, computers are still no match to our brains in some tasks like hand-eye coordination; face recognition, handwriting recognition, and natural speech recognition to name a few. Also, our brains are far better in handling uncertainty and noisy inputs and are remarkably adaptable to ever changing contexts.

With inspirations from nature, biology, cognition, and computational theories a set of computational paradigms were born to address these tasks, that are challenging to our traditional computational paradigms yet seemingly done relatively at ease inside our brains. An umbrella term for this set of paradigms is computational intelligence (CI). CI covers disciplines such as artificial neural networks, fuzzy logic, and evolutionary computation. It embraces nature inspired algorithms that are derived from the principles and foundations of ant colonies, swarm intelligence, and artificial immune system. It has applications in many fields such as image and speech processing, natural language processing, computer vision, and data mining.

In the following sections, we will show several examples of CI applications in the automotive industry. The first two examples cover NN-based CI applications. We will start by an application in which a NN is learned from example data how to detect an intruder hiding in a vehicle based on his/her heartbeat. Next, we present NNs that are learned to optimize the fuel economy in a vehicle with a hybrid powertrain (internal combustion engine and an ultra-capacitor), while maintaining the average state of charge of the ultra-capacitor at a preferred target level. The third example CI application relates to fuzzy control as a tool for incorporating additional subjective knowledge and intelligence to the conventional hybrid electric vehicle (HEV) control algorithms. In our last CI application example, we present a Hybrid Model combining a set of discrete Markov chains and an associated fuzzy rule-base of contextual conditions. We discuss the structure of the Hybrid Model and the methodology for learning and predicting driver preferences and its application to the problem estimating the next driving destination based on the information about the trips between the most frequent stop locations.

26.2. Vehicle Intrusion Detection

The first application that we present is detecting an intruder, who may be lurking in a vehicle, waiting to ambush an unsuspecting lonely driver as he/she is entering in. We sought a system that may alleviate this scenario and allows one to query his/her vehicle, before approaching it, to make sure that the vehicle is vacant of intruders. The system we present is based on detecting the intruder heartbeat. The system utilizes signals from a sensor that responds to the intruder heartbeat, breathing, or both (Eagen *et al.*, 2008).

This detection problem is not straight forward and has many challenges. One challenge is the wide range of weather conditions and the variety of contextual surroundings which may affect and interfere with the sensor signals and can even excite the sensor into quasi-periodic oscillations that resemble a beating heart. Another is the wide range of heart beats and breathing patterns of different individuals. In addition, the space for packaging and resources such as memory and CPU available for embedded system implementation are limited, favoring compact signal processing algorithms. The problem is further compounded by the absence of a known signature differentiating an unoccupied vehicle from an occupied one. Figure 26.1 illustrates several five second intervals of conditioned sensor signals, some of them are taken while the vehicle was occupied (top panel) and the others are taken while the vehicle is unoccupied (bottom panel).

A block diagram of an intruder detection system that is based on recurrent neural networks is shown in Figure 26.2.

The first block in the diagram is a sensor which is a highly sensitive accelerometer with a wide dynamic range capable of responding to the minute vibrations caused by the human heart when carefully placed in a proper location inside the vehicle. Next, the signal is filtered and amplified in the signal conditioning block. The conditioned signal is then sampled and converted to a digital signal in the A/D block and then preprocessed (mainly scaled) in the preprocessing block in order for the trained neural network in the NN block to render its decision on whether the vehicle is occupied or not.

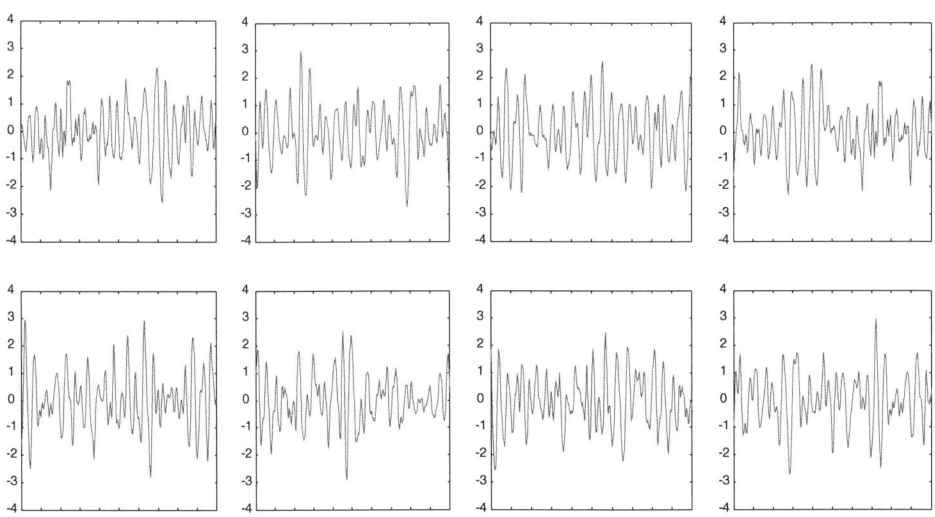

Figure 26.1: Various five seconds intervals of conditioned sensor signals representing an occupied (top panel) and an unoccupied (bottom panel) vehicle. It is difficult to visually discern a distinguishing signature for occupancy. The horizontal axis is time (0.5 s), and the vertical axis is the voltage (mv) proportional to the accelerometer signal.

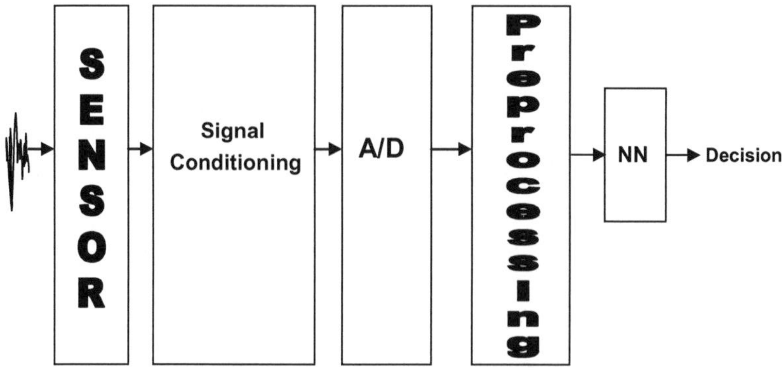

Figure 26.2: Block diagram of the intruder detection system.

26.2.1. *Data-Driven Intruder Detection Neural Network Development*

In a data-driven problem solving approach like neural networks data acquisition is of paramount importance. Methods and procedures for collecting and accurately labeling the data have to be decided upon and followed meticulously to ensure successful neural network development. Mislabeled data can affect NN training process and can drive the conclusions in the wrong direction. In addition, the collected dataset should be representative of all possible conditions that the detection NN may encounter in real-life.

For this problem, several instrumented vehicles were used to acquire data representing a variety of individuals, of different ages, genders, weights, heart rates who hid in different locations inside the car. Data acquisition sessions were structured so that recordings of when the car was occupied and when it was empty were collected in consecutive sessions or at least within a very short interval of time to minimize the potential for varying external conditions that may mislead the NN training process. This process was repeated in different locations both in Europe and in the United States e.g., parking lots, garages, and different levels of parking structures. Also it was repeated in different weather conditions (wind, rain, snow) and varying proximities to different traffic patterns (heavy, moderate, and low or no traffic).

We have experimented with different recurrent neural architectures in terms of number of layers and number of nodes within each layer. The node activation functions in all of our experiments/tests were bipolar sigmoids. Our initial experiments found that we can obtain about the same performance from all architectures ($\sim$95% accuracy, $\sim$2.4% false negative). Embedded implementation for vehicle deployment imposes constraints on CPU computations and memory utilization. Hence, we focused more on smaller architectures in our development. As expected, we have found that the detection performance of the NN is directly related to the richness and variety of the data in the training set. The recurrent networks were trained with extended Kalman filter (EKF) training algorithms. For more detail and description of this training method please see Feldkamp and Puskorius (1998).

26.2.2. *Intruder Detection NN Performance Examples*

In Figure 26.3, we show the response of a trained NN with an architecture that is comprised of one input which is the conditioned and normalized sensor signal, six bipolar sigmoid nodes which are also fully recurrent in the first layer and three bipolar sigmoid nodes in the hidden layer and one bipolar sigmoid node as an output node. Panel (a) is the instantaneous (every 1/100 s) response of this network to the sensor signal that is shown in panel (b) from an occupied car. The NN indicates the detection of a person in the vehicle, with a positive output value. Panel (c) on the other hand is the instantaneous response of the same trained network to the sensor signal that is shown in panel (d) from an unoccupied car. In this case the NN indicates that it did not detect a person with a negative output value.

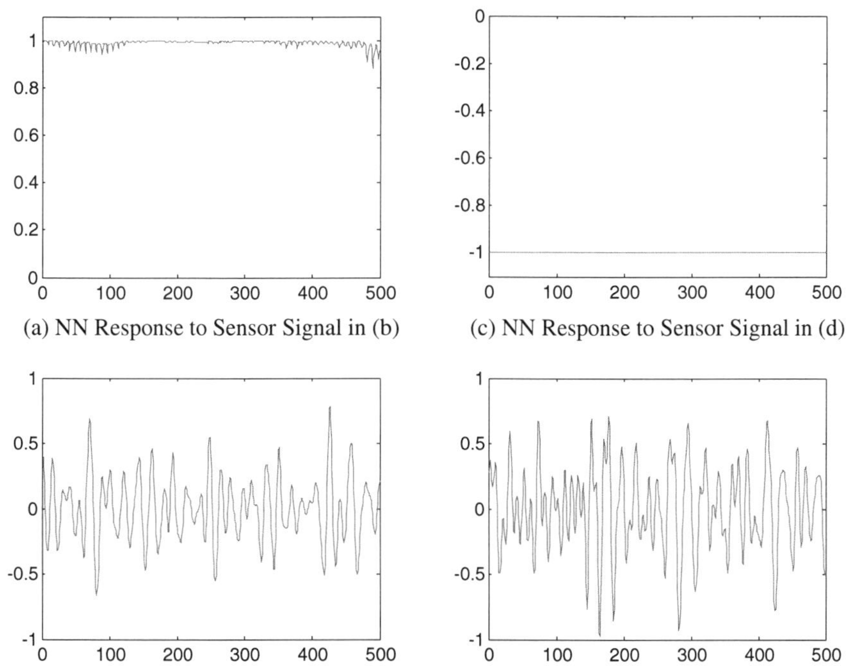

(a) NN Response to Sensor Signal in (b)

(c) NN Response to Sensor Signal in (d)

(b) Sensor Signal (Occupied Vehicle)

(d) Sensor Signal (Unoccupied Vehicle)

Figure 26.3: Trained neural network response to sensor signals. Panel (a) is the normalized NN Response to the normalized conditioned sensor signal from an occupied vehicle that is shown in Panel (b). Panel (c) is the normalized NN response to the normalized conditioned sensor signal from an unoccupied vehicle that is shown in panel (d). The horizontal axis in all figures is time (0.01 s). The vertical axis in figures (c) and (d) is the normalized NN output while the vertical axis in figures (b) and (d) is the normalized NN input representing the conditioned sensor signal.

26.3. Energy Management in a Hybrid Powertrain

The next application that we present is the problem of energy management in a hybrid powertrain with an ultra-capacitor as shown in Figure 26.4. In this configuration, the primary energy source is an internal combustion engine (ICE) and the power to the wheels may be delivered through either the ICE or an electric motor connected to the ultra-capacitor or both.

Ultra-capacitors have high specific power and efficiency even at low temperatures, a quick response, efficient regenerative braking energy acceptance, and long projected cycle and calendar life. On the other hand, they have low energy storage capacity (low specific energy) and they self-discharge which may limit their use in serious hybrid applications. Unlike HEVs with conventional batteries, ultra-capacitors can be easily discharged during regular driving. Obviously, when an ultra-capacitor is discharged, it cannot supplement the energy power which may lead to drivability issues of the sort of a degraded response during an acceleration event, especially if the primary energy source (ICE in this case) is downsized or unable to respond quickly. A fully charged ultra-capacitor is not desirable either, as it will not be able to harvest energy from regenerative braking events.

For these reasons, incorporating ultra-capacitors in a hybridization strategy has its own challenges which could be even harder than the ones encountered in typical HEV's with batteries.

To overcome the ultra-capacitor limitations, HEV powertrain control strategies must optimally manage their charging and discharging behavior while driving. In this regard, a control strategy aims at prescribing a power split between the ICE engine and the electric motor in such a way as to sustain (on average) the state of charge of the ultra-capacitor, while attaining reduction in fuel consumption. The strategy must be sophisticated enough to be able to incorporate knowledge of the driving patterns, vehicle conditions, and possibly road terrain.

Researchers have explored different techniques to achieve these objectives in energy management control strategies, including dynamic programming (DP),

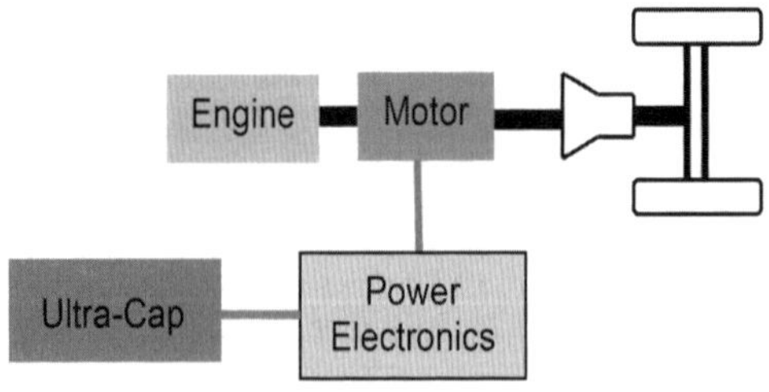

Figure 26.4: Schematic of an HEV configuration with an ultra-capacitor.

rule-based, and model predictive control. In the following we elucidate a technique for achieving these two objectives in an energy management strategy for HEV with ultra-capacitor.

The technique is based on recurrent (dynamic) NNs which are employed in two modalities: A plant model and an optimizer. The plant model NN learns the information regarding fuel consumption and the ultra-capacitor state of charge as a function of the vehicle speed, requested wheel power, and power split factor between the ICE and the electric motor. An approximation to the optimum value of this split factor is determined by the optimizer NN online (as the vehicle is driven) in real-time, after training the optimizer network offline on sample drive cycles.

NNs have successful applications in scientific, industrial, and financial applications as classifiers, pattern recognizers, and in regression and function approximation. In control applications they have been traditionally employed for model identification when analytical models are not feasible or too complex. Researchers have also proposed frameworks for applying NNs beyond their traditional successful applications. One such application is approximate dynamic programming (ADP) for obtaining approximate solutions to DP problems. In Abou-Nasr and Filev (2013); Balakrishnan *et al.* (2008); Prokhorov and Wunsch (1997); Werbos (1992), example frameworks for obtaining these solutions with NNs are presented. In the following, we will formulate the hybrid powertrain energy management problem as a DP problem. Then, we will obtain an approximate solution to it with NNs.

26.3.1. *ADP with Recurrent Neural Networks*

In deterministic, discrete, dynamic programming problems, an objective function J that is the sum of a utility function values U over a horizon of N sequential events is to be minimized (or maximized).

$$J = \sum_{n=1}^{N} U(\mathbf{x}(n), \mathbf{u}(n)). \tag{1}$$

The sequence of controls (policy) $\mathbf{u}^*(n)$ that minimizes (or maximizes) J in Equation (1) as a function of the system states $\mathbf{x}(n)$is the what we seek as a solution to the dynamic programming problem, and is obtained by the Bellman principle of optimality recursion:

$$J(\mathbf{x}(n)) = \max(U(\mathbf{x}(n), \mathbf{u}(n)) + \langle J(\mathbf{x}(n+1))\rangle). \tag{2}$$

From Equation (2), it follows that in order for the sequence $\mathbf{u}^*(n)$ to be optimal; all the individual controls in each step of the sequence have to be optimal. Another

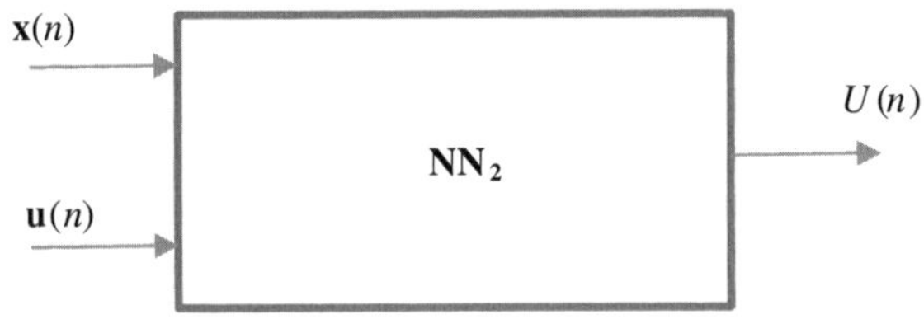

Figure 26.5: Approximating the utility function U with a recurrent NN.

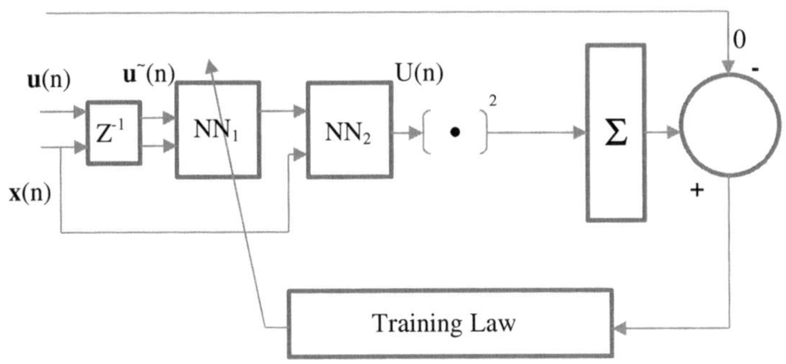

Figure 26.6: Approximate solution to a dynamic programming problem with NNs. The Z^{-1} is a unit time delay.

way of stating this is that we can obtain the sequence $\mathbf{u}^*(n)$ by searching for the individual optimum control for the upcoming step. With a recurrent (dynamic) NN, one may approximate with high fidelity the utility function U. This recurrent NN will have the inputs of $\mathbf{x}(n)$ and $\mathbf{u}(n)$ and an output that represents the utility function $U(n)$ as depicted in Figure 26.5.

With the help of another recurrent NN that is initialized to random weights that we shall refer to as the optimizer network in Figure 26.6, we transform the problem into a supervised learning problem. In this supervised learning problem, we are training the optimizer network to find the sequence $\mathrm{u}(n)$ that produces a sum of the square of the utility function $U(n)$ that is as close as possible to zero, since the minimum of a quadratic function is greater than or equal to zero. This sequence is an approximate solution to the dynamic programming problem. Handling problem constraints can be readily done by including them within the objective function weighted by Lagrange multipliers.

26.3.2. *Hybrid Powertrain Energy Management with Neural Networks*

The problem of hybrid powertrain energy management with an ultra-capacitor can be posed as a dynamic programming problem in which the objective is to minimize the powertrain fuel consumption over a driven trajectory, while maintaining the ultra-capacitor state of charge at a certain target level.

$$J(n) = \sum_{n=1}^{N} F(n) \quad n = 1 \to N,$$

s.t.

$$1/N \sum C(n) = \mathrm{C}_T \quad n = 1 \to N, \tag{3}$$

$F(n)$ is the fuel consumption rate at instance n, $C(n)$ is the state of charge of the ultra-capacitor at instance n, C_T is the ultra-capacitor target average state of charge and N is the duration of the drive cycle.

The fuel consumption rate which is also a function of the vehicle speed $V(n)$, the wheels power $W(n)$, and the split factor $S(n)$. The utility function neural network can be extended from Figure 26.5 to this particular problem as in Figure 26.7 where,

$$\mathbf{u}(n) = S(n), \tag{4}$$

$$\mathbf{x}(n) = (V(n), W(n)), \tag{5}$$

$$U(n) = F(n). \tag{6}$$

In order to implement the constraint on the ultra-capacitor state of charge, we first train another recurrent neural network to represent the functional relationship between the state of charge and the inputs of $S(n)$, $V(n)$, and $W(n)$ as depicted in Figure 26.7. Equation (7) depicts how the output of the state of charge network is

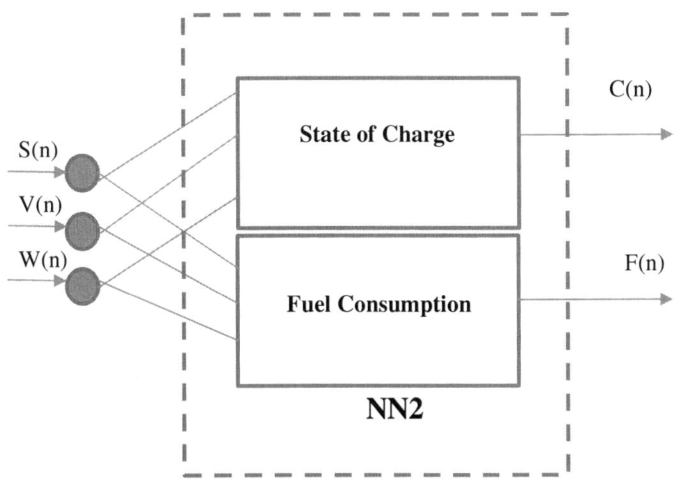

Figure 26.7: The NN_2 neural network for hybrid powertrain energy management.

combined with the output of the fuel network to form the output of the Σ block of Figure 26.6.

$$sum = F^2(n) + \lambda(\bar{C}(n) - C_T)^2, \tag{7}$$

λ is a Lagrange multiplier and $\bar{C}(n)$ is obtained by Equation (8).

$$\bar{C}(n) = \alpha C(n) + (1 - \alpha)\bar{C}(n - 1), \tag{8}$$

where $\bar{C}(n)$ is the exponentially weighted moving average of $C(n)$ over the last $(1/\alpha - 1)$ samples.

26.3.3. *Comparison of the ADP with NN to Dynamic Programming (DP)*

In the following we compare the approximate solution obtained by the trained NN to the solution obtained by DP. For the drive cycle of Figure 26.8, the split factor between the ICE and the ultra-capacitor as prescribed by DP is shown in Figure 26.9 and the one prescribed by the NN is shown in Figure 26.10. The corresponding sate of charge of the ultra-capacitor for the DP solution is shown in Figure 26.11 and the one corresponding to the NN solution is shown in Figure 26.12.

With the prescribed controls (split factor) shown in Figure 26.10, the NN has saved 10% of fuel, and the DP solution has saved 13% of fuel as compared to driving with ICE all the time. The savings could be improved further by improving the NN_2 models of fuel consumption and the ultra-capacitor state of charge. On the other hand, the trained neural optimizer allows us to obtain an approximate solution for a DP problem online on a sample by sample basis, as opposed to the traditional DP solutions which require the knowledge of the whole path before solving the optimization problem, and can be impractical if the problem has more

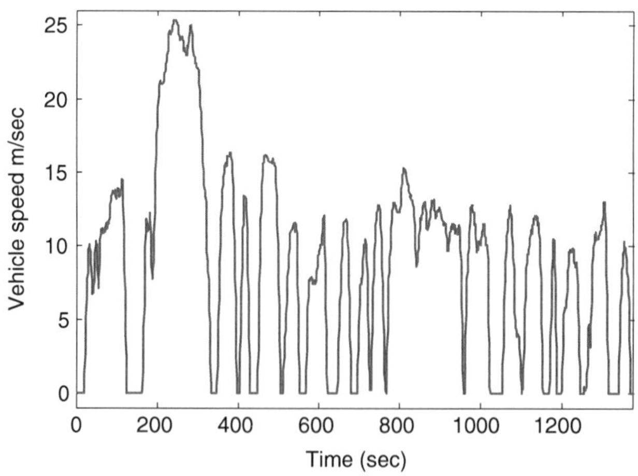

Figure 26.8: Drive cycle employed in the comparison of the DP solution to the NN solution.

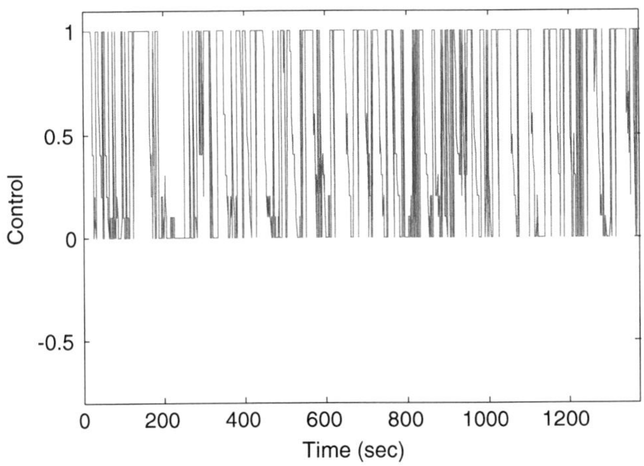

Figure 26.9: Split factor (control) prescribed by DP over the drive cycle of Figure 26.8.

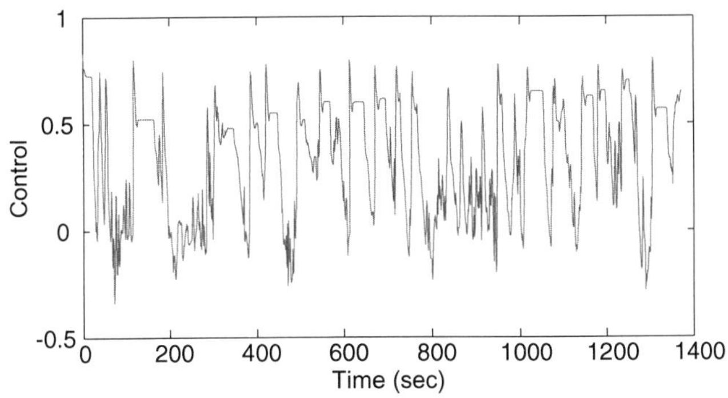

Figure 26.10: Split factor (control) prescribed by NN_1 over the drive cycle of Figure 26.8.

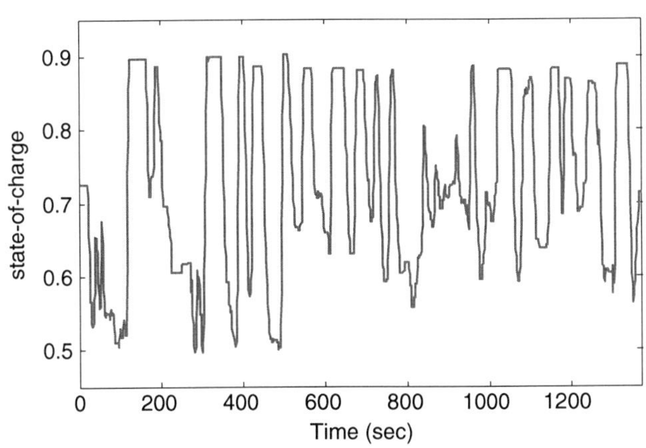

Figure 26.11: State of charge prescribed by DP over the drive cycle of Figure 26.8.

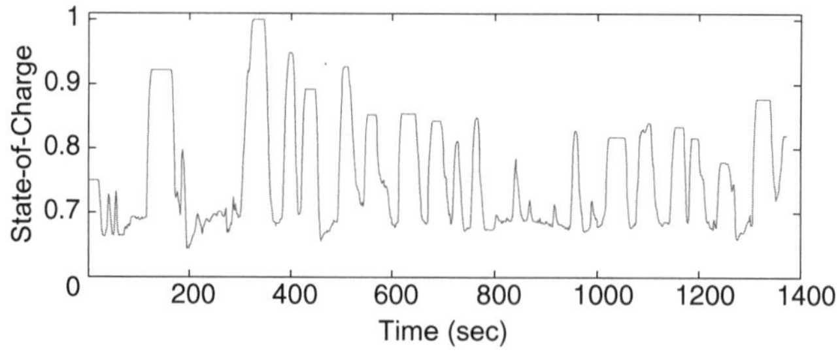

Figure 26.12: State of charge prescribed by NN_1 over the drive cycle of Figure 26.8.

than a few dimensions. Thus, we conclude that the our approximate solution to the hybrid powertrain energy management problem is very competitive with the dynamic programming solution in terms of fuel savings, but also has advantages in terms of applicability in real-world problems that more often than none will have high dimensionality, and seldom afford us the luxury of previewing the path ahead nor the time traditionally required by DP to find a solution.

26.4. A Fuzzy Rule-Based Control System for Minimizing High Voltage Battery Power Limits Violations

In a conventional gasoline internal combustion engine based vehicle, the delivered engine torque or power can be different from commanded engine torque or power. When the perceived acceleration by the driver, as a result of the delivered torque or power, does not match what he or she is expecting, then the driver compensates for it by modifying his or her foot position on the accelerator pedal. In such systems, the control system does not need to estimate engine torque or power for delivering desired vehicle performance and any mismatch in the performance is compensated by the driver accordingly. However, in a power-split HEV, the wheel torque command is calculated from the actual engine torque or power. If the engine power can be estimated perfectly, then the control system can command or deliver the wheel torque such that the battery power limits are not violated. However, if the engine power or torque estimate is not accurate, then, the wheel torque command is incorrect and the high voltage (HV) battery power limits may be violated. Even in this scenario, any mismatch in desired vehicle acceleration can be compensated by the modifying the accelerator pedal, but the battery power violation cannot be addressed by the driver. Thus a control system is used to ensure that battery power limits are not violated, while meeting the driver desired vehicle acceleration or performance (McGee *et al.*, 2007).

The driveline vibrations or disturbances can result in driveline oscillations or vehicle speed oscillations (Farshidianfar *et al.*, 2001). Power-split is more prone to this issue since there is direct mechanical coupling between engine, generator, and motor to the driveline. As there is no mechanism of passive damping of such disturbances in power-split HEV, this requires use of sophisticated active damping control system approach to suppress the driveline oscillations in a power-split hybrid electric vehicle. As shown in Syed *et al.* (2009), such an approach is very effective in damping the driveline oscillations. Since part of such an approach requires the use of high-order narrow band notch filter resulting in real-time filtering of actual engine power, such filtering results in inaccuracy or mismatch of engine power estimate during transient event due to the phase delays introduced by filtering. These inaccuracies in the engine power estimate can ultimately, under extreme conditions result in violation of HV battery power limits.

In this section, an intelligent controller that can differentiate between various driving conditions and minimize HV battery power limit violations is described. This approach for improving the HV battery power controls in power-split HEV uses fuzzy weight-scheduling to determine appropriate weight for the Feedback Weighted Narrow Band Notch Filter used for engine power estimation based on the system's operating conditions. This fuzzy logic-based controller's performance is validated through simulation environment. The fuzzy logic-based controller's behaviors in simulation environment for the driving conditions that severely impacts HV battery power control or results in violations are compared with the performances of the original simple weighted engine power estimation controller (SWEC) Syed *et al.* (2009).

26.4.1. *HV Battery and Power Limitations*

There are three power producing devices in a power-split HEV powertrain — the generator, the motor, and the engine (McGee *et al.*, 2007; Syed *et al.*, 2006). A vehicle system controller (VSC) control system determines the desired engine speed, desired engine torque, and desired wheel torque to meet the driver demand.

For a given driver demand, this system also has two degrees of freedom which provides more choices available in the selection of desired engine speed (due to the e-CVT nature of power-split architecture) and desired engine torque (due to the motor) as compared to conventional vehicles. The existence of extra degree of freedom also imposes additional constraint on power limit that must be met. Power-split HEV architecture consists of the HV battery, the generator, and the motor inverters, and the HV wiring that connects the two. The HV battery acts as a buffer on the HV bus. Any difference in the power consumed by the two electric machines is reflected as power discharged from or power charged into the HV battery. Due to the nature of the HV battery, there are limits on how much power can be put into or taken out of the HV battery (McGee *et al.*, 2007; Syed *et al.*, 2006). Violation of these limits can result in damage of the HV battery and/or reduction of HV battery life, both of which can have serious consequences in terms of vehicle warranty cost. It is important in the power split HEV that the HV battery's discharge and charge power limits violations are minimized (McGee *et al.*, 2007).

26.4.2. *Advanced Wheel Torque Controller and its impact on HV Battery Power Limits Control*

The wheel torque controller main control blocks are described in Syed *et al.* (2009). A sophisticated wheel torque control system was designed in Syed *et al.* (2009) that is capable of actively damping the driveline oscillations in a HEV. This controller for determining desired wheel torque is represented by the following simplified equations (Syed *et al.*, 2009):

$$P_{sys\_min} = P_{elec\_chg\_lim} + P_{eng\_min}, \tag{9}$$

$$P_{sys\_max} = P_{elec\_dch\_lim} + P_{eng\_max}, \tag{10}$$

$$P_{mod} = \begin{cases} P_{sys\_max}, & \text{if } P_{drv} + P_{loss} > P_{sys\_max} \\ P_{drv} + P_{loss}, & \text{if } P_{sys\_min} \le P_{drv} + P_{loss} \le P_{sys\_max} \\ P_{sys\_min}, & \text{if } P_{drv} + P_{loss} < P_{sys\_min}, \end{cases} \tag{11}$$

$$P_{elec\_des} = \begin{cases} P_{elec\_dch\_lim}, & \text{if } f(P_{mod}, P_{eng\_act}) > P_{elec\_dch\_lim} \\ f(P_{mod}, P_{eng\_act}), & \text{if } P_{elec\_chg\_lim} \le f(P_{mod}, P_{eng\_act}) \le P_{elec\_dch\_lim} \\ P_{elec\_chg\_lim}, & \text{if } f(P_{mod}, P_{eng\_act}) < P_{elec\_chg\_lim}, \end{cases} \tag{12}$$

$$T_{wh\_des} = \frac{P_{elec\_des} - P_{loss} + P_{eng\_act}}{\omega_{wheel}}, \tag{13}$$

where ω_{wheel} is the wheel speed, T_{wh_des} is the desired wheel torque, P_{loss} is the system power losses, $P_{elec\_chg\_lim}$ is the electrical charge power limit, $P_{elec\_dch\_lim}$ is the electrical discharge power limit, P_{eng_min} is the minimum engine power, P_{eng_max} is the maximum engine power, and P_{elec_des} is the desired electrical power such that it is bounded between the electrical charge power limit ($P_{elec\_chg\_lim}$) and the electrical discharge power limits ($P_{elec\_dch\_lim}$). Note that $P_{elec\_chg\_lim} \le 0$ and $P_{eng\_min} \le 0$. Similarly, $P_{elec\_dch\_lim} \ge 0$ and $P_{eng\_max} \ge 0$. Also note that $P_{elec\_chg\_lim}$ includes the HV battery charge power limit ($P_{bat\_chg\_lim}$) constraint and $P_{elec\_dch\_lim}$ includes the HV battery discharge power limit ($P_{bat\_dch\_lim}$) constraint. Equation (9) to represents the minimum system power ($P_{sys\_\min}$) which is the sum of electrical charge power limit ($P_{bat\_chg\_lim}$) and the minimum engine power ($P_{eng\_\min}$). Similarly, Equation (10) represents the maximum system power ($P_{sys\_\max}$) which is the sum of electrical discharge power limit ($P_{bat\_dch\_lim}$) and the maximum engine power ($P_{eng\_\max}$). Equation (11) represents the modified driver power requested

(P_{mod}) which is clipped sum of driver power (P_{drv}) and the system power losses (P_{loss}) and is limited between the minimum and maximum system power. Equation (12) represents the desired electrical power (P_{elec_des}) which is the difference between the modified driver power (P_{mod}) and the actual engine power (P_{eng_act}) and is limited between the electrical charge and discharge power limits. Equation (13) represents the desired wheel torque (T_{wh_des}) which is determined from the sum of desired electrical power (P_{elec_des}) and actual engine power (P_{eng_act}) minus the system power losses (P_{loss}) at a given wheel speed (ω_{wheel}).

The actual engine power in this controller, as described in Syed *et al.* (2009), is estimated as follows:

$$P_{eng\_act} = \left(\frac{T'_{wh\_des}}{k_{m2w}}\omega_{mot} + T_{mot}\omega_{mot} + T_{gen}\omega_{gen}\right) \times \left((1-W) + W\frac{b_1 + b_2z^{-1} + b_3z^{-2} + b_4z^{-3} + b_5z^{-4} + b_6z^{-5}}{a_1 + a_2z^{-1} + a_3z^{-2} + a_4z^{-3} + a_5z^{-4} + a_6z^{-5}}\right), \tag{14}$$

$$W = \begin{cases} 1, & \text{if } f(\omega_{mot}) > 1 \\ f(\omega_{mot}), & \text{if } 0 \le f(\omega_{mot}) \le 1 \\ 0, & \text{if } f(\omega_{mot}) < 0, \end{cases} \tag{15}$$

where T_{mot} is the motor torque, T_{gen} is the generator torque, ω_{mot} is the actual motor speed, ω_{gen} is the actual generator speed, k_{m2w} is the gear ratio between motor and the wheel (driveshaft), and W is the notch filtering weight for deciding the contribution of notch (band stop) filtering, with $b_1 \ldots b_6$ and $a_1 \ldots a_6$ representing the coefficients for poles and zeros of the sixth order narrow band notch filter respectively. The actual delivered wheel torque estimate, T'_{wh_des}, is the result of the desired wheel torque (T_{wh_des}) command from VSC to transaxle controller module (TCM) which is responsible for delivering the desired wheel torque. The actual delivered wheel torque estimate is described as $T'_{wh\_des} = z^{-k}T_{wh\_des}$ with k representing the time step delay in z-domain, which is the time that TCM takes to deliver the requested desired wheel torque command from VSC. Equation (15) can be rewritten as follows:

$$P_{eng\_act} = P_{eng\_act\_inst} \times \left((1-W) + W\frac{b_1 + b_2z^{-1} + b_3z^{-2} + b_4z^{-3} + b_5z^{-4} + b_6z^{-5}}{a_1 + a_2z^{-1} + a_3z^{-2} + a_4z^{-3} + a_5z^{-4} + a_6z^{-5}}\right), \tag{16}$$

where

$$P_{eng\_act\_inst} = \left(\frac{T'_{wh\_des}}{k_{m2w}}\omega_{mot} + T_{mot}\omega_{mot} + T_{gen}\omega_{gen}\right) \tag{17}$$

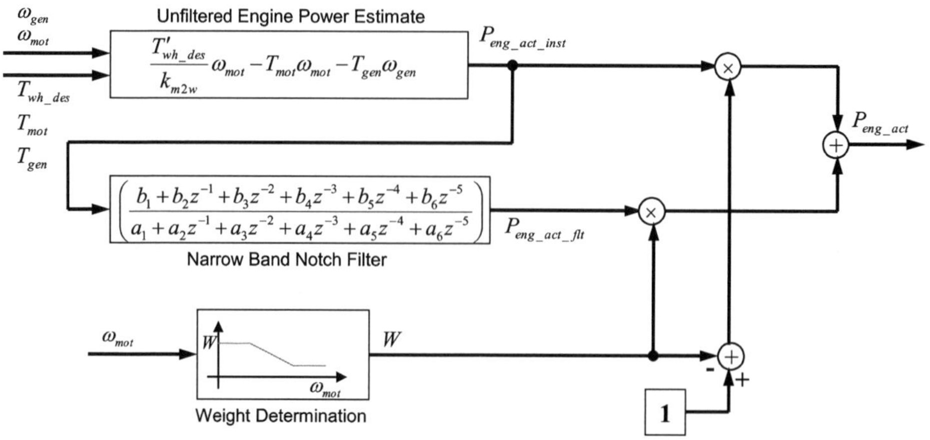

Figure 26.13: Simple weight engine power estimation control system.

Note that $P_{eng\_act\_inst}$ is the unfiltered actual instantaneous engine power.

Figure 26.13 shows the controller for determining the engine power estimate. Note that a Feedback Weighted Narrow Band Notch Filter is used for engine power estimation which determines the final weighted engine power estimate by taking the weighed contribution from the actual engine power estimate and the filtered engine power estimate (Syed *et al.*, 2009). As mentioned in Syed *et al.* (2009), one of the key factor to improve drivability (suppress driveline oscillations) is to achieve decoupling between VSC and TCM. This was achieved by using a narrow band notch (band stop) filter [× 4]. It is clear that if the actual engine power were to change fast or quick, there will be an error between estimated engine power and actual engine power which can result in HV battery power limits violations under certain conditions. This can mathematically be written as follows:

$$P_{eng\_act\_error} = P_{eng\_act\_inst} - P_{eng\_act}. \tag{18}$$

Since, actual HV battery power is the sum of generator power and the motor power, the actual HV battery power can be represented as follows:

$$P_{bat\_act} = T_{mot}\omega_{mot} + T_{gen}\omega_{gen} + P_{loss}. \tag{19}$$

Solving Equations (19) and (17) results in following:

$$P_{bat\_act} = P_{eng\_act\_inst} - \frac{T'_{wh\_des}}{k_{m2w}}\omega_{mot} + P_{loss}. \tag{20}$$

Substituting the value of $P_{eng\_act\_inst}$ from Equation (18) into Equation (20) results in following equation for actual HV battery power:

$$P_{bat\_act} = P_{eng\_act\_error} + P_{eng\_act} - \frac{T'_{wh\_des}}{k_{m2w}}\omega_{mot} + P_{loss}. \tag{21}$$

It is clear from Equation (21) that any non-zero value of $P_{eng\_act\_error}$ will appear in actual HV battery power, hence consequently can result in HV battery power limits violations (More probable when HV battery charge or discharge limits are low).

In order to address this issue, a simple weight determination process in the previously designed advanced wheel torque controller design (Syed *et al.*, 2009) was used to determine the value of the weight, W(between 0 and 1), in Equation (15) to minimize the inaccuracies in actual engine power estimation error ($P_{eng\_act\_error}$), and was calibrated and tuned as a function of vehicle speed (motor speed) to minimize the phase delays or essentially the inaccuracies in $P_{eng\_act\_error}$ thereby minimizing the effect on transient actual HV battery power (Note that if there are no inaccuracies in $P_{eng\_act\_error}$, then $P_{eng\_act\_error}$ will be zero). However, as we will demonstrate later that the use of such simple weighted engine power estimation to improve transient HV battery power control is not the most efficient approach for minimizing HV battery power limits violations.

Use of simple weighted engine power estimation could result in violations of HV battery power limits. The amplitude of these violations are critical as they can degrade HV battery and impact HV battery life (McGee *et al.*, 2007). Since fuzzy-control systems do not require a mathematical model of the system to be controlled, and allow for the development of a knowledge based nonlinear controller, a desirable candidate for improving engine power estimation or minimizing HV battery power limits violations is to use fuzzy-logic based nonlinear control system.

26.4.3. *Fuzzy Weight Scheduling Engine Power Estimation for the Power-Split HEV — Controller Design*

As mentioned in Section 26.4.2, to improve drivability (suppress driveline oscillations) decoupling between VSC and TCM is necessary. This was achieved by using a narrow band notch (band stop) filter which results in phase delays and hence inaccuracies in the engine power estimation, especially during transient conditions. Since all driving conditions do not result in impacting drivability due to driveline oscillations, an intelligent controller can be designed which can detect such scenarios and conditions, and schedule appropriate weights for feedback weighted narrow band notch filter used for the estimation of engine power. This intelligent fuzzy weight-scheduling engine power estimation controller is shown in Figure 26.14.

The fuzzy weight-scheduling engine power estimation controller block in Figure 26.14 improves engine power estimation and hence results in improved HV battery power limits control. In other words, this controller is capable of minimizing HV battery power limits violations. The fuzzy weight-scheduling controller improves HV battery power limits management behavior in a power-split HEV by utilizing the human control knowledge and experience to intuitively

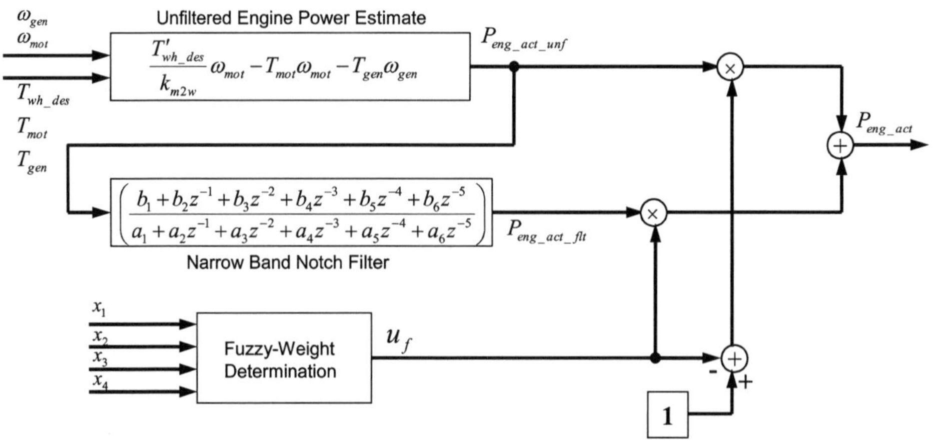

Figure 26.14: Fuzzy weight-scheduling engine power estimation control system.

construct an intelligent controller so that the resulting controller will emulate the desired control behavior to a certain extent (Ying, 2000). A multiple input, single output (MISO) Mamdani fuzzy weight-scheduling controller (Ying, 2000) is utilized. The formulation of the proposed fuzzy weight-scheduling controller can be described as follows:

$$P_{eng\_act} = \left(\frac{T'_{wh\_des}}{k_{m2w}}\omega_{mot} + T_{mot}\omega_{mot} + T_{gen}\omega_{gen}\right) \times \left((1-u_f) + u_f\frac{b_1+b_2z^{-1}+b_3z^{-2}+b_4z^{-3}+b_5z^{-4}+b_6z^{-5}}{a_1+a_2z^{-1}+a_3z^{-2}+a_4z^{-3}+a_5z^{-4}+a_6z^{-5}}\right), \tag{22}$$

where u_f is the dynamically adjusted fuzzy scheduled weight output of the MISO fuzzy logic weight-scheduler controller.

Equation (22) can be re-written as follows:

$$P_{eng\_act} = (1-u_f)\, P_{eng\_act\_inst} \times u_f P_{eng\_act\_flt}, \tag{23}$$

where

$$P_{eng\_act\_inst} = \left(\frac{T'_{wh\_des}}{k_{m2w}}\omega_{mot} + T_{mot}\omega_{mot} + T_{gen}\omega_{gen}\right), \tag{24}$$

$$P_{eng\_act\_flt} = \left(\frac{T'_{wh\_des}}{k_{m2w}}\omega_{mot} + T_{mot}\omega_{mot} + T_{gen}\omega_{gen}\right) \times \frac{b_1+b_2z^{-1}+b_3z^{-2}+b_4z^{-3}+b_5z^{-4}+b_6z^{-5}}{a_1+a_2z^{-1}+a_3z^{-2}+a_4z^{-3}+a_5z^{-4}+a_6z^{-5}}, \tag{25}$$

where $P_{eng\_act\_inst}$ is the pre-filtered (or unfiltered) engine power estimate and $P_{eng\_act\_flt}$ is the filtered engine power estimate. Comparing Equations (14) and (22) it can be seen that fuzzy weight scheduling engine power estimation controller replaces the term W with the fuzzy scheduled weight output u_f.

At this point, it is important to emphasize that if $u_f = W$ under all operating conditions, then the fuzzy weight-scheduling engine power estimation controller reduces to SWEC.

To effectively design a fuzzy-logic based weight-scheduler, input variables, output variables, and input and output fuzzy sets need to be defined. Firstly, since the driver demand wheel torque (T_{mod}) can affect drivability, it was used as a predictive input to determine if filtering of the actual engine power is needed to achieve improved drivability. On the other hand, to ensure that HV battery power is with-in its limits effectively, the magnitude of the error between the pre-filtered engine power estimate and the final engine power estimate was selected as one of the other inputs to the fuzzy logic weight-scheduler. Similarly, HV battery power limits provide a buffer to amount of inaccuracy in engine power estimate that can be tolerated, therefore the difference between the HV battery discharge power limit ($P_{bat\_dch\_lim}$) and desired electrical power (P_{elec_des}) was used as one of the other inputs. Finally, the motor speed (or vehicle speed) was used as the final input, because it can be used as the predictor of expected drivability issue at various vehicle or motor speeds. The input variables for the controller can be written as follows:

$$x_1(n) = T_{\mathrm{mod}}(n) = \frac{P_{\mathrm{mod}}(n)}{k_{m2w}\omega_{mot}(n)}, \tag{26}$$

$$x_2(n) = \left|P_{eng\_act\_unf}(n) - P_{eng\_act}(n)\right|, \tag{27}$$

$$x_3(n) = P_{bat\_dch\_lim}(n) - P_{elec\_des}(n), \tag{28}$$

$$x_4(n) = \omega_{mot}(n). \tag{29}$$

The input fuzzy sets or membership functions for $x_1(n)$, $x_2(n)$, $x_3(n)$, and $x_4(n)$ are chosen as trapezoidal and triangular functions. The input fuzzy sets or membership functions for $x_1(n)$, $x_3(n)$, and $x_4(n)$ are chosen to be low and high trapezoidal functions where b_{1L}, b_{3L}, b_{4L} representing the low value of the trapezoidal function for the three input membership functions and b_{1H}, b_{3H}, b_{4H} representing the high value of the trapezoidal functions for the three input membership functions. The input fuzzy sets or membership functions for $x_2(n)$ are chosen to be low, medium, and high trapezoidal/triangular functions where, b_{2L} and b_{2H} represents the low and high value of the trapezoidal functions respectively for the $x_2(n)$ input membership function, and b_{2M}, representing the medium value of the triangular functions for the $x_2(n)$ input membership function. The output fuzzy sets are of singleton type for the fuzzy scheduled weight representing maximum (max or h_{MX}), high (h_H), medium (med or h_{ME}), low (h_L), minimum (min or h_{MN}), and zero (h_Z) values.

The fuzzy rules are laid out in a manner such that they can distinguish between various HEV powertrain behaviors and makes decision of the current and future states of the powertrain. This way these fuzzy rules can anticipate and optimize to cover conditions where HV battery power violations can be improved while maintaining improved drivability of the vehicle. A sample description of these fuzzy rules is shown in Table 26.1.

Among these fuzzy rules, some of the rules are intended to cover both steady state and transient conditions under various driving conditions, such as scenarios where HV battery limits or driver demand torque or vehicle speed (motor speed) conditions are important for acceptable drivability and reduced HV battery power limits violations. For example, Rules 1, where $x_1(n)$ is either low or high and $x_2(n)$, $x_3(n)$, and $x_4(n)$ are all low, depict a steady state, or close to a steady state predictive condition where, under current state, the error from filtering effect of the engine power estimate is low but the vehicle speed and the difference between the HV battery discharge power limit and the desired electrical power are also low. Under such conditions, if the driver were to perform a transient event the drivability will be severely affected due to driveline oscillations unless a very high or max (h_{MX}) fuzzy-scheduled weight is used. Similarly, rules where $x_1(n)$ is low, $x_2(n)$ is high, $x_3(n)$ is either low or high, and $x_4(n)$ is high describes conditions, where due to low

Table 26.1: Some fuzzy rules for the fuzzy weight-scheduler.

Rule No.	If $x_1(n)$ is	if $x_2(n)$ is	if $x_3(n)$ is	if $x_4(n)$ is	Then $u_f(n)$ is	Example Explanation
1	low	low	low	low	Max	Steady state condition where drivability can be improved and there is no concern of HV battery power control.
2	low	low	low	high	Med	Steady state condition with less chance of drivability issues due to higher vehicle speed and so HV battery power control can be improved.
⋮	⋮	⋮	⋮	⋮	⋮	⋮
24	high	high	high	high	Min	Fast transient condition where HV battery power controls can be improved, as wheel torque is high but HV battery power limits are also available.

driver demand torque and high vehicle speeds, the impact of zero fuzzy-scheduled weight (h_{MX}) on drivability is negligible but since it is a transient event, using such a lower fuzzy-scheduled weight will significantly reduce HV battery power limits violation or in other words, it will improve the transient HV battery power control. In summary, these rules provide a method to schedule weights for engine power estimation which can significantly improve HV battery power control (or reduce HV battery power limits violations) without compromising the vehicle's drivability.

If Ω represents the total number of fuzzy rules ($\Omega = 24$ in our case) and $\mu_j(x_i, \tilde{\mathbf{A}}_{i,j})$ represents the combined membership value from the antecedent of the jth rule, the output, $u_f(n)$, of the fuzzy weight scheduler can be written as follows (Ying, 2000) when the centroid defuzzifier is employed.

$$u_f(n) = \frac{\sum_{j=1}^{\Omega} \mu_j(x_1, \tilde{\mathbf{A}}_{1,j})\mu_j(x_2, \tilde{\mathbf{A}}_{2,j})\mu_j(x_3, \tilde{\mathbf{A}}_{3,j})\mu_j(x_4, \tilde{\mathbf{A}}_{4,j})\tilde{h}_j}{\sum_{j=1}^{\Omega} \mu_j(x_1, \tilde{\mathbf{A}}_{1,j})\mu_j(x_2, \tilde{\mathbf{A}}_{2,j})\mu_j(x_3, \tilde{\mathbf{A}}_{3,j})\mu_j(x_4, \tilde{\mathbf{A}}_{4,j})}, \tag{30}$$

where x_i represents all the inputs ($i = 1 \dots 4$) and $\tilde{\mathbf{A}}_{i,j}$ is a vector involving all the input fuzzy sets and $\tilde{h}_j$ represents the output fuzzy set for the jth rule.

Using Equation (23), the complete fuzzy controller system for the engine power estimation can be described by the following equation:

$$\begin{aligned} P_{eng\_act} = {}& \left(1 - \frac{\sum_{j=1}^{\Omega} \mu_j(x_1, \tilde{\mathbf{A}}_{1,j})\mu_j(x_2, \tilde{\mathbf{A}}_{2,j})\mu_j(x_3, \tilde{\mathbf{A}}_{3,j})\mu_j(x_4, \tilde{\mathbf{A}}_{4,j})\tilde{h}_j}{\sum_{j=1}^{\Omega} \mu_j(x_1, \tilde{\mathbf{A}}_{1,j})\mu_j(x_2, \tilde{\mathbf{A}}_{2,j})\mu_j(x_3, \tilde{\mathbf{A}}_{3,j})\mu_j(x_4, \tilde{\mathbf{A}}_{4,j})}\right) P_{eng\_act\_inst} \\ & \times \left(\frac{\sum_{j=1}^{\Omega} \mu_j(x_1, \tilde{\mathbf{A}}_{1,j})\mu_j(x_2, \tilde{\mathbf{A}}_{2,j})\mu_j(x_3, \tilde{\mathbf{A}}_{3,j})\tilde{h}\mu_j(x_4, \tilde{\mathbf{A}}_{4,j})\tilde{h}_j}{\sum_{j=1}^{\Omega} \mu_j(x_1, \tilde{\mathbf{A}}_{1,j})\mu_j(x_2, \tilde{\mathbf{A}}_{2,j})\mu_j(x_3, \tilde{\mathbf{A}}_{3,j})\mu_j(x_4, \tilde{\mathbf{A}}_{4,j})}\right) P_{eng\_act\_flt}. \end{aligned} \tag{31}$$

26.4.4. *Evaluation of Fuzzy Control System*

To evaluate the improvements from the fuzzy weight-scheduling engine power estimation controller, simulation environment to study the SWEC and fuzzy weight-scheduling engine power estimation controller (FWEC) is presented. After the description of the simulation environment, simulation results using the simple weighted and fuzzy weight-scheduling engine power estimation controller is presented. Finally experimental results using a test vehicle at test track is used to compare the simple weighted engine power estimation controller and fuzzy weight-scheduling engine power estimation controller. A validated simulation environment (Syed *et al.*, 2006) consisting of the vehicle model for a power-split HEV together with the subsystem models of the various hybrid specific systems was used for the testing and evaluation of this fuzzy weight-scheduling engine power estimation control system. In order to study the performance of the controllers, a custom test that could emphasize on the controller's HV battery power limits violations was devised. In this test, the vehicle is tested at the speeds of 10 mi/hour, 20 mi/hour, 30 mi/hour, 40 mi/hour, 50 mi/hour, and 60 mi/hour where the HV battery power limits are set to 0 kW, and the driver demand, driver accelerator pedal position, is changed from 0% to 100% and then from 100% back to 0% at a particular vehicle speed. This results in large changes in the desired engine power and hence will also result in large changes in the actual engine power. Such a test emphasizes on the change of actual engine power to monitor the HV battery power limits violations.

To study the improvements of the fuzzy weight-scheduling engine power estimation controller, it is compared to the performance of simple weighted engine power estimation controller. A validated simulation environment described in Syed *et al.* (2006) is used. To test the effectiveness of the fuzzy weight-scheduling engine power estimation controller versus the simple weighted engine power estimation controller, simulations using the test conditions described earlier were performed using these two controllers.

Figure 26.15 shows the HV battery power limits violations using the simple weighted engine power estimation controller. Note that in this test the HV battery power limits were set to zero (0 kW) which is a very extreme case and then the driver demand changed dramatically between its minimum and maximum by changing the driver accelerator pedal position from 0% to 100% and then back from 100% to 0% at a particular vehicle speed. These maneuvers results in large changes in the desired engine power and so also result in large changes in actual engine power. Plot [A] in Figure 26.15, shows the results of HV battery power violation during this maneuver at 10 mi/hour. Similarly other plots in Figure 26.16 shows the HV battery power violations at speeds of 20 mi/hour, 30 mi/hour, 40 mi/hour, 50 mi/hour, and 60 mi/hour. As a result of actual engine power change, the HV battery power limits violations ranged from about −7 kW to 7 kW or the average range of power limit violations (average of the magnitude of HV battery discharge power limit violation and HV battery charge power limit violation) was around 7 kW under worst cases.

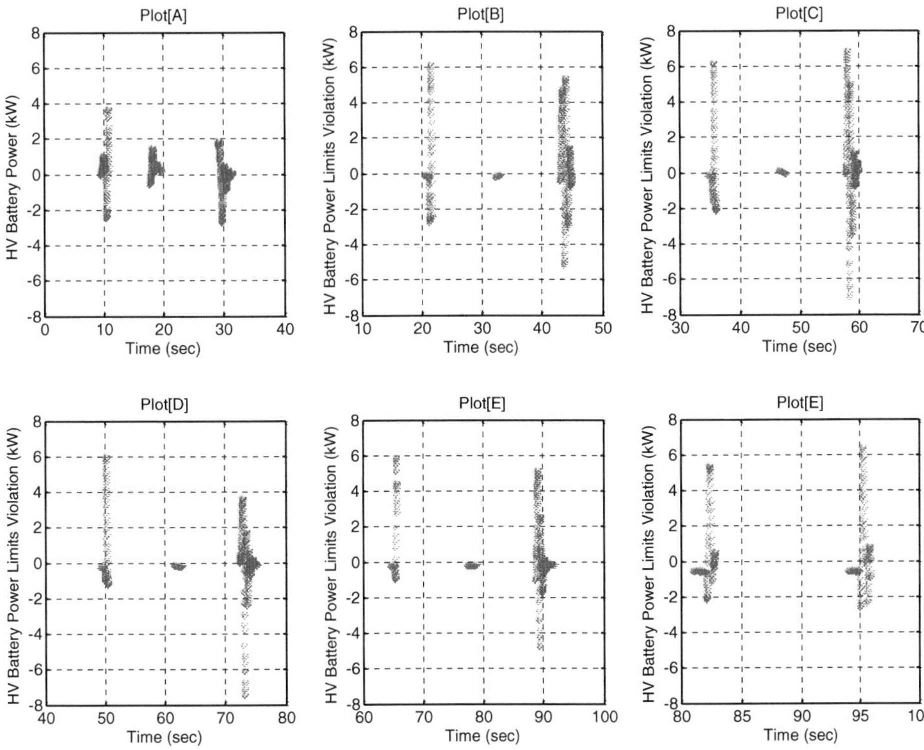

Figure 26.15: Simulation results for HV battery power limits violation using the simple weighted engine power estimation control system during the custom test. Plot[A] shows the results at vehicle speeds of around 10 mi/hr, plot[B] shows the results at vehicle speeds of around 20 mi/hr, plot[C] shows the results at vehicle speeds of around 30 mi/hr, plot[D] shows the results at vehicle speeds of around 40 mi/hr, plot[E] shows the results at vehicle speeds of around 50 mi/hr and plot[F] shows the results at vehicle speeds of around 60 mi/hr.

It is important to emphasize that such HV power limits violations can reduce or degrade HV battery life overtime.

Next the simulations are performed for the same custom test using the fuzzy weight schedule engine power estimation control system. Figure 26.16 shows the HV battery power limits violations. It can be seen from these results that the HV battery power limits violations are reduced and they ranged on from about −5 kW to 5 kW or the average range of power limit violations was around 5 kW under worst cases. Such an improvement or reduction in HV power limits violations can improve HV battery life overtime. These simulation results are described in Table 26.2.

It can be seen from Table 26.2 that using the fuzzy weight-scheduling engine power estimation controller, improvements or reduction in HV battery power limits violations are seen at all vehicle speeds from 10 mi/hr to 60 mi/hr and the overall average power limit violations reductions ranged from 17 to 55%. Such huge

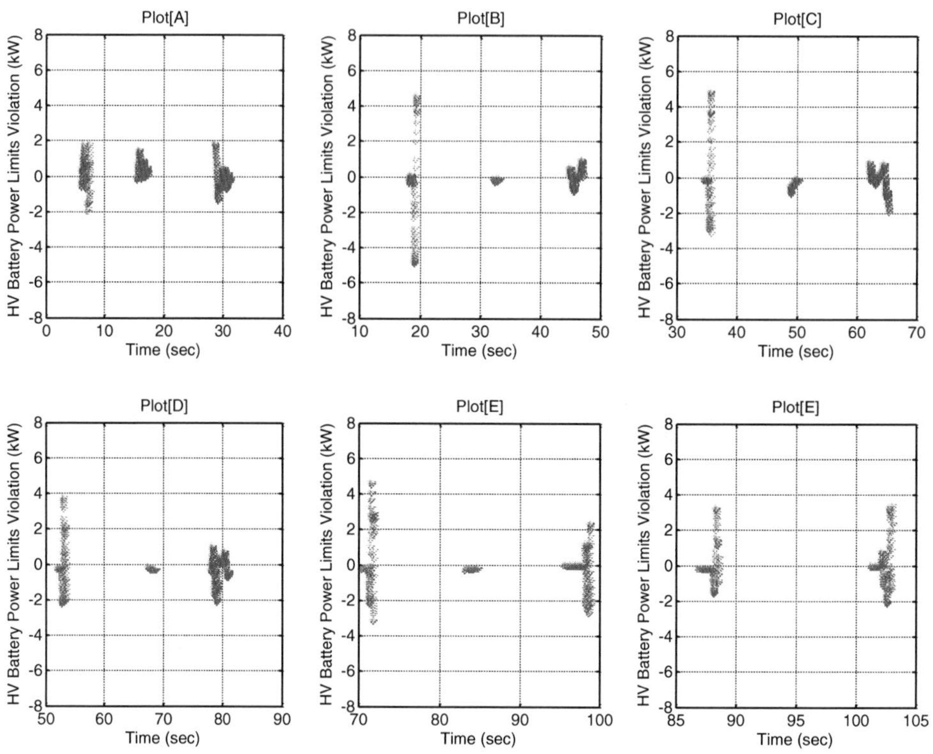

Figure 26.16: Simulation results for HV battery power limits violation using the fuzzy weight-scheduled engine power estimation control system during the custom test. Plot[A] shows the results at vehicle speeds of around 10 mi/hr, plot[B] shows the results at vehicle speeds of around 20 mi/hr, plot[C] shows the results at vehicle speeds of around 30 mi/hr, plot[D] shows the results at vehicle speeds of around 40 mi/hr, plot[E] shows the results at vehicle speeds of around 50 mi/hr and plot[F] shows the results at vehicle speeds of around 60 mi/hr.

improvement can provide ability to improving HV battery life and decreasing HV battery damages or degradations.

26.5. Hybrid Models for Contextual Learning of Driver's Preferences

The concept of a "driver-aware" vehicle determines a type of vehicle that is capable to estimate and learn driver's preferences. This presumes well-developed algorithms for perception and learning driver's actions and decision. The learning mechanism is driver specific and is able to identify and summarize the driver preferred actions in different situations and states. The final goal is to incrementally develop and update families of models that characterize the driver under diverse set of conditions. The models are used by the vehicle systems to anticipate driver's actions and to proactively respond/advise the driver for the most appropriate actions

Table 26.2: Simulation test results comparison for HV battery power limits (charge and discharge limit) violations using SWEC versus FWEC.

Vehicle Speed (mi/hr)	HV battery charge limit violation using SWEC (kW)	HV battery discharge limit violation using SWEC (kW)	HV battery power limit average violation range using SWEC (kW)	HV battery charge limit violation using FWEC (kW)	HV battery discharge limit violation using FWEC (kW)	HV battery power limit average violation using FWEC (kW)	HV battery power limit violation improvement using FWEC (%)
10	−2.65	3.78	3.22	−1.92	1.89	1.91	40.68
20	−5.14	6.26	5.70	−4.86	4.61	4.74	16.84
30	−6.98	6.93	6.96	−3.10	4.92	4.01	42.39
40	−7.41	6.10	6.76	−2.20	3.83	3.02	55.33
50	−4.72	5.97	5.35	−3.15	4.71	3.93	26.54
60	−2.56	6.48	4.52	−2.10	3.50	2.80	38.05

under specific circumstances. Examples include models for contextual learning preferred destinations, most likely music selection, level of acceptance of advisory information, etc.

One of the main advantages of introducing models for contextual learning is the opportunity for better utilization of the flexibility of the current vehicle systems. The goal is to satisfy not only the hypothetical nominal driver but to meet the requirements of as many as possible individual members of the customer group that is targeted by a specific vehicle model. An obvious area of implementation of this concept is the vehicle infotainment system. A good understanding of the driver preferred destinations and music/news/route selections under different conditions can introduce a level of intelligence that has a significant impact on the driver, while minimally affecting the critical vehicle attributes related to performance, comfort, and safety. One can expect that the final goal will be achieving personalized vehicle performance, i.e., performance that depends on the specific driver's choice. In a broad sense this may lead to the creation of customizable and reconfigurable vehicles — an automotive equivalent of the growing trend of customization of information, news, and entertainment.

26.5.1. *Switching Contextual Model of Most Frequent Destinations*

One specific contextual model for estimating the most likely destinations was introduced in Filev *et al.* (2011). Alternative techniques for predicting most frequent routes and destinations have been proposed in Ashbrook and Starner (2003); Krumm and Horvitz (2012); Krumm *et al.* (2013). The contextual model assumes a finite set of M frequent destinations and provides an estimate for the next most likely driving destination. In this section we extend and generalize this model.

If we consider the selection of the next destination as a random process in which the decision for the next destination depends only on the current destination then we can model the mechanism of selecting new destinations as a Markov process with states corresponding to the set of destinations. For a finite set of destinations $S = \{\bar{x}_j, j = 1, \ldots, M\}$ we model the decision-making process as a finite state Markov chain with transition probabilities (Figure 26.17)

$$\pi_{ij} = P\left(x^+ = \bar{x}_j | x = \bar{x}_i\right), \tag{32}$$

defining an (MXM) size transition probability matrix Π:

$$\Pi = \left\{\pi_{ij}, i, j = 1, \ldots, M\right\}. \tag{33}$$

Consequently, the rows of the transition probability matrix are positive and sum to one, i.e.,:

$$\sum_{j=1}^{M} \pi_{ij} = 1, \quad i = 1, \ldots, M; \;\; \pi_{ij} \geq 0. \tag{34}$$

For a given $x = \bar{x}_i$ the next state inferred by the Markov chain is the one that maximizes the probability distribution that is conditioned by the state $\bar{x}_i$:

$$x^+ = \bar{x}_j, \quad \text{if } x = \bar{x}_i, \;\; j \in \arg\max_t \pi_{it}. \tag{35}$$

In order to include the option of different decision strategies under alternative contextual conditions, e.g., time of the day, day of the week, the mood, and emotional state of the driver, the traffic, road, and weather conditions, etc., we introduced the Switching Contextual Model of Most Frequent Destinations (Filev *et al.*, 2011).

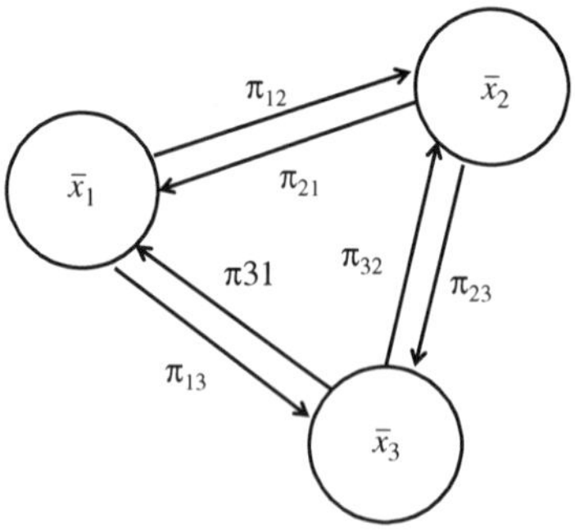

Figure 26.17: Markov chain model of most frequent destination (no context).

Due to the hybrid nature of this model — finite state Markov Model combined with continuous inputs — we partition the inputs into intervals. Assuming that the two inputs — *Time of the Day* and *Day of the Week* denoted by U_1, U_2 — are defined on universes u_1 and u_2 that are partitioned into S_1 and S_2 countable set of disjunct intervals I_p, $p = \{1, S_1\}$, and I_q, $q = \{1, S_2\}$ we can decompose the input space into a countable set of granules. The input granules are defined in the Cartesian product space $(u_1 \times u_2)$. The total number of granules is $S = S_1 S_2$. Each granule $\bar{u}_s = I_p \times I_q$, $\mathrm{s} = \{1, S\}$, is formed by the Cartesian products of the intervals I_p, $p = \{1, S_1\}$, and I_q, $q = \{1, S_2\}$; the input granule $\bar{u}_s$ expresses a combination of conditions belonging to a Cartesian product of intervals $I_p \times I_q$.

Using the granular decomposition of the input space we can define Contextual Model of Most Frequent Destination as a set of conditional probabilities:

$$\pi_{ij}^{(s)} = P\big(x^+ = \bar{x}_j \mid x = \bar{x}_i, U = \bar{u}_s\big), \quad i, j = \{1, m\}, \ s = \{1, S\}. \tag{36}$$

The model (36) represents probabilities of transitioning from the current destination $\bar{x}_i$ to a new destination $\bar{x}_j$ under the condition that the pair of random inputs $U = (U_1, U_2)$ take values from the input granule $\bar{u}_s = I_p \times I_q$, $\mathrm{s} = \{1, S\}$.

It is easy to see that for all input pairs $U = (U_1, U_2)$ belonging to the same input granule, i.e., $U \in \bar{u}_s$, the contextual model is essentially identical to the Markov model $\Pi^{(s)}$ expressing the transitions between the Markov states under the condition defined by the granule $\bar{u}_s$. Thus, the contextual model can be viewed as composed by s switching Markov models $\Pi^{(s)}$ each one associated with one of the s granules of input conditions. This contextual model is equivalent to a collection of s Boolean logic rules with disjunct predicates:

$$\text{If } U \in \bar{u}_s \text{ } \textit{Then } \pi_{ij}^{(s)} = P\big(x^+ = \bar{x}_j | x = \bar{x}_i\big), \quad i, j = \{1, m\}, \ \mathrm{s} = \{1, S\}. \tag{37}$$

The role of the granular encoding of the input space is to determine a switching mechanism linking the current pair of conditions $U = (U_1, U_2)$ to the corresponding transition probability matrix $\Pi^{(s)}$, $\mathrm{s} = \{1, S\}$. The specific transition probability matrix $\Pi^{(s)}$ defines the transitions between the states for that given pair of conditions. For a given pair of conditions $U = (U_1, U_2)$ and current state $\bar{x}_i$ the next state $\bar{x}_j$ predicted based conditional probability (36) can be expressed as follows:

$$\begin{gathered} j = arg\ max_k\big(\Pi_{ik}^{(s)}\big), \quad \text{where } U_1 \in I_p \text{ and } U_2 \in I_q \text{ and} \\ \mathrm{s} = \mathrm{ind}\ \big[\{(p, q)\} \equiv \{1, S_1\} \times \{1, S_2\}\big]. \end{gathered}$$

Similarly, for a given pair of conditions $U = (U_1, U_2)$, the elements π_{ij} of the corresponding transition probability matrix $\Pi^{(s)}$ are learned according to the algorithm for real time learning of Markov Models (Filev and Kolmanovsky, 2010):

$$\pi_{ij}^{(s)}(k) = \frac{F_{ij}^{(s)}(k)}{F_{oi}^{(s)}(k)} = \frac{F_{ij}^{(s)}(k-1) + \alpha\big(f_{ij}(k) - F_{ij}^{(s)}(k-1)\big)}{F_{oi}^{(s)}(k-1) + \alpha\big(f_i(k) - F_{oi}^{(s)}(k-1)\big)}, \tag{38}$$

where

$$F_{ij}^{(s)}(k) = F_{ij}^{(s)}(k-1) + \alpha(f_{ij}(k) - F_{ij}^{(s)}(k-1)), \tag{39}$$

$$F_{oi}^{(s)}(k) = F_{oi}^{(s)}(k-1) + \alpha(f_i(k) - F_{oi}^{(s)}(k-1)) \tag{40}$$

and

(i) $F_{ij}^{(s)}$ is the moving average of all transition events $f_{ij}(k)$ from state $\bar{x}_i$ to state $\bar{x}_j$ (a transition event takes the values 1 or 0 if the transition occurs or not):

i.e.,:

$$f_{ij}(k) = \begin{cases} 1 & \text{if } x^+ = \bar{x}_j,\ x = \bar{x}_i \\ 0 & \text{otherwise} \end{cases} \tag{41}$$

(ii) $F_{oi}^{(s)}$ is the mean the moving average of the transition events that start from state i:

$$f_i(k) = \begin{cases} 1 & \text{if } x = \bar{x}_i \\ 0 & \text{otherwise} \end{cases}. \tag{42}$$

The forgetting factor α assigns weight to the recent observed transition, exponentially distributes the rest of the weighs, and defines the memory depth (the length of the moving window) of the weighted averaging aggregating operator. It can be shown that the memory depth K_α is approximately reciprocal to the forgetting factor, i.e., $K_\alpha = 1/\alpha$. Therefore, by properly choosing the parameter α we can calculate the transition probabilities within a specified moving window K_α addressing the possible nonstationarity of the data and updating the transition probabilities online. That is recursively calculated over the transition events belonging to the soft interval $\{k - K_\alpha + 1, k]$ where symbol $\{$indicates a soft lower interval limit which includes values with lower indexes than $(k - K_\alpha)$ that have relatively low contribution.

The Switching Contextual Model assumes interval partitioning of the inputs. Its switching mechanism activates only one of the Markov models and cannot account for the cases when the conditions are very similar, e.g., 2:55 pm and 3:01 pm on weekend. It also cannot interpret efficiently the uncertainties in defining the context. In the following, we provide a generalization of the results from the previous section by introducing a fuzzy partitioning of the input variables.

26.5.2. *Hybrid Contextual Model*

We assume multiple factors determining the context, i.e., r inputs $U_1, U_2, \ldots, U_r$ defined over the universes $u_1, u_2, \ldots, u_r$ that are partitioned into $S_1, S_2, \ldots, S_r$ fuzzy subsets $E_{11}, E_{12} \ldots, E_{1s_1}; \ldots; E_{r1}, E_{r2} \ldots, E_{rs_r}$. This fuzzy partitioning decomposes the Cartesian input space $(u_1 \times u_2 \times \cdots \times u_r)$ input space into a countable set of $S = \prod_{i=1}^{r} S_i$ granules $\bar{u}_s = E_{1s} \times E_{2s} \times \cdots \times E_{rs}$. Each input granule $\bar{u}_s$ expresses a combination of conditions belonging to the Cartesian product of the fuzzy subsets $E_{1s} \times E_{2s} \times \cdots \times E_{rs}$.

Using the granular decomposition of the input space we can define the Hybrid Contextual Model as a family of rules with fuzzy predicates and a set of Markov models as consequents. The antecedents of the rules provide a possibilistic description of the context while the consequents represent the corresponding models of transitional probabilities that are associated with these conditions.

$$\begin{aligned} &\mathit{IF}\ U_1\ \mathit{is}\ E_{1s}\ \mathit{AND}\ U_2\ \mathit{is}\ E_{2s}\ \mathit{AND} \ldots \mathit{AND}\ U_r\ \mathit{is}\ E_{rs} \\ &\qquad\qquad \mathit{THEN}\ \Pi^{(s)},\ s = [1, 2, \ldots, S]. \end{aligned} \tag{43}$$

This set of rules resembles the well-known Takagi–Sugeno model with the Markov models replacing the conventional linear equation type consequents. Following the theory of approximate reasoning, the Hybrid Contextual Model is a Markov model that is obtained by the weighted average of the individual models $\Pi^{(s)}$:

$$\Pi = \sum_{s=1}^{S} w_s \Pi^{(s)}, \tag{44}$$

with weights

$$w_s = \frac{\tau_s}{\sum_{j=1}^{S} \tau_j}, \quad s = [1, 2, \ldots, S], \tag{45}$$

that are determined by the degrees of matching the inputs to the antecedents of the rules, i.e., the degrees of firing the rules τ_s:

$$\tau_s = \prod_{j=1}^{r} E_{js}(U_j), \quad s = [1, 2, \ldots, S].$$

where by $E_{js}(U_j)$ is denoted the membership grade of the U_jth input with respect to the E_{js}th fuzzy subset (Yager and Filev, 1994).

Proposition. If each of the granules $\bar{u}_s = E_{1s} \times E_{2s} \times \cdots \times E_{rs}$ is associated with a Markov model then the Hybrid Contextual Model is also a Markov model.

Proof: Assuming the transition probability matrices $\Pi^{(s)}, s = [1, 2, \ldots, S]$ satisfy condition (3), then for each raw of the transition probability matrix Π of Hybrid Contextual Model Equation (44) we have:

$$\sum_{j=1}^{M} \pi_{ij} = \sum_{s=1}^{S} \sum_{j=1}^{M} w_s \pi_{ij}^{(s)} = 1, \quad i = 1, \ldots, M. \tag{46}$$

We have used that the weights w_s are positive and sum to one as implied by (16).

According to Equation (45), the Hybrid Contextual Model interpolates and provides smooth transition between the Markov models that are associated with individual contexts. The switching contextual model can be considered a special case of it for the cases when the fuzzy subsets degenerate into disjunct intervals.

Figure 26.18 shows an example of a collection of 56 Markov models of 10 frequent stop locations associated with a fuzzy partitioning of the two conditions — Time of the Day and Day of the Week into 8, respectively 7 fuzzy subsets. In reality not all of the 56 Markov models include the complete set of states since only some of the stop locations are visited under certain conditions. These active states along with

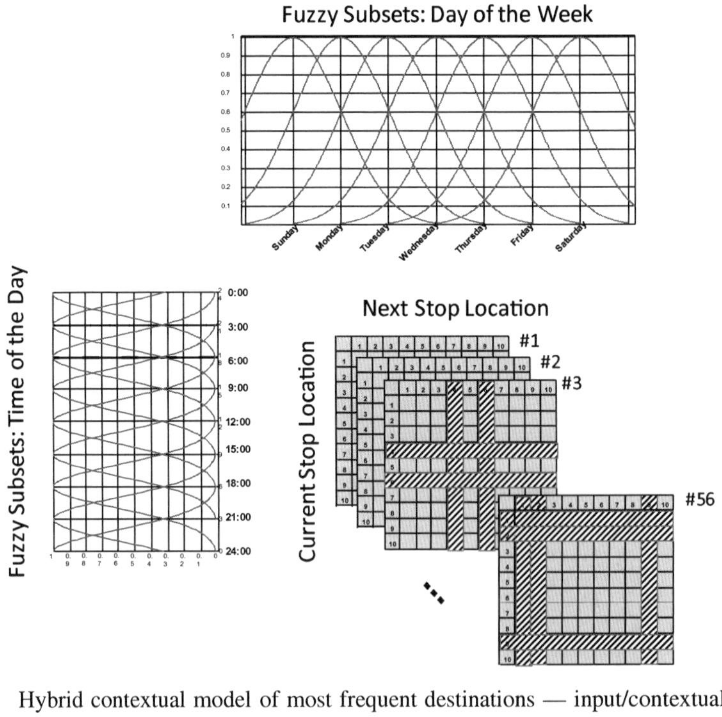

Figure 26.18: Hybrid contextual model of most frequent destinations — input/contextual space is granulated into 56 regions; corresponding Markov models include only the active Markov states (the visited stop locations under specific contextual conditions).

their transition probabilities are estimated during the learning phase. For example, in Figure 26.18 the models #3 and #56 do not have states #4 and #6, respectively #1, #2, and #9.

26.5.3. *Online Learning the Hybrid Contextual Model*

The interpolative nature of the Hybrid Contextual Model affects the algorithm for its learning from data. While the switching model can be learned as a collection of independent Markov models since only one of them is active when the specific set of conditions is satisfied, the Hybrid Contextual Model requires parallel updating of all of the individual Markov models.

During the learning the weights w_s by Equation (45) provide different interpretation of the new information about the current context and the transitions between the Markov states. In order derive the algorithm for learning the Hybrid Contextual Model we consider the following cases:

If the current input set of input values $U_1(k), U_2(k), \ldots, U_r(k)$ completely matches a set of conditions that are captured by a granule, e.g., $\bar{u}_s = E_{1s} \times E_{2s} \times \cdots \times E_{rs}$, then the corresponding Markov model transition probability matrix $\Pi^{(s)}$ is updated with the information for the specific transition between the according to expressions (38)–(42) assuming that a transition between states $\bar{x}_i$ and $\bar{x}_j$ has occurred; the rest of the transition probabilities in $\Pi^{(s)}$ remain unchanged. If the rest of the conditions are not matched, the remaining transition probability matrices $\Pi^{(t)}, t = 1, 2, \ldots, S, t \neq s$, are not updated. Note that this assumption corresponds to the following set of weights:

$$w_s = 1; \quad w_t = 0, \;\; t = 1, 2, \ldots, S, \;\; t \neq s. \tag{47}$$

If the current input set of input values $U_1(k), U_2(k), \ldots, U_r(k)$ partially matches the conditions in multiple granules, then the corresponding Markov model transition probability matrices are updated with the information for the specific transition between the according to expressions (38)–(42) assuming that a transition between states $\bar{x}_i$ and $\bar{x}_j$ has occurred; the rest of the transition probabilities in $\Pi^{(s)}$ remain unchanged. Note that this assumption corresponds to a set of non-zero weights w_s, $s = 1, 2, \ldots, S$.

We combine the three cases of matching by scaling the learning rate α in (39) and (40) with the corresponding weight w_s, $s = 1, 2, \ldots, S$, as follows:

$$F_{ij}^{(s)}(k) = F_{ij}^{(s)}(k-1) + \alpha w_s\big(f_{ij}(k) - F_{ij}^{(s)}(k-1)\big), \tag{48}$$

$$F_{oi}^{(s)}(k) = F_{oi}^{(s)}(k-1) + \alpha w_s\big(f_i(k) - F_{oi}^{(s)}(k-1)\big), \tag{49}$$

$$\pi_{ij}^{(s)}(k) = \frac{F_{ij}^{(s)}(k)}{F_{oi}^{(s)}(k)} = \frac{F_{ij}^{(s)}(k-1) + \alpha w_s\big(f_{ij}(k) - F_{ij}^{(s)}(k-1)\big)}{F_{oi}^{(s)}(k-1) + \alpha w_s\big(f_i(k) - F_{oi}^{(s)}(k-1)\big)}. \tag{50}$$

The algorithm for online learning the Hybrid Contextual Model was validated on a dataset including 623 trips over 48 unique start–stop location combinations and incremental learning of the transition probabilities. The granularity of contextual conditions — Time of the Day and Day of the Week — was 3 hours and 1 day corresponding to 8, respectively 7 fuzzy subsets consistent with the partitioning shown in Figure 26.18. The algorithm demonstrated prediction rate of 71.95%. Prediction accuracy varied between different drivers based on the percentage of repetitive trips and similarity of corresponding contextual information (Filev *et al.*, 2011).

26.6. Conclusions

In this chapter, we presented several diverse automotive applications of computational intelligence. Our goal was to demonstrate the potential of CI for solving wide range of practical problems related to driver safety (intrusion detection), neural net-based dynamic optimization of hybrid powertrain energy management of HEV that was coupled with an ultra-capacitor, fuzzy control of HV battery in power-split HEV, and learning driving patterns and prediction of the next destination. These cases clearly show that the methodology of computational intelligence combined with conventional techniques, e.g., dynamic programming, control theory, Markov models, etc., provides a strong foundation and opportunities for developing new original technical solutions, and innovative vehicle systems, and features.

References

Abou-Nasr, M. A. and Filev, D. P. (2013). Dynamic adaptation of a vehicle's cruising speed with recurrent neural networks for enhancing fuel economy, 2013 *IEEE International Conference on Cybernetics* (*CYBCONF*), pp. 249–254.

Ashbrook, D. and Starner, T. (2003). Using GPS to learn significant locations and predict movement across multiple users. *Pers. and Ubiquit. Comput.*, 7(5), pp. 275–286.

Balakrishnan, S. N., Ding, J. and Lewis, F. L. (2008). Issues on stability of ADP feedback controllers for dynamical systems. *IEEE T. Syst. Man Cy. B*, 38(4), pp. 913–917.

Eagen, C., Feldkamp, L., Ebenstein, S. *et al.* (2008). System and method for detecting presence of a human in a vehicle, US20060089753 A1701/1.

Farshidianfar, A. Ebrahimi, M. and Bartlett, H. (2001). Hybrid modelling and simulation of the torsional vibration of vehicle driveline systems. *P. I. MECH. ENG. D-J. Aut.*, 215, pp. 217–229.

Feldkamp, L. A. and Puskorius, G. V. (1998). A signal processing framework based on dynamic neural networks with application to problems in adaptation, filtering, and classification. *Proc. IEEE*, 86(11), pp. 2259–2277.

Filev, D. and Kolmanovsky, I. (2010). Markov chain modeling approaches for on board applications. *Proc. Am. Control Conf.* (*ACC*), pp. 4139–4145.

Filev, D., Tseng, F., Kristinsson, J. and McGee, R. (2011). Contextual On-Board Learning and Prediction of Vehicle Destinations, In *2011 Symp. on Intelligent Vehicles and Vehicular Systems, IEEE Symp. Comput. Intell.*, April 11–15, 2011, Paris, France.

Krumm, J. and Horvitz, E. (2012). Some help on the way: Opportunistic routing under uncertainty. *Proc. 2012 ACM Conf. Ubiquit. Comput. UbiComp'12*, pp. 371–380.

Krumm, J., Gruen, R. and Delling, D. (2013). From destination prediction to route prediction. *Journal of Location Based Services*, 7, pp. 98–120.

McGee, R., Syed, F., Hunter, S. and Ramaswamy, D. (2007). Power control for the escape and mariner hybrids. *SAE 2007 World Congress and Exhibition, Paper No.* 2007-01-0282.

Pettersson, M. and Nielsen, L. (2000). Gear shifting by engine control. *IEEE T. Cont. Syst. T.*, 8(3), pp. 495–507.

Prokhorov, D. V. and Wunsch II, D. C. (1997). Adaptive critic designs. *IEEE T. Neural. Networ.*, 8(5), pp. 997–1007.

Syed, F., Kuang, M., Czubay, J. and Ying, H. (2006). Power-split hybrid electric vehicle model development and validation. *IEEE T. Veh. Technol.*, 55(6), pp. 1731–1747.

Syed, F., Ying, H. and Kuang, M. (2009). Active damping wheel-torque control system to reduce driveline oscillations in a power-split hybrid electric vehicle. *IEEE T. Veh. Technol.*, 58(9), pp. 4769–4785.

Werbos, P. J. (1992). Approximate dynamic programming for real-time control and neural modeling, In White, D. A. and Sofge, D. A. (eds.), *Handbook of Intelligent Control*, New York: Van Nostrand Reinhold, Ch. 13.

Yager, R. and Filev, D. (1994). *Essentials of Fuzzy Modeling and Control*. New York: John Wiley & Sons.

Ying, H. (2000). *Fuzzy Control and Modeling*. New York: IEEE Press.

Index

D

K

L

M

N

U

V

W

Z